LIQUID CRYSTALS 3

Part I

LIQUID CRYSTALS 3

The 3rd International Liquid Crystal Conference

Part I

Edited by

GLENN H. BROWN

Kent State University

and

M. M. LABES

Department of Chemistry,
Temple University, Philadelphia

1972

GORDON AND BREACH SCIENCE PUBLISHERS

LONDON · NEW YORK · PARIS

CHEMISTRY

Library of Congress catalog card number: 76–190444. ISBNs: 0 677 12620 4 (Part I); 0 677 12630 1 (Part II). All rights reserved. No part of this book may be reproduced or utilized in any form or by any means, electronic or mechanical, including photocopying, recording, or by any information storage and retrieval system, without permission in writing from the publishers. Printed in Great Britain.

Preface

The papers appearing in *Liquid Crystals 3* were presented at the Third International Liquid Crystal Conference held in Berlin, West Germany, August 24–28, 1970. Over one hundred papers were presented authored by scientists from eleven countries. Nine of these were plenary lectures and the remainder were contributed papers. The papers presented at the conference but not included in these bound volumes are listed by abstract at the end of Part II.

The highlight of the opening session of the conference was the citation of five distinguished scholars who had made outstanding contributions to research in the field of liquid crystals (this appears at the beginning of Part I). These citations are recorded in this volume. It is with regret we inform you that Dr. A. S. C. Lawrence died in January 1971. Professor W. Kast served as honorary chairman of the Third International Conference and his message to the conference was presented by recording. Dr. G. Meier has translated Dr. Kast's lecture into English.

The papers cover a large spectrum of subjects from theory to medical subjects. The plenary lectures focus on " the state of the art " in a variety of areas. Only three of the authors of plenary lectures prepared papers for publication. Contributed papers show considerable concentration on molecular properties. The interest in the synthesis of new compounds continues, especially for low temperature nematic liquid crystals. The impact of the room temperature nematic liquid crystal, p-methoxybenzylidene-p'-n-butylaniline (MBBA), on applied research in display media has been extensive. Synthetic work is advancing at a rapid pace with the goal being liquid crystalline materials with a crystal–nematic transition well below zero.

There has been an increasing interest during the past few years in theoretical studies of the liquid crystalline state. Experimental techniques have continued to attract more scientists and optical measurements appear to be the most popular. Other experimental

v

techniques such as inelastic neutron scattering and X-ray are showing more activity.

Lyotropic liquid crystals in inanimate and animate systems received attention in about 15 per cent of the papers presented. There is certainly a need for a larger involvement in this important aspect of liquid crystals.

From a practical point of view, the two items which received the most attention were the preparation of liquid crystalline compounds of a high degree of purity and compounds exhibiting low temperature nematic liquid crystalline properties. The most interest in the use of liquid crystals focused on display systems. The interest in the use of liquid crystals as temperature sensors has decreased in the past two years.

This volume covers many facets of liquid crystals and will be of value to scientists in many areas. It should find its place in scientific, engineering and medical circles as a valuable reference.

Those persons closely involved with the conference are indebted to all authors who gave papers and especially to those who prepared their papers for publication. Professor R. Hosemann and his associates deserve a vote of thanks for the excellent manner in which they handled all details of the conference. Many other people helped make the conference a success and sincere thanks are extended to each. The members of the Planning and Steering Committee merit special thanks for their sound counsel throughout the planning for and carrying out of the conference. This committee is planning the fourth conference for August 1972. They are listed on the following page.

Along with the intellectual aspects of the conference, all who attended will remember the delightful Waterway Tour and delicious picnic dinner following the tour.

GLENN H. BROWN
M. M. LABES

Planning and Steering Committee

E. J. Ambrose (England)

G. H. Brown (U.S.A.), *Chairman*

I. Chistyakov (U.S.S.R.)

R. D. Ennulat (U.S.A.)

G. W. Gray (England)

R. Hosemann (Germany)

R. S. Porter (U.S.A.)

A. Saupe (U.S.A.)

A. Skoulios (France)

G. T. Stewart (U.S.A.)

Contents of Part I

INVITED PAPERS

CONTRIBUTED PAPERS

1 Optical Properties

2 Theory (Statistical or Continuum)

3 NMR and EPR

Contents of Part II

xiii

8   Cholesteric Phases

9   Mechanical Behaviour, Transport Phenomena and Thermodynamics

10 Polymer Formation

Opening Ceremony

Glenn H. Brown, *Presiding*

It is my pleasure to call the Third International Liquid Crystal Conference into session. Our first two conferences were in Kent, Ohio, U.S.A. in 1965 and 1968. It is fitting that the third conference be held in Germany, the site of early work in the field, and a country whose scientists have a record of research in liquid crystals from the date of their discovery.

Professor Kast has made the observation that when he started research in liquid crystals, 50 years ago, he could count on the fingers of one hand all the scientists in Europe working in the field. When I entered the field in the mid-1950's that number throughout the world had no more than doubled. When I attempted to organize the first conference, I wrote 10 chemists and physicists at home and abroad seeking their opinions on organizing a conference. The responses varied from enthusiastic support to the rejection of the idea. As we look backward to those days, we can conclude that the decision to proceed to call a conference in 1965 was a wise one. At the first conference we had approximately 40 papers and 120 attendees. In 1968 at the second conference we had approximately 75 papers and 260 attendees. This conference has over 100 papers on the program and an attendance of approximately 300.

As I travel about my own country and from there across Europe and Asia, I find a great interest in liquid crystals in academic, industrial and governmental laboratories. It seems reasonable to say that ours is one of the " hottest " research areas in science today.

The plans for this conference have been efficiently prepared and executed by Professor Hosemann and his organizing committee; you may find their names on Page 1 of the program book. I am sure that you join me in expressing our thanks to Professor Hosemann, the organizing committee and the personnel in Fritz Haber Institute for their work on this conference.

The purpose of this opening ceremony is to honor several scientists who have reached retirement, or nearly so, and who have made significant contributions to liquid crystal research. On the recommendation of a number of individuals and with the approval and guidance of the Planning and Steering Committee five individuals are recognized at this time. Each has made important contributions to the field. One of the number whom we recognize today died in October 1969 after the idea for this ceremony was finalized. Another of the group whom we honor will speak to us through a recording.

It is a pleasure to introduce, in turn, those who will present citations. Our first speaker is Mr. John Dreyer, Polacoat Inc., Cincinnati, Ohio, U.S.A. who will read the citation for Dr. Hans Zocher. Our second speaker is Dr. Gordon Stewart, Tulane University, Medical School, New Orleans, Louisiana, U.S.A. who cites Dr. A. S. C. Lawrence. The third speaker is Dr. George Gray of Hull University, Great Britain, who reads the citation for Professor P. Chatelain. The fourth speaker is Dr. A. J. Ambrose of Chester Beatty Research Institute, Great Britain, who cites Professor J. D. Bernal.

I now present the Chairman of the Organizing Committee for the Third International Liquid Crystal Conference who will present by recording Professor W. Kast. Professor Kast was one of the five persons cited for distinguished service in the field of liquid crystals. His lecture which appears in this volume outlines his career in liquid crystal research. This recording from Professor Kast concludes the opening session of the Third International Liquid Crystal Conference.

The Planning and Steering Committee for Liquid Crystal Conferences recommended that the citations be published as a part of the Proceedings of the Third International Liquid Crystal Conference. We record, in the Proceedings, the English translation of the recording presented by Professor W. Kast and the citations of the other four persons whom we honored.

GLENN H. BROWN

August 24, 1970

Professor WILHELM KAST

Address
of the Honorary Chairman

Professor Dr. phil. nat. Wilhelm Kast, *Freiburg i. Br., Germany*

It is a great privilege and pleasure for me to address the Third International Conference on Liquid Crystals which is the first to be held in the country of their discoverer Otto Lehmann. And I am grateful that I can do so in absentia because, unfortunately, I am not able to travel to Berlin at present for reasons of health.

It was 80 years ago (1889 and 1890) that the first papers of Otto Lehmann on *Fließende Kristalle* (flowing crystals) and *Kristalline Flüssigkeiten* (crystalline fluids) were published. The term *flüssige Kristalle* (liquid crystals), which he used for the first time in 1900, met with a lot of opposition, especially from Tamman, the well-known physical chemist at Göttingen. Rudolf Schenk at Marburg, however, who devoted many careful measurements to the " turbid melts ", was able to demonstrate in his book on *Kristallinische Flüssigkeiten*, edited in 1905, that Lehmann's fluid crystals were, in fact, homogeneous optically anisotropic fluids, thus disproving Tamman's emulsion theory.

Still, I too have given preference to the term *Kristalline Flüssigkeiten* because, after all, they are fluids. I can still remember the first lecture on *Kristalline Flüssigkeiten* which I delivered in Vorländer's Chemistry colloquium shortly after my appointment as full professor at the University of Halle. In the discussion following the lecture Vorländer made the humorous remark: " Now that you are full professor you can also use the term *flüssige Kristalle*! " Nevertheless, in my publications—and even in my Table in Landolt-Börnstein in 1960—I retained the name " Kristalline Flüssigkeiten ".

Today, however, there exists a " Liquid Crystal Institute " which, going back to Lehmann's original bold nomenclature for its official title, has contributed decisively to awakening interest in this field, as is shown quite impressively not only by the previous two conferences in Kent, Ohio, but also by the present Third International Conference on Liquid Crystals here in Berlin with its 120 contributions: 9 General Lectures, 103 Short Communications and 8 Meetings.

How different the situation was when I started on my doctoral thesis 50 years ago! At that time it would have been possible to count on one's fingers all the chemists and physicists engaged in liquid crystal research in Europe. Particularly favourable circumstances, however, prevailed at the University Halle, which I attended as a student: Here was Vorländer to whom we are indebted for discovering many materials with crystalline liquid phases on account of his systematic synthesis of organic compounds with somewhat long and stiff molecules. And here was my Ph.D. sponsor, Gustav Mie, who himself had been assistant of Otto Lehmann for some time. No wonder that this atmosphere stimulated my interest in liquid crystals.

Thus, when I was free to decide what problem I would like to investigate with the newly developed method of beats for measuring small changes in capacitances, I decided to look for a change in the dielectric constant of liquid crystal layers when these are placed in a magnetic field, since Bose had demonstrated that under similar circumstances their turbidity disappears. The result is well-known and was confirmed in the following years both by Jezewski at Krakau and by Freedericks and Repiewa at Petersburg.

Above all, L. S. Ornstein, at whose Institute at the University of Utrecht, Netherlands, several studies on liquid crystals had already been made, was able to demonstrate on account of my measurements that the field dependence of the decrease of the dielectric constant in a magnetic field is in good agreement with the calculation of the orientation of diamagnetically and dielectrically anisotropic domains. In this way, his and Bose's swarm theory of crystalline melts found a confirmation over and above the one furnished by previous experiments at Utrecht which demonstrated that light scattering can be calculated on the assumption of unoriented doubly refracting domains.

In the meantime I went with Gustav Mie to Freiburg, completed the dielectric measurements with different orientations of the magnetic field and could prove the magnetic orientation in a new way by observing the splitting into two halves of the blurred X-ray interference ring, which is produced by liquids. After my habilitation at Freiburg on the basis of this work I became more and more engaged in the field of atomic physics. Nevertheless I still remained in contact with Ornstein and as a consequence was invited 1932–1933 as a guest and Rockefeller Fellow in his institute for an enjoyable and rewarding year. This episode yielded some papers in collaboration concerning the behaviour of crystalline liquids in magnetic and electric fields and ended with the attendance by both of us at the first conference on Liquid Crystals arranged by the Faraday-Society in London April 24–25, 1933. At this conference 20 different contributions were discussed. Among the participants were Vorländer, Schenk, Herrmann, Herzog, Paneth and Zocher.

After my return to Freiburg I started, together with my assistants, dielectric measurements with different high frequency amplitudes and measurements of the specific heat and the transformation heat at the clearing point. In 1937 the University of Halle offered me a full professorship, at the same time expressing the hope that I might continue their tradition of liquid crystal research. At the *Diskussions-Tagung der Deutschen Bunsen-Gesellschaft über Übergänge zwischen Ordnung und Unordnung in festen und flüssigen Phasen* in 1938 at Darmstadt I had the opportunity, the first one in Germany, to give a review on " Anisotropic Liquids ". Here I could use the results of calorimetric measurements which, at this time, had been nearly completed.

My graduate student Wilhelm Maier who performed the electrical measurements accompanied me to Halle where he got his doctoral degree and his habilitation. Later on he became a full professor at Freiburg but his fruitful work broke off abruptly in 1964 in a fatal accident on a lecture tour abroad.

However, he left us several of his former students who opened up the way to important applications of liquid crystals to technology. First of all the extremely useful introduction of liquid crystals as solvents in NMR measurements is to be mentioned. Further, let me refer to investigations on the behaviour of thin liquid crystalline layers in electric fields. Now that room temperature liquid crystals have been created by Farbwerke Hoechst, such thin layers may

become very important for the development of flat T.V.
screens.

Due to various circumstances at Halle I myself could only follow
and collect the literature in the field of liquid crystals. The comprehensive material of Vorländer which was kept in the Chemical
Institute at Halle proved very useful in collecting data for the table
of crystalline fluid compounds in the 6th edition of Landolt-
Börnstein. Moreover, I enjoyed the valuable assistance of the
chemist Weygand who continued the work of his teacher Vorländer
at Leipzig. In 1960 I could publish a table of 1412 liquid crystalline
compounds with their characteristic temperatures whereas in the
1912 edition there were only 90. My friend Weygand unfortunately
died before the publication of this table. However, in a lecture which
I delivered in 1955 at the " Gessellschaft Deutscher Chemiker " in
Köln, and which I published later in *Angewandte Chemie,* I was able
to present his work, especially those papers which deal with the
clearing point in homologous series which he had synthesized or at
least augmented himself. To my delight, Rudolf Schenk, even
though 85 years old, made a special trip from Aachen to Köln in
order to listen to my talk. Furthermore, when the tables were
published five years later, he sent me a letter thanking me for men-
tioning his papers of 1905 in the preface and emphasizing their
importance—an indication as to how little attention they had
formerly received. Incidentally, our meeting in Köln was the last
one. On his 95th birthday I happened to be abroad and when I
returned he was no longer alive.

I am very glad to have won Dr. Kelker from Farbwerke Hoechst
to continue this table. I would like to use this opportunity to ask all
colleagues to support Dr. Kelker in his task by kindly informing him
of any new compounds with liquid crystal phases that they discover
or hear of.

Today I could only speak about the special line of liquid crystal
research which has been carried out by me and has been pursued by
my students and their students. In order not to detract from the
work of authors belonging to other groups, I have avoided naming
living persons.

By the way, " living? " ! Otto Lehmann once published a paper
on *Die flüssigen Kristalle und ihr scheinbares Leben* whereupon one

of his colleagues in Karlsruhe asked him " How are your liquid crystals doing? Are they eating already? "

Certainly this conference clearly demonstrates: " The liquid crystals are alive "!

Professor J. D. BERNAL

Citation

Professor J. D. Bernal

Professor J. D. Bernal, F.R.S., carried out research in Crystallography at the Davy Faraday Laboratory and at Cambridge from 1923 to 1937, and was Professor of Physics at Birkbeck College from 1937 to 1963 and Professor of Crystallography there from 1963 to 1968. His pioneering work on the investigation of corpuscular proteins structure using X-ray diffraction, in association with Dr. Dorothy Hodgkin (née Crowfoot), is well known. The later determination of the structure of myoglobin and haemoglobin by Kendrew and Perutz stems from the recognition by Bernal that the X-ray diffraction methods could be used on protein crystals.

His interest in the relevance of the phenomena observed in liquid crystals stemmed from X-ray work in 1933 with Crowfoot on crystalline substances showing the mesophases. Here he was in close contact with K. Hermann and A. S. C. Lawrence who were also pioneers in the study of materials in this field. The extension of such studies to molecular biology arose in the investigation of the properties due to particle arrangements in tobacco mosaic virus which began in collaboration with Bawden and Pirie. Bernal has always taken an interest in molecular biology and in 1967 published a book on the Origin of Life which reveals his ideas on the close connections between the molecular basis of life and his ideas on generalised crystallography.

We owe a debt to Bernal for showing us the relevance of liquid crystalline properties to living systems, a field of investigation which is attracting increasing interest at the present time.

A. J. AMBROSE

Professor PIERRE CHATELAIN

Citation

Professor Pierre Chatelain

To all who have made a study of Liquid Crystals, the names of European scientists such as Friedel, Kast, Lehmann, Oseen, Ornstein, Vorländer and Zocher stand pre-eminent amongst those who so securely laid the foundations of our present-day knowledge of liquid crystals. During the forty-five years between the discovery by Reinitzer, in 1888, that melts of cholesteryl benzoate were optically anisotropic and the occasion of the Faraday Society Discussion in London in April, 1933, knowledge about liquid crystals accumulated rapidly because of the efforts of scientists such as those mentioned above. Then followed a period of relative quiescence, due partly perhaps to an abating of the first flush of enthusiasm for a new topic, and partly no doubt to the international situation which existed in Europe at that time and which was soon to lead to war.

However, work on liquid crystals did go on during the late 1930's and the 1940's, and outstanding amongst those who continued to study and advance knowledge about these systems was Pierre Chatelain, on whose behalf it is my honour and privilege to make this citation in recognition of his scientific contributions in the field of liquid crystals. Professor Chatelain's researches were carried out in the Department of Mineralogy and Crystallography at the University of Montpellier, and in addition to scientific papers on other topics, have led to more than twenty-five important publications concerning liquid crystals.

In the early stages of his research, beginning in about 1935, his main interest was concentrated upon the optical properties of nematic melts, and his precise quantitative studies of the refractive indices of such melts and of the manner in which these melts scattered and diffused light added greatly to the depth of understanding of molecular organisation in the nematic state. During these studies, Professor Chatelain first recognised the vital influence of the orienting properties of surfaces on the nematic state and how this could be used to impose a specific orientation on a film of nematic material, producing in effect a single nematic liquid crystal. The eventual importance of this discovery in the production of light polarising filters is recognised by us all today, and to those who are involved in the active present-day study of the use of nematic materials in display systems, the significance and value of Professor Chatelain's discovery of the influence of rubbed or stroked surfaces on nematic liquid crystals, and indeed of the results of all his optical studies on such systems, are obvious.

It was my privilege to meet Professor Chatelain when I spent a short period in his laboratories at Montpellier in 1957. This visit to Montpellier was one of particular importance to me, for during it I was able to consult many papers on liquid crystals hitherto unavailable to me and to discuss with Professor Chatelain and his colleagues current ideas and thinking about liquid crystals. Indeed it was the inspiration which Professor Chatelain gave me which led me to begin work on the book " Molecular Structure and the Properties of Liquid Crystals " which was published some years later and I hope in some measure contributed to the resurgence of interest in liquid crystals during the last ten years. I need hardly add that during that visit I found Professor Chatelain to be deeply knowledgeable of his subject and a charming man who extended to me great courtesy and hospitality. Indeed, as a result of our meeting, I came to have an even higher regard for his scientific attainments in the realisation that these had been achieved in the face of considerable physical handicaps.

Professor Chatelain's contributions to knowledge of the optical properties of nematic liquid crystals continued through the 1940's and 1950's, and outstanding amongst his many publications was his article entitled " Liquid Crystals ", published in the Bulletin de la Société Française de Minéralogie et de Cristallographie, a review covering the twenty years of research on liquid crystals prior to 1954. This is a review which anyone working in the field today could read with considerable profit.

During the last ten years, his research contributions have not diminished and in collaboration with colleagues such as R. Cano, M. Germain, and J. C. Martin, he has continued his work and paid increased attention to the cholesteric state and its relationship to the nematic state. These studies have centred upon the properties of pure optically active systems which exhibit cholesteric behaviour, of the corresponding racemic systems which are nematic in behaviour, and of mixtures containing intermediate ratios of the stereoisomers. The studies have centred upon the changes in optical rotatory power and in periodicity of the Grandjean planes which occur with changes in concentration of the active species and have provided experimental agreement with the de Vries formula postulating proportionality between periodicity and optical rotatory power. These studies have been extended to mixtures of a non-optically active nematic substance with an optically active cholesteric compound, and again provide verification of the theory. Recently too, continued studies of the nematic state—in this case of the refractive indices of the nematic state produced by mixtures of two nematic substances—have given results supporting the Maier–Saupe theory of the nematic state.

A brief citation of this kind cannot do full justice to the scientific achievements of Professor Chatelain, but I hope that it is clear from what I have said, that I personally have the highest regard for his attainments. I am sure too that his fellow scientists in France feel the same and that the recent French Symposium on Liquid Crystals in June 1969 was held at the University of Montpellier as a tribute to Professor Chatelain. It is therefore my pleasure and privilege to convey now to Professor Pierre Chatelain, through the medium of this citation, our recognition—that of all the delegates and organisers of this Third International Conference on Liquid Crystals held in Berlin in August, 1970—of the value, importance and scientific merit of his researches during the last thirty-five years in this field of study which we call Liquid Crystals.

G. W. GRAY

Professor A. S. C. LAWRENCE

Citation

Professor A. S. C. Lawrence

Professor Lawrence is a pioneer in the study of phase equilibrium, and one of the first to describe the lyotropic mesophase. He has now reached the age of retirement so, even though the inclination to work, think and write is strongly within him, it is fitting that we should honor his name at this meeting of his peers, many of whom are his friends of long standing.

Stuart Lawrence was born in Southern England in 1902. He began his scientific career in 1919 as a laboratory assistant but not for long. In 1920, at the age of 18, he was appointed as a junior lecturer at the Royal Institution where he served Sir James Dewar and, later, Sir William Bragg as research assistant. During this time, he attended evening classes at Battersea Polytechnic to work for the external B.Sc. of London University. Possibly this early association with the great unwashed of the academic world made its mark, for he began to develop his lifelong interest in amphiphiles and, in 1927 (during an illness) wrote a book on soap films. 1927 saw him at Cambridge University as a research worker in Rideal's Laboratory of Colloid Science where he remained until 1934. Some of you may remember his important communications on lyotropic mesomorphism and the viscosity of liquid crystals to the Faraday Society in 1933, based on his work at Cambridge.

Following his excursion into theory, Lawrence turned his attention again to practical matters—fuel research, lubrication, paraffins and soaps—working successively for Government and Industrial projects. During World War II, he served the British Navy as a scientific expert on fuel and lubrication, donning the uniform of a naval officer in Arctic Voyages for the purpose. In 1946, he attended the World Power Conference at The Hague as British Naval representative. Then he discarded his uniform for an academic gown (probably hired) at the University of Sheffield where he served, successively, as

Senior Lecturer, Reader and Professor in the Department of Chemistry.

Lawrence's work is painstakingly but elegantly described in about 80 papers in major scientific journals, in numerous reports and communications to learned societies, in chapters in books and in plenary lectures delivered at Glasgow, Brussels, Moscow, Lund (Sweden), Kent (Ohio) and elsewhere. His outstanding contribution to physical chemistry is his definition of the conditions governing phase equilibrium and molecular interaction at interfaces. His experiments and reasoning in this field have elucidated problems of lubrication, cleansing, detergence, membrane structure, flow, colloid stability, muscle contraction and even (so I am told) cosmetology. Most of his papers are written solo, partly because for many years he ploughed a lonely field, partly because he was and is a self-sufficient resource; but this should not obscure the thoroughness of his teaching and his ability to collaborate with academic and industrial colleagues at all levels in the solution—or, should I say, in the dispersion!—of a great variety of practical problems. He is one of the few chemists who has effectively penetrated the protoplasmic curtain to find himself now, very appropriately, at this interdisciplinary meeting, equally at home and equally respected on both sides.

Of Lawrence's other accomplishments and other interests, I would mention especially his interest in students and apprentice scientists, and his services to important committees and conferences. He enjoys home life and a wonderful companionship with his sister. He is himself convivial, with a sense of humor, of history, of occasions and of youthfulness. But, above all, he stands out as a very fine type of academic scientist—thorough, modest, imaginative and unselfish. It is a pleasure to know him as a friend, a stimulus to know him as a scientist and a privilege to present his name to this distinguished assembly in this great Institute of Physical Science here in West Berlin.

DR. GORDON T. STEWART

NOTE: It is with regrets that we report the death of Dr. Lawrence in January 1971.

DR. HANS ERNST WERNER ZOCHER

Citation

Professor Dr. Hans Ernst Werner Zocher

On October 16, 1969, in Rio de Janeiro, Hans Zocher died at the age of 76 years after a short illness. Hans Zocher, one-time professor at the German Technical University in Prague, author of nearly 100 publications, still lives in the memory and esteem of his many friends, his colleagues and his former students.

He was born on April 27, 1893 at Bad Liebenstein, a small town in Germany. From 1912 to 1914 he attended Leipzig and Jena Universities, studying Chemistry, Physics, Mathematics and Mineralogy. From 1914 to 1916 he took part in the war as a soldier. He had been at the front only two weeks when he received a wound in the face and so spent most of this period in a military hospital. On being discharged, he continued his studies at Berlin University, where he attained his doctor's degree in 1920.

In 1921 he became assistant of H. Freundlich at the Kaiser-Wilhelm-Institut für Physikalische Chemie und Elektrochemie at the time when Fritz Haber was its director. During the ten years he stayed there he did research on many subjects, among them mesophases, chemiluminescence, photochemistry, passivity and anisotropy. There he also met his future wife who was at the time secretary and librarian at the Institute. In 1931 he was called to the German " Technische Hochschule " in Prague as extraordinary professor where he became the director of the Institute for Physical Chemistry and Electrochemistry, and, in 1936, also director of the photographic laboratory. He became ordinary professor in 1937.

In the meantime, political events in Europe were rapidly reaching their climax. The German occupation of Czechoslovakia brought a sudden halt to his career. Forced to leave his position at the University and not allowed to publish, his position was restricted to that of technical adviser to the " Society for Chemical and Metallurgical Production ". His situation under the regime was most precarious.

Apart from the fact that his wife was Jewish, his democratic attitude was very well known. At the end of the war, when communication was again possible, his friends, now scattered throughout the world, helped him to find a new position. He went to Rio de Janeiro in 1946 where he worked in the Laboratorio da Producao Mineral as a research scientist for the Brazilian Government and the Brazilian National Research Council until the time of his death last year. He had been a member of the Brazilian Academy of Science since 1949. In 1963 he was accorded the degree of *doctor honoris causa* at the University of Brazil, and in 1965 he was awarded the Einstein Prize of the Brazilian Academy of Science.

His publications, of which there are more than 90, show the great variety of his interests. His methods of investigation were chiefly optical, as with the use of polarized light. Very early in his career he investigated anisotropy. He reported that directional optical quality can be produced in nearly all dyestuffs mechanically by rubbing or polishing. Another discovery was the orienting effect of a rubbed surface on solutions. The first mention of this was in 1923 in the Zeitschrift für Physikalische Chemie, and, as he said, he rediscovered it later in 1928. He was one of the earliest to realize the potential of surface oriented dichroic films as light polarizers and he obtained a patent in 1932.

On the subject of discovery he once wrote: " Who discovered America? Columbus? The Vikings? The ancestors of the Indians coming from East Asia? The concept of discovery is a relative one, depending on the level of general knowledge, on the consequences following and, therefore, on the activity of the discoverer and his successors."

Many of his papers deal with photochemical problems such as chemiluminescence, the Weigert effect, optical activity caused by photochemical action of circular-polarized light on photohalogenides, and the polarized fluorescence of dyestuffs dissolved in smectic phases.

He often made use of polarization optics in order to investigate submicroscopic structures such as the iridescent scales of butterfly wings, of lignine, of crystals in stretched rubber sheets, the orientation of chlorophyll molecules in the chloroplasts of plants and in lipoids, collogene fibres, etc.

He was able to demonstrate the presence of thin layers of oxide on iron produced either by anodic passivation or the action of air.

Since his arrival in Brazil he published several papers on the symmetry of crystals, on optical asymmetry and on space-time asymmetry, some of them in collaboration with Dr. C. Torok.

He is best known, however, for the extensive work on mesophases, or " liquid crystals ". Many of his earlier and most of his latest papers were devoted to their study. He investigated their optics their mechanics and the effect of electrical, magnetic and mechanical influence on them. Several of his concepts are now widely accepted. He was one of the original propounders of the Deformation and Continuum theory of liquid crystals, and he always upheld it, contributing much to it and refuting the Swarm theory. Of the nematic liquid crystal phase, he gave the following definition, heretofore unpublished:

" A nematic phase is one of the states of matter known as mesophases, mesomorphic phases or liquid crystals, which are intermediate between the amorphous and crystalline phases in relation to their structure and properties.

It is characterized by an arrangement of the molecules, so that they are with one of their axes almost completely parallel to each other. Consequently, the volume element has a rotational symmetry axis, corresponding to an anisotropy of the physical behaviour, especially to uniaxial birefringence and dichroism.

The lack of any translational periodicity permits fluidity for all translational movements, unless prevented by resinous or glassy consistence.

Deformations producing flexure, divergence or torsion of the symmetry axis, meet weak elastic resistance forces, comparable in weakness to magnetic forces.

Homogenous orientation may be produced by contact with an anisotropic surface or by a magnetic field.

Enantiomorphic (optically active) substances form twisted nematic phases (cholesteric phases), reflecting interference colours."

To the field of liquid crystals also belong his discoveries of " Tactosols ". They constitute special mesophases whose structural elements are of inorganic constituents. Some of these, more specifically those of tungstenic acid, show beautiful " lustre-layers " with a metallic brilliance. He also recognized " Superphases."

Hans Zocher was a scientist with profound knowledge, an acute intelligence, great powers of observation, and also great technical skill and ingenuity. These qualities coupled with an infinite patience made him a great research scientist. He made interesting and beautiful demonstrations which were the delight of all his visitors.

His open and endearing personality included a ready sense of humor and a love of puns. At the Kent University Symposium, while going to the picnic grounds at the commons, he remarked, " We are the plebeians going to the commons."

Dr. Zocher's vitality was that of a person who is happy in his work, who is doing exactly what he likes doing and for which he has all the aptitude. It was his intense interest in his work and the world about him, which kept him so active up to the last few days of his life.

JOHN F. DREYER

August 24, 1970

INVITED PAPERS

Ultraviolet, Infrared and Magnetic Resonance Spectroscopy on Liquid Crystals†

ALFRED SAUPE

Liquid Crystal Institute
Kent State University
Kent, Ohio 44242

Received April 7, 1971

1. Introduction

Liquid crystals comprise the states of intermediate order that may have properties in common with normal isotropic liquids as well as with solid crystals and, for this and other reasons, provide a matrix for experiments on oriented molecules which has considerable advantages:

(1) With nematic liquid crystals and some smectic liquid crystals it is easy to obtain uniformly aligned samples corresponding to single crystals with solids.

(2) Nematic liquid crystals have solvent properties practically as good as isotropic liquids and there should be no difficulty to find a suitable solvent for nearly any organic compound.

(3) The combination of orientational order and of high molecular mobility which can be obtained with many nematic solvents is extremely useful in magnetic resonance studies. It provides us with a method for the study of molecular geometries.

Experiments with oriented molecules are only one aspect of spectroscopy in liquid crystals. We may use spectroscopical methods also to study the structure and the molecular order of the liquid crystal itself and draw conclusions on the molecular interactions connected with the formation of these states. Measurements of relaxation times in magnetic resonance experiments give in addition

---

† Invited Paper presented at the Third International Liquid Crystal Conference, Berlin, August 24–28, 1970.

3

information on the dynamics of orientational fluctuations in these systems.

In recent years a large number of spectroscopical studies have been published, especially on magnetic resonance spectroscopy. Several review articles and a monograph covering the latter field are available.[1-4] The field is much too extensive for a comprehensive representation in a lecture. We regard, therefore, only some general features of spectroscopy in liquid crystals and discuss a few topics in more details which seem to me of special interest in connection with molecular structure and interactions in liquid crystals.

2. General Features and Comparison of UV, IR and Magnetic Resonance Spectra

With respect to their optical properties uniformly aligned nematic liquid crystals and smectic liquid crystals of type A are uniaxial. For a complete determination of their UV and IR absorption spectra measurements should be made with linear polarized light for the direction of polarization parallel and perpendicular to the optical axis.

These absorption measurements on liquid crystals are often difficult because the absorption may be very high and extremely thin layers may be needed. In the UV range it may be necessary to use layers as thin as 0.1 micron. The use of two polarizers, one in front of the layer and the second one as analyzer behind the layer, can be useful to suppress errors due to incomplete uniformity in alignment in such cases of high absorption.

Fortunately these difficulties do not arise when the liquid crystal is used as a matrix.[5-7] It can of course only be used in wavelength ranges when the absorption of the liquid crystal solvent itself is weak. The concentration of the solute molecules can always be kept low enough for a reasonably high transmission.

Many nematic liquid crystals can be relatively easily aligned in thin layers by surface action. Figure 1 shows, as an example, an aligned layer of nematic liquid MBBA (4-methoxybenzylidene 4-n-butylaniline) between crossed polarizers. The alignment was produced by rubbing the surfaces. The polarization of the incoming light is parallel to the direction of rubbing. The bright double lines

follow inversion walls, which separate areas in which the preferred
orientation differs 180°. In the center of the walls the molecules are
preferably perpendicular to the direction of rubbing, while in the
outside area they are preferably parallel to it. The preferred orientation changes continuously when we cross a wall until a complete

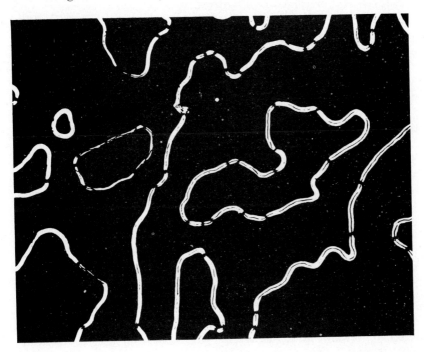

Figure 1. Surface aligned layer of nematic liquid 4-methoxybenzal-4-*n*-
butylaniline, ca. 0.1 mm thick, crossed polarizers parallel and perpendicular
to direction of rubbing.

turn of 180° is made and a physically equivalent orientation is
regained. Inversion walls are common disturbances of alignment
which are often difficult to avoid.

Figure 2 shows the UV spectra of heptyloxyazoxybenzene in the
isotropic liquid phase, the nematic liquid crystal state and the
smectic state. Positions and intensities of the absorption bands are
practically unchanged which demonstrates that no change of the
π-electronic structure of the molecules is connected with these phase
transitions.

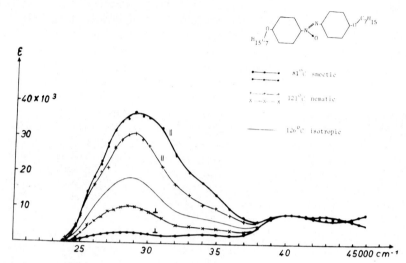

Figure 2.   UV-absorption, molar extinction coefficient of 4,4'-di-*n*-heptyloxy-azoxybenzene for linear polarized light, parallel (‖) and perpendicular (⊥) to optical axis. (According to Ref. 8).

The dichroism in the nematic phase is a function of the temperature it increases with decreasing temperature. In the smectic C phase, the dichroism is stronger than in the nematic phase and it shows only little temperature dependence.

There is a difficulty which should be mentioned here. Heptyloxy-azoxybenzene forms a smectic phase of type C that is optically biaxial.[9]   For the evaluation of the absorption measurements it has been treated as uniaxial which, however, is probably a fairly good approximation.

In Fig. 3 parts of the infrared absorption spectrum of undecadienic acid is reproduced. It demonstrates the similarity of line positions and intensities in the isotropic and nematic phase. The inner molecular vibrational frequencies are not noticeable shifted at the phase transition. The dichroism in the nematic phase is again larger at lower temperatures.

Figure 4 shows Raman lines of the normal isotropic liquid, the nematic liquid crystal and the solid crystalline phase of PAA (4,4'-di-methoxyazoxybenzene). The alignment of the nematic sample has not been specified. It is not uniform. The solid spectrum is taken with a polycrystalline sample.

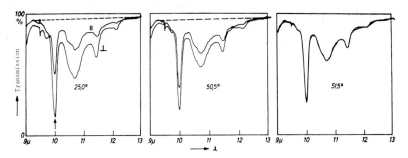

Figure 3. Sections of the infrared spectra of 2,4-nonadienic acid with linear polarized light, parallel (∥) and perpendicular (⊥) to optical axis; nematic phase at 25 and 50.5 °C and normal liquid at 51.5 °C. (According to Ref. 10).

Again the nematic spectrum is very similar to the spectrum of the isotropic phase. There are, however, additional features which indicate that the absorption peaks of low frequency vibrations where the molecules react approximately like rigid bodies are somewhat better defined in the nematic phase. In the solid crystal, these frequencies are fairly sharp and can be well observed in the 50 to 100 cm^{-1} region. Also a splitting of the inner molecular vibration frequencies can be observed.

As we have seen, the frequencies and intensities of the electronic transitions and between molecular vibrational states are about the same in the nematic liquid crystalline state as in the isotropic liquid state and the spectrum of the different states are very similar. This is completely different for magnetic resonance spectroscopy. Especially proton magnetic resonance spectra change dramatically at the normal liquid to liquid crystal phase transition.

Figure 5 shows as an example the proton magnetic resonance spectrum of PAA in different states: normal liquid, nematic liquid crystal and solid crystal. The absorption curve is shown for the isotropic liquid. The nematic spectrum and the solid spectrum is for technical reasons represented by the derivative curves of the absorption. The changes in the spectra are due to changes in the molecular orientation and molecular mobility. They are not due and do not indicate changes of the molecular structure at the phase transitions.

The resonance frequencies of the nuclei are in the first place determined by the Zeeman splitting of the spin levels in the applied

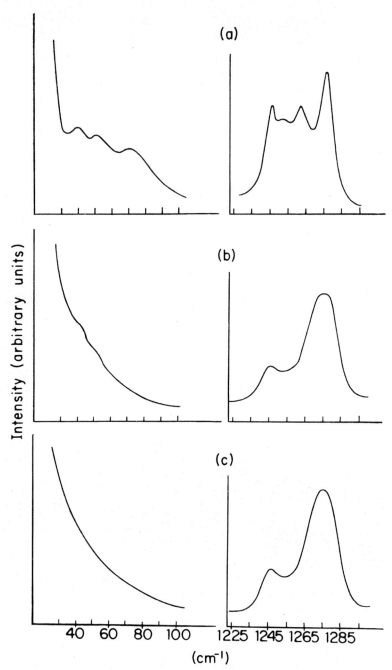

Figure 4.   Sections of Raman spectra of 4,4′-dimethoxy-azoxybenzene, (a) solid, (b) nematic, (c) normal liquid.   (According to Ref. 11).

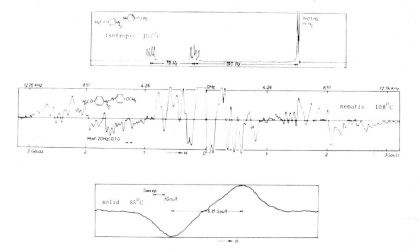

Figure 5. PMR spectra of 4,4'-dimethoxy-azoxybenzene. (According to G. Englert, see Ref. 12).

strong magnetic field. The local fields differ somewhat for different protons because of the screening by the surrounding electron clouds.

In the spectrum of the isotropic liquid phase these differences in screening or, in other words, the chemical shifts determine the overall splitting of about 270 Hz at the resonance frequency of 60 MHz. The overall splitting in the liquid crystal is nearly two orders of magnitude larger. In the solid crystal it is another factor 2 larger. While in the nematic phase a detailed fine structure is observed, there is only a broad band without structure in the solid.

The large splitting in the nematic and the solid phase is due to the direct magnetic interaction between the protons, which in normal liquids with a high molecular mobility reduces to zero. The fine structure is lost in the solid for two reasons:

(1) The solid sample was a polycrystalline sample and not uniformly aligned, contrary to the nematic liquid crystal which is aligned by the magnetic field.

(2) The molecules in the solid have little mobility and therefore the intermolecular spin–spin interactions are effective.

The fine structure in the nematic phase is not always observable. It disappears with molecules that have many more protons than PAA

because there are too many interacting nuclei.   When nematic
liquids are used as solvents for NMR experiments this is an advantage
because the resonance lines of the solute can then be observed on a
smooth background.

3. Orientational Order and S-Matrix

The dichroism in UV and IR spectra, the direct magnetic couplings
and quadrupole splitting observable in magnetic resonance experiments are all due to the orientational order of the molecules in liquid
crystals.   To characterize this orientational order for spectroscopic
purposes it is useful to introduce a set of average values of spherical
functions of second order (see for information References 1–4 or 13).
This set of values can be written as a matrix which transforms by a
change of the molecular coordinate system as a second rank tensor.

Let ξ, η, ζ, denote the axes of a molecular cartesian coordinate
system and θ_ξ, θ_η, θ_ζ, the angles between these axes and the symmetry
axis of the nematic liquid crystal.   Then the elements of the matrix
are given by:

$$S_{lk} = 1/2 \langle 3 \cos \theta_l \cos \theta_k - \delta_{lk} \rangle,$$

$$l, k = \xi, \eta, \zeta. \tag{1}$$

The trace $\sum S_{ll}$ is zero and there exists always a principle molecular
coordinate system where the matrix is diagonal.

It is convenient to refer to the diagonal elements S_{ll} as degree of
order or S-value of the corresponding axis.   When β_ξ, β_η, β_ζ are the
direction cosines of a given molecular axis p, q in the ξ, η, ζ-system
then its S-value can be expressed by the elements of the S-matrix

$$S_{pq} = \sum_{l,k} \beta_l \beta_k S_{lk}. \tag{2}$$

Since the S-matrix has only five independent elements, more than
five S-values are always linearly dependent on each other.   These
considerations are, however, only valid for rigid molecules.   The
number of independent S-values is reduced in the case of symmetrical
molecules.   It reduces to one when the molecule has a three or more
fold symmetry axis.   The relation between the S-values is of major
importance.   It is, for instance, essential for geometrical structure
determination of molecules by NMR studies.

The S-matrix contains all information on molecular orientational order that we may obtain from infrared and UV-spectroscopical studies as well as from the analysis of magnetic resonance spectra, provided in the latter case that the molecular mobility is high so that effective coupling constants obtained by averaging over the molecular motions may be used.

When we regard an absorption band of a linear polarized electronic or vibrational transition, then the degree of order of the transition axis determines the dichroism. We have the relation

$$S_{tr} = \frac{f_1 - f_2}{f_1 + f_2} \tag{3}$$

which allows to calculate the S-value of the transition axis out of the integrated intensities f_1 and f_2 of the absorption band measured with linear polarized light, polarized parallel and perpendicular to the optical axis.

In ESR experiments information on the orientation of the radical in the liquid crystal can be obtained from the change of the hyperfine coupling. The hyperfine coupling constants are changed because of the direct magnetic interaction between the nuclei and the electron. The change of the coupling constant is given by

$$\delta A = \sum_{ij} S_{ij} A_{ij} \tag{4}$$

where A_{ij} are the components of the coupling tensors in the molecular coordinate system. It is assumed here that the magnetic field is parallel to the symmetry axis of the nematic liquid. When the coupling tensor has a rotational symmetry as it is the case for many interesting radicals, we can write

$$\delta A = S_{sym} \Delta A. \tag{5}$$

Here S_{sym} is the degree of order of the axis of the coupling tensor and $\Delta A = A_{\parallel} - A_{\perp}$ the difference between its principle values parallel and perpendicular to the symmetry axis.

In case of electric quadrupole interactions of the nucleus with the electron cloud we have again equations analogous to (4) and (5) for the resulting quadrupole interaction constant.

The coupling constant for the direct magnetic coupling between two nuclei p and q may be defined as

$$B_{pq}^{\mathrm{dir}} = -\frac{h}{8\pi^2}\gamma_p\gamma_q\left\langle\frac{3\cos^2\theta_{pq}-1}{r_{pq}^3}\right\rangle \tag{6}$$

where h is Planck's constant, γ denotes the gyromagnetic ratio. r_{pq} is the distance between the two nuclei and θ_{pq} the angle between the nuclear axis and the magnetic field. The angle brackets indicate that the average over the molecular orientational motion has to be taken. Here it has to be assumed that the molecule has a sufficiently high mobility.

For rigid molecules when the expectation value $\langle r_{pq}^{-3}\rangle$ is independent of θ_{pq} we have

$$B_{pq}^{\mathrm{dir}} = -\frac{h}{4\pi^2}P_2(\alpha)\gamma_p\gamma_q\frac{1}{\mathbf{r}_{pq}^3}S_{pq}. \tag{7}$$

$\mathbf{r}_{pq}$ may be defined as the NMR distance between the nuclei and S_{pq} is the degree of order. We have included here the case that the magnetic field is not parallel to the nematic symmetry axis. α denotes the angle between the magnetic field and this symmetry axis and

$$P_2(\alpha) = \tfrac{1}{2}(3\cos^2\alpha - 1) \tag{8}$$

is the spherical function of second order. It is equal to 1 for $\alpha = 0$.

4. Orientation and Interactions

The information on molecular orientations that we obtain by spectroscopical measurements allows us to study the interactions that determine the molecular orientational order. By what factors this orientation is determined depends much on the kind of liquid crystal under consideration.

The orientation, for instance, that was found for the solvent molecules of nematic liquid polypeptide solutions is supposed to be due to associations of the small solvent molecules with the oriented polymers. The comparison of the orientation found for dimethyl formamide in different nematic polypeptide solutions supports this assumption.[14] The orientation varies considerably and depends, therefore, obviously on specific solute solvent interactions.

In lyotropic systems, e.g. in soap water solutions, it is of importance whether a molecule dissolved in such a system stays preferably in the water or prefers to stay inside the aggregates formed by the amphiphilic compounds. Benzene, for instance, is hydrophobic and it has been found to have an orientation in these systems comparable in extent to that in thermotropic liquid crystals.[15] For hydrophilic compounds which stay outside the aggregates one expects, on the other hand, only very little orientation.

TABLE 1   Orientation of acetylene and ethylene in nematic solution.   The first column indicates the position of the molecular coordinate system.   (See Refs. 16 and 17).

	S_{11}	S_{22}	S_{33}
H—C≡C—H	− 0.014	0.007	0.007
H₂C=CH₂ (ethylene)	0.064	− 0.033	− 0.031

The discussion of the orientation in thermotropic liquid crystals is in some respects less complicated than in the above systems since here we have not only macroscopically but also microscopically homogeneous systems and specific intermolecular interactions seem to be less important.   It is often assumed that the molecular shape is the dominating factor for the orientation in thermotropic liquid crystals.   And indeed for larger molecules it has always been found that they follow this assumption.   An elongated molecule always orients preferably with the long molecular axis parallel to the optical axis of the liquid.   The long axis has accordingly the largest positive S-value.   On the other hand, the shortest axis has the most negative S-value.   With small molecules the rule does not always hold.

In Table 1 it can be seen that, contrary to the expectations, the symmetry axis of acetylene has a negative S-value.   Ethylene is also an exception.   The axis 3, normal to the molecular plane, which corresponds to the shortest molecular dimension has an S-value slightly less negative than that of axis 2.   The examples show that the geometrical molecular shape can not explain the observation quantitatively.

For a more detailed and more quantitative discussion of the molecular orientation in thermotropic liquid crystals we regard the free energy of the molecule as a function of its orientation.

$$F = F(\theta_1, \theta_2, \theta_3). \tag{9}$$

It is defined so that $e^{-F/kt}$ gives the Boltzmann factors or statistical weight for an orientation characterized by the values θ_1, θ_2 and θ_3. We expand F into a power series of $\cos \theta_i$. In the principle coordinate system where S_{lk} is diagonal, this gives up to terms in third order

$$F = -(a_0 + a_1 \cos^2 \theta_1 + a_2 \cos^2 \theta_2). \tag{9'}$$

If we use (10) the measured S-values allow us to determine the coefficients a_1 and a_2 and, therefore, in our approximation the explicit expression for the orientation dependent part of the free energy.

It is on the other hand possible to estimate theoretically the relative values of the energy coefficients of similar molecules. This has been done for instance for fluorobenzene derivatives.[18]

It was assumed that the difference of the coefficients of different fluorobenzenes is due only to the changes in dispersion forces. With additional assumptions and simplifications, it becomes possible starting from the experimental values of one fluorobenzene to derive the coefficients and calculate the S-values of other fluorobenzenes in the same solution.

Table 2 gives the experimental results and the comparison with calculated values obtained in both solvents by adapting the coefficients a_1 and a_2 for 1,4 fluorobenzene.

It is especially interesting to compare the orientation of ortho- and meta-difluorobenzene. Both molecules have a permanent electrical dipolemoment, but for ortho difluorobenzene the axis 2 which is the axis with the highest S-value is parallel to the dipolemoment while for meta-fluorobenzene it is perpendicular to the dipolemoment. According to the theoretical estimation, both molecules should orient equal and it turns out that they indeed orient very similar. It demonstrates that the permanent dipolemoment is of minor importance for the molecular orientation.

The general agreement is an argument for the importance of dispersion forces. The differences of the experimental results in the different solvents show also clearly that a simple interaction model which does not take into account specific solvent properties can only give a rough approximation and cannot explain finer details of orientation effects. It indicates that in the discussion of molecular structure and crystallinity specific intermolecular interactions have to be considered at least when smaller shifts in clearing temperatures are discussed.

5. The Orientational Distribution Function

The expression for the free energy used in the previous calculations give us, by definition, the complete orientational distribution function. It is, of course, of interest to compare the theoretical distribution function as given in the approximation (10) with the actual distribution in a nematic solvent.

The distribution function can in some cases in fact be experimentally determined by magnetic resonance spectroscopy as first shown by Schwerdtfeger and Diehl.[19] When the viscosity of the liquid crystal is very high, the mobility of the molecules becomes too low for the use of an effective spin-Hamiltonian in ESR experiments.

Instead of averaging over the molecular motion, we have to consider the other extreme that each radical has a quasi-fixed orientation and that all motion can be neglected. When measurements are made under these conditions at different angles between magnetic field and symmetry axis of the liquid it becomes possible to evaluate numerically the distribution function.

Only one radical, vanadyl-acetylaceton has so far been studied in a suitable high viscosity nematic solvent.[19,20] Unfortunately, the experiment gives only the distribution function of the symmetry axis of the coupling tensor. The radical has however no three or more fold symmetry axis which coincides with the axis of the coupling tensor and for that reason a direct check of the approximation (10) is not possible by these results.

TABLE 2 Experimental and calculated S-values and energy coefficients (according to Ref. 18). The position of the molecular coordinate system is indicated in the first column. Values in parenthesis are calculated with parameters adapted for 1,4-difluorobenzene. Solvent I 4,4'-di-n-hexyloxyazoxybenzene, solvent II 3:2 mixture of 4-heptanoyloxy- and 4-hexanoyloxy-4'-ethoxyazobenzene

$\begin{smallmatrix}1\\\uparrow\\\;\to 2\end{smallmatrix}$	Solvent I				Solvent II			
	S_1	S_2	a_1/kT	a_2/kT	S_1	S_2	a_1/kT	a_2/kT
(benzene)	0.05	0.05	0.82	0.82	0.05	0.05	0.82	0.82
	(0.05)	(0.05)	(0.81)	(0.81)	(0.04)	(0.04)	(0.55)	(0.55)
(fluorobenzene)	0.10	0.01	1.09	0.70				
	(0.11)	(0.01)	(1.25)	(0.81)	(0.12)	(−0.01)	(1.11)	(0.55)
(1,4-difluorobenzene)	0.18	−0.03	1.68	0.81	0.20	−0.06	1.66	0.55
	(0.18)	(−0.03)	(1.68)	(0.81)	(0.20)	(−0.06)	(1.66)	(0.55)
(1,3-difluorobenzene)	0.02	0.10	0.83	1.17	0.00	0.14	0.88	1.47
	(0.02)	(0.13)	(1.03)	(1.46)	(0.00)	(0.13)	(0.83)	(1.39)

1.36	1.41	1.92	1.52	3.10
(1.39)	(1.39)	(2.22)	(1.39)	(2.22)
1.03	1.41	1.28	1.95	3.10
(0.83)	(1.39)	(1.11)	(1.94)	(2.22)
0.11	0.08	0.17	0.04	0.14
(0.13)	(0.08)	(0.23)	(0.02)	(0.11)
0.03	0.08	0.01	0.15	0.14
(0.00)	(0.08)	(−0.04)	(0.16)	(0.11)
1.36	1.41	1.95	1.42	3.10
(1.46)	(1.46)	(2.12)	(1.46)	(2.12)
1.03	1.41	1.23	1.82	3.10
(1.03)	(1.46)	(1.24)	(1.90)	(2.12)
0.11	0.08	0.18	0.04	0.14
(0.13)	(0.08)	(0.21)	(0.04)	(0.11)
0.03	0.08	0.00	0.14	0.14
(0.02)	(0.08)	(−0.02)	(0.15)	(0.11)

6. Thermal Fluctuations and Spin-Lattice Relaxation Times

In nematic solutions of low viscosity the positions of the magnetic resonance lines are given by an effective Hamiltonian obtained by averaging over the molecular orientational motion. It gives us the orientation parameters. Measurements of the spin-lattice relaxation times give us some information on the motion itself.

It is known from light scattering and other optical observations that in nematic liquid crystals strong thermal fluctuations of relatively long wavelengths are present. It can, therefore, be expected that there are low frequency components in the molecular orientational motion which will lead to unusual effects in the spin-lattice relaxation times.

A first theoretical treatment was made by Pincus.[21] His starting point is the general relation for T_1 valid in the case of two interacting nuclei of spin 1/2 at a fixed distance r

$$\frac{1}{T_1} = \frac{9}{8}\gamma^2 \frac{h^2}{4\pi^2 r^2}[\zeta_1(\omega) + \zeta_2(2\omega)]. \tag{10}$$

$\zeta_1(\omega)$ and $\zeta_2(2\omega)$ are Fourier transforms of orientational correlation functions for the motion of the nuclear axis.

For the calculation of the Fourier transforms, Pincus used the theory of thermal fluctuations as developed by de Gennes and coworkers.[22] He assumed that the axis of the considered pair is parallel to the long axis of the molecule and assumed further that this can be identified with the director **L** used in the continuum theory. Including possible effects due to diffusion this leads to

$$\frac{1}{T_1} = \frac{9}{16\sqrt{2}\pi^3} \cdot \frac{\gamma^2 h^2}{r^6} - \frac{kT}{(\kappa/\eta + D)^{1/2}} \cdot \frac{1}{\kappa\omega^{1/2}}. \tag{11}$$

Here κ, η, and D denote mean values for an elastic constant, a viscosity coefficient and a diffusion constant.

The frequency dependence predicted by Pincus was in fact found experimentally. The temperature dependence, however, turned out to be not at all in agreement with (11). There is an obvious objection against the treatment by Pincus. It is not justified to identify the momentary orientation of the molecule with the director **L** which is defined as the preferred orientation.

Doane and Johnson[23] avoided this difficulty in their treatment. They introduced a local coordinate system in which one axis coincides with the preferred orientation as obtained by averaging over a sufficiently large area surrounding the considered molecule. The orientational fluctuations of the molecule in this local coordinate system are assumed to contribute nothing to the frequency dependence of T_1. The latter is determined, therefore, by the orientational motions of the local coordinate system which can be described by de Gennes theory. The final expression is

$$\frac{1}{T_1} = \frac{9}{16\sqrt{2\pi^3}} \cdot \frac{\gamma^2 h^2}{r^6} \frac{kT}{(\kappa/\eta + D)^{1/2}} \cdot \frac{S^2}{\kappa\omega^{1/2}}. \tag{12}$$

It differs from the previous one only by the factors S^2. The frequency dependence is unchanged, but the temperature dependence is different. In agreement with the experiment, Eq. (12) gives little temperature dependence, because the ratio S^2/κ has been found to be nearly temperature independent. The problem is, however, still not yet solved satisfactorily. Other difficulties in the explanation of T_1 experiments have turned up (see Ref. 24).

Finally it is interesting to mention that pretransitional effects near the normal liquid to nematic liquid transition point have also observable effects on relaxation times and line widths in the normal liquid. This has first been noticed by Blinc et al.[25] Very recently, careful line width measurements for N^{14} resonances have been made with PAA by Cabane and Clark.[26]

They find a temperature dependence of the line width which agrees very good with the much earlier studies of magnetic birefringence in PAA.[27] The Cotton–Moutton constant has a very similar temperature dependence as the line width, and by extrapolation it is found that both go to infinity at a temperature which is a few degrees lower than the transition temperature. It confirms that the transition is of first order although in many respects it is not very far from a second order transition. Correlations between pretransitional effects have been discussed theoretically some time ago by de Gennes[28] and these experimental results confirm his predictions.

REFERENCES

1. Meiboom, S. and Snyder, L. C., *Science*, **162**, 1337 (1968). *Mol. Crystals and Liq. Crystals*, **7**, 181 (1969).
2. Luckhurst, G. R., *Quarterly Rev. (London)*, **22**, 179 (1968).
3. Saupe, A., *Magnetic Resonance*, 339; Eds. Coogan, C. K., Ham, N. S., Stuart, S. N., Pilbrow, J. R. and Wilson, G. V. H., Plenum Press, New York 1970.
4. Diehl, P. and Khetrapal, C. L., *NMR Basic Principles and Progress*, Vol. 1, Springer-Verlag Berlin, 1969.
5. Ceasar, G. P. and Gray, H. B., *J. Amer. Chem. Soc.*, **91**, 191 (1969).
6. Ceasar, G. P., Levenson, R. A. and Gray, H. B., *J. Amer. Chem. Soc.*, **91**, 772 (1969).
7. Hansen, T. S., *Z. Naturforsch.*, **24a**, 866 (1969).
8. Saupe, A., *Z. Naturforsch.*, **18a**, 336 (1963).
9. Taylor, T. R., Fergason, J. L. and Arora, S. L., *Phys. Rev. Letters*, **24**, 359 (1970).
10. Maier, W. and Markau, K., *Z. Physik. Chem.*, NF **28**, 190 (1961).
11. Amer, N. M., Shen, Y. R. and Rosen, H., *Phys. Rev. Letters*, **24**, 718 (1970).
12. Saupe, A., *Z. Naturforsch.*, **19a**, 161 (1964).
13. Buckingham, A. D. and McLauchlan, K. A., in *Progress in NMR Spectroscopy*, Vol. 2; Eds. Emsley, J. W., Feeney, J. and Sutcliffe, L. H., Pergamon Press, Oxford, 1967.
14. Samulski, E. T. and Tobolski, A. V., *Liquid Crystals and Ordered Fluids*, 117, Eds. Johnson, J. F. and Porter, R. S., Plenum Press, New York 1970.
15. Black, P. J., Lawson, K. D. and Flautt, T. J., *J. Chem. Phys.*, **50**, 542 (1969).
16. Englert, G., Saupe, A. and Weber, J. P., *Z. Naturforsch.*, **23a**, 153 (1968).
17. Spiesecke, H. and Saupe, A., *Mol. Cryst. and Liq. Cryst.*, **6**, 287 (1970).
18. Nehring, J. and Saupe, A., *Mol. Cryst. and Liq. Cryst.*, **8**, 403 (1969).
19. Schwerdtfeger, C. F. and Diehl, P., *Mol. Phys.*, **17**, 417 (1969).
20. James, P. G. and Luckhurst, G. R., *Mol. Phys.*, **19**, 484 (1970).
21. Pincus, P., *Solid State Commun.*, **7**, 415 (1969).
22. Orsay Liquid Crystal Group, *J. Chem. Phys.*, **51**, 816 (1969).
23. Doane, J. W. and Johnson, D. L., *Chem. Phys. Letters*, **6**, 291 (1970).
24. Visintainer, J. J., Doane, J. W. and Fishel, D. L., Lecture at the Int. Liq. Cryst. Conference, Berlin 1970; *Mol. Crystals and Liq. Crystals*, **13**, 69 (1971).
25. Blinc, R., Hogenboom, D. L., O'Reilly, D. E. and Peterson, E. M., *Phys. Rev. Lett.*, **23**, 969 (1969).
26. Cabane, B., Clark, W. G., *Phys. Rev. Letters*, **25**, 2 (1970).
27. Zadoc-Kahn, J., *C.R.*, **191**, 1002 (1930).
28. de Gennes, P. G., *Phys. Letters*, **30a**, 454 (1969).

Short Range Order Effects in the Isotropic Phase of Nematics and Cholesterics†

P. G. DE GENNES‡

Department of Physics
Simon Fraser University
Burnaby 2, B. C., Canada

Received September 22, 1970

Abstract—We assume that (1) the local state of order in the isotropic phase is a symmetric traceless tensor $Q_{\alpha\beta}$, proportional to the anisotropic part of a tensor property such as the magnetic susceptibility; (2) the free energy may be expanded in powers of $Q_{\alpha\beta}$ and of its gradients. This allows a unified description covering the anomalous magnetic birefringence, the intensity of light scattering, and the properties of the nematic/isotropic interface. For a cholesteric, although the optical rotation is huge in the ordered phase, we predict that it should *not* be anomalous just above the transition point T_c. We also investigate the dynamics of fluctuations of $Q_{\alpha\beta}$, and discuss the flow birefringence, the frequency width of the Rayleigh scattering, and the attenuation of ultrasonic shear waves, in terms of 3 viscosity coefficients.

1. Introduction

The nematic↔isotropic transition is of first order, but weak.[1] In most thermotropic materials, the isotropic phase still shows some remarkable short range order effects above the transition point T_c; we give here a short list of the relevant experiments:

(a) *magnetic birefringence*[2-4]: the refractive indices $n_{\parallel}$ and $n_{\perp}$ (measured for polarisations respectively parallel and normal to the magnetic field H) differ by an amount

$$n_{\parallel} - n_{\perp} = \alpha(T)\,H^2 \tag{1.1}$$

Near T_c, α may be a hundred times larger than in conventional organic liquids. Plots of $1/\alpha$ versus T are roughly linear and extra-

---

† Invited Paper presented at the Third International Liquid Crystal Conference, Berlin, August 24–28, 1970.

‡ Permanent address: Physique des solides, Faculté des Sciences, 91 Orsay, France.

21

polation suggests that α would diverge at a temperature T^* which is only slightly smaller than T_c ($T_c - T^* \gtrsim 1 \, °\mathrm{K}$).

(b) *intensity of light scattering I*: although smaller than in the nematic phase[5] I is still significant.[6] It is essentially independent of the scattering angle θ, and the ratio $I_\perp / I_\parallel$ (for the two conventional polarisation set ups) is $\frac{3}{4}$ as it is for a collection of anisotropic scattering objects with random orientations.[6] Since I is independent of θ, the size of these objects, or, more accurately, the " coherence length " $\xi(T)$, is smaller than the optical wavelength. Typically we expect $\xi(T_c)$ to be of order 10 times the molecular length (i.e. $\sim 200 \, \text{Å}$): This is still large enough to allow a macroscopic description of fluctuation and correlation effects. One of the aims of the present paper is to give a detailed definition of these coherence lengths.

(c) *flow birefringence[2]*: with a flow velocity v, in the x direction, and under a velocity gradient $\partial v / \partial z$, the isotropic phase becomes birefringent, with two optical axes (1) and (2) at 45° from x and z. The difference in refraction indices $n_1 - n_2$ is proportional to the rate of shear

$$n_1 - n_2 = \tau(T) \frac{\partial v}{\partial z} \tag{1.2}$$

τ has the dimension of time, and is much larger than in conventional liquids.

The Zvetkov measurements of τ[2] were not very accurate, but, they do show a strong increase of τ when T decreases down to T_c.

(d) *frequency width of the scattered light*: this has been measured with a Fabry–Perot interferometer.[3,6] The observed line is a single Lorentzian, of half width ($\Gamma/2\pi$). Γ is small (in the megacycle range) when $T = T_c$, and increases with T. The presence of only one Lorentzian is remarkable, and will be discussed in detail in section 4.

More generally, the aim of the present paper is to give a unified discussion of short range order effect, in terms of a Landau model for the nematic isotropic transition. The principles have been sketched in an earlier short communication.[7] The first problem is to define an adequate order parameter—here a tensorial object $Q_{\alpha\beta}$, as explained in section 2. Then we assume that the free energy F may be expanded in powers of $Q_{\alpha\beta}$: the symmetry properties of $F(Q)$ then force the transition to be first order. However, just above

T_c, the fluctuations may be large. This is discussed in section 3, together with some static applications, including effects (a) and (b) above, plus the properties of the nematic/isotropic interface. Section 4 discusses the dynamics of fluctuations, using the thermodynamics of irreversible processes as a framework, and including the coupling between molecular rotation and flow. Finally we try to extend these considerations to cholesteric materials: the new feature here is the presence of a term proportional to Q grad Q in the free energy. We discuss the physical implications of this unusual term on the static optical properties in section 5.

2. Definition of an Order Parameter

(a) *microscopic approach*: For a system of rod-like molecules, the natural order parameter, in a nematic phase, is

$$S = \langle \tfrac{1}{2}(3 \cos^2 \theta - 1) \rangle \tag{2.1}$$

where θ is the angle between rod axis and nematic axis. For rigid molecules of more general shape, a natural generalisation of (2.1) amounts to use

$$S_{ij}^{\alpha\beta} = \langle \tfrac{1}{2}(3i_\alpha j_\beta - \delta_{ij}\delta_{\alpha\beta}) \rangle \tag{2.2}$$

where i, j, k are three orthonormal vectors linked to the molecule, while α and β are indices referring to the laboratory frame. In a uniaxial nematic of optical axis parallel to z, the only non 0 components of $S_{ij}^{\alpha\beta}$ are the following

$$\left. \begin{array}{c} S_{ij}^{zz} = S_{ij} \\ S_{ij}^{xx} = S_{ij}^{yy} = -\tfrac{1}{2}S_{ij} \end{array} \right\} \tag{2.3}$$

(b) *macroscopic approach*: Many nematic molecules are partly flexible, and different parts of one same molecule would give different S_{ij} tensors. Also, from a thermodynamic point of view, it is preferable to define the amount of order from a macroscopic property, independently of any assumption on the rigidity of the molecules. Consider for instance the anisotropy of the magnetic susceptibility: let us define[8]

$$Q_{\alpha\beta} = \chi_{\alpha\beta} - \tfrac{1}{3}\chi_{\gamma\gamma}\delta_{\alpha\beta} \tag{2.4}$$

$Q_{\alpha\beta}$ is a symmetric, traceless tensor: we call it the *tensor order parameter*. It must be emphasized that any other tensor property (i.e. the dielectric constant $\epsilon_{\alpha\beta}$) could have been used to define $Q_{\alpha\beta}$. In the isotropic phase, where $Q_{\alpha\beta}$ is small, any other anisotropic effect is linear in Q. For instance we may write

$$\delta\epsilon_{\alpha\beta} \equiv \epsilon_{\alpha\beta} - \tfrac{1}{3}\epsilon_{\gamma\gamma}\,\delta_{\alpha\beta} = M_{\alpha\beta\gamma\delta}\,Q_{\gamma\delta} \qquad (2.5)$$

The only matrix M relating two symmetric traceless tensors ($\delta\epsilon$ and Q) and compatible with rotational invariance is a multiple of the unit matrix. Thus Eq. (1) reduces to

$$\delta\epsilon_{\alpha\beta} = M\,Q_{\alpha\beta} \qquad (2.6)$$

For simple rod-like molecules M is simply the ratio of dielectric/magnetic anisotropies in the ordered phase.

We have chosen here to define $Q_{\alpha\beta}$ through the diamagnetic anisotropy for the following reason: theoretical calculations of $\chi_{\alpha\beta}$ are feasible, since magnetic interactions between different molecules are negligible. For instance, with a rigid molecule, let us assume that we know the suspectibility tensor (per molecule) in the molecular frame χ^{ij}. Then $\chi_{\alpha\beta}$ is simply a superposition of individual responses, and if n is the number of molecules/cm³, we may write

$$Q_{\alpha\beta} = nS_{ij}^{\alpha\beta}\,\chi^{ij}$$

In a uniaxial nematic, the difference between parallel and perpendicular susceptibilities is

$$\chi_{\parallel} - \chi_{\perp} = Q_{zz} - Q_{xx} = \tfrac{3}{2}S_{ij}\chi^{ij} \qquad (2.7)$$

Equation (2.7) gives, for rigid molecules, the link between the microscopic definition of order (via S) and the macroscopic (via Q). If we had chosen to define Q from the dielectric anisotropy, we could not have produced such explicit formulae—the present theory of dielectric constants in liquids being unable to take into account correctly the electric interactions between different molecules.

(c) *biaxial versus uniaxial nematics*: Our definition of the order parameter covers both uniaxial and biaxial nematic systems: the matrix $Q_{\alpha\beta}$, when diagonalized, may have the form

$$Q_{\alpha\beta} = \begin{bmatrix} \dfrac{-Q+P}{2} & & 0 \\ 0 & \dfrac{-Q-P}{2} & 0 \\ 0 & & 2 \quad Q \end{bmatrix} \qquad (2.8)$$

Depending on the form of the free energy F as a function of Q and P, the minimum of F may correspond to $P = 0$ (uniaxial nematic) or $P \neq 0$ (biaxial nematic). The possible existence of biaxial phases has been stressed in particular by Freiser.[9]

3. Free Energy and Static Properties

3.1. LANDAU EXPANSION OF THE FREE ENERGY

Let us assume that the free energy F (per unit volume) may be expanded in powers of $Q_{\alpha\beta}$. Then, retaining only terms which have rotational invariance, we may expect the following structure

$$\bar{F} = F_0 + \tfrac{1}{2}A Q_{\alpha\beta}Q_{\beta\alpha} + \tfrac{1}{3}B Q_{\alpha\beta}Q_{\beta\gamma}Q_{\gamma\alpha} + 0(Q^4) - \tfrac{1}{2}Q_{\alpha\beta}H_\alpha H_\beta \quad (3.1)$$

where F_0 is independent of Q. Because Q is symmetric traceless there is only one invariant of order Q^2 (with the coefficient $A/2$) and one invariant of order Q^3 (there would be two invariants of order Q^4). $A(T)$ is expected to be small near T_c. More precisely we can put

$$A(T) = a(T - T^*)^\gamma \quad (3.2)$$

where T^* is a temperature slightly below T_c, and γ an unknown exponent.

($\gamma = 1$ in a mean field theory such as the Maier Saupe theory.)

The last term in (3.1) is the anisotropic part of the diamagnetic energy, in a field H. The presence of a cubic term BQ^3 in (3.1) imposes a first order transition, as explained in Fig. 1. If one assumed that an expansion to order Q^4 is acceptable even in the ordered phase, one could derive formulas for the order parameter just below T_c, the latent heat, etc; however, it is not obvious that the terms of order Q^5, etc., are indeed negligible in the ordered phase. For this reason we shall mainly restrict our attention to the isotropic phase ($T > T_c$) where Q is indeed small.

3.2. APPLICATION TO THE MAGNETIC BIREFRINGENCE

In a non 0 external field, the minimum of F (Eq. 3.1) corresponds to a non 0 Q, i.e. to a finite anisotropy in the optical properties. Minimizing F with respect to $Q_{\alpha\beta}$, and keeping in mind the constraint of 0 trace ($Q_{\alpha\alpha} = 0$) one finds (to order H^2) for the thermal average of Q:

$$\langle Q_{\alpha\beta} \rangle = \frac{1}{2A}\left(H_\alpha H_\beta - \tfrac{1}{3}H^2 \delta_{\alpha\beta}\right) \quad (3.3)$$

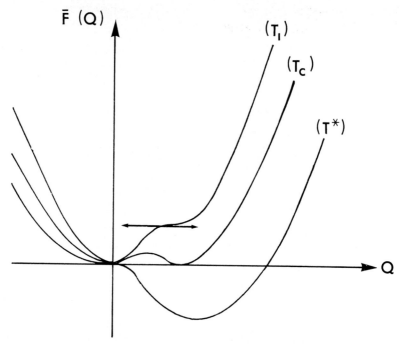

Figure 1.   Plot of free energy $\bar{F}$ versus order parameter Q, in zero magnetic field, at various temperatures. T_c is the equilibrium transition point. T^* is the temperature below which the isotropic phase is absolutely unstable. T_1 is the temperature above which the nematic phase is absolutely unstable.

Take for instance H along Z.   Then

$$Q_{zz} - Q_{xx} = \frac{H^2}{2A}$$

and from Eq. (2.6), the dielectric anisotropy is

$$\delta\epsilon_{zz} - \delta\epsilon_{xx} = \frac{MH^2}{2A}$$

(where ϵ and M are defined for the frequency of the optical measurement)

Finally the birefringence is obtained by writing $n_{\parallel}^2 = \epsilon_{zz}, n_{\perp}^2 = \epsilon_{xx}$

$$n_{\parallel} - n_{\perp} = \frac{MH^2}{4A\bar{n}} = \alpha(T)H^2 \qquad (3.4)$$

We do not expect any strong variation in M or $\bar{n}$ near T_c, thus

$1/\alpha(T)$ is essentially proportional to $A(T)$. The existing data suggest that $1/\alpha$ is nearly linear in T ($\gamma \cong 1$).

3.3. DEFINITION OF COHERENCE LENGTHS

Let us now add terms in F which can describe situations where the order parameter varies slowly from point to point. In a nematic fluid, the first terms allowed by symmetry are quadratic in the gradients of Q and have the form

$$F_g = \tfrac{1}{2} L_1 \partial_\alpha Q_{\beta\gamma} \partial_\alpha Q_{\beta\gamma} + \tfrac{1}{2} L_2 \partial_\alpha Q_{\alpha\gamma} \partial_\beta Q_{\beta\gamma} \tag{3.5}$$

where $\partial_\alpha \equiv \partial/\partial x_\alpha$. L_1 and L_2 may be called the elastic constants in the isotropic phase. Their number is smaller than in the ordered phase (where there are three constants[10]) because in Eq (3.5) we restrict our attention to terms of order Q^2, i.e. to small Q. To get more information on the meaning of L_1 and L_2 let us consider the case where Q depends only on one co-ordinate, say z. Then

$$F_g = \frac{L_1}{2} [(\partial_z Q_{zz})^2 + (\partial_z Q_{xx})^2 + (\partial_z Q_{yy})^2] + L_1 [(\partial_z Q_{xy})^2 + (\partial_z Q_{yz})^2$$

$$+ (\partial_z Q_{zx})^2] + \frac{L_2}{2} [(\partial_z Q_{zz})^2 + (\partial_z Q_{zx})^2 + (\partial_z Q_{zy})^2] \tag{3.6}$$

From Eq. (3.6) we may derive a number of inequalities which must be satisfied by the elastic constants to ensure stability (i.e., F_g must be positive for all distortions of Q).

Let us start with a situation where Q_{xy} is the only non-vanishing component. Then from Eq. (3.6) we get the stability condition

$$L_1 > 0 \tag{3.7}$$

Similarly with Q_{xz} (or Q_{yz}) we obtain

$$L_1 + \tfrac{1}{2} L_2 > 0 \tag{3.8}$$

Considerations involving the diagonal terms Q_{xx}, Q_{yy}, Q_{zz} are more delicate because the sum of these three terms must vanish identically. Let us consider first a case where, at all points, the nematic axis is parallel to $0z$. (Fig. 2a) (at $T = T_c$, this would describe a nematic/isotropic interface with the optical axis normal to the interface). In such a situation we may put

$$Q_{zz} = Q \quad Q_{xx} = Q_{yy} = -\frac{Q}{2} \quad Q_{xy} = Q_{yz} = Q_{zx} = 0$$

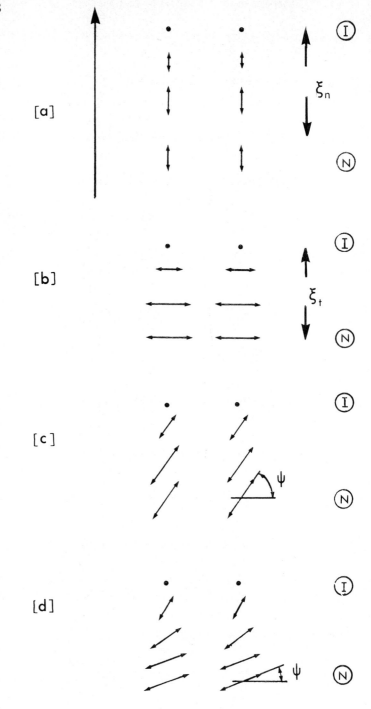

and we get from Eq. (3.6)

$$F_g = \frac{3L_1 - 2L_2}{4}\left(\frac{dQ}{dz}\right)^2 \tag{3.9}$$

Adding the other terms of order Q^2 from Eq. (3.1) we get for the free energy

$$F = \bar{F} + F_g = \tfrac{3}{4}AQ^2 + \frac{3L_1 + 2L_2}{4}\left(\frac{dQ}{dz}\right)^2$$

$$= \tfrac{3}{4}A\left[Q^2 + \xi_n^2\left(\frac{dQ}{dz}\right)^2\right] \tag{3.10}$$

$$\xi_n^2(T) = \frac{(L_1 + \tfrac{2}{3}L_2)}{A(T)} \tag{3.11}$$

where we have defined the " normal coherence length " $\xi_n(T)$. ξ_n^2 must be positive = this implies the inequality

$$L_1 + \tfrac{2}{3}L_2 > 0$$

Now let us go the tangential case of Fig. (2b). Here we assume

$$Q_{xx} = Q \quad Q_{yy} = Q_{zz} = -\frac{Q}{2} \quad Q_{xy} = Q_{yz} = Q_{zx} = 0$$

and we obtain for the free energy, to order Q^2

$$F = \tfrac{3}{4}A\left[Q^2 + \xi_t^2(T)\left(\frac{dQ}{dz}\right)^2\right] \tag{3.12}$$

where the " tangential coherence length " $\xi_t(T)$ is given by

$$\xi_t^2(T) = (L_1 + \tfrac{1}{6}L_2)\frac{1}{A(T)} \tag{3.13}$$

We also have the stability requirement:

$$L_1 + \tfrac{1}{6}L_2 > 0$$

but, if the conditions (3.7) and (3.11) are satisfied, the other conditions will also be satisfied. The two lengths ξ_n and ξ_t are expected

---

Figure 2.   Possible structures for the nematic/isotropic interface:
   (a) normal case; (b) tangential case; (c) conical case with constant angle in the transition layer; (d) conical case with variable angle.

to be comparable in magnitude (for qualitative discussions we will sometimes replace them by a single length $\xi(T)$). Near T_c the coherence lengths are large (but finite) since $A(T_c)$ is small (but non 0). Qualitatively, neglecting all indices, and neglecting the difference between ξ_n and ξ_t) we may say that the QQ correlation function has the form:

$$\langle Q(0)\, Q(R) \rangle = \frac{\text{const. } k_B T}{L_1 R}\, e^{-R/\xi} \quad (R \gtrsim \xi) \tag{3.14}$$

At first sight we might hope to measure the coherence lengths ξ_n and ξ_t (or suitable admixtures of these two) by a study of the scattered light intensity I. However, the data of Litster and Stinson[6] show that I is essentially independent of the scattering wave vector q. This means then $q\xi \ll 1$ and in this limit we cannot measure ξ.

The magnitude of the scattered intensity is easily derived for $q\xi \ll 1$. Consider for instance the case where the incident light is polarized along x, while the outgoing light is polarized along y. The corresponding intensity $I_\perp$ is proportional to the average square.

$$I_\perp \cong \langle |\, \delta\epsilon_{zx} |^2 \rangle = M^2 \langle Q_{zx}^2 \rangle \tag{3.15}$$

To order Q^2 the only terms in the free energy (3.1) involving Q_{zx} are $\frac{1}{2} A(Q_{zx}^2 + Q_{xz}^2) = A Q_{zx}^2$. The gradient terms (3.5) are negligible for $g\xi \ll 1$. Then applying the equipartition theorem gives (per unit volume)

$$A \langle Q_{zx}^2 \rangle = \tfrac{1}{2} k_B T$$

$$I_\perp \cong \langle |\, \delta\epsilon_{zx} |^2 \rangle = \frac{M^2 k_B T}{2A}. \tag{3.16a}$$

Similarly, when both polarizations are parallel to X, we get

$$I_{\|} \cong \langle |\, \delta\epsilon_{zz} |^2 \rangle = \tfrac{2}{3} \frac{M^2 k_B T}{A} \tag{3.16b}$$

Thus the intensities are proportional to $1/A$. This has been verified by Stinson and Litster.[6]

3.4. The Nematic/Isotropic Interface

In the present paragraph we shall assume that the distortion free energy is correctly described by Eq. (3.5), even when the variations of Q take place in a distance comparable to $\xi(T)$. (This is equivalent to a mean field approximation). We can then apply our earlier Eqs. (3.10) and (3.12) to a discussion of the N/I interface, at $T = T_c$. Here Q goes from a finite value (at $z = -\infty$) to 0 (at $z = +\infty$), the variations taking place in a thickness $\xi(T_c)$ which is large compared with the molecular dimensions a.

Consider first the "normal" case where Q has the structure defined immediately before Eq (3.9). We may write the surface tension γ_r in the form

$$\gamma_n = \int_{-\infty}^{\infty} dz \left[\bar{F}(Q) + b_n^2 \left(\frac{dQ}{dz} \right)^2 \right] \tag{3.17}$$

Here $b_n^2 = (3L_1 + 2L_2)/4$ and $\bar{F}(Q)$ is the free energy (3.1), including now all powers of Q. The origin of free energies is such that $\bar{F}(0) = \bar{F}(Q*) = 0$ where $Q*$ is the order parameter in the nematic phase, at $T = T_c$. Writing that the form of $Q(z)$ minimizes γ we get the equation

$$2b_n^2 \frac{d^2Q}{dz^2} = \frac{\partial \bar{F}}{0Q} \tag{3.18}$$

This equation has the first integral

$$b_n^2 \left(\frac{dQ}{dz} \right)^2 = \bar{F}(Q) \tag{3.19}$$

where the integration constant must vanish, since both dQ/dz and $\bar{F}(Q)$ are zero far from the transition layer. Inserting Eq. (3.19) into (3.17) we get

$$\gamma_n = 2 \int_{-\infty}^{\infty} b_n^2 \frac{dQ}{dz} dQ = 2b_n \int_0^{Q*} [\bar{F}(Q)]^{1/2} dQ \tag{3.20}$$

Similarly, for the tangential case, we get

$$\left. \begin{array}{l} \gamma_t = 2b_t \int_0^{Q*} [\bar{F}(Q)]^{1/2} dQ \\[2mm] b_t^2 = \tfrac{1}{4}(3L_1 + \tfrac{1}{2}L_2) \end{array} \right\} \tag{3.21}$$

Comparing (3.20) and (3.21) we see that, if $L_2 > 0$, b_t is smaller than b_n, and $\gamma_t < \gamma_n =$ the tangential conformation is favoured. On the other hand, if $L_2 < 0$, the normal conformation is favoured.

A word of caution should be inserted at this point: the actual conformation at the interface may be different from the normal and tangential cases considered above. In macroscopic terms, we may say that the preferred angle between the director and the N/I surface need not be 0, or $\pi/2$: it might be some intermediate angle. To compute the interface tension γ for such cases is difficult. We have only carried out a simple variational calculation, assuming that at all points in the transition layer the medium is uniaxial, with an optical axis which is the same everywhere (making a constant angle ψ with the surface—Fig. 2c). Within this approximation we can show that the minimum of γ occurs either at $\psi = 0$ if $L_2 > 0$) or at $\psi = \pi/2$ if $L_2 < 0$), but not at an intermediate ψ value. But a much more elaborate calculation would be required to elucidate this point completely.

4. Dynamics of Fluctuations

4.1. FLUXES AND FORCES

In the nematic phase we know both from theory [5] and from experiment [11] than an orientational fluctuation of wave vector q relaxes in a purely viscous way (no oscillations) with a time constant τ_g given qualitatively by

$$\frac{1}{\tau_g} \cong \frac{Kg^2}{\eta_{\text{eff}}} \qquad (4.1)$$

where K is an average of the Frank elastic constants, [10] and η_{eff} an average viscosity. This result suggests that, above T_c, where the fluid is more disordered, we will also find a strongly dissipative behaviour: such a behaviour may then be analyzed in terms of the thermodynamics of irreversible processes, introducing *fluxes* and *forces*.

(a) *Fluxes.* One group of such fluxes is given by the rate of change in time of $Q_{\alpha\beta}$

$$R_{\alpha\beta} = \frac{\delta Q_{\alpha\beta}}{\delta t} \qquad (4.2)$$

The differentiation symbol $\delta/\delta t$ denotes the variation (along one flow line) with respect to the background fluid; in particular, if the fluid is in rotation, the part of the change of Q due to this rotation must be subtracted, as explained in Ref. (7). However, in all what follows, we shall treat v_α and $Q_{\alpha\beta}$ as infinitesimal quantities of first order. Then the difference between $\delta/\delta t$ and the partial derivative $\partial/\partial t$ is of second order and may be neglected:

$$R_{\alpha\beta} \to \frac{\partial Q_{\alpha\beta}}{\delta t} \tag{4.3}$$

Another group of fluxes which is important here is the hydro-dynamic shear rate tensor

$$e_{\alpha\beta} = \partial_\alpha v_\beta + \partial_\beta v_\alpha \tag{4.4}$$

We restrict our attention to incompressible flow ($e_{\alpha\alpha} \equiv 0$). As explained in Ref. (5), this appears to be justified because the fluctuations of Q have a frequency spectrum much lower than the sound waves.

(b) *Forces.* The force $\phi_{\alpha\beta}$, conjugate to $Q_{\alpha\beta}$, may be obtained directly from the free energy F (e.g., 3.1, 3.5). We restrict our attention to terms of F which are quadratic on Q, giving linear contributions to ϕ. Furthermore, in most of the applications to be discussed below, the wave vectors q of interest will turn out to be small ($q\xi \ll 1$) and the derivative terms from (3.5) will be negligible; then:

$$\phi_{\alpha\beta} = \frac{-\delta F}{\delta Q_{\alpha\beta}} = -AQ_{\alpha\beta}. \tag{4.5}$$

The force conjugate to $e_{\alpha\beta}$ is $\frac{1}{2}\sigma_{\alpha\beta}$, where $\sigma_{\alpha\beta}$ is the viscous stress tensor.

Finally the entropy source may be written as a bilinear function of fluxes and forces

$$TS = \phi_{\alpha\beta} R_{\alpha\beta} + \tfrac{1}{2}\sigma_{\alpha\beta} e_{\alpha\beta} \tag{4.6}$$

Our choice of fluxes and forces purposely omits certain effects (such as temperature fluctuations) which are not anomalously large and not strongly coupled to the order parameter Q.

4.2. Hydrodynamic Equations in the Isotropic Phase

We now write down a phenomenological system of linear equations coupling the fluxes and the forces. Since all these quantities are symmetric traceless tensors of rank 2, the most general form for these equations, which is compatible with rotational invariance and the Onsager relations, is[12]:

$$\tfrac{1}{2}\sigma_{\alpha\beta} = \tfrac{1}{2}\eta\, e_{\alpha\beta} + \mu R_{\alpha\beta} \tag{4.7}$$

$$\phi_{\alpha\beta} = \mu\, e_{\alpha\beta} + \gamma R_{\alpha\beta} \tag{4.8}$$

If Q is taken as dimensionless, both R and e have the dimension of frequency. A and σ have the dimension of pressure. The three coefficients η, μ, ν have the dimension of a viscosity.

Imposing that the entropy source (4.6) be positive leads to the inequality

$$2\mu^2 > \nu\eta \tag{4.9}$$

In addition we need the hydrodynamic acceleration equation

$$\rho \frac{dv_\alpha}{dt} \sim \rho \frac{\partial v_\alpha}{\partial t} = \partial_\beta \sigma_{\alpha\beta} - \partial_\beta p \tag{4.10}$$

where ρ is the density and p the scalar pressure, Eqs. (4.5, 8, 9, 10) together with the incompressibility condition ($e_{\alpha\alpha} = 0$) define entirely the problem of small motions.

4.3. DISCUSSION OF EXPERIMENTS

(a) *flow birefringence*: with a flow velocity v along x, and a velocity gradient $e_{xz} = \partial v/\partial z$, we have a steady state ($R_{\alpha\beta} = 0$) corresponding to $\phi_{xz} = \mu e_{xz}$ from Eq. (4.8). Inserting Eq. (4.5) for ϕ_{xz} we arrive at

$$Q_{xz} = -\frac{\mu}{A}\frac{\partial v}{\partial z} \tag{4.11}$$

all other components of Q being 0. This implies that two principal axes of the Q tensor (1) and (2) are the bisectors of the x and z axis. The dielectric anisotropy is

$$\left| \epsilon_1 - \epsilon_2 \right| = M \left| Q_{11} - Q_{22} \right| = M Q_{xy} \tag{4.12}$$

The difference in refracting indices is

$$\left| n_1 - n_2 \right| = \frac{M}{2n}\left| Q_{xy} \right| = \left| \frac{M\mu}{2nA} \right| \frac{\partial v}{\partial z} \tag{4.13}$$

Thus the characteristic time $\tau(T)$ defined in Eq. (1.3) is given by

$$\tau(T) = \frac{M\mu}{2nA(T)} \tag{4.14}$$

In Eq. (4.14) the most important temperature effects come from $A(T)$. The factors M and n are probably temperature insensitive. The friction coefficient μ might vary significantly with T. The data of Zvetkov[3] are not accurate enough to decide on this point.

(b) *inelastic scattering of light—simplified treatment*: For small wave vectors q, it turns out that the characteristic frequencies of the fluctuations of Q are very different from the frequencies associated with v. In such case, the coupling between v and Q is uneffective: in the dynamical Eq. (4.8) for $Q_{\alpha\beta}$ we may neglect the v term. Then we find a simple exponential relaxation for $Q_{\alpha\beta}$, involving one single relaxation rate:

$$\frac{\partial Q_{\alpha\beta}}{\partial t} = -\Gamma Q_{\alpha\beta} \qquad (4.15)$$

$$\Gamma(T) = \frac{A(T)}{\nu} \qquad (4.16)$$

The consequences of Eq. (4.16) have been investigated by Stinson and Litster.[3] Taking $A(T)$ from the magnetic birefringence, they find that the temperature dependence of Γ can be accounted for if one assumes that ν varies in temperature just as the average viscosity η. Cases where Eq. (4.15) is not applicable (because of the coupling between Q and v) will be discussed in paragraph 4.4.

(c) *shear wave attenuation*: Let us assume that the liquid crystal is driven at an angular frequency ω, with shear waves propagating along z, the flow velocity being along x. The shear stress is from Eq. (4.7)

$$\sigma_{xz} = \eta \frac{\partial v}{\partial z} + 2\mu \frac{\partial Q_{xz}}{\partial t} \qquad (4.17)$$

and the equation for the order parameter is:

$$\frac{\partial Q_{xz}}{\partial t} + \Gamma Q_{xz} = -\frac{\mu}{\nu} \frac{\partial v}{\partial x} \qquad (4.18)$$

Replacing $\partial/\partial t$ by $i\omega$ and eliminating Q_{xz} between (4.17) and (4.18) we arrive at a simplified form of the acceleration equation

$$i\omega \rho v = \eta(\omega) \frac{\partial^2 v}{\partial x^2} \qquad (4.19)$$

where the effective viscosity $\eta(\omega)$ is defined by

$$\eta(\omega) = \eta - \frac{2\mu^2}{\nu} \frac{i\omega}{\Gamma + i\omega} \qquad (4.20)$$

Thus $\eta(\omega)$ goes from η (for $\omega \ll \Gamma$) to $\eta - (2\mu^2/\nu)$ (for $\omega \gg \Gamma$) Dispersion anomalies in this frequency range have indeed been observed very recently,[13] but it is not known yet whether the simple form (4.20) accounts for them or not.

The concept of an effective viscosity $\eta(\omega)$ applies only when the penetration depth of the shear waves $(\eta/\rho\omega)^{1/2} = \delta$ is much larger than the coherence length $\xi(T)$. This is indeed correct when $\omega \sim \Gamma$, as can be seen from the following argument:

$$\frac{\xi^2}{\delta^2} = \xi^2 \frac{\rho\Gamma}{\eta} \sim \frac{\rho A L_1}{\eta\gamma A} = \frac{L_1\rho}{\eta\gamma} \qquad (4.21)$$

The parameter $L_1\rho/\eta\gamma$ is similar in magnitude and in physical content to the parameter $K\rho/\eta^2$ ($K = $ Frank elastic constant) which is central to the discussion of the fluctuation modes in the ordered phase. As pointed out in Ref. (5) this parameter is of order 10^{-4} or less: thus $\xi/\delta \gtrsim 10^{-2}$ and the concept of an effective viscosity is acceptable.

4.4. COUPLED MODES OF BIREFRINGENCE AND FLOW

We now discuss in more detail the coupled relaxation modes of Q and v, for a Fourier component of given wave vector q. The characteristic frequency associated with v is $\eta q^2/\rho$. The characteristic frequency associated with Q is the Litster width Γ. For small q values, these two frequencies are widely different, and the coupling between v and Q has very little influence on the power spectrum of Q, as measured by light scattering: we made use of this observation in paragraph 3b of this section. Here, we shall focus our attention on the opposite case, where both frequencies are comparable:

$$\Gamma \sim \frac{\eta q^2}{\rho} \qquad (4.22)$$

It should be emphasized that (4.22) is compatible with our general assumption $q\xi \ll 1$. In fact, from Eq. (4.16) we see that the condition (4.22) corresponds to

$$q\xi \sim \left(\frac{\eta v}{L_1\rho}\right)^{1/2} \sim 10^{-2}$$

Let us put the z axis of our reference frame along q ($\partial/\partial x \to 0$ $\partial/\partial y \to 0$ $\partial/\partial z \to iq$). Because of the incompressibility condition we have only two non 0 components of v (v_x and v_y). v_x is coupled to Q_{xz} by Eqs. (4.7, 4.8). Similarly v_y is coupled to Q_{yz}. All the other components of Q ($Q_{zz}, Q_{xx}, Q_{xy}, \dots$) are not coupled to the hydrodynamic flow, and relax with a single relaxation rate Γ. From now on, we shall concentrate on Q_{xz} and v_x. With suitable polarizations, the light scattering experiment (performed at wave vector q and frequency shift ω) measures the quantity:

$$S(q\omega) = \int dt < Q_{xy}(-q, 0) Q_{xy}(qt) e^{-i\omega t} > = -\frac{k_\beta T}{\pi \omega} IM[\chi(q\omega)]$$

$$(4.23)$$

$\chi(q\omega)$ is a response function giving Q_{xy} when the system is submitted to an external perturbation $(H_x H_z)$ modulated at wave vector q and frequency ω. Equation (4.23) is a statement of the fluctuation dissipation theorem for χ. Our use of response functions is similar in spirit to Ref. (5). χ may be derived very directly from Eqs. (4.7, 4.8, 4.10), which give, after inclusion of the external pertubation:

$$iq\frac{\mu}{\nu} v_x + (i\omega + \Gamma)Q_{xz} = \Gamma \chi_0 H_x H_z \qquad (4.24)$$

$$\left(i\omega + \frac{\eta}{\rho} q^2\right) v_x + \frac{2\mu}{\rho} q\omega Q_{xz} = 0 \qquad (4.25)$$

Here $\chi_0 = 1/2A$ is the static susceptibility (Eq. 3.3). Solving Eq. (4.24, 4.25) for $Q_{xz} \equiv \chi(q\omega) H_x H_z$ and taking the imaginary part of χ leads to:

$$S(q\omega) = \frac{k_\beta T}{2\pi\nu} \frac{\omega^2 + ab\,q^4}{(\omega^2 - \Gamma aq^2)^2 + \omega^2(\Gamma + bq^2)^2} \qquad (4.26)$$

where

$$a = \frac{\eta}{\rho}$$

$$b = \frac{\eta}{\rho} - \frac{2\mu^2}{\nu\rho}$$

Equation (4.26) shows that in general the power spectrum of Q_{xz} is not composed of a single Lorentzian. However, when $aq^2 \ll \Gamma$ we recover a single Lorentzian of width Γ. In the opposite limit $(aq^2 \gg \Gamma)$ we also find a single Lorentzian, but with a modified width:

$$\Gamma' = \frac{a}{b} \Gamma \qquad \left(\frac{\Gamma}{a} < q^2 < \xi^{-2}\right) \qquad (4.27)$$

The more complicated scattering law described by Eq. (4.26) has not been observed by Litster and Stinson [2,6] but it might be worthwhile to search for it with suitable q values and polarization indices.

5. Extension to Cholesterics

5.1. STRUCTURE OF THE FREE ENERGY

With an optically active material, it is still possible to define an order parameter $Q_{\alpha\beta}$ by Eq. (2.7). The static magnetic susceptibility tensor is always symmetric, and $Q_{\alpha\beta}$ is symmetric traceless. The expansion of the free energy $\bar{F}$ in powers of Q retains the structure (3.1) and Eq. (3.4) for the magnetic birefringence is always valid. Thus, if T^* is only slightly below T_c, cholesterics will show a large magnetic birefringence anomaly, just like nematics.[14]

New features appear when we investigate the terms involving the gradients of Q in the free energy: symmetry allows for a new term

$$F_c = q_0 L_1 \epsilon_{\alpha\beta\gamma} Q_{\alpha\mu} \, \partial_\gamma Q_{\beta\mu} \qquad (5.1)$$

In this formula $\epsilon_{\alpha\beta\gamma}$ is the alternant symbol ($\epsilon_{xyz} = 1$, $\epsilon_{xxx} = 0$, etc.) and is antisymmetric with respect to all pairs of indices. The energy density F_c is a pseudoscalar, and its coefficient must vanish in a nematic. But in a cholesteric F_c must be included: the complete free energy contains (a) the term $\bar{F}$ for a uniform Q; (b) the term F_c (linear in grad Q); (c) the usual term F_g quadratic in the gradients (Eq. 3.5). The coefficient in F_c has been written as $q_0 L_1$ where L_1 is still defined by Eq. (3.5), and q_0 has the dimension of an inverse length. Qualitatively we may say that $2\pi/q_0$ is the helical pitch which the isotropic phase would tend to display for T just above T_c. We shall now explore some consequences of the presence of F_c in the free energy.

5.2. INTENSITY OF LIGHT SCATTERING

Let us now discuss the magnitude of the fluctuations of Q for a Fourier component of given wave vector q. As in section 4, we take our z axis parallel to Q. From Eqs. (3.1, 3.5 and 5.1) we get for the free energy associated with this Fourier component, to order Q^2:

$$F(q) = \tfrac{1}{2}(A + L_1 q^2)[\tfrac{3}{2}Q^2 + \tfrac{1}{2}P^2 + 2(|Q_{xy}|^2 + |Q_{yz}| + Q_{zx}{}^2|)]$$
$$+ \tfrac{1}{2}L_2 q^2[Q^2 + |Q_{xz}|^2 + |Q_{zy}|^2]$$
$$+ 2q_0 L_1[P'' Q'_{xy} - P' Q''_{xy} + Q''_{xz} Q'_{yz} - Q'_{xz} Q''_{yz}] \qquad (5.2)$$

In Eq. (5.2) we have used the notation of Eq. (2.8) for the diagonal components of $Q_{\alpha\beta}$. We have also analyzed the Fourier component $Q_{\alpha\beta}(q)$ in its real and imaginary part $Q_{\alpha\beta}(q) = Q'_{\alpha\beta}(q) + iQ''_{\alpha\beta}(q)$. Diagonalizing the quadratic form (5.2) and applying the equipartition theorem we arrive at the following averages:

$$\langle Q_{zz} \rangle \equiv \langle Q^2 \rangle = \frac{2k_\beta T}{3(A + L_1 q^2) + 2L_2 q^2} \tag{5.3}$$

$$\langle |Q_{xy}|^2 \rangle = \tfrac{1}{4}\langle P^2 \rangle = \frac{k_\beta T(1 + \xi_1^2 q^2)}{2A[(1 + \xi_1^2 q^2)^2 - 4q_0^2 q^2 \xi_1^4]} \qquad \xi_1^2 = \frac{L_1}{A} \tag{5.4}$$

$$\langle |Q_{xz}|^2 \rangle = \langle |Q_{yz}|^2 \rangle = \frac{k_\beta T \tilde{A}}{2[\tilde{A}^2 - q_0^2 L_1^2 q^2]} \tag{5.5}$$

$$\tilde{A} = A + (L_1 + \tfrac{1}{2}L_2) q^2$$

The fluctuations of Q_{zz}, as defined by Eq. (5.3), are not different from what they are in the nematic state. But all other averages are modified. Let us focus our attention on $I_{xy}(q) = \langle |Q_{xy}|^2 \rangle$. Examination of Eq. (5.5) shows the following features

   –if $q_0 \xi_1(T) < \tfrac{1}{2}$ the maximum of $I_{xy}(q)$ is at $q = 0$

as it is in a nematic

   –if $q_0 \xi_1(T) > \tfrac{1}{2}$ the maximum of $I_{xy}(q)$ is at a

finite q (comparable to q_0): we then have a broad scattering peak which is reminiscent of the Bragg peak in the ordered phase.

However $q_0 \xi_1$ cannot become much larger than $\tfrac{1}{2}$: in fact, if $q_0 \xi_1$ would reach the value 1, the fluctuations $\langle |Q_{ky}|^2 \rangle$ would diverge for $q = q_0$. The temperature T^{**}, such that $q_0 \xi_1(T^{**}) = 1$, is thus the temperature below which the isotropic phase is absolutely unstable. A first order transition from isotropic to cholesteric must occur (because of the Q^3 terms in F) at a temperature $T_c > T^{**}$. Thus $q_0 \xi(T_c) < 1$.

In many cases we may in fact have $q_0 \xi(T_c) < \tfrac{1}{2}$: then $I_{xy}(q)$ has a central peak at all temperatures above T_c, and the tendency to build up a spiral is not strongly apparent in the properties of the isotropic phase.

A similar discussion can be carried out for the components Q_{xz} and Q_{yz}, with qualitatively similar conclusions. It can be shown, however, (using the inequalities of section III on L_1 and L_2) that the fluctuations of Q_{xy} are more singular: if we were able to supercool below T_c, the onset of instability would occur (at $T = T^{**}$) through Q_{xy}, while Q_{xz} is still comparatively small.

5.3. Optical Rotation at Long Wavelengths

Cholesterics in their ordered phase show a huge optical rotation: thus, if the cholesteric → isotropic transition is nearly of second order, we might, at first sight, expect a large optical rotation just above T_c. This is not correct, however, as shown by the following argument.

To derive the optical rotation we essentially look at the forward scattering amplitude for a process where a photon is absorbed at point (1), a virtual photon propagates from (1) to (2), and a final photon is emitted from (2). This gives a second order correction to the non local polarisability tensor, proportional to

$$p_{\alpha\beta}(\mathbf{R}) = \langle Q_{\alpha\gamma}(\mathbf{r}_1)\, T_{\gamma\mu}(\mathbf{R})\, Q_{\mu\beta}(\mathbf{r}_2)\rangle$$

$$\mathbf{R} = \mathbf{r}_1 - \mathbf{r}_2 \tag{5.6}$$

Here $T'_{\gamma\mu}$ represents the virtual photon propagator, and in the long wavelength limit ($\lambda \gg R$) it essentially describes the field of a static dipole:

$$T_{\gamma\mu} = \frac{1}{R^3}\delta_{\gamma\mu} - \frac{3}{R^5}R_\gamma R_\mu \tag{5.7}$$

The optical rotation is proportional to Ω/λ^2, where Ω is the integral:

$$\Omega = \int d\mathbf{R}\, p_{xy}(\mathbf{R})\, R_z \tag{5.8}$$

Ω may be computed in detail from the Eqs. (5.4 and 5.5). Qualitatively, we may estimate Ω as follows: the chiral part of the $\langle QQ\rangle$ correlation function which occurs in (5.6) is of order

$$\langle Q(0)\, Q(\mathbf{R})\rangle_{\text{chiral}} \simeq \frac{k_B T}{L_1 R}\, e^{-R/\xi}\, q_0\, R \tag{5.9}$$

Inserting this in (5.8) we have

$$\Omega \sim q_0 \int 4\pi R^2\, dR\, \frac{1}{R^2}\frac{k_\beta T}{L_1}\, e^{-R/\xi} \sim \text{const}\, \frac{k_\beta T}{L_1}\, q_0\, \xi \tag{5.10}$$

We have seen that $q_0\, \xi \gtrsim 1$. Thus $\Omega \sim k_\beta T/L_1$ is non singular near T_c. It is our hope that this point will soon be checked experimentally.

6. Concluding Remarks

We know that there are spectacular short range effects in the isotropic phase of nematics, and we know how to correlate them in terms of a small number of phenomenological constants. We do not have, however, any measurement of the coherence lengths ξ_n and ξ_t; light scattering involves wavelengths which are too large; studies on the reflectance of the nematic/isotropic interface might be helpful. Qualitatively, since the enhancement factor found in the magnetic birefringence or the flow birefringence reaches values of order 100, we expect the ratio coherence length/molecular length to be of order $\sqrt{100} \sim 10$.

Another attractive direction for experimental work is the study of *metastable phases*. Is it possible to observe a metastable isotropic phase in the small interval $T^* < T < T_c$, and to follow the fluctuations in such a phase? Also, can one measure the temperature T_1 above which the nematic phase is absolutely unstable? Finally, from the nucleation processes of one phase in the other, can one obtain significant information on ξ_n or ξ_t?

All our analysis has been restricted to properties which are quasi-macroscopic (spatial variations slow on the molecular scale). However, certain microscopic properties can be estimated from it: in particular the Pincus calculation of nuclear relaxation rates[15] may be extended to temperatures above T_c, using equations such as (5.26), suitably generalized to cover situations where $q\xi \sim 1$. A qualitative estimate has been described in Ref. (7), but more detailed calculations are clearly required.

Acknowledgments

The present author is greatly indebted to R. B. Meyer for a number of discussions on pretransitional phenomena in liquid crystals. He would also like to thank D. Litster and A. Arrott for some very stimulating conversations. Part of this work was done during a visit at the General Electric Research and Development Center, and the author would like to thank M. Fiske and C. P. Bean for their hospitality.

REFERENCES

1. A useful list of latent heats and other characteristics of the transition is given in the review by A. Saupe. *Angurandte Chemie* (English Version) **7**, 97 (1968).
2. Zadoc Kahn, J., *Annales de Physique* **6**, 31 (1936),
   Zvetkov, V., *Acla Physicochemica USSR* **19**, 86 (1944).
3. Stinson, T. W., Litster, J. D. To be published.
4. Allain, Y. Private communication.
5. For an analysis of the scattering in the ordered phase, see Orsay group on liquid crystals, *Journ. Chem. Phys.*, **51**, 816 (1969).
6. Litster, J. D., Stinson, T., *Journ. App. Phys.*, **41**, 996 (1970).
7. de Gennes, P. G., *Physics Letters*, **30A**, p. 454 (1969).
8. Summation over repeated indices is always implied in the equations.
9. Freiser, M. J., *Phys. Rev. Lett.* **24**, 1041 (1970).
10. Frank, F. C., *Faraday Soc. discussions* **25**, 19 (1958).
    Ericksen, J. L., *Arch. Rat. Mech. Anal.* **10**, 189 (1962).
11. Orsay group on liquid crystals. *Phys. Rev. Letters*, **22**, 1361 (1969).
12. The proof is similar to that leading to Eq. (2.6) and can be found in the book by de Groot: " Thermodynamics or irreversible processes ", North Holland 1954.
13. Private communication from Dr. Candau.
14. Of course the magnitude of the birefringence may be smaller than in nematics, because the anisotropy of the electric polarisability is rather small for cholesterol esters.
15. Pincus, P., *Solid State Comm.* **7**, 415 (1969).

Liquid Crystallinity in Relation to Composition and Temperature in Amphiphilic Systems†

P. A. WINSOR

Shell Research Ltd.
Thornton Research Centre
P.O. Box I
Chester CHI 3SH, England

Received October 12, 1970

Abstract—The purpose of this paper is to give a broad review of the " fused " type of liquid crystalline phases formed by amphiphilic compounds and to examine the constitutional relationships of these phases to one another and to the amorphous liquid phase. Further, an account will be given of how, on changes in composition and temperature, the various phases undergo reversible interconversions through first-order phase transitions. It will be shown how these transitions follow a regular pattern which, qualitatively, can be satisfactorily interpreted on a molecular basis.

Distinction between Semicrystalline and Fused Mesophases

The fused liquid crystalline phases to be considered are formed by amphiphilic compounds either in the pure state or, more generally, in binary or multicomponent solutions. Before they are discussed the restriction in scope expressed in the term " fused " will be examined.

Among the most comprehensively studied of amphiphilic compounds are the sodium soaps. At room temperature the sodium soaps from lamellar crystals of the character indicated diagrammatically in Fig. 1. Both the hydrocarbon groups and the polar groups are arranged in regular three-dimensional solid-crystalline order. When the sodium soaps are heated they undergo a regular series of first-order phase transitions before the amorphous liquid melt is finally produced. It has been shown by Luzzati and associates[1] by X-ray

---

† Invited Paper presented at the Third International Liquid Crystal Conference, Berlin, August 24–28, 1970.

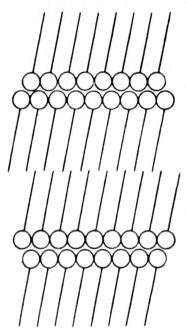

Figure 1.   Character of solid lamellar soap crystal.   Both the hydrocarbon groups and the polar groups are arranged in regular three-dimensional solid crystalline order.

diffraction studies that this behaviour arises because the three-dimensional crystalline organization of the hydrocarbon groups breaks down at a temperature a little above 100 °C, while the crystalline arrangement of the polar groups persists, in some measure, up to considerably higher temperatures.   With rising temperature, however, this crystalline order breaks down in a series of steps at definite transition points that are characteristic for each soap, and thus gives rise to a succession of mesophases which are both partly crystalline and partly liquid in character.   Such semicrystalline mesophases will not be further considered in this discussion.

At a temperature in the region of 300 °C, depending on the particular sodium soap, the crystalline arrangement of the polar groups is finally lost, but even then the amorphous liquid phase is not at first produced.   It is preceded by a smectic (Greek, smegma–soap) mesophase or liquid crystal whose structure will shortly be considered. This " fused " mesophase undergoes a first-order phase transition

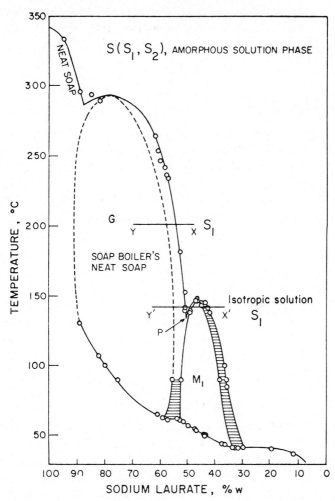

Figure 2. Phase diagram for the sodium laurate/water system showing homogeneous fields of each of the different solution phases and isothermal tie lines connecting the phases in heterogeneous equilibria.[5]

to the amorphous melt at a somewhat higher temperature (cf. Fig. 2).

It should be remarked here that, at lower temperatures under certain conditions, semicrystalline soap mesophases arise in which, while the hydrocarbon groups retain crystalline order, the polar groups have been brought into the " labile " or fused condition through the solvent action of water. This situation, according to

Vincent and Skoulios[2] is found in the lamellar " gel " phases formed at room temperatures by, for example, potassium or rubidium stearates in the presence of water. This second class of semicrystalline mesophase is again outside the scope of this paper.

Fused Mesophases

The present paper is thus concerned only with the amorphous liquid phase (pure melt or solution) and with those mesophases in which both the hydrocarbon and polar zones are in the " fused " or " labile " state.

Amphiphilic compounds, depending on their constitution, form a number of individually distinct types of fused mesophase. Further, depending on temperature and the presence of additional components, a particular amphiphile may give rise to several types of mesophase. Each type is constructed according to a definite structural pattern which confers on it clearly defined diagnostic features of behaviour such as optical properties,[3] X-ray diffraction spectra,[1] N.M.R. spectra[4] etc. The individual types of mesophase and their interconversions under the influence of changes in composition and temperature will now be considered, with the help of some specific examples.

THE LAMELLAR MESOPHASE G: " NEAT " PHASE

Figure 2[5] illustrates the ranges of stability of the " fused " phases in the sodium laurate/water system. These phases are the amorphous liquid phase, the " neat soap " phase, the " soap boiler's neat soap " phase and the " middle " phase. The last three are birefringent liquid crystalline phases. The structure of the " neat soap " phase consists essentially of a succession of planar liquid monolayers of soap molecules.[1] These monolayers are arranged alternately so that, as in the solid crystal, like is juxtaposed to like. The juxtaposed hydrocarbon chains constitute a layer of the character of a fused hydrocarbon while the juxtaposed polar groups have the character of a fused salt. Limited amounts of additional hydrocarbon may be incorporated into the hydrocarbon layer and limited amounts of water may be incorporated into the polar zone before any phase change occurs. Incorporation of hydrocarbon will be referred to later in this article and the discussion at the present stage will be restricted to binary aqueous systems.

The neat soap phase is able to incorporate only a small amount of water before undergoing a phase transition which, depending on temperature (Fig. 2), leads to the formation either of the amorphous solution phase or of the " soap boiler's neat " phase. The transition to this second, more aqueous, lamellar phase probably involves a change in the mutual orientation of the polar groups within the individual monolayers. This point will be considered further later.

The second, more aqueous, lamellar liquid crystalline solution phase is stable over a wide range of composition and temperature. This type of aqueous lamellar mesophase is formed in many other binary amphiphile/water systems, as for example with Aerosol OT

$$CH_2.CO.O.CH_2.CH(C_2H_5).CH_2.CH_2.CH_2.CH_3$$
$$|$$
$$CH(SO_3Na).CO.O.CH_2.CH(C_2H_5).CH_2.CH_2.CH_2CH_3$$

(Fig. 3),[6] N,N,N-trimethylaminododecanomide (Fig. 4),[7] dodecyl-trimethylammoniumchloride (Fig. 5),[8] as well as in many ternary and multicomponent systems.[9,10,11] In the speaker's system of nomenclature it was termed the G phase on account of its usually rather thin gel-like consistency. Other nomenclatures have also been used, for example, neat phase, phase D (Ekwall and associates) and phase LL (lamellar labile, Luzzati and associates).

The fact, established by X-ray and optical studies, that in the G phase the amphiphilic monolayer $\bar{C}$ remains statistically planar, except where subject to mechanical deformation, shows that in this phase, whose structure is represented diagrammatically in Fig. 6, the tendencies of the $\bar{C}$ monolayer to become convex towards its lipophilic environment, $\bar{O}$, on the one hand and towards its polar environment, $\overline{W}$, (usually aqueous) on the other, are equally balanced. Barred symbols are used here to indicate (i) that $\bar{C}$ may be a mixed monolayer containing several amphiphilic species; (ii) that the lipophilic region $\bar{O}$, which in the simplest case contains the liquid juxtaposed hydrocarbon groups of two $\bar{C}$ monolayers, may also contain in solution, besides a fraction of the amphiphile, added hydrocarbon-soluble additives, such as hydrocarbons or halo-hydrocarbons; and finally (iii) that the $\overline{W}$ region, which in the

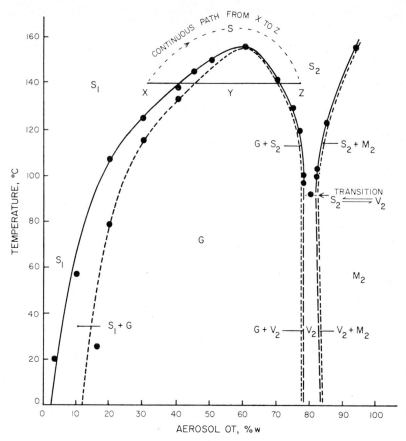

Figure 3.   Phase diagram for the Aerosol OT/water system.[6]   The bound-
aries indicated by broken lines are tentative.
$S(S_1, S_2)$ = Mobile isotropic phase; G = Neat phase;
M_2 = Inverse middle phase; V_2 = Inverse viscous isotropic phase

simplest case contains the fused juxtaposed polar groups of two $\bar{C}$
monolayers, more usually contains water which may contain in
solution, besides a fraction of the amphiphile present (Fig. 6), such
water-soluble additives as inorganic salts, sugars, the lower organic
hydroxy compounds etc.

    If we define a ratio $R^{(10,11)}$ as

$$\frac{\text{tendency of } \bar{C} \text{ layer to become convex towards } \bar{O}}{\text{tendency of } \bar{C} \text{ layer to become convex towards } \bar{W}} ,$$

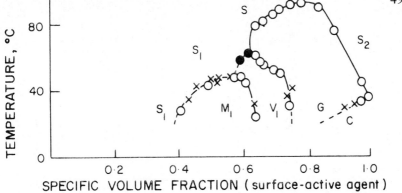

Figure 4. Phase diagram for the N,N,N-trimethylaminododecanoimide/ water system.[7] Phase boundaries were determined from optical ○, density x and X-ray diffraction ● measurements. $S(S_1, S_2)$, mobile isotropic solution (amorphous solution). M_1, middle phase; V_1, viscous isotropic phase; G, neat phase; C, crystals; the two-phase zones are narrow and are not indicated.

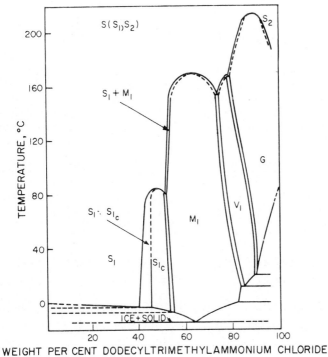

Figure 5. Phase diagram for the dodecyltrimethylammonium chloride/water system.[8] ———, Experimental boundary; – – –, interpolated boundary.

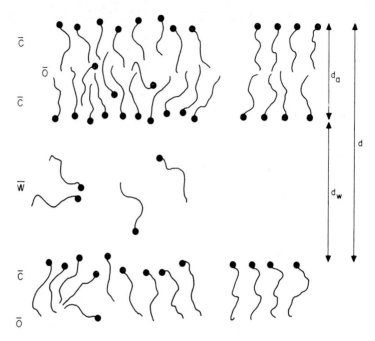

Figure 6. Diagrammatic representation of the structure of the G phase in a binary amphiphile water system. Left, situation in principle: $\bar{C}$ layer contains most of the amphiphile but both amphiphile and water are distributed throughout the $\bar{C}, \bar{O}$ and $\bar{W}$ regions so as to maintain their respective activities statistically uniform throughout. Right, working approximation usually employed in X-ray studies: $\bar{C}$ layer contains only and entirely all the amphiphile present.

then within the G phase, since the planar lamellar structure is stable, $R = 1$.

The ratio R will be largely dependent on the ratio

$$\frac{\text{tendency of } \bar{C} \text{ layer to spread out into the } \bar{O} \text{ region}}{\text{tendency of } \bar{C} \text{ layer to spread out into the } \bar{W} \text{ region}}.$$

The tendency of the $\bar{C}$ layer to spread out into the $\bar{O}$ region will be promoted by attractive molecular interactions between $\bar{C}$ and $\bar{O}$, $A_{\bar{C}\bar{O}}$, and opposed by attractive interactions (cohesion) within $\bar{O}$ itself, $A_{\bar{O}\bar{O}}$. Similarly, the tendency of the $\bar{C}$ layer to spread out into the $\bar{W}$ region will be promoted by a factor $A_{\bar{C}\bar{W}}$ and opposed by a factor $A_{\overline{W}\overline{W}}$. Thus we may say that R will increase with increase in the ratio

$$\frac{A_{\overline{C}\overline{O}} - A_{\overline{O}\overline{O}}}{A_{\overline{C}\overline{W}} - A_{\overline{W}\overline{W}}}$$

where $A_{\overline{C}\overline{O}}$ etc. are energies of interaction per unit area of interface at the $\overline{C}$–$\overline{O}$ and $\overline{C}$–$\overline{W}$ interfaces respectively.

Further, for a given $\overline{O}$ and $\overline{W}$, R will increase with increase in the ratio $A_{\overline{C}\overline{O}}/A_{\overline{C}\overline{W}}$. This relationship we will denote by the expression

$$R \rightarrow \frac{A_{\overline{C}\overline{O}}}{A_{\overline{C}\overline{W}}}$$

The intermolecular attractive forces responsible both for $A_{\overline{C}\overline{O}}$ and for $A_{\overline{C}\overline{W}}$ will be partly electrokinetic (forces of lipophilic character, A_L) and partly electrostatic (forces of hydrophilic character, A_H).

The effects of changes in composition and temperature on the ratio R, and consequently on micellar shape, may therefore be considered from the point of view of their probable effects on

$$\left[\frac{A_{\overline{C}\overline{O}}}{A_{\overline{C}\overline{W}}}\right]$$

or more explicitly, on

$$\left[\frac{A_{L\overline{C}\overline{O}} + A_{H\overline{C}\overline{O}}}{A_{L\overline{C}\overline{W}} + A_{H\overline{C}\overline{W}}}\right]$$

In many systems, of which the sodium laurate/water and the Aerosol OT/water systems may be taken as specific examples, the G phase is stable over a wide range of temperature and composition. Over this range the form of the $\overline{C}$ monolayer remains statistically planar ($R = 1$), although thermal fluctuations will give rise to small local distortions ($R > 1$ or $R < 1$) (Fig. 6). Just why the lamellar structure and a statistically unit value of R are maintained over a wide range of compositions and temperatures is not obvious. However, the mechanism by which this is effected is fairly clear, mainly from evidence afforded by X-ray diffraction studies.[1]

The repeat distance, d, (Fig. 6) for any particular experimental G phase may usually be determined directly by X-ray diffraction measurements. The dimensions of other features of the G phase may then be calculated from d, the composition of the G phase and the experimentally estimated partial specific volumes of its components, provided one adopts certain working approximations (see right-hand side of Fig. 6).

For binary aqueous G phases the approximations most frequently adopted may be collectively expressed in the assumption that the G phase may be treated as if the double $\bar{C}$ layers are effectively planar and include only and entirely all the amphiphile molecules present.

If one adopts this assumption, whose acceptability cannot here be discussed in detail, one may readily calculate[1]

d_a ... the thickness of the double $\bar{C}$ layer

d_w ... the thickness of the aqueous layer, and

S ... the mean area populated by one polar group at the interface or, more shortly, the " area per polar group ". Gallot and Skoulios,[12] using this assumption, have calculated from their measurements of d values the changes with concentration in the area per polar group within the G phases formed by the homologous potassium soaps (C_8—C_{2z}). It was found that, at constant temperature, the calculated area increases with decreasing concentration and depends only on the concentration, N, when this is expressed as gram molecules of soap per litre of water (Fig. 7). This result implies that, at constant temperature, the unique area per polar group which at a given value of N leads to unit value of R, is insensitive to the chain length of the soap and consequently to the thickness of the $\tilde{O}$ layer.

This suggests that, in the expression $R \to A_{\bar{C}\bar{O}}/A_{\bar{C}\bar{W}}$ (cf. p. 6), (i) at a given temperature over the range of stability of the G phase (in which $R = 1$), $A_{\bar{C}\bar{O}}$ is not highly sensitive to those changes in the thickness of the $\tilde{O}$ layer which necessarily accompany either variation in chain length at a given value of S (corresponding to a given value of N) or variation in S (resulting from variation in N) with a soap of given chain length: (ii) the tendency for increase in $A_{\bar{C}\bar{W}}$, which might be expected to follow increase in water content, is offset by an increase in S, that is by a reduction in the number of polar groups per unit area of interface, which maintains the balance of $A_{\bar{C}\bar{W}}$ with $A_{\bar{C}\bar{O}}$ corresponding to $R = 1$.

For each soap, at a given temperature, there is a minimum thick-

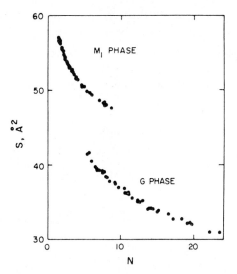

Figure 7. Variation in the area S per polar group with change in concentration N (moles soap/litre water) in M_1 and G solutions of potassium soaps (n-alkanoates) at 86 °C.[12]

ness of the $\bar{O}$ layer (corresponding to a maximum value of S) consistent with the stability of the G phase. At concentrations lower than that at which this minimum thickness is reached, transition to a second phase (either S_1 or M_1 according to the temperature (cf. Fig. 2)) occurs. Since at a given concentration N (with its corresponding unique value of S) the thickness of the $\bar{O}$ layer is approximately proportional to the chain length, it might be expected that the stability of the G phase would extend to lower concentrations with the soaps of higher molecular weight. This behaviour is observed. The points at the left-hand side of the curve for the G phase in Fig. 7 thus correspond to values obtained with soaps of higher molecular weight (up to C_{22}).

The increase in effective area per polar group on dilution probably derives from a decrease in the degree of binding of the counter-ions (K^+) to the micellar surface with increasing water content. Further, a change in the interfacial concentration of the polar groups will be necessary in order to maintain equilibrium with that concentration of the amphiphile (regarded as negligible in the calculations of Gallot and Skoulios) which is actually dissolved in the interlamellar solution

$\overline{W}$ (Fig. 6, left-hand side). That this interlamellar concentration is appreciable, particularly with shorter-chain amphiphilic salts, and that it diminishes with bulk dilution is shown by the colligative properties of amphiphile/water systems. It must be remembered that in these equilibrium systems the activity of each chemical species must necessarily be statistically uniform throughout, although the concentrations within the different zones may differ greatly on account of the large local differences in activity coefficients. Figure 8[13] shows curves of vapour pressure against composition for

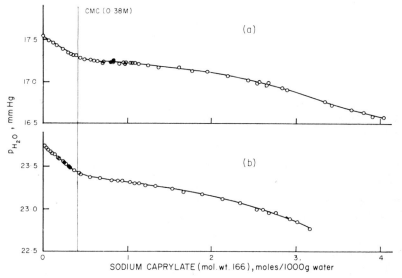

Figure 8.   (a) Vapour pressure of sodium caprylate solutions at 20 °C measured by the iso-piestic method.   (b) Vapour pressure of sodium caprylate solutions at 25 °C measured by the Mechrolab Osmometer method.[13]

amorphous solutions (S_1) of sodium caprylate. It is clear that in the more concentrated solutions the composition of the $\overline{W}$ region, whose vapour pressure must be equal to that of the system as a whole, cannot approximate to that of pure water. It must, in fact, be of markedly higher concentration (perhaps more than three times) than the critical micelle concentration (cmc about 5%). This conclusion must apply also to the liquid crystalline solutions of sodium caprylate (in this case the M_1 phase which will be considered shortly) formed at still higher concentrations. With the more lipophilic amphiphile,

Aerosol OT (cmc about 0.2%), which is however of similar effective chain length, X-ray studies suggest a concentration within the interlamellar solution $\overline{W}$ of the G phase of the order of 5% at 20 °C and of 3% at 83 °C.[14] In the solutions of the higher members of the soaps (C_8—C_{22}) studied by Gallot and Skoulios the interlamellar soap concentrations may, however, well be considerably lower. Where, however, they are still significant, the effect of neglecting them in calculating S values from measured values of d will be to give underestimates of S.[14] The values for S in Fig. 7 may therefore be taken as minimum estimates.

It may be mentioned at this point that for the G solutions of the soaps studied by Gallot and Skoulios and also for the solutions of Aerosol OT studied by Rogers and Winsor, the measured d-spacing diminishes with rise of temperature. The area per polar group, when calculated using the simplifying approximations 1–4 above, correspondingly shows an increase. With the Aerosol OT system, however, when reasonable allowance is made for amphiphile included in the $\overline{W}$ region, this apparent increase in S with rise of temperature largely disappears.[14]

Breakdown of the G Phase on Dilution to Give the Amorphous Solution Phase S_1

In the sodium laurate/water system (Fig. 2) at temperatures above about 150 °C and in the Aerosol OT/water system at room temperatures, dilution of the G phase beyond its lower concentration limit of stability leads to the separation of a mobile amorphous solution phase S_1. The S_1 phase at first exists in equilibrium with the conjugate G phase, each phase, in accordance with the phase rule, being of fixed composition at a given temperature.

The phase sequence $S_1 \rightarrow (S_1 + G) \rightarrow G$ may be interpreted as follows. Over the range of stability of the G phase, the general tendency of dilution to decrease R, i.e. to favour convexity of the $\overline{C}$ monolayer towards the aqueous region $\overline{W}$, is compensated, as just discussed, by increase in the area per polar group. This compensation process, however, reaches a limit. At this limit the local thermal fluctuations in the form of the C monolayer (Fig. 6), which with progressive dilution increasingly lead to areas convex towards $\overline{W}(R < 1)$, attain a magnitude which causes fragmentation of the lamellae. As would be expected on this view, breakdown occurs sooner, the higher the temperature. At those loci within the lamellar G phase where thermal fluctuations have momentarily produced the highest water content, with consequent lowest momentary value of R, separation of a more dilute aqueous phase S_1 is initiated. This phase is in equilibrium with the residual G phase and therefore, although it is considerably more dilute, shows the same colligative properties (partial vapour pressures, osmotic properties, etc.).

It is this insensitiveness of the osmotic properties to composition which permits those local thermal fluctuations in composition and micellar form within the G phase which, at the limiting dilution, lead to the separation of the relatively more dilute S_1 phase. Complementarily, fluctuations within this conjugate S_1 phase, which is at its upper limit of concentration, lead to separation of the relatively more concentrated G phase. In the S_1 phase, which is thus maintained in equilibrium with the G phase, the form of the $\overline{C}$ monolayer is, on balance, convex towards $\overline{W}(R < 1)$. However, on the fluctuation hypothesis, it would be expected that, locally, lamellar regions would be present within it similar in internal dimensions to those of the G phase itself but of limited extent. X-ray diffraction studies support this view.[15,16] On progressive dilution of the S_1 phase below its upper limit of concentration, i.e. at concentrations at which it is no longer in equilibrium with the G phase, the mean form of the $\overline{C}$ layer tends towards the spherical form, characteristic of the " S_1 " or " Hartley micelles " found at concentrations not too greatly above the cmc.

BREAKDOWN OF THE LAMELLAR MESOPHASE G ON DILUTION TO GIVE THE HEXAGONAL OR " MIDDLE " MESOMORPHOUS SOLUTION PHASE M_1

In the sodium laurate/water system (Fig. 2) at temperatures below $150\,^\circ\mathrm{C}$ breakdown of the G phase on dilution does not lead directly to the amorphous solution phase S_1, but a second mesomorphous solution phase, the " middle phase " M_1, is first produced. The essential architecture of this mesophase (Fig. 9) has been definitively established by X-ray diffraction measurements[1] taken in conjunction with optical studies.[17] The amphiphile molecules are, for the most part, aggregated into indefinitely extended parallel

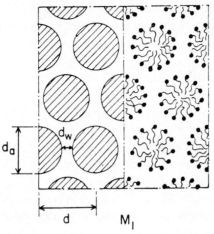

Figure 9.   The structure of the middle M_1, phase in relation to the measured X-ray long spacing, d.[1]

cylindrical or fibrous micelles which are ordered in two-dimensional hexagonal array.   In the M_1 phase, as in the G phase and all other amphiphilic solution phases, there is a kinetic equilibrium of molecules between the $\bar{C}$, $\overline{W}$ and $\bar{O}$ regions, the activity of each molecular species necessarily being statistically uniform throughout the equilibrium system.   However, in X-ray diffraction studies of the M_1 phase the simplifying approximation is usually adopted that the fibrous micelles contain solely and entirely all the amphiphile present as represented in Fig. 9.

In the M_1 phase, except when subject to mechanical constraint, the liquid fibrous micelles maintain their indefinitely extended parallel arrangement.   It is therefore clear that, parallel to the fibre axis, $R = 1$, while circumferentially, $R < 1$.   This implies that the force fields around the micellized amphiphile molecules do not interact in a statistically symmetrical manner about the long axes of adjacent molecules.

It appears from its solvent behaviour and from X-ray diffraction studies, that the micellar $\bar{O}$ region is essentially of " random liquid " character.[1]   The dissymmetry of R in the M_1 phase therefore seems to imply that there is mutual ordering of the polar groups at the $\bar{C}$—$\overline{W}$ interface.   At the $\bar{C}$—$\overline{W}$ interface the polar groups in the M_1 phase must therefore be regarded as constituting a two-dimensional liquid crystalline interfacial solution in equilibrium with the $\overline{W}$ region. In relation to the orientation of the polar groups within the $\overline{C}$ layer, we may denote the direction in which R is a minimum by x and the direction in which R is a maximum by y. With this convention, in the M_1 phase, around the micelles $R_x < 1$ while along them $R_y = 1$.

From their X-ray diffraction measurements with the G and M_1 phases formed by the homologous potassium soaps, Gallot and Skoulios[12] have calculated, using the approximations noted above, the area, S, per polar group in the two phases at various compositions and temperatures (Fig. 7).

In both phases, with increasing dilution, there is a progressive increase in S which, in each phase, is dependent only on N, as already considered above for the G phase. Further, corresponding to the change of phase $G \to M$, there is a marked increase in S. These calculated increases would be even greater if allowance were made for intermicellar amphiphile within the $\overline{W}$ region.

It seems unlikely that the mutual ordering of the polar groups, indicated in the case of the M_1 phase by the dissymmetry of R, will be lost in the conjugate G phase in which the polar groups are closer together. The fact that, in the G phase, $R = 1$ in all directions must therefore imply that in passing from the M_1 phase ($R_x < 1$; $R_y = 1$) to the G phase on increase in concentration, differential compression of the polar groups in the x and y directions produces the condition in which both $R_x = 1$ and $R_y = 1$. In spite of this, the ordering of the polar groups would be expected to make each individual mono-layer optically biaxial. The fact that the G phase is optically uniaxial would then imply that the successive parallel monolayers are stacked at random.

BREAKDOWN OF THE M_1 PHASE ON DILUTION TO GIVE THE S_1 PHASE

The M_1 phase, like the G phase, is stable over a considerable range of compositions. The condition, $R_x < 1$; $R_y = 1$, is maintained with increasing water content by a progressively increasing area per polar group, in a manner analogous to that discussed for the G phase. However, with increasing dilution, thermal fluctuations will increasingly tend to produce local convexities towards $\overline{W}$ along the length of the fibrous micelles. A limiting dilution is ultimately reached at which fragmentation of the micellar fibres and breakdown of the M_1 phase occur at loci where fluctuations have momentarily given rise to a relatively high water content. The amorphous S_1 phase, which is of higher water content than the residual conjugate M_1 phase, separates. This S_1 phase contains locally regions of M_1 structure,[18] the situation being analogous to that already discussed for the $G \rightarrow (G + S_1)$ sequence. On further dilution and further increase in R the local M_1 regions diminish in significance and the average micellar form approaches the spherical S_1 or Hartley type.[18]

It is of particular interest that Aerosol OT and many other amphiphiles in which the lipophilic moiety is laterally relatively bulky do not yield an M_1 phase on dilution of the G phase. This is presumably because the laterally bulky lipophilic groups prevent sufficiently close mutual approach of the polar groups for the occurrence of the mutual orientation that is required for the formation of the M_1 phase.

BREAKDOWN OF THE G PHASE ON INCREASE IN CONCENTRATION
TO GIVE THE AMORPHOUS SOLUTION PHASE S_2

We have already discussed how the general tendency of R to decrease with dilution can lead to the phase sequence,

$$G \rightarrow (G + S_1) \rightarrow S_1,$$
$$R = 1 \qquad R < 1$$

as indicated in Fig. 2 and Fig. 3 for dilution along the lines marked YX.

In certain circumstances, as indicated in Fig. 3 along the line marked YZ, increase in concentration with consequent increase in R may lead to the complementary sequence

$$G \rightarrow (G + S_2) \rightarrow S_2.$$
$$R = 1 \qquad R > 1$$

In the amorphous S_2 solution the mean form of the $\bar{C}$ monolayer will be convex towards $\bar{O}$, complementarily to its convexity towards $\overline{W}$ in the S_1 solution. There is, however, usually no uniform micellar form nor long-range order in either the S_1 or S_2 solutions, but rather a thermal equilibrium of fluctuating micellar forms. By following the path indicated by the dotted line in Fig. 3 it is possible to pass continuously from the S_1 solution, X, to the S_2 solution, Z, without encountering any change in phase or any abrupt discontinuity in properties, such as are found in proceeding along the discontinuous path, XYZ. "S_1" and "S_2" should therefore be considered as parts of a single solution phase S rather than as distinct individual phases. The designations S_1 and S_2 conveniently distinguish those regions of the S phase in which the mean form of the $\bar{C}$ monolayer predominantly tends to convexity towards $\bar{W}$ and to convexity towards $\bar{O}$ respectively.

FORMATION OF THE "INVERSE MIDDLE MESOPHASE" M_2

An "inverse middle" phase, M_2, complementary in character to the M_1 phase is found in the Aerosol OT/water system (Fig. 3) at concentrations somewhat higher than the upper limit of concentration for the G phase. The M_2 phase is also found in many similar systems derived from other amphiphiles with laterally bulky hydrocarbon groups—for example, from the sodium and potassium salts of di(2-ethylhexyl)acetic acid or di(2-ethylhexyl)ethylsulphuric acid. Ekwall and associates have also observed this phase (their phase F) in certain ternary aqueous systems containing two n-alkyl amphiphiles, for example, sodium caprylate with decanol–1.[9] The structure of the M_2 phase, like that of the M_1 phase, consists of parallel fibrous micelles in two-dimensional hexagonal array. In the M_2 phase however, it is the polar groups and aqueous region $\bar{W}$ that form the micellar cores while the hydrocarbon groups constitute a liquid continuum between these cores. Clearly in this phase, $R_x = 1$ along the fibres while $R_y > 1$ around them.

In the Aerosol OT/water system, the M_2 phase extends, at room temperature, from a concentration of about 84% up to the anhydrous salt. The anhydrous soaps of the metals of Group II of the Periodic Table, although crystalline at room temperature, apparently yield M_2 mesophases at elevated temperatures.[19]

The reason why fibrous M_2 mesophases are formed in these cases although, under comparable conditions, the alkali metal soaps of the n-alkanoic acids yield lamellar G mesophases, probably involves steric effects. With the straight-chain soaps the packing of the n-alkyl groups diverging around a system of fibrous or spherical polar cores, so as to form a liquid continuum between them, might well present difficulties in space filling. On the other hand, with Aerosol OT, accommodation of the highly branched and laterally bulky hydrocarbon groups around the fibrous polar cores would be an easier matter. With the soaps of the divalent metals the presence of two alkyl chains per metal ion would likewise facilitate space filling within a fibrous aggregate. Finally, space filling in the interfibre continuum of Ekwall's F phases, which contain two straight-chain amphiphiles, is probably permitted by the location of a considerable proportion of the less polar amphiphile outside the $\bar{C}$ layer and included within the interfibre continuum or $\bar{O}$ region. Evidence for such a distribution of amphiphile within the F phase in the sodium caprylate/decanol system has been advanced on the basis of X-ray diffraction studies.[9]

The M_2 phases of certain magnesium and cadmium soaps exist in two modifications,[19,1] stable at different temperatures. These two forms probably arise from a change in the mutual orientation of the polar groups with change in temperature. Analogous changes could arise with other fused mesophases. Indeed, as already noted, the transition from the lamellar neat soap phase to the lamellar soap boiler's neat phase, which occurs on dilution at high concentrations in the sodium laurate/water (Fig. 2) and other similar systems,[5] is probably of this type.

PHASES INTERMEDIATE BETWEEN THE M_1 AND G PHASES

It can be seen in Fig. 2 and Fig. 3 that both the M_1 and G phases show maxima in thermal stability at particular concentrations which, for convenience, we will term C_{M_1} and C_G respectively. At these concentrations the M_1 and G micellar structures respectively attain their greatest stabilities and are least readily disintegrated by thermal fluctuations. At concentrations somewhat above $C_{M_1}(R_x < 1, R_y = 1)$ the fibrous micelles of the M_1 phase tend to undergo thermal breakdown in virtue of those thermal fluctuations which lead to loci of higher concentrations where R_x tends to become unity. At concentrations somewhat below C_{M_1} the M_1 micelles tend to breakdown in virtue of those fluctuations which lead to loci of lower concentration where R_y tends to fall below unity. Analogous considerations apply to thermal breakdown of the G phase on either side of C_G.

In proceeding in Fig. 2 along a line such as $X'\,Y'$, we encounter the phase sequence

$$S_1 \rightarrow (S_1 + M_1) \rightarrow M_1 \rightarrow (M_1 + S_1) \rightarrow S_1 \rightarrow (S_1 + G) \rightarrow G$$

The S_1 phase, as constituted between the compositions C_{M_1} and C_G, will contain locally both G and M_1 micellar loci in thermal equilibrium. This underlies the eutectic phenomena associated with the point P in Fig. 2. At temperatures below that corresponding to this point, the G and M_1 mesophases undergo direct transition on changes in bulk composition, without intermediate formation of the amorphous solution phases S_1. At higher temperatures, cooling of the S_1 phase, intermediate in composition between M_1 and G, leads, dependent on composition, to separation of either the G phase or the M_1 phase or, when S_1 has the eutectic composition P, of both.

Although the behaviour observed in the sodium laurate/water system is as just described, with certain other soaps cooling of a S_1 phase intermediate in composition between M_1 and G may lead to the separation of a number of individual mesophases intermediate in composition between M_1 and G. According to Luzzati and associates the following succession of " intermediate phases ", each named in accordance with its X-ray diffraction pattern, can arise in binary soap/water systems:[1,20] " deformed middle "; " rectangular "; " hexagonal complex "; " cubic ".

Not all of these phases are found in any particular soap/water system but, according to Luzzati, those which do arise always follow one another with increasing concentration in the order given. The experimental study of these intermediate phases is difficult since the range of composition of each individual phase is narrow, the systems are highly viscous and mixtures of the phases are frequently present. The credentials of certain of these phases may therefore be regarded as less certain than those of the M_1, G and M_2 phases just considered.[9] The cubic phase, or viscous isotropic phase, V_1, has however been observed by numerous workers in a variety of systems (cf. e.g., Fig. 4 and Fig. 5) and is fully authenticated. It was first characterized by Luzzati and associates as formed in aqueous systems containing the higher potassium soaps at temperatures in the region of 100 °C. It has also been studied at room temperature in binary aqueous systems containing potassium caprylate, sodium 2-ethylhexyl sulphate, N,N,N-trimethylaminododecanoimide and N,N-dimethyl-dodecylamine oxide. It has also been observed in ternary aqueous systems containing two amphiphiles, one more and one less polar.[9] In these ternary systems a further intermediate phase, Ekwall's phase C, is often found intermediate between G (Ekwall's phase D) and M_1 (Ekwall's phase E).

Although X-ray diffraction measurements provide information concerning the arrangement and the repeating distances between the micellar units of the various intermediate phases, they do not establish the nature of the units themselves. A number of tentative micellar models for the individual intermediate phases have been suggested by several workers but these models have often later been revised or discarded. None can be considered as unequivocally established.

STRUCTURE OF THE V_1 PHASE

A number of structural models have been proposed for the well-defined V_1 phase. Chronologically, these include:

(i) spherical S_1 micelles arranged in a face centred cubic lattice within an aqueous continuum [20,21] (" Cubic I " structure);

(ii) inverse spherical S_2 micelles similarly arranged, the hydrocarbon chains forming a hydrocarbon continuum between the polar cores [22] (" Cubic II " structure); and, most recently,

(iii) a structure consisting of two interpenetrating networks composed of rods, each rod having the character of a short segment of an M_1 micellar fibre.[23] The interpenetrating networks crystallographically constitute a body-centred cubic structure (" Q_1 structure ").

Neither the " Cubic I " nor the " Cubic II " structure fits conformably between the M_1 and G structures. Moreover, a structure of the " Cubic I " type must apparently now be assigned to the recently characterized cubic phase S_{1c} which, as will shortly be discussed, occasionally arises between the S_1 and M_1 phases.

With regard to the Q_1 structure it is difficult to see what intermolecular forces could stabilize the postulated network in a system in which the $\bar{O}$, $\bar{C}$ and $\bar{W}$ regions are all fluid in character.

To the writer it seems that, somewhat as the M_1 and G phases arise on cooling the intermediate S_1 phase by homo-aggregation of either M_1 or G micellar units respectively, so the " intermediate mesophases " may arise by aggregation of both M_1 and G units jointly or of some type of hybrid unit.

Such hybrid aggregation might occur in various ways according to the relative abundance and extension of the M_1 and G units present. This would be expected to vary in a regular manner with concentration. The proposal of detailed hybrid structures for the successive individual intermediate phases must however await further studies.

It may be mentioned that, whereas the S_1 and V_1 phases show high resolution NMR spectra, the M_1, M_2 and G phases do not.[24,17] This may possibly be related to the presence of indefinitely extended micellar systems in the M_1, M_2 and G phases in contrast to the presence of smaller and more mobile units in the S_1 and V_1 phases. This seems in better accord with the idea of a hybrid structure for the V_1 phase than with the indefinitely extended Q_1 network model. NMR studies of other " intermediate phases " would be of much interest.

The Inverse Cubic or Inverse Viscous Isotropic Phase V_2

A cubic phase, which is complementary to the V_1 phase, arises intermediate between the G and M_2 phases in the Aerosol OT/water system (Fig. 3) and in many other binary and ternary systems. This phase, which shows a high resolution NMR spectrum,[17] may possibly possess a hybrid structure derived jointly from M_2 and G units.

The V_2 phase is apparently to be identified with the cubic Q_2 phase observed by Spegt and Skoulios[19] in the case of the anhydrous fatty acid soaps of strontium and barium at high temperatures and with calcium ω-phenylundecanoate at room temperature. It was for these Q_2 phases that the interpenetrating network structure (here of inverse form) was first postulated by Luzzati and Spegt.[25] This interpretation was later extended to cover the Q_2 phase found in lecithin/water systems at high concentrations, and to the Q_1 phase observed in other systems of higher water content.[23,26,27]

The Hydrophilic Cubic Phase S_{1_c}

Analogous to the formation of the M_1 and G phases by the mutual long-range ordering of M_1 and G micelles respectively, in certain circumstances mutual ordering of spherical S_1 micelles can apparently give rise to a mesophase in which these micelles are arranged in some form of cubic lattice. This phase was recorded by Fontell, Mandell and Ekwall[28] in the decaethyleneglycol monolaurylether/water system at room temperature at 40–44% concentration. It has recently also been characterized by Balmbra, Clunie and Goodman[8] in the dodecyltrimethylammonium chloride/water system (Fig. 5). It also occurs with the C_{10} and C_{14} but not with the C_{16} and C_{18} trimethylammonium chlorides nor with any of the corresponding bromides.

For the formation of a phase having the structure S_{1c} in a binary amphiphile/water system it is clear that the amphiphile must be constituted so that the replacement of the S_1 micelles with other forms, which normally occurs with increasing concentration, does not take place over a concentration range that is so low that the S_1 micelles never attain sufficient proximity for their mutual ordering. It would be expected that the asymmetry in the interfacial interaction of polar groups, which is believed to promote the formation of M_1 micelles, would, at a given concentration, be less with the $-N(CH_3)_3Cl$ group than with the more bulky $-N(CH_3)_3Br$ group. This view is supported by the X-ray diffraction studies of Reiss–Husson and Luzzati[18] who found evidence that while at 27 °C in the cetyl trimethylammonium bromide/water system conversion of spherical to fibrous micelles commences at a concentration of about 5%, with the corresponding chloride spherical micelles are still predominant even at a concentration of 40%. This type of difference probably accounts for the formation of the S_{1c} phase by the C_{10}, C_{12} and C_{14} trimethylammonium chlorides although not by the corresponding bromides. The non-formation of the S_{1c} phase by the C_{16} and C_{18} trimethylammonium chlorides is probably due to displacement of the $S_1 \rightarrow M_1$ interconversion process to lower concentrations on increase of molecular weight. At these lower concentrations the S_1 micelles are insufficiently close together for mutual long-range ordering to occur. It is of interest that the S_{1c} phase is produced on solution of hydrocarbon in S_1 solutions of sodium caprylate of suitable concentration although, in absence of hydrocarbon, increase in concentration (accompanied by reduction in area per polar group) leads to formation of the M_1 mesophase.[28] This is probably because solution of hydrocarbon increases the size and mutual proximity of the S_1 micelles without markedly affecting R or the area per polar group.   Increase in concentration, on the other hand, produces a decrease in area per polar group and leads to the condition, $R_x < 1$; $R_y = 1$, which gives rise to formation of the M_1 phase.

IDEALIZED PHASE DIAGRAM INCLUDING THE AMORPHOUS SOLUTION PHASE AND THE SUCCESSION OF FUSED MESOMORPHOUS SOLUTION PHASES FORMED IN BINARY AMPHIPHILE/WATER SYSTEMS

An idealized phase diagram showing the relationships between the amorphous solution phase and the succession of fused mesomorphous solution phases found in binary amphiphile/water system is shown in Fig. 10.   Of the " intermediate phases " only the V_1 and V_2 phases are included.

In this idealized diagram the ranges of existence of all the mesophases are drawn of similar extent, the peaks are represented as of equal heights and the eutectics of equal depth.   In real systems, as already instanced by Figs. 2–5, not all the phases arise and the temperatures of the peaks and eutectics vary widely.   Nonetheless, in real systems those phases that do appear apparently always follow the sequence shown with increasing concentration.   With amphiphiles of analogous constitution a particular peak tends to arise at a lower concentration the higher the molecular weight of the amphiphile (cf. Method Ic of Table 1 below).

In the sequence of phases illustrated in Fig. 10 the effect of increasing concentration can reasonably be assigned to its tendency to increase R and thus regularly to affect micellar conformation.   The effect of increasing temperature can be interpreted mainly in terms of the effect of increased thermal motion in increasing fluctuations in micellar form and in tending to break down long-range order.   Although the influence of increasing temperature on the ratio R is usually small it may in some specific cases be either to increase or to decrease R.   In these cases, in addition to the general disintegrating effect just noted, the various peaks in Fig. 10 will tend to be bent towards the left or right respectively.   The former effect is evident in Figs. 4 and 5.

TABLE 1   General methods for influencing phase equilibria by variation of $\bar{R}$ in amphiphile solutions containing an organic liquid O_1, an amphiphilic salt C_1 and water W_1

Note: R increases with A_{CO}^-/A_{CW}^-, i.e. with $\left[(A_{H_2O}^- + A_{CO}^-)/(A_{H_2O}^- + A_{CW}^-)\right]$

Method classification	Details of method	Influence on R	Probable mechanism of influence on R	Effect on the phase ratio in an initially heterogeneous system containing any two in the following succession of phases: $O_1^*, S_1, S_1^*, M_1, V_1, G, V_2, M_2, S_2, W_1^*$
Ia	Reduction in the relative proportion of W_1	R tends to be increased	A_{CW}^- diminished by mass action	
Ib	The addition to O_1 of an oil-soluble compound of more polar (hydrophilic) character than O_1. Alternatively, this may be regarded as the addition to C_1 of an amphiphilic compound less polar than C_1	R tends to be increased	Reduction of $A_{H_2O}^-$ by incorporation of amphiphilic additive in C layer and/or increase of $A_{H_2O}^-$	Increase in proportion of the right-hand phase present
Ic	Increase in the relative lipophilic character of C_1, e.g., by increase of molecular weight, substitution of an organic for an inorganic counter-ion, or by certain changes in constitution[10]	R tends to be increased	A_{CO}^- increased and/or $A_{H_2O}^-$ diminished	
Id	The addition to W_1 of an inorganic salt	R tends to be increased	$A_{H_2O}^-$ diminished	
IIa	Reduction in the relative proportion of O_1	R tends to be decreased	A_{CO}^- diminished by mass action	
IIb	The addition to W_1 of a water-soluble organic liquid of more lipophilic character	R tends to be decreased	A_{CW}^- increased	Increase in proportion of the left-hand phase present
IIc	Increase in the relative hydrophilic character of C_1, i.e., method Ic in reverse	R tends to be decreased	$A_{H_2O}^-$ increased and/or A_{CO}^- diminished	
IId	The addition to O_1 of a less hydrophilic oil-soluble component, e.g., medicinal oil	R tends to be decreased	Reverse of mechanism of method Ib	

Where a single-phase system is initially involved, the progressive application of a particular method will finally tend to the precipitation from this phase of the neighbouring successional phase. With particular systems certain phases of the sequence do not appear, but the general order of succession with variation in R remains the same. Superimposed on the directional effects of methods Id and IIb is the general tendency of W-soluble materials to inhibit the formation of liquid crystalline solutions

O_1^*, W_1^* Excess non-solubilized organic or aqueous phase if present. If no organic liquid has been added O_1 must be taken to indicate the hydrocarbon region of the micellar system.

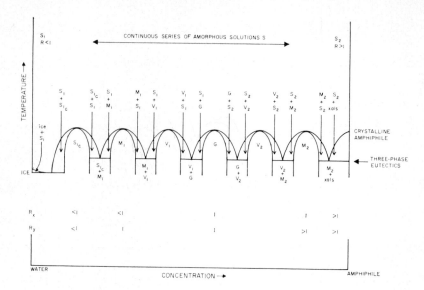

Figure 10.   Idealized phase diagram including the amorphous solution phase $S(S_1, S_2)$ and the succession of fused mesomorphous solution phases realizable in binary amphiphile/water systems.   In individual real systems not all the phases arise, but those that do succeed one another with increasing concentration in the order indicated; further the heights of the different peaks and the depths of the eutectics vary greatly.

DIAGRAMMATIC REPRESENTATION OF INTERMICELLAR EQUILIBRIA AND ASSOCIATED PHASE CHANGES

The generalizations of Fig. 10 are also expressed in Fig. 11 in which, again, micellar form is correlated with the ratio R.

Within the individual mesophases (with the possible exception of the " intermediate phases ", V_1, V_2, etc.) the micellar form is characteristic and uniform and there is long-range intermicellar order.

Within the amorphous solution phase S there is an equilibrium of thermally fluctuating micellar forms.   If, within the S phase, under particular conditions of composition and temperature, a particular micellar form attains a sufficient concentration and extension, then micellar interaction leads to mutual ordering of the micelles and to the separation of the corresponding homo-mesophase (S_{1c}, M_1, G, M_2). Further, it appears possible that under certain conditions there may be micellar interactions involving more than one micellar type that

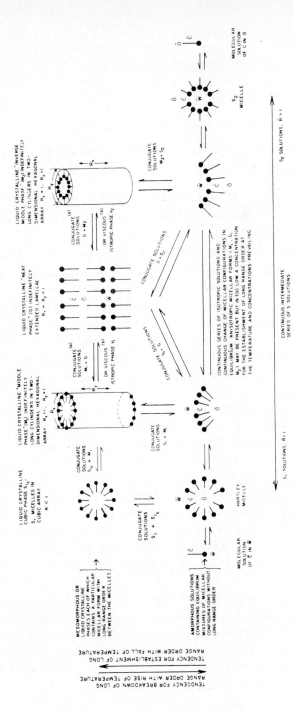

Figure 11. Correlation between the ratio R and the micellar form in the fused amorphous and mesomorphous phases produced in amphiphilic systems.

lead to the separation of hybrid mesophases (V_1, V_2 and other " intermediate " mesophases).

Mesophase Formation in Multicomponent Systems

In the remainder of this article a brief account will be given of mesophase formation in multicomponent amphiphilic systems.

SYSTEMS CONTAINING WATER, HYDROCARBON AND TWO AMPHIPHILES, ONE HYDROCARBON-SOLUBLE AND ONE WATER-SOLUBLE

Many systems of this type, often including additional components, were examined by the writer in a study initially concerned with the formulation of storage-stable emulsifiable concentrates.[10]

From the point of view of this technical objective both crystal and liquid crystal formation are usually undesirable. In the systems examined branched-chain salts were mainly used, because, in comparison with the n-alkyl compounds, they crystallize much less readily and are less inclined to give highly viscous and technically intractible liquid crystalline solutions. Indeed, in the particular systems examined, of all the mesophases included in Fig. 10, only the comparatively non-viscous lamellar liquid crystalline phase G was encountered. This fortunately considerably simplified these early phenomenological and orientative studies. It was to correlate and interpret the observations made in this work that the R-theory[10,11] was first developed. Since the only micellar phases encountered were the amorphous solution phase $S(S_1, S_2)$ and the lamellar liquid crystalline phase G, only the possibilities $R < 1$, $R = 1$ and $R > 1$ were envisaged. The possibility of dissymmetry in R, for example $R_x < 1$, $R_y = 1$ as in the M_1 phase, did not at that time suggest itself.

As a typical example of the approach adopted, the behaviour observed when octanol–1 is gradually added to a mixture of equal volumes (10 ml total) of an aqueous solution of undecane–3 sodium sulphate (20%w) and an aromatic-free hydrocarbon fraction (b.p. 188–213 °C) will be discussed. The observed sequence of phase changes, which are readily reversible with changes in composition or temperature, is illustrated by Fig. 12, (1)–(8).

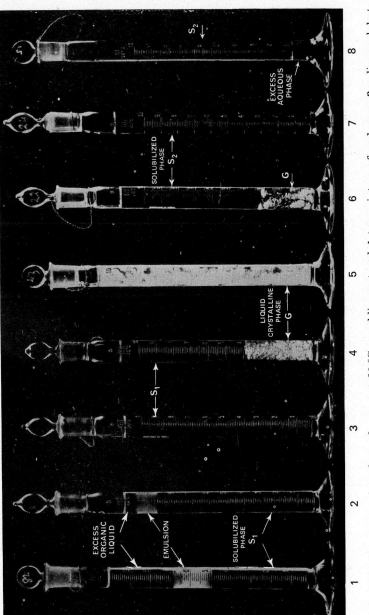

Figure 12. Accompanying phase changes at 20 °C on adding octanol-1 (5 ml, 20w%) to a mixture of undecane-3 sodium sulphate solution (5 ml) with aromatic-free hydrocarbon (5 ml); systems photographed between crossed polaroid sheets. Note that S_1 and S_2 solutions are clear and the persistent orientation in certain regions of G phases.

(1) No octanol added, (S_1+excess hydrocarbon phase)
(2) 0.85 ml octanol-1 added
(3) 0.91 ml octanol-1 added, S_1 (isotropic)
(4) 1.00 ml octanol-1 added, $S_1 + G$
(5) 1.20 ml octanol-1 added, G (birefringent)
(6) 1.38 ml octanol-1 added, $G+S_2$
(7) 1.70 ml octanol-1 added, S_2 (isotropic)
(8) 2.13 ml octanol-1 added, S_2+excess aqueous phase

In (1) the undecane–3 sodium sulphate is dissolved in the aqueous phase mainly as spherical S_1 micelles (Hartley micelles). Solution (or " solubilization ") of hydrocarbon in the micellar interior, which necessarily involves reduction in the curvature of the $\overline{C}$ monolayer, is strictly limited by the condition, $R < 1$.

In (2) the added octanol, although distributed between the excess hydrocarbon and the $\overline{W}$, $\overline{O}$ and $\overline{C}$ regions of the aqueous amphiphile phase so as to be of uniform activity throughout, principally enters the S_1 micelles between the alkyl sulphate molecules, C_8 hydrocarbon groups beside C_{11} hydrocarbon groups and $-OH$ groups beside $-SO_4Na$ groups. The highly polar $-SO_4Na$ groups are thus diluted at the interface by the less polar $-OH$ groups. $A_{\overline{C}\overline{W}}(=A_{H\overline{C}\overline{W}}+A_{L\overline{C}\overline{W}})$ is thus diminished by reduction in $A_{H\overline{C}\overline{W}}$ and the value of $A_{\overline{C}\overline{O}}/A_{\overline{C}\overline{W}}$ and hence of the ratio R is thus increased. This permits reduction in curvature of the micellar surface so that further hydrocarbon can enter the micellar interior.

In (3) the continuation of these processes results in complete solution of the hydrocarbon in the amorphous solution phase S_1.

In (4), with further addition of octanol–1 the processes envisaged under (2) and (3) reach a stage where thermal fluctuations establish an equilibrium between the two conjugate phases S_1, in which R is statistically less than unity, and G in which $R = 1$. The character of the equilibrium between the S_1 and G phases has already been discussed for the case of the sodium laurate/water system (p. 153).

In (5), on further addition of octanol–1, unit value of R is established throughout the system which now constitutes a single lamellar liquid crystalline solution phase G.

In (6) further addition of octanol–1 tends to produce the condition $R > 1$ and thermal fluctuations establish an equilibrium between two conjugate phases, the amorphous solution phase S_2, in which R is statistically greater than unity, and the residual G phase ($R = 1$).

In (7) further addition of octanol results in complete conversion of the system to the amorphous solution phase $S_2(R > 1)$.

In (8) continuing increase in R results in extrusion of an excess aqueous phase from the micellar interior. This is complementary to the extrusion of an excess hydrocarbon phase on reduction of R on following the reverse sequence, (3) to (2), that is $S_1 \rightarrow (S_1 + \text{excess}$ hydrocarbon phase).

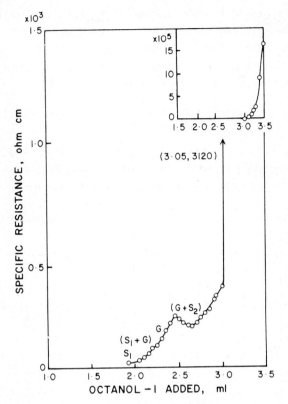

Figure 13. Changes in specific resistance at 20 °C when passing through S_1, G and S_2 stages on gradual addition of octanol–1 to a mixture of undecane–3 sodium sulphate solution (10 ml, 20w%) with 10 ml of aromatic-free hydrocarbon.

Phase changes of the type illustrated by Fig. 12 are accompanied by characteristic changes in electrical resistance. These are shown, for the system of Fig. 12, in Fig. 13. The curves for both the S_1 and S_2 branches of the S phase show a continuous increase in electrical resistance as R is increased and the thermally fluctuating micellar system progressively tends from $\overline{W}$-continuity towards $\overline{O}$-continuity. Further, the S_1 and S_2 branches appear to form parts of a single curve which is interrupted by the interposition of the G phase. The resistance of the G phase itself is higher than that of either the S_1 or S_2 phases of neighbouring composition. This is probably because a crystallographic unit of the G phase, although both $\overline{O}$-continuous and $\bar{W}$-continuous in a plane normal to its optic axis, is both $\bar{O}$-discontinuous and $\bar{W}$-discontinuous in all other planes. Under conditions of temperature or composition where a G phase is not interposed, the continuous transition $S_1 \rightarrow S_2$ is accompanied by a continuous increase in electrical resistance (cf. Fig. 15 on p .174).

INFLUENCE OF A VARIETY OF COMPOSITIONAL CHANGES ON THE RATIO R

By noting the effect of stepwise modification in the composition or temperature of series of systems similar to that illustrated by Figs. 12 and 13 on the amounts of hydrocarbon-soluble amphiphile required

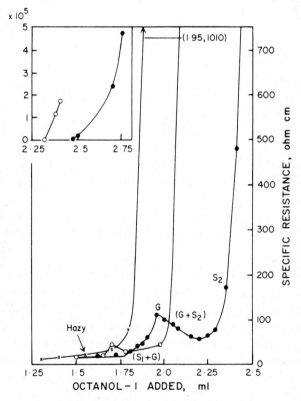

Figure 14.   Changes in specific resistance at 20 °C when passing through S_1, G and S_2 stages on gradual addition of octanol–1 to a mixture of undecane–3 sodium sulphate solution (10 ml, 20w%) containing sodium sulphate: ●0.1 g, or ○0.2 g, or ×0.4 g) with 10 ml of aromatic-free hydrocarbon.

to reach corresponding stages in the phase progression, the qualitative influence of the modification on the ratio R may be inferred. For example it can be seen from Fig. 14 that corresponding points on the curves of resistance against octanol–1 addition are displaced to lower octanol contents by progressive addition of sodium sulphate. It may be inferred that addition of sodium sulphate increases the ratio R.

As a result of many experiments on these lines a table correlating the effects of various types of compositional change on the ratio R and on the formation of the S_1, G and S_2 phases was compiled. This compilation as extended, to some extent tentatively, to cover systems in which the additional mesophases of Fig. 10 are produced, is given in Table 1. Space does not permit its detailed discussion. The following points may be noted:

(1) The table as originally compiled applied to systems in which the more hydrophilic amphiphile was ionic. The same behaviour is broadly followed if this amphiphile is a polyethanoxy compound. The effect of added water-soluble lower alkanols is however reversed (cf. Method IIb). This is probably because, with the polyethanoxy amphiphile, the water-soluble organic compound is distributed in favour of the polyethanoxy zone of the $\bar{C}$ layer, whereas with the ionic amphiphiles it predominantly enters the $\bar{W}$ region. [11]

(2) The effect of inorganic salts on amphiphilic phases has mainly been investigated in systems in which only the S_1, G and S_2 phases arise. [10] In this case the effect of added sodium sulphate is both to increase R and to decrease the range of compositions forming the G phase at a given temperature. Both effects are evident in Fig. 14. Other additives which enter the $\bar{W}$ region, also restrict the range of the G phase independently of whether they increase or decrease R. The effect is probably associated with interruption of water-to-water and water-to-amphiphile hydrogen bonding.

The effect of inorganic salts on the stability of other amphiphilic mesophases needs further study. The effects on the formation of the " intermediate " phases might prove particularly interesting. In certain 1-monoglyceride/water systems Krog and Larsson have found that the V phase (whether of V_1 or V_2 character seems uncertain [9,11]) is stabilized relative to the G phase by sodium chloride. [29]

(3) Independently of its general effect in promoting thermal fluctuations and the breakdown of long-range order, increase in

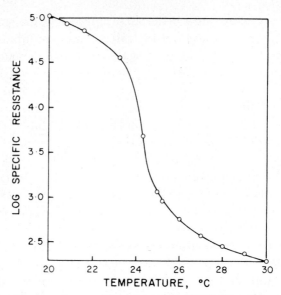

Figure 15. Changes in specific resistance with change of temperature of a solution containing aromatic-free hydrocarbon (10 ml), octanol–1 (2.25 ml), undecane–3 sodium sulphate solution (10 ml, 20w%) and sodium sulphate (0.2 g).

temperature may either increase or decrease R. In the systems in which the amphiphile is mainly non-ionic, increase of temperature usually increases R (Fig. 4) probably by reducing $A_{H\bar{c}\bar{w}}$ through dissociation of hydrogen bonds. With ionic amphiphiles a reduction in R with rising temperature is sometimes found. A striking result of this effect is provided by the electrical resistance changes illustrated by Fig. 15. In this system rise of temperature, by decreasing R, produces a continuous transition within the S phase from S_2 to S_1; that is a thermally fluctuating amorphous micellar system which is predominantly $\bar{O}$-continuous (S_2) is progressively transformed into one that is predominantly $\overline{W}$-continuous (S_1). Although in Fig. 15 the change $S_2 \rightarrow S_1$ is continuous and involves no change of phase, with certain other similar systems intermediate separation of the G phase occurs with rising temperature,[10] i.e., $S_2 \rightarrow (S_2 + G) \rightarrow G \rightarrow (G + S_1) \rightarrow S_1$.

TERNARY AQUEOUS SYSTEMS

A number of ternary systems have been carefully investigated,

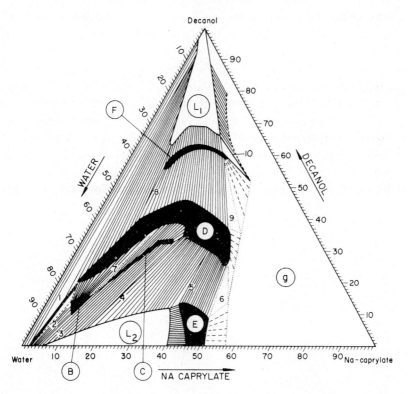

Figure 16. Phase diagram for the three-component system sodium caprylate/decanol/water at 20 °C. The concentrations are % by weight.[9]

L_1–Homogeneous isotropic solutions in water.

L_2–Homogeneous isotropic solutions in decanol.

B, C, D, E, F–Homogeneous mesomorphous phases.

g–Solid crystalline sodium caprylate and hydrated sodium caprylate with fibre structure.

1–10–Three-phase triangles.

Note In the system of nomenclature used in the present paper:

$$L_1 = S_1$$
$$L_2 = S_2$$
$$D = G; \quad B = \text{a second form of } G$$
$$C = \text{an intermediate phase}$$
$$E = M_1$$
$$F = M_2$$

particularly by Ekwall and associates.[9]   Results have usually been represented on triangular isothermal phase diagrams.

The phase equilibria in the most intensively studied system are illustrated in Fig. 16.   Many other systems of this type containing two amphiphiles, one relatively hydrophilic (A_1) and the other relatively lipophilic (A_2) have also been investigated.   They give phase diagrams broadly similar to Fig. 16.   All of the phases indicated in Fig. 10 are represented in one or other of these systems.

In such diagrams, phase sequences encountered with changes in composition directed along lines such as WP in Fig. 17 can be regarded as following the application of Method Ia of Table 1 to an amphiphile of composition P.   Except in zones where conjugate phases occur, P is found to behave much as a single amphiphile of polarity inter-

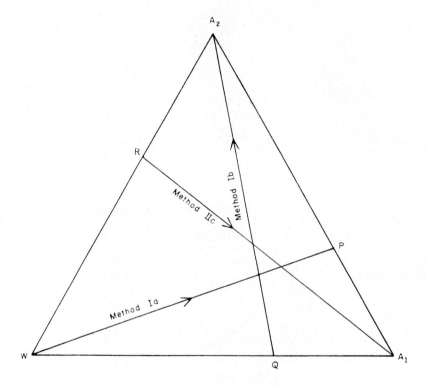

Figure 17.   Composition changes following Methods 1a and 1b of Table 1 in a ternary aqueous system containing two amphiphiles, one relatively hydrophilic (A_1) and the other relatively lipophilic (A_2).

mediate between A_1 and A_2. However, as already noted in discussing the formation of the M_2 phase in these systems, there will be appreciable fractionation of A_1 and A_2 between the $\bar{C}$, $\bar{O}$ and $\bar{W}$ zones within the individual phases. Where conjugate phases occur, macroscopic fractionation of P takes place, A_1 being distributed in favour of the phase richer in water.

Phase sequences encountered with changes in composition directed along lines such as QA_2 and RA_1 may be regarded as following the application of Methods Ib and IIc respectively of Table 1.

When Ekwall's phase diagrams, which have recently been collected and discussed,[9] are examined from this point of view they are found, apparently without exception, to be in good accord with Table 1 and with the generalizations suggested in Figs. 10 and 11.

REFERENCES

1. Luzzati, V., " Biological Membranes ", Chap. 3, p. 71, Academic Press, London (1968) and references.
2. Vincent, J. M. and Skoulios, A. E., *Acta Cryst.* **20**, 441 (1966).
3. Rosevear, F. B., *J. Amer. Oil Chemists Soc.* **31**, 628 (1954), see also Hartshorne, N. H., in " Liquid Crystalline Systems ", Van Nostrand (in preparation).
4. Lawson, K. D. and Flautt, T. J., *Mol. Cryst.* **1**, 241 (1966); cf. also Hanson, J. R. and Lawson, K. D., *Nature* **225**, 542 (1970).
5. McBain, J. W. and Lee, W. W., *Oil and Soap* **20**, 17 (1943).
6. Rogers, J. and Winsor, P. A., *Nature* **216**, 477 (1967).
7. Clunie, J. S., Corkhill, J. M. and Goodman, J. F., *Proc. Roy. Soc.* **285A**, 520 (1965).
8. Balmbra, R. R., Clunie, J. S. and Goodman, J. F., *Nature* **222**, 1159 (1969).
9. Ekwall, P., Mandell, L. and Fontell, K., *Mol. Cryst. and Liq. Cryst.* **8**, 157 (1969) and references.
10. Winsor, P. A., " Solvent Properties of Amphiphilic Compounds ", Butterworths, London (1954) and references.
11. Winsor, P. A., *Chem. Rev.* **68**, 1 (1968) and references.
12. Gallot, B. and Skoulios, A., *Kolloid Zeit. u. Zeit. für Polymere* **213**, 143 (1966).
13. Ekwall, P., Lemström, K. E., Eikrem, H. and Holmberg, P., *Acta Chem. Scand.* **21**, 1401 (1967).
14. Park, D., Rogers, J., Toft, R. W. and Winsor, P. A., *J. Coll. and Interface Sci.* **32**, 81 (1970).
15. Skoulios, A. E. and Luzzati, V., *Acta Cryst.* **14**, 278 (1961).
16. Larsson, K., *Zeit. für Physikal. Chem. Neue Folge*, **56**, 173 (1967).
17. Gilchrist, C. A., Rogers, J., Steel, G., Vaal, E. G. and Winsor, P. A., *J. Coll. and Interface Sci.* **25**, 409 (1967).

18. Reiss-Husson, F. and Luzzati, V., *J. Phys. Chem.* **68**, 3504 (1964).
19. Spegt, P. and Skoulios, A., *Acta Cryst.* **21**, 892 (1966).
20. Luzzati, V., Mustacchi, H., Skoulios, A. and Husson, F., *Acta Cryst.* **13**, 660 (1960); Luzzati, V. and Husson, F., *J. Cell Biol.* **12**, 207 (1962).
21. Clunie, J. S., Corkhill, J. M. and Goodman, J. F., *Proc. Roy. Soc.* **A285**, 520 (1965).
22. Luzzati, V. and Reiss-Husson, F., *Nature* **210**, 1351 (1966).
23. Lecture presented by Luzzati *et al.* at the symposium " Molecular Basis of Membrane Function ", Duke University, Aug. 1968 (in press); cf. also Refs. 25, 26, 27.
24. Lawson, K. D. and Flautt, T. J., *J. Phys. Chem.* **72**, 2066 (1968); cf. also Ref. 4.
25. Luzzati, V. and Spegt, P. A., *Nature* **215**, 701 (1967).
26. Luzzati, V., Tardieu, A. and Gulik-Krzywicki, T., *Nature* **217**, 1028 (1968).
27. Luzzati, V., Gulik-Krzywicki, T., and Tardieu, A., *Nature* **218**, 1031 (1968).
28. Fontell, K., Mandell, L. and Ekwall, P., *Acta Chem. Scand.* **22**, 3209 (1968).
29. Krog, N. and Larsson, K., *Chem. Phys. Lipids* **2**, 129 (1968).

CONTRIBUTED PAPERS

1   Optical Properties

Light Scattering Spectrum of a Nematic Liquid†

IVAN HALLER and J. D. LITSTER‡

IBM Thomas J.Watson Research Center
Yorktown Heights
New York 10598

Abstract—We measured the intensity and the spectrum of light scattered by the nematic liquid crystal p-methoxybenzylidene p-n-butylaniline as a function of temperature. The measurements yield the temperature dependence of the amplitude and dynamics of orientational fluctuations in the ordered phase. We analyze the results in terms of two theories of normal modes of liquid crystals, and examine the extensions required to make the macroscopic elastic theory consistent with experiment.

Introduction

We report here the results of an experimental study of the temperature dependence of the intensity and spectrum of light scattered by fluctuations in the nematic phase of p-methoxybenzylidene p-n-butylaniline (MBBA). From these measurements we deduce the mean squared amplitude and time dependence of the fluctuations, and we compare our results with two phenomenological theories of the normal modes of a liquid crystal.

The ordered phase of nematic liquid crystal is characterized by a long range parallel orientational ordering of the anisotropic rod-like molecules that constitute the compound. The cooperative interaction means the molecules are not free to rotate about directions perpendicular to their long axis, and the normal modes of the ordered phase consist of collective orientational oscillations about the equilibrium direction. Since the electric polarizability of the molecules is highly anisotropic, the orientational fluctuations cause large changes in the refractive index and are, therefore, readily studied by light scattering.

---

† Presented at the Third International Liquid Crystal Conference in Berlin, August 24–28, 1970.
‡ Permanent address: Department of Physics, MIT, Cambridge, Mass.

Let incident light of wave vector $\mathbf{k}_i$ with polarization along $\mathbf{i}$ be scattered in a direction with wave vector $\mathbf{k}_f$ and polarization along $\mathbf{f}$. Then this light will be scattered[1] only by a particular spatial Fourier component of the fluctuations in the element ϵ_{if} of the dielectric constant tensor whose wave vector is $\mathbf{q} = \mathbf{k}_f - \mathbf{k}_i$. The intensity of the scattered light is proportional to the mean squared fluctuations, $\langle \delta\epsilon_{if}{}^2(\mathbf{q}) \rangle$. The spectrum gives the Fourier transform of the correlation function $\langle \delta\epsilon_{if}(\mathbf{q}, 0)\, \delta\epsilon_{if}(\mathbf{q}, \tau) \rangle$ and hence the time dependence of $\delta\epsilon_{if}(\mathbf{q})$. Exponentially decaying fluctuations, for example, give therefore a Lorentzian spectrum to the scattered light.

Phenomenological Theories

There are at present two phenomenological theories of the normal modes of liquid crystals. In this section of our paper we outline the basic features of these two models and how their predictions may be compared with the results of light scattering experiments. In a subsequent section we shall present the measurements we made and compare our results with each model.

If we consider a nematic liquid crystal of uniaxial symmetry, the order on a macroscopic scale may be specified by two quantities: (i) the average alignment direction (optic axis) of the molecules in a small volume, and (ii) the degree of alignment (birefringence) of the molecules along this direction. Therefore, we may write the Cartesian dielectric constant and susceptibility tensors as

$$\epsilon_{\alpha\beta} = \bar{\epsilon}\delta_{\alpha\beta} + (Q\Delta\epsilon/3)(3n_\alpha n_\beta - \delta_{\alpha\beta}) \tag{1}$$

$$\chi_{\alpha\beta} = \bar{\chi}\delta_{\alpha\beta} + (Q\Delta\chi/3)(3n_\alpha n_\beta - \delta_{\alpha\beta}) \tag{2}$$

Here, n_α, n_β are the Cartesian components of a unit vector (called the director) parallel to the local optic axis. An order parameter that specifies the degree of alignment[2] is $Q = \frac{1}{2}\langle 3\cos^2\theta - 1\rangle$ where θ is the angle between the long axis of a molecule and the optic axis. The quantities $\Delta\epsilon$ and $\Delta\chi$ are, respectively, the anisotropies of the dielectric constant and diamagnetic susceptibility for a completely ordered ($Q = 1$) liquid crystal. It is clear from (1) that both fluctuations in Q and $\mathbf{n}$ will scatter light. In the nematic phase the most intense scattering comes from thermally excited fluctuations in the orientation of $\mathbf{n}$; it is these fluctuations we have studied in MBBA. From (1) it is also apparent that re-orientations of the director cause large fluctuations only in ϵ_{31} and ϵ_{32} if we choose the undisturbed director to lie along the 3 direction. Then, for example, we may carry out experiments with the incident polarization **i** along 3 and the scattered polarization **f** along 1 or 2, respectively, to study the mean squared fluctuations in n_1 or n_2 (from the intensity) and the time dependence of these fluctuations (from the spectrum).

The Orsay Liquid Crystal Group[3] has proposed a model to explain the intensity and spectrum of the scattered light. In this model they derive an equation of motion for the director using the Frank[4] elastic model for liquid crystals and Leslie's hydrodynamic equations[5] for anisotropic fluids. The fluctuations in **n** are heavily overdamped and lead to a Lorentzian spectrum of the scattered light. Since the Orsay theory deals directly with optic axis (director) motions, we may obtain directly from it expressions for the intensity and spectrum of the scattered light.

The theory of Martin, Pershan, and Swift (MPS)[6] discusses the normal modes of a liquid crystal in terms of strains $u_{ij} = \frac{1}{2}(\partial_i u_j + \partial_j u_i)$. Coordinates are chosen so that the 3 axis is a symmetry axis in the unstrained crystal. In order to use the MPS theory to interpret optical and magnetic measurements on liquid crystals it is necessary to relate the optic axis displacements to the strains u_{ij}. In the unstrained uniaxial liquid the dielectric polarizability tensor is diagonal at any point; the major axis of the corresponding polarizability ellipsoid (the optic axis) coincides at any location with the overall symmetry axis. The polarizability ellipsoid can be distorted through rotations, which correspond to fluctuations in the off-diagonal elements of the tensor, or by deformations, which involve only the diagonal elements of the corresponding dielectric polarizability tensor. The fluctuations measured by our experiments (i.e., those that arise from the reorientation of the optic axis) will in general be given by ($j = 1$ or 2)

$$\delta\epsilon_{3j} = Q\Delta\epsilon(A\,\partial_3 u_j + B\,\partial_j u_3) \tag{3}$$

where A and B are parameters relating the optic axis motion to the MPS displacements u_i. Note that, in general, the optic axis can be rotated both by the symmetric part (center of mass flow) and the antisymmetric part (reorientation of molecular axis) of the displacement gradient.†

A comparision of Eqs. (1) and (3) shows that director displacements are related to strains ($j = 1$ or 2) as

$$\delta n_j = A\, \partial_3 u_j + B\, \partial_j u_3 \tag{4}$$

Analysis of Light Scattering Experiments

Since the liquid crystal possesses symmetry about the 3 axis, we may, without loss of generality, choose the scattering wave vector $\mathbf{q}$ to lie in the 1–3 plane. Our experiments were carried out, as detailed in the Appendix, under three different conditions which led to the following configurations:[8] (a) $q_1{}^2 < 0.078\, q_3{}^2$, $\mathbf{i}$ along 3 and $\mathbf{f}$ in the 1–3 plane; (b) $q_1{}^2 < 0.0026\, q_3{}^2$, $\mathbf{i}$ along 2, and $\mathbf{f}$ in the 1–3 plane; (c) $q_3 = 0$, $\mathbf{i}$ along 3, and $\mathbf{f}$ along 1. Under the conditions a, b, and c, we therefore measured the mean squared amplitude and time dependence of $f_1\, \delta\epsilon_{13}$, $f_3\, \delta\epsilon_{23}$, and $\delta\epsilon_{13}$, respectively, where f_1 and f_3 are the components of the unit vector $\mathbf{f}$ along 1 and 3, respectively.

We may then use the Orsay model to calculate the intensities for our three configurations to be proportional to:

$$\langle \delta\epsilon_{if}{}^2(\mathbf{q})\rangle = Q^2 \Delta\epsilon^2 f_1{}^2\, kT / K_{33}\, q_3{}^2 \tag{5a}$$

$$= Q^2 \Delta\epsilon^2 f_3{}^2\, kT / K_{33}\, q_3{}^2 \tag{5b}$$

$$= Q^2 \Delta\epsilon^2 kT / K_{11}\, q_1{}^2 \tag{5c}$$

Here we have ignored the small contributions of $q_1{}^2$ in configurations a, and b, and have used the notation of the original references[3] for the elastic constants. Equations (5a)–(5c) refer to the configurations a–c, respectively.

From the MPS theory and Eq. (3) we obtain:

$$\langle \delta\epsilon_{if}{}^2(\mathbf{q})\rangle = Q^2 \Delta\epsilon^2 A^2 f_1\, kT / M_5\, q_3{}^2 \tag{6a}$$

$$= Q^2 \Delta\epsilon^2 A^2 f_3{}^2\, kT / M_5\, q_3{}^2 \tag{6b}$$

$$= Q^2 \Delta\epsilon^2 B^2\, kT / L_5\, q_1{}^2 \tag{6c}$$

where, again, we use the notation of the original reference[6] for elastic constants.

---

† Amazingly enough, this point in the case of solids has only recently been noted.[7]

We used the known temperature dependence of the refractive indices of MBBA[9] to correct for the variation of reflection at the liquid crystal surfaces, the geometrical factors f_1 or f_3, and the wave vectors q_1 or q_3. In Fig. 1 we show kT divided by the intensity of

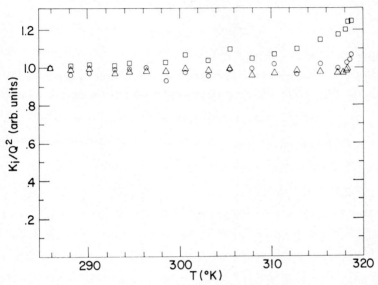

Figure 1. The temperature dependence of normalized light intensity scattered by fluctuations in the nematic phase of MBBA. The squares, triangles, and circles correspond respectively to the experimental configurations a, b and c discussed in the text.

the scattered light normalized to unity at 286 °K. We see that K_{33}/Q^2, K_{11}/Q^2, M_5/A^2Q^2, and L_5/B^2Q^2 are all independent of temperature within the accuracy of our measurements. (We did not correct for the temperature dependence of the effect of the q_1 component in a; we believe this explains the slight rise near the transition temperature for this configuration in Fig. 1).

The spectrum of the scattered light was found to be a Lorentzian line centered about the incident laser frequency. If $\Gamma/2\pi$ is the half-width at half height (in Hz) for the scattered spectrum, the Orsay theory predicts:

$$\Gamma_a = K_{33}q_3^2/\eta_B \tag{7a}$$

$$\Gamma_b = K_{33}q_3^2/\eta_B \tag{7b}$$

$$\Gamma_c = K_{11}q_1^2/[\gamma_1 - (\gamma_1+\gamma_2)\alpha_3/\alpha_s] \tag{7c}$$

where the notation of Ref. 3 has been used for the viscosity coefficients.

From the MPS model, we calculate:

$$\Gamma_a = M_5 q_3{}^2/\eta_5 \tag{8a}$$

$$\Gamma_b = M_5 q_3{}^2/\eta_5 \tag{8b}$$

$$\Gamma_c = L_5 q_1{}^2/\eta_5 \tag{8c}$$

using the notation of Ref. 6.

We give the measured linewidths as a function of temperature in
Fig. 2. The Orsay theory is consistent with our experimental results

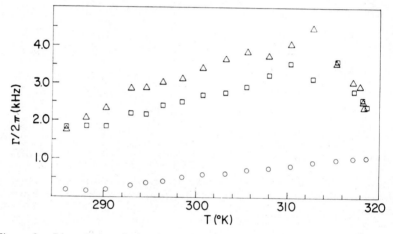

Figure 2. Linewidth of the Lorentzian spectrum of light scattered by
fluctuations in the nematic phase of MBBA. The squares, triangles, and
circles correspond to experimental configurations a, b and c discussed in the
text.

within experimental errors and allows evaluation of the temperature
dependence of the viscosity coefficients (Fig. 3). From the different
temperature dependences of Γ_a and Γ_c, however, we see the MPS model
is consistent with our data only if M_5 and L_5 have different temperature dependences. Our intensity measurements then show that the
coefficients A and B must vary differently with temperature.

Equation 3 permits rotation of the optic axis by both the symmetric and the anti-symmetric part of the displacement gradient.
The anti-symmetric part is pure rotation and might naively be
thought of as the unique or predominant contributor to optic axis

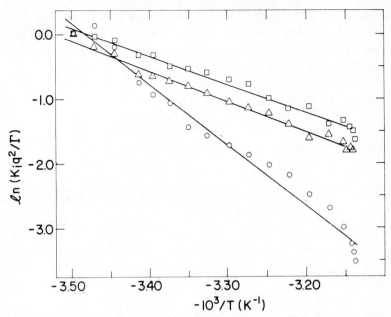

Figure 3. Temperature dependence of the viscosity coefficients for damping of director motions in the Orsay model. The squares, triangles, and circles correspond to η_a, η_b, and η_c, respectively.

rotation. If in the strained medium the optic axis merely rotated according to the rotational part of the strain, then we should have $A = -B = 1$ at all temperatures. This, however, is ruled out by our experiments.

Discussion

It is interesting to speculate on the mechanism by which the strains u_{ij} cause re-orientations of the optic axis. Since the strains u_{ij} are thermally excited fluctuations, they are not static distortions. A plausible mechanism which might result in different temperature dependences for A and B would be flow alignment[10] of the molecular axes.

The anisotropy of the diamagnetic susceptibility enables one, however, to study the elastic constants under static conditions, by using magnetic fields to exert torques on the liquid crystal molecules. For certain experimental configurations the applied magnetic field has no effect until a critical field has been reached.[11]   The Frank theory can be used to treat finite distortions and hence to obtain the rotation of the molecular axis as a function of field.   A detailed theoretical discussion may be found in a paper by Saupe.[12]

The critical field at which distortion can first occur, is given[12] in terms of the Frank theory by

$$H_{c\perp} = (\pi/d)(K_{33}/Q\Delta\chi)^{1/2}$$

for the perpendicular configuration and by

$$H_{c\parallel} = (\pi/d)(K_{11}/Q\Delta\chi)^{1/2}$$

for the parallel configuration.   In the perpendicular configuration the nematic sample of thickness d is enclosed by plane parallel plates which have been pretreated such that the optic axis in the absence of a magnetic field is perpendicular to the boundary, and the field is applied in the plane.   In the parallel configuration the nematic liquid is aligned in a direction parallel to and the field is applied perpendicular to the plates.

Assuming Eq. (4) also relates the optic axis displacement to static strains, an analogous derivation of critical fields using the MPS theory yields

$$H_{c\perp} = (\pi/d)(M_5/Q\Delta\chi A^2)^{1/2},$$

and

$$H_{c\parallel} = (\pi/d)(L_5/Q\Delta\chi B^2)^{1/2}$$

The temperature dependence of the critical field has been studied by Saupe[12] for p-azoxyanisole (PAA).   He found that K_{33}/Q^2 and K_{11}/Q^2 were independent of temperature.   This is in agreement with our light scattering intensity results for MBBA and means that Eq. (4) relating the optic axis rotation to static strains provides consistency between experiment and the MPS model.   Since the magnetic field exerts a steady torque on the optic axis and a steady restoring torque is supplied by the elastic constants M_5 and L_5 under static conditions, it is clear that flow alignment cannot be the mechanism for the coupling of the optic axis to the strains.

We have seen that our measurements of the temperature dependence of the intensity and spectrum of the light scattered in the nematic phase of MBBA may be interpreted with either the Orsay model or the MPS model for liquid crystals.   For the MPS model to be consistent with our data it is necessary to postulate a rather involved temperature dependent relation between the strain variables u_{ij} of the model and the motion of the optic axis of the liquid crystal. Comparision with static experiments in a magnetic field suggest that the coupling between the director orientation and the strains is the same for static strains or thermally excited time dependent ones; this rules out flow alignment as a possible mechanism for this coupling. It appears that the strains consist of a mixture of center of mass translation and axial realignment of the liquid crystal molecules; the relative amount of each type of molecular motion for a given strain seems to depend on temperature. In the Orsay model restoring forces are produced only for reorientations of the molecular axis, but it seems that in the MPS model there must also be restoring forces resulting from displacements of the molecules.

A complete version of the MPS model will require the introduction of an equation of motion for the director in order to determine the temperature and frequency dependence of the coupling constants A, and B. The model then loses the attractive simplicity which distinguished it from earlier approaches.

Acknowledgements

We are grateful to M. J. Freiser for many stimulating and helpful discussions. We have also benefited from conversations with P. G. DeGennes, G. J. Lasher, P. C. Martin, P. S. Pershan, and N. S. Shiren. We thank W. R. Young and D. C. Green for the preparation and purification of the MBBA used.

Appendix: Experimental and Computational Details

The spectrum of the scattered light was measured with the technique of self-beating spectroscopy. The 6328 Å light from a Spectra Physics model 119 He–Ne laser was focused on the aligned MBBA sample contained between two Pyrex microscope slides 25 mm square. The sample thickness of $50\,\mu$ was maintained by a Teflon gasket. To obtain good alignment, the slides were cleaned in chrome-sulfuric acid and rubbed repeatedly on cheesecloth: the extinction ratio between crossed and parallel polars was better than

100. The sample assembly was mounted in an aluminum block whose temperature was controlled to better than 8 mdeg. Temperatures were measured with a platinum resistance thermometer. Parallel light scattered by the sample was focused on an EMI 9558B photomultiplier tube. The spectrum of the photo-current was analyzed with a Hewlett Packard 310A wave analyzer.

The MBBA was purified by vacuum distillation. To minimize decomposition, the scattering chamber was purged with dry nitrogen. The nematic–isotropic transition temperature of the sample was frequently checked and observed to stay in the range 45.45 ± 0.15 °C.

We studied light scattered in three configurations: (a) $\mathbf{n}$, $\mathbf{i}$, and $\mathbf{f}$ in the scattering plane; (b) $\mathbf{n}$ and $\mathbf{f}$ in the scattering plane with $\mathbf{i}$ normal to them; (c) $\mathbf{i}$ parallel to $\mathbf{n}$ and normal to the scattering plane with $\mathbf{f}$ in the scattering plane. Light entered perpendicular to the glass slides, and the laboratory scattering angle, θ_1 was fixed at 45.0°. The corresponding internal scattering angles, θ, varied from 24.0° to 25.3° in configurations (a) and (b), and from 27.2° to 26.8° in configuration (c) over the temperature range from 12.8 °C to the clearing point.

In configuration (c) f_2 vanishes only at a single, temperature-dependent scattering angle. The ratio f_2^2/f_1^2 is easily computed, however, from trigonometric relations and was shown to be smaller than 0.0086 under the conditions of our experiments.

The dielectric constant fluctuations appearing in Eq. (5) and (6) relate the electric displacement associated with the scattered wave to the incident electric field, within the liquid crystal medium. To obtain them from the intensities measured in air, the temperature dependent reflectivities of the two glass-MBBA interfaces need to be taken into account. The multiplicative coefficients C_a, C_b, and C_c, for configuration (a), (b) and (c), respectively, were obtained from the Fresnel coefficients for uniaxial bodies. They are listed, along with relations used for other temperature dependent quantities below:

Configuration (a):

$$\sin \theta = (1/n_f) \sin \theta_1$$
$$n_f = [n_e^2 - (n_e^2/n_0^2 - 1) \sin^2 \theta_1]^{1/2}$$
$$q_1^2 = (2\pi/\lambda_0)^2 (n_f \cos \theta - n_0)^2$$

$$q_3{}^2 = (2\pi/\lambda_0)^2 \sin^2\theta_1$$
$$f_1 = \sin\theta$$
$$C_a = [(n_f n_g \cos\theta + n_e{}^2 \cos\theta_g)(n_0 + n_g)/4n_g \cos\theta]^2$$

Configuration (b):

$$n_f = [n_e{}^2 - (n_e{}^2/n_0{}^2 - 1) \sin^2\theta_1]^{1/2}$$
$$q_1{}^2 = (2\pi/\lambda_0)^2 (n_f \cos\theta - n_e)^2$$
$$q_3{}^2 = (2\pi/\lambda_0)^2 \sin^2\theta_1$$
$$f_3 = \cos\theta$$
$$C_b = [(n_f n_g \cos\theta + n_e{}^2 \cos\theta_g)(n_0 + n_g)/4n_g \cos\theta]^2$$

Configuration (c):

$$n_f = n_0$$
$$q_1{}^2 = (2\pi/\lambda_0)^2 (n_e{}^2 + n_0{}^2 - 2n_e n_0 \cos\theta)$$
$$q_3 = 0$$
$$f_1 = n_e \sin\theta/(n_e{}^2 + n_0{}^2 - 2n_e n_0 \cos\theta)^{1/2}$$
$$f_2 = (1 - f_1{}^2)^{1/2}$$
$$C_c = [n_0(n_g \cos\theta + n_0 \cos\theta_g)(n_e + n_g)/4n_g \cos\theta]^2$$

Here n_e and n_0 are extraordinary and ordinary indices of refraction and n_f the effective index for the scattered light in MBBA. $n_g = 1.473$ is the refractive index of glass, and

$$\cos\theta_g = [1 - (1/n_g)^2 \sin^2\theta_1]^{1/2}.$$

REFERENCES

1. Benedek, G. B., in Statistical Physics of Phase Transitions and Super-fluidity (Gordon and Breach, New York, 1969).
2. Maier, W. and Saupe, S., Z. Naturforsch. 15a, 287 (1960).
3. Groupe d'Etude des Cristaux Liquides (Orsay), J. Chem. Phys. 51, 816 (1969); Phys. Rev. Letters 22, 1361 (1969).
4. Frank, F. C., Disc. Faraday Soc. 25, 19 (1958).
5. Leslie, F. M., Quart. J. Mech. Appl. Math. 19, 357 (1966).
6. Martin, P. C., Pershan, P. S. and Swift, J., Phys. Rev. Letters 25, 844 (1970).
7. Nelson, D. F. and Lax, M., Phys. Rev. Letters 24, 379 (1970).
8. Haller, I. and Litster, J. D., Phys. Rev. Letters 25, 1550 (1970).
9. Haller, I., Huggins, H. A. and Freiser, M. J., to be published.
10. Helfrich, W., J. Chem. Phys. 50, 100 (1969).
11. Freedericksz, V. K. and Zolina, V., Trans. Faraday Soc. 29, 919 (1933).
12. Saupe, A., Z. Naturforsch. 15a, 810 (1960).

Scattering of Light by Liquid Crystalline p-Azoxyanisole†

D. KRISHNAMURTI and H. S. SUBRAMHANYAM

Department of Physics
University of Mysore
Mysore, India

Received October 8, 1970; in revised form December 18, 1970

Abstract—Chatelain's theory of light scattering in nematic liquid crystals is modified and extended to obtain expressions for the intensities V_H, H_H, H_V and V_V in three cases, i.e., when the optic axis of the medium lies (i) normal to the scattering plane, (ii) along the direction of the incident light and (iii) perpendicular to incident direction and in the scattering plane. The theory is developed assuming that the molecules are arranged parallel to one another in spherical volume elements, but no specific orientation distribution function is used here. The intensity data available for p-azoxyanisole are analysed by modifying the theoretical expressions by an empirical form-factor to represent the effect of the orientation correlation between neighbouring volume elements. From the consistency of the analysis it emerges that the volume elements have a radius of about $800\,\text{Å}$. Also, the average value $\overline{\cos^4\theta}$ is calculated, θ being the angle between the optic axis and the orientation direction in a volume element.

1. Introduction

The scattering of light in the nematic phase of p-azoxyanisole at $125\,^\circ\text{C}$ was investigated by Chatelain[1,2] in detail, using plane polarized incident light with the electric vector lying (i) in the plane of scattering and (ii) perpendicular to it. In each case the scattered light was analysed and the intensities of the H component with the electric vector in the plane of scattering and the V component with electric vector normal to the plane of scattering were determined mainly over the range of angles of scattering from 8° to 50°. The intensities of the different components may be denoted here by H_H, V_H, V_V and H_V, the respective subscripts H or V being used to denote that the incident electric vector is in the plane of scattering or normal to it. In his studies Chatelain made use of oriented specimens corresponding to two cases, wherein the optic axis of the

† Presented at the Third International Liquid Crystal Conference in Berlin, August 24–28, 1970.

97

medium was lying (i) normal to the plane of scattering and (ii) in the plane of scattering.

A striking angular dissymmetry in the intensities of the scattered light, analogous to that encountered with colloidal scattering was observed with regard to all the components. Further, at small angles it was observed that the intensity V_H was several times greater than H_H. Falgueirettes[3] who studied the intensity V_H for various angles of scattering in the case of nematic parabutyloxy-benzoic acid, found the intensity to be large at small angles.

A theory of scattering of light in nematic liquid crystals was proposed by Chatelain[4] on the basis of the following assumptions. The intensity of scattering due to fluctuations in orientation (anisotropic scattering) is large compared to that arising from density fluctuations so that the latter part (isotropic scattering) may be neglected. The molecules are arranged with their long axes parallel to one another in the form of " paquets "-bundles which are spherical volume elements whose size is small compared to the wavelength of light, and phase correlation exists between the scattered waves from the molecules within a volume element. The different volume elements in the medium have different orientations for their optic axes and the orientation distribution function is assumed to be of the form $e^{-\beta \theta^2}$, where θ is the angle between the orientation axis of a volume element and the optic axis of the medium. Also the values of θ are restricted so that $0 \leqslant \theta \leqslant \theta_0$. Besides, Chatelain has also considered the case where the molecules may not form " paquets " but have an orientation distribution given by $e^{-\beta \theta^2}$. The results of the theory proposed by him gave the right order of magnitude for the depolarisation factors at small angles. However, detailed comparison of the intensities of scattering for different angles, from the standpoints of theory and experiment have not been made.

Chatelain has dealt with only the case corresponding to the optic axis of the medium lying normal to the plane of scattering. In the following, we theoretically consider, on the basis of an approach similar to his, but without using any specific distribution function, three cases of interest viz., where the optic axis of the medium lies (i) normal to the plane of scattering, (ii) along the direction of the incident light and (iii) in the plane of scattering and in a direction perpendicular to that of the incident light. An analysis of the intensity data of Chatelain is also carried out in this paper with the aid of the results of the theory, and in conjunction with a simple empirical relation to represent some of the effects which it is not possible to treat theoretically.

2. Theoretical

We consider the medium to be composed of spherical volume elements of average radius R, each volume element containing on an average l molecules which are arranged parallel to one another. The size of the volume element may be considered as equivalent to an average value of the persistent length for the orientational order in the medium, although one cannot altogether rule out correlations in the orientations between neighbouring volume elements. For the case where the orientations of the different volume elements are independent of one another, the average intensity of anisotropic scattering per unit volume is given by

$$I = \tfrac{1}{2}\nu[\overline{A_i^2} - (\overline{A}_i)^2] \tag{1}$$

where ν is the number of volume elements per unit volume, A_i is the amplitude of the scattering from the ith volume element and $\overline{A_i^2}$ and $\overline{A}_i$ are the mean values of A_i^2 and A_i, averaged over the different volume elements (see, for example, Cabannes[5]). Since the molecules in any particular spherical volume element are aligned parallel to one another, the phase correlation between the scattered waves from them may be taken into account by assuming that the average propagation characteristics of the incident and scattered waves in the volume elements, are defined by the extraordinary and ordinary indices n_e and n_0 of the medium (see, for example, Rocard,[6] Chatelain[4]).

If r is the distance of the detector of the scattered light from the scattering volume, $\mathbf{p}_i$ the electric moment induced in the molecule at the centre of the volume element, l the number of molecules in the volume element and $\mathbf{0}$ the unit vector along the direction of the electric vector of the scattered component in which we are interested, we have,

$$A_i = \frac{4\pi^2 l}{\lambda^2 r}(\mathbf{p}_i \cdot \mathbf{0})G_{ii} \tag{2}$$

where $\qquad G_u = \dfrac{3/u^3}{\sin u - u \cos u}$ and $\qquad u = \dfrac{2\pi R/\lambda}{|\,n_1\mathbf{s} - n_2\mathbf{s}_0\,|}$.

Here λ is the wavelength of light, R is the radius of the volume element, $\mathbf{s}_0$ and $\mathbf{s}$ are unit vectors along the incident and scattered directions and n_1 and n_2 the appropriate refractive indices for the scattered and incident waves. For the various cases to be discussed, the expressions for u are shown in Table 1.

TABLE 1

Orientation of the optic axis of the medium	Scattered component	Expressions for u
Case I: Normal to the plane of scattering	V_H	$\dfrac{2\pi R}{\lambda}\,(n_e^2 + n_0^2 - 2n_e n_0 \cos \theta_s)^{1/2}$
	H_H	$\dfrac{4\pi R}{\lambda}\,n_0 \sin\,(\theta_s/2)$
	V_V	$\dfrac{4\pi R}{\lambda}\,n_e \sin\,(\theta_s/2)$
	H_V	$\dfrac{2\pi R}{\lambda}\,(n_e^2 + n_0^2 - 2n_e n_0 \cos \theta_s)^{1/2}$
Case II: along the direction of incident light	V_H	$\dfrac{4\pi R}{\lambda}\,n_0 \sin\,(\theta_s/2)$
	H_H	$\dfrac{2\pi R}{\lambda}\,(n^2 + n_0^2 - 2nn_0 \cos \theta_s)^{1/2}$
	V_V	$\dfrac{4\pi R}{\lambda}\,n_0 \sin\,(\theta_s/2)$
	H_V	$\dfrac{2\pi R}{\lambda}\,(n^2 + n_0^2 - 2nn_0 \cos \theta_s)^{1/2}$
Case III: In the scattering plane and perpendicular to the direction of incident light.	V_H	$\dfrac{2\pi R}{\lambda}\,(n_e^2 + n_0^2 - 2n_e n_0 \cos \theta_s)^{1/2}$
	H_H	$\dfrac{2\pi R}{\lambda}\,(n^2 + n_e^2 - 2nn_e \cos \theta_s)^{1/2}$
	V_V	$\dfrac{4\pi R}{\lambda}\,n_0 \sin\,(\theta_s/2)$
	H_V	$\dfrac{2\pi R}{\lambda}\,(n^2 + n_0^2 - 2nn_0 \cos \theta_s)^{1/2}$

NOTE: In the above n is the extraordinary index for the scattered wave along θ_s and is given by $n^2 = n_0^2 n_e^2 (n_0^2 \sin^2 \theta_0 + n_e^2 \cos^2 \theta_0)^{-1}$, where θ_0 is the angle between the scattering direction and the optic axis of the medium.

To calculate the induced moment $\mathbf{p}_i$, we assume that the molecules have two principal polarizabilities $\alpha_{\parallel}$ and $\alpha_{\perp}$ respectively parallel and perpendicular to the long axis of the molecules. The direction of the long axis of the molecule may be denoted by the unit vector $\mathbf{a}_i$, which also corresponds to the orientation axis of the volume element. For p-azoxyanisole we assume $\alpha_{\parallel} = C$ and $\alpha_{\perp} = (A + B)/2$ where A, B, C are the principal polarizabilities. If the incident electric vector $\mathbf{E}$ is represented by $E_0\mathbf{b}$ where $\mathbf{b}$ is the unit vector along $\mathbf{E}$ we have, $\mathbf{p}_i = E_0\{\alpha_{\parallel}(\mathbf{b} \cdot \mathbf{a}_i)\mathbf{a}_i + \alpha_{\perp}[\mathbf{b} - (\mathbf{b} \cdot \mathbf{a}_i)\mathbf{a}_i]\}$ and

$$\mathbf{p}_i \cdot \mathbf{0} = E_0\{\delta(\mathbf{b} \cdot \mathbf{a}_i)(\mathbf{a}_i \cdot \mathbf{0}) + (\alpha_0 - \delta/3)(\mathbf{b} \cdot \mathbf{0})\} \tag{3}$$

where $\delta = \alpha_{\parallel} - \alpha_{\perp}$ and $\alpha_0 = (\alpha_{\parallel} + 2\alpha_{\perp})/3$. Using Eqs. (1), (2) and (3) the average intensity of anisotropic scattering per unit volume can be shown to be given by

$$I = KG_u^2 \delta^2\{\overline{(\mathbf{b} \cdot \mathbf{a}_i)^2(\mathbf{a}_i \cdot \mathbf{0})^2} - \overline{[(\mathbf{b} \cdot \mathbf{a}_i)(\mathbf{a}_i \cdot \mathbf{0})]^2}\} \tag{4}$$

where K is a proportionality constant and the factor within the braces represents averages taken over all the volume elements. In arriving at Eq. (4), the terms involving $(\alpha_0 - \delta/3)$ and $2\delta(\alpha_0 - \delta/3)$ vanish owing to $(\mathbf{b} \cdot \mathbf{0})$ being a constant for a given angle of scattering and not related to the orientation of the volume elements.

The factor within the braces in Eq. (4) can be more explicitly written for the various cases by employing a Cartesian coordinate system defined by unit vectors $\mathbf{i}, \mathbf{j}, \mathbf{k}$. The optic axis of the medium is taken as the direction $\mathbf{k}$. The vibration direction of the scattered light which is defined by $\mathbf{0}$ is then expressible in terms of the unit vectors $\mathbf{i}, \mathbf{j}, \mathbf{k}$ and the angle of scattering θ_s and Table 2 gives the details regarding the directions of $\mathbf{b}$ and $\mathbf{0}$ for the various cases in terms of $\mathbf{i}, \mathbf{j}, \mathbf{k}$. We denote the direction cosines $(\mathbf{a}_i \cdot \mathbf{i})$, $(\mathbf{a}_i \cdot \mathbf{j})$, $(\mathbf{a}_i \cdot \mathbf{k})$ by α, β, γ and recognize that for the nematic phase which is uniaxial, $\overline{\alpha^2} = \overline{\beta^2} \neq \overline{\gamma^2}$; $\overline{\alpha^2\gamma^2} = \overline{\beta^2\gamma^2} \neq \overline{\alpha^2\beta^2}$ and $\overline{\alpha^4} = \overline{\beta^4} \neq \overline{\gamma^4}$. Making use of Table 2 and the above relations, the intensity expressions obtained for the various cases are given below. The constant of proportionality K involves the square of the effective electric field inside the medium. It was shown by Chandrasekhar and Madhusudana[7] that in the case of nematic liquid crystals the polarization field is satisfactorily represented by a new and simple formula proposed by Vuks.[8] Accordingly, the effective field here would be $(\overline{n^2} + 2)/3$ times that of the external field, $\overline{n^2}$ being equal to $(n_e^2 + 2n_0^2)/3$. Hence, in the following the constant of proportionality K is the same for all cases.

Case I.   Optic axis normal to the plane of scattering

$$V_H = KG_u^2 \delta^2(\overline{\alpha^2\gamma^2}) \tag{5}$$

$$H_H = KG_u^2 \delta^2\{[\overline{\alpha^4 - (\alpha^2)^2}] \cos^2 \theta_s + (\overline{\alpha^2\beta^2}) \sin^2 \theta_s\} \tag{6}$$

$$V_Y = KG_u^2 \delta^2[\overline{\gamma^4 - (\gamma^2)^2}] \tag{7}$$

$$H_V = KG_u^2 \delta^2(\overline{\alpha^2\gamma^2}) \tag{8}$$

Case II.   Optic axis along the direction of the incident light

$$V_H = KG_u^2 \delta^2(\overline{\alpha^2\beta^2}) \tag{9}$$

$$H_H = KG_u^2 \delta^2\{[\overline{\alpha^4 - (\alpha^2)^2}] \cos^2 \theta_s + (\overline{\alpha^2\gamma^2}) \sin^2 \theta_s\} \tag{10}$$

$$V_V = KG_u^2 \delta^2[\overline{\alpha^4 - (\alpha^2)^2}] \tag{11}$$

$$H_V = KG_u^2 \delta^2[(\overline{\alpha^2\beta^2}) \cos^2 \theta_s + (\overline{\alpha^2\gamma^2}) \sin^2 \theta_s] \tag{12}$$

Case III.   Optic axis lying in the plane of scattering and perpendicular to incident direction

$$V_H = KG_u^2 \delta^2(\overline{\alpha^2\gamma^2}) \tag{13}$$

$$H_H = KG_u^2 \delta^2\{[\overline{\gamma^4 - (\gamma^2)^2}] \cos^2 \theta_s + (\overline{\alpha^2\gamma^2}) \sin^2 \theta_s\} \tag{14}$$

$$V_V = KG_u^2 \delta^2[\overline{\alpha^4 - (\alpha^2)^2}] \tag{15}$$

$$H_V = KG_u^2 \delta^2[(\overline{\alpha^2\gamma^2}) \cos^2 \theta_s + (\overline{\alpha^2\beta^2}) \sin^2 \theta_s] \tag{16}$$

Chatelain[4] gives the expressions for only Case I. In his paper the averages are represented by integrals involving the orientation distribution function. In the above, the u values to be used in G_u^2 for the various cases are those tabulated in Table 1. It may be noted that $V_H = H_V$ is satisfied only for Case I as is to be expected. Making use of the fact that $\alpha^2 + \beta^2 + \gamma^2 = 1$ and that $(\alpha^2 + \beta^2 + \gamma^2)^2 = 1$ and also that in the nematic phase any orientation distribution would be a function of only θ ($= \cos^{-1} \gamma$), it can be shown that in the above expressions,

$$\overline{\alpha^4} = \overline{3\alpha^2\beta^2}; \qquad \overline{\alpha^2\beta^2} = \tfrac{1}{8}(1 - \overline{2\gamma^2} + \overline{\gamma^4})$$

and
$$\overline{\alpha^2\gamma^2} = \tfrac{1}{2}(\overline{\gamma^2} - \overline{\gamma^4}). \tag{17}$$

Hence, the intensity expressions involve only the averages $\overline{\gamma^2}$ and $\overline{\gamma^4}$. Further, it may be noted that $\overline{\gamma^2}$ is obtainable from the order para-

TABLE 2

Orientation of the optic axis of the medium: **k**	Direction of incident light	Scattered component	**b**	**0**
Case I Normal to the plane of scattering	**i**	V_H	**j**	**k**
	i	H_H	**j**	$\mathbf{j}\cos\theta_s - \mathbf{i}\sin\theta_s$
	i	V_V	**k**	**k**
	i	H_V	**k**	$\mathbf{j}\cos\theta_s - \mathbf{i}\sin\theta_s$
Case II Along the direction of the incident light	**k**	V_H	**j**	**i**
	k	H_H	**j**	$\mathbf{j}\cos\theta_s + \mathbf{k}\sin\theta_s$
	k	V_V	**i**	**i**
	k	H_V	**i**	$\mathbf{j}\cos\theta_s + \mathbf{k}\sin\theta_s$
Case III In the scattering plane and perpendicular to the direction of incident light	**i**	V_H	**k**	**j**
	i	H_H	**k**	$\mathbf{k}\cos\theta_s + \mathbf{i}\sin\theta_s$
	i	V_V	**j**	**j**
	i	H_V	**j**	$\mathbf{k}\cos\theta_s + \mathbf{i}\sin\theta_s$

meter S calculable from the birefringence of the medium using the well-known relation that $\overline{\gamma^2} = (2S + 1)/3$.

3. Analysis of the Experimental Data

In our calculations we make use of the values of $n_e = 1.819$ and $n_0 = 1.568$ obtained from the measurements of Chatelain and Germain[9] for p-azoxyanisole. Calculations of the S factors for p-azoxyanisole at various temperatures were made by Chandrasekhar and Madhusudana[7] using the Vuk's formula.[8] At 125 °C the values of S and $\overline{\gamma^2}$ are respectively 0.4618 and 0.6412. The relative intensities V_H, H_H, etc., for cases I and II as reported by Chatelain are shown in Table 3. Case III has not so far been experimentally investigated. The values of V_H and H_H (for Case I) shown, are the revised values from Ref. 2. All the other values are from Ref. 1 and require a correction by a factor of $\cos\theta_s$ as pointed out by Chatelain in his later paper, Ref. 4. Accordingly, this correction will be made for purposes of the analysis of these data.

If the orientations of the spherical volume elements are mutually independent of one another it follows from Eq. (5) that the intensity V_H (Case I) should be proportional to G_u^2. Chatelain[4] has estimated

TABLE 3

Components	θ_s										
	8°	9°	11°	15°	20°	25°	30°	40°	50°	160°	172°
V_H†	137	100	75	46	27	—	13	—	5	5	3.5
H_H†	15	13	11	9	6.4	—	5.1	—	3.7	—	—
V_V†	18	16	13	10.5	7.5	6	5.8	4.9	4.9	—	—
V_H‡	86	73	53	32	20	14	11	8.5	8	4.2	3.5
H_H‡	22	19	16	11	8.5	8	7	6.8	6.7	—	—
V_V‡	14	12	10.5	7	5.2	4.5	4	3.3	3.1	—	—
H_V‡	67	58	43	24	15	10	8	5.5	5	3.9	4.2

† Optic axis normal to the plane of scattering.
‡ Optic axis along the incident direction.

from the ratio of the observed intensities of the scattering at θ_s and $(180 - \theta_s)$ that the radius of the volume elements should be about 0.1μ. Four pairs of such ratios are reported by Chatelain and from these it was deduced by us that if R/λ, ($\lambda = 5893$ Å) were to lie between 0.18 and 0.13 the correct order of magnitude of the ratio would be obtained. However, it was found on calculation that no one particular value of R/λ when used for calculating G_u^2, would give a straight line plot for the data of the intensities V_H against G_u^2. In fact, the rapid increase of intensity in the nearly forward directions could not be accounted for, because of the slow variation of G_u^2 with θ_s. Evidently, the assumption made in the theory that the orientations of the neighbouring volume elements are independent of each other cannot be valid for a dense anisotropic medium. A large proportion of the variation of intensity with the angle of scattering probably arises due to the correlation between the orientations of the molecules in neighbouring volume elements. Debye[10] has discussed an analogous problem in the case of colloidal scattering by solutions which are neither too dilute nor too strong and shown that the intensity expression would involve an additional form factor—which is a function of θ_s—arising from the phase correlation in the scattering from the different particles. However, his formula cannot be used here owing to its validity being restricted to cases where the concentrations are not too high. In addition to the above effect, there is also the possibility of the enhancement of intensity by multiple scattering; this is a complex problem to treat theoretically, especially in the case of anisotropic media.

In the following, we show that the present theory enables us to analyse the experimental data and obtain the average value $\overline{\gamma^4}$. Let us consider a system of oriented spherical groups of molecules with correlation in their orientations. Let $\overline{\gamma^2}$ and $\overline{\gamma^4}$ be the averages for this system. The intensity of anisotropic scattering for this system may be denoted by I (dependent) $= f(\theta_s)$. Now, for a hypothetical system with the same averages $\overline{\gamma^2}$ and $\overline{\gamma^4}$, but in which there are no orientational correlations, the intensity of anisotropic scattering would be different. Let I_{ind} be equal to a function $g(\theta_s)$. The theory developed by us gives $g(\theta_s)$. We can write,

$$(I_{dep})/(I_{ind}) = f(\theta_s)/g(\theta_s) = h(\theta_s)$$

and $I_{dep} = f(\theta_s) = g(\theta_s)h(\theta_s)$. If the form of the function $(I_{dep})/g(\theta_s)$ could be obtained at least over a range of θ_s where there are no discontinuities in the functions, it would enable us to calculate the average value of $\overline{\gamma^4}$ appearing in $g(\theta_s)$.

Chatelain had earlier found that he could represent the various observed intensities by an empirical formula $I = A (\sin \theta_s)^x$ where A and x are constants, x being negative. The values of x for the different cases are in the range of -1 to -2. There are also other instances of correlated systems, where the function for the intensity takes this form. For example, it is well-known[11] that in the case of critical opalescence where strong correlations exist between the fluctuations of the neighbouring volume elements, the intensity formula involves a factor $kT/[\beta^{-1} + \{(2\pi g/\lambda') \sin \tfrac{1}{2}\theta_s\}^2]$ and β^{-1} tends to zero near the critical point. Another example which may be cited here is the case of medium density polyethylene wherein the orientational correlations between the crystallites give rise to very strong small angle scattering. We find that the data for the scattered intensity H_V reported by Stein[12] can be well represented by the function $(\sin \theta_s)^x$ with $x = -2.64$. Therefore it appeared that $h(\theta_s)$ itself could most probably be represented by $(\sin \theta_s)^x$.

We have analysed the data for V_H (case I) by plotting $\log (V_H/G_u^2)$ versus $\log (\sin \theta_s)$ for various values of (R/λ). It was found that a value of $(R/\lambda) = 0.141$ gave the best straight line fit, as shown in Fig. 1. The data for H_V (case I) are not reproduced here in a graphical plot since H_V is experimentally found to be equal to V_H. The data for V_H (case II) also gave a reasonable straight line fit as

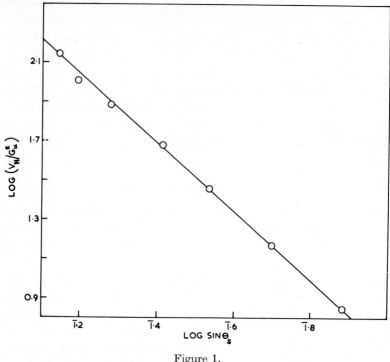

Figure 1.

shown in Fig. 2, again in confirmation of the choice of the factor as $(\sin \theta_s)^x$. We have adopted the same value of $(R/\lambda) = 0.141$ for calculating the G_u^2 appearing in all the cases analysed here. Further confirmation of the validity of our approach is obtained from the analysis of the data for H_H (cases I and II) and H_V (case II); for these cases the $g(\theta_s)$ itself is more complicated and involves also functions like $[(\overline{\alpha^2\beta^2}) \cos^2 \theta_s + (\overline{\alpha^2\gamma^2}) \sin^2 \theta_s]$ and these will have to be calculated for the different angles before the analysis is made.

The cases of V_V and H_H evidently involve also isotropic scattering, although conceivably it is a small value. The intensity of isotropic scattering, which arises due to density fluctuations, may be considered as proportional to α_0^2 where $\alpha_0 = (\alpha_\| + 2\alpha_\perp)/3$. For the intensities V_V (I and II cases) the isotropic scattering should be representable therefore by a constant C, so that the anisotropic part of scattering is $[V_V \text{(obs)} - C]$. In the case of H_H on the other hand, the isotropic scattering which is dependent on θ_s should be repre-

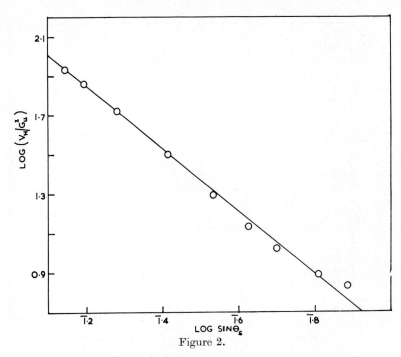

Figure 2.

sentable by $C \cos^2 \theta_s$, so that the anisotropic part of the scattering becomes equal to $[H_H \text{(obs)} - C \cos^2 \theta_s]$. On including the empirical factor, the observed values of the intensities may be expressed as follows:

Case I:
$$V_H = H_V = KG_u^2 \delta^2(\overline{\alpha^2\gamma^2})(\sin \theta_s)^x \tag{18}$$

where
$$\left. \begin{aligned} H_H - C \cos^2 \theta_s &= KG_u^2 \delta^2 F_1(\theta_s)(\sin \theta_s)^x \\ F_1(\theta_s) &= [\overline{\alpha^4} - (\overline{\alpha^2})^2] \cos^2 \theta_s + \overline{\alpha^2\beta^2} \sin^2 \theta_s \end{aligned} \right\} \tag{19}$$

$$(V_V - C) = KG_u^2 \delta^2[\overline{\gamma^4} - (\overline{\gamma^2})^2](\sin \theta_s)^x \tag{20}$$

Case II:
$$V_H = KG_u^2 \delta^2(\overline{\alpha^2\beta^2})(\sin \theta_s)^x \tag{21}$$

where
$$\left. \begin{aligned} H_H - C \cos^2 \theta_s &= KG_u^2 \delta^2 F_2(\theta_s)(\sin \theta_s)^x \\ F_2(\theta_s) &= [\overline{\alpha^4} - (\overline{\alpha^2})^2] \cos^2 \theta_s + (\overline{\alpha^2\gamma^2}) \sin^2 \theta_s \end{aligned} \right\} \tag{22}$$

$$(V_V - C) = KG_u^2 \delta^2[\overline{\alpha^4} - (\overline{\alpha^2})^2](\sin \theta_s)^x \tag{23}$$

where
$$\left. \begin{aligned} H_V &= KG_u^2 \delta^2 F_3(\theta_s)(\sin \theta_s)^x \\ F_3(\theta_s) &= (\overline{\alpha^2\beta^2}) \cos^2 \theta_s + (\overline{\alpha^2\gamma^2}) \sin^2 \theta_s \end{aligned} \right\} \tag{24}$$

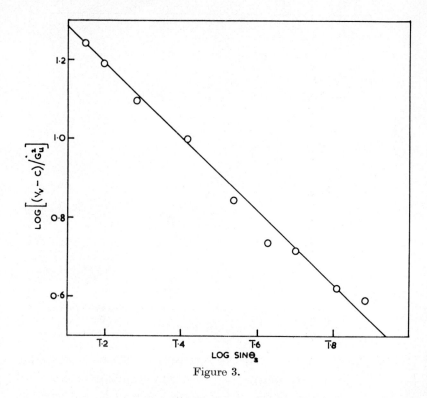

Figure 3.

In the above, the intensities V_H, H_H etc. are the observed intensities. As already mentioned, Eqs. (18) and (21) are verified from the graphical plots shown in Figs. 1 and 2. Graphical plots of $\log [(V_V - C)/G_u^2]$ versus $\log (\sin \theta_s)$ for Cases I and II were made and it was found that with $C = 0.5$, straight line plots were obtainable as shown in Figs. 3 and 4. Before proceeding to the other three cases which involve $F_1(\theta_s)$, $F_2(\theta_s)$, $F_3(\theta_s)$, a calculation of $\overline{\gamma^4}$ was made, using the graphical plots of Figs. 1, 3 and 4. If we write Eqs. (18), (20) and (23) in the form of $V_H/G_u^2 = A_1(\sin \theta_s)^{x_1}$, $(V_V - C)/G_u^2 = A_2(\sin \theta_s)^{x_2}$ and $(V_V - C)/G_u^2 = A_3 (\sin \theta_s)^{x_3}$, the corresponding constants x and A can be determined from the slopes and intercepts of Figs. 1, 3 and 4. Then, we have from Eqs. (18), (20) and (23),

$$\frac{A_1}{A_2} = \frac{\overline{\alpha^2 \gamma^2}}{\overline{\gamma^4} - (\overline{\gamma^2})^2} \tag{25}$$

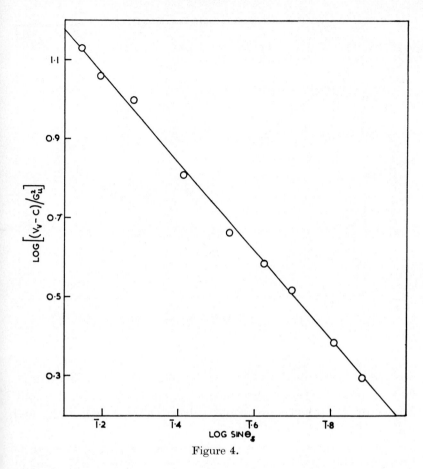

Figure 4.

and

$$\frac{A_1}{A_3} = \frac{\overline{\alpha^2 \gamma^2}}{\overline{\alpha^4} - (\overline{\alpha^2})^2} \qquad (26)$$

Using Eq. (17) and the value of $\overline{\gamma^2} = 0.6412$, two values for $(\overline{\gamma^4})$ were calculated and found to be 0.466 and 0.453 respectively. The values are in reasonable agreement, considering that the intensity data are accurate to about 10%. Similar calculations were made using Eqs. (18) and (21), but the value of $\overline{\gamma^4}$ turns out to be about 0.4. This discrepancy arises presumably because in the case of specimens used in Case II the orientation of the optic axis (parallel to the thickness of the specimen) was easily disturbed and the optic axis

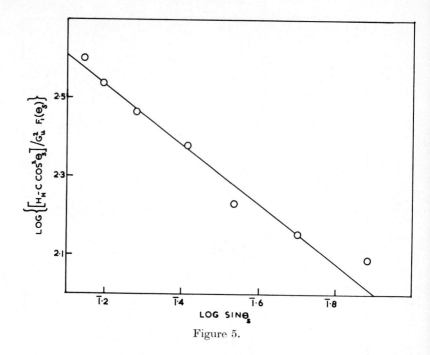

Figure 5.

was only approximately defined, as remarked by Chatelain.[1] Hence, we prefer to use the value of $\overline{\gamma^4} = 0.466$, calculated wholly from Case I, for purposes of our calculation of $F_1(\theta_s)$, $F_2(\theta_s)$ and $F_3(\theta_s)$ in the following.

It may be remarked here that the values of $\overline{\gamma^4}$ calculated from Eqs. (25) and (26) are in reasonable agreement with the value of 0.49 (at 125 °C) calculated by Chandrasekhar and Madhusudana,[13] in connection with the statistical theory of orientational order in nematic liquid crystals, proposed by them. We are thankful to them for providing this value which has not been included in their paper.

Graphical plots of

$$\log\left[(H_H - C \cos^2 \theta_s)/G_u^2 F_1(\theta_s)\right],$$

$$\log\left[(H_H - C \cos^2 \theta_s)/G_u^2 F_2(\theta_s)\right]$$

and $\log\left[H_V/G_u^2 F_3(\theta_s)\right]$ versus $\log(\sin \theta_s)$ verifying Eqs. (19), (22) and (24) are shown in Figs. 5, 6 and 7. The fit obtained in the above three cases shows again that the value of $\overline{\gamma^4}$ obtained from the analysis of the data is a reasonably good estimate.

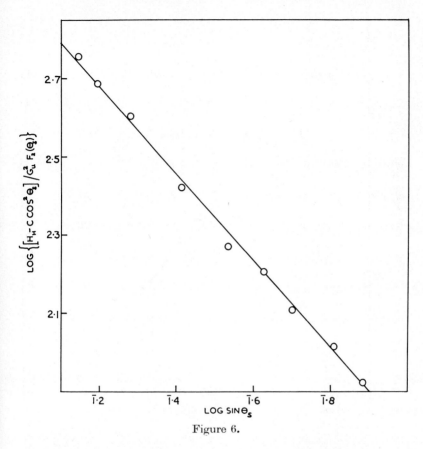

Figure 6.

It may be remarked here that the intensity data of V_H (Case I) for backward scattering[2] cannot be represented accurately using the same empirical factor $(\sin \theta_s)^x$, although the correct order of magnitude may be obtained at about $\theta_s = 165°$. This shows that the empirical factor would not be valid for large angles of scattering. However, we wish to stress that for all the seven cases analysed, the (R/λ) value used is the same, the same form of the empirical factor is used, and that the value of $\overline{\gamma^4}$ is in reasonable agreement with the value independently calculated by Chandrasekhar and Madhusudana. Besides, Gravatt and Brady[14] have recently reported from their studies on the small angle X-ray scattering with p-azoxyanisole, that the correlation length for molecular ordering, at the nematic–isotropic transition point, is about 1900 Å. This is in satisfactory

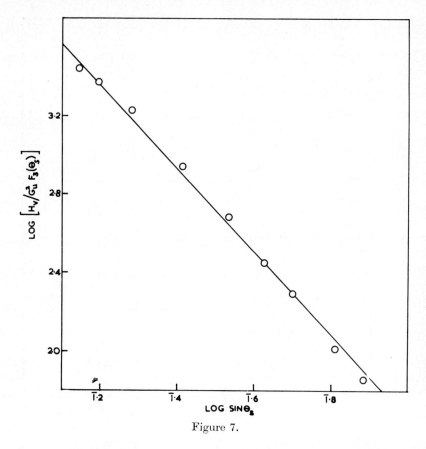

Figure 7.

agreement with the value of 1600 Å for the diameter of the spherical volume elements discussed in this paper. In the foregoing analysis we have not considered the effect of scattering by unattached molecules, as we presume that it is likely to be negligible and further because it would not give rise to strong dependence of the intensities on the angle of scattering. Although one can envisage the possibility of accounting for all the observed facts in terms of correlations between the orientations of the molecules, the use of correlation functions involves a number of constants and can be fruitful only if the intensities of scattering are available over a very wide range of angles for the different cases.

In the case of the nematic phase of parabutyloxybenzoic acid also the intensity data for V_H is available and it is possible to reasonably represent them by a graphical plot of log (V_H/G_u^2) versus log $(\sin \theta_s)$. But, in the absence of data with regard to the other components of intensities, we have not gone into that case in detail.

Acknowledgement

The authors wish to thank Professor S. Chandrasekhar, for his kind interest in this investigation.

REFERENCES

1. Chatelain, P., *Acta Cryst.* **1**, 315 (1948).
2. Chatelain, P., *Bull. Soc. Franc. Miner. et Crist.* **77**, 353 (1954).
3. Falgueirettes, J., *C.R. Acad. Sci., Paris*, **234**, 2619 (1952).
4. Chatelain, P., *Acta Cryst.* **4**, 453 (1951).
5. Cabannes, J., *Recueil des Conferences rapports de documentation sur la physique* **16**, 211 (1929).
6. Rocard, Y., *Rev. Opt. (theor. instrum.)* **9**, 97 (1930).
7. Chandrasekhar, S. and Madhusudana, N.V., *J. de Physique* **30**, c4–24 (1969).
8. Vuks, M. F., *Optics and Spectroscopy* **20**, 361 (1966).
9. Chatelain, P. and Germain, M., *C.R. Acad. Sci., Paris* **259**, 127 (1964).
10. Debye, P. J. W., *Topics in Chemical Physics*, based on the Harvard Lectures—Edited by Prock, A. and McConkey, G., p. 183 (Elsevier Publishing Company, Amsterdam–New York, 1962).
11. Condon, E. U. and Odishaw, H., *Handbook of Physics*, page **6**–126 (McGraw Hill Book Company, Inc., 1958).
12. Stein, R. S., *Electromagnetic Scattering—Proceedings of the interdisciplinary Conference*—Edited by Kerker, M., p. 451 (Pergamon Press, 1963).
13. Chandrasekhar, S. and Madhusudana, N. V., *Mol. Cryst. and Liq. Cryst.* **10**, 151 (1970).
14. Gravatt, C. C. and Brady, G. W., *Acta Cryst.* **a25** (Pts 3), S20 (1969).

Orientational Order in Anisaldazine in the Nematic Phase†

N. V. MADHUSUDANA, R. SHASHIDHAR and S. CHANDRASEKHAR

Department of Physics
University of Mysore
Mysore, India

Received October 16, 1970

Abstract—The refractive indices of anisaldazine,
$$CH_3OC_6H_4CH:NN:CHC_6H_4OCH_3,$$
have been measured in the crystalline, nematic and isotropic phases and the orientational order parameter in the mesophase has been evaluated by the application of the Vuks formula. The curve for the order parameter versus the relative temperature $(T_c - T)$ is nearly parallel with those for p-azoxyanisole and p-azoxyphenetole and lies approximately midway between them.

1. Introduction

A precise determination of the orientational order parameter in nematic liquid crystals from optical anisotropy requires a knowledge of the polarization field in the medium. Recently, it was shown[1] that a new and simple formula proposed by Vuks[2] for the highly anisotropic polarization field in certain organic molecular crystals gives accurate and internally consistent values of the order parameter in p-azoxyanisole and p-azoxyphenetole. We report in this paper measurements of the refractive indices of anisaldazine,

$$CH_3OC_6H_4CH:NN:CHC_6H_4OCH_3,$$

in the crystalline, nematic and isotropic phases and the application of the Vuks formula for calculating the order parameter in the nematic phase.

2. Experimental

The commercial sample of anisaldazine (supplied by Eastman

† Presented at the Third International Liquid Crystal Conference in Berlin, August 24–28, 1970.

Organic Chemicals) was purified by double recrystallization from its solution in toluene.   Oriented specimens were prepared in a small-angled hollow glass prism.   The inside surfaces of the prism were rubbed vertically, i.e., parallel to the refracting edge, and the liquid crystal was allowed to flow along the edge by melting a few crystals placed at the top.   The combined effect of rubbing and flow produced a homogeneous nematic specimen with the optic axis vertical.   The single crystal was grown by slow cooling of the mesophase.

The prism was mounted in a copper block whose temperature could be controlled electrically.   The temperature was measured by means of a thermocouple calibrated previously against the melting points of pure benzoic acid and salicylic acid.   The thermocouple junction was imbedded in a thin copper foil suitably wrapped round the prism to ensure good thermal contact.   The relative temperatures $(T_c - T)$ could be determined to an accuracy of $\pm 0.1\,°C$ and could be maintained constant to within the same limits during any set of observations.

The aperture of the optical system was so arranged that an area of only about 2×2 mm^2 of the specimen was used for the experiments. The refractive index measurements were carried out on a precision spectrometer reading to $2''$ of arc.   The homogeneity and orientation of the nematic and crystalline phases were tested by (i) the clarity of the image of the slit of the spectrometer for both horizontal and vertical polarizations and, (ii) the constancy at a given temperature of the refractive index for vertical polarization irrespective of the angle of incidence.

The principal refractive indices n_x and n_y of the crystal for horizontal polarization were derived from the observed values of n at various angles of incidence by constructing the principal section of the index ellipsoid according to the equation

$$\frac{1}{n^2} = \frac{\sin^2 \theta}{n_x{}^2} + \frac{\cos^2 \theta}{n_y{}^2}, \tag{1}$$

where θ is the inclination of the direction of the ray in the crystal with respect to its X axis.   Such a procedure was necessary as the geometry of the set up did not allow the entire $90°$ range of θ to be investigated.   One of the principal refractive indices was determined directly, whilst the other had to be derived from (1).

Measurements on two specimens in the crystalline and nematic phases gave consistent results. The refractive indices are reckoned to be accurate to ± 0.001. The data are presented in Tables 1 and 2.

TABLE 1   Refractive indices of the crystal at room temperature

$\lambda(\text{Å})$	n_x	n_y	n_z
5893	1.519	1.602	2.201
5461	1.522	1.613	2.251

TABLE 2   Refractive indices in the nematic and isotropic phases ($T_c = 454\,°\text{K}$)

$T_c - T$	$\lambda 5893\,\text{Å}$		$\lambda 5461\,\text{Å}$		$\lambda 4358\,\text{Å}$	
	n_e	n_o	n_e	n_o	n_e	n_o
0.5	1.781	1.560				
1.0	1.784	1.559	1.807	1.569	1.950	1.626
2.5	1.798	1.555	1.820	1.564	1.968	1.619
3.8	1.806	1.552	1.830	1.561	1.980	1.615
4.8	1.810	1.550	1.835	1.559	1.988	1.612
5.4	1.815	1.549	1.840	1.558	1.993	1.611
6.6	1.819	1.547	1.845	1.556	2.001	1.608
8.0	1.828	1.546	1.853	1.555	2.012	1.606
9.2	1.833	1.545	1.858	1.554	2.019	1.605
11.8	1.842	1.543	1.867	1.552	2.030	1.601
13.8	1.848	1.542	1.875	1.550	2.042	1.599
15.5	1.853	1.541	1.880	1.550	2.049	1.597
17.4	1.858	1.540	1.885	1.548	2.056	1.595
18.9	1.862	1.540	1.890	1.548	2.062	1.595
20.6	1.867	1.539	1.894	1.547	2.068	1.593
24.7					2.077	1.588
26.7	1.878	1.533	1.906	1.542	2.085	1.587
$T_c + 0.5$	$n = 1.628$		1.643		1.729	

3. Calculation of the Order Parameter in the Nematic Phase

The Vuks formula is

$$\frac{n_i^2 - 1}{\overline{n^2} + 2} = \frac{4\pi\nu}{3}\,\alpha_i\,, \qquad i = x, y, z, \tag{2}$$

where $\overline{n^2} = \frac{1}{3}\sum_i n_i^2$,

ν the number of molecules/cc and α_i the principal polarizabilities of the medium. To test the applicability of (2) we consider Born's relation[3] between the refractive indices and densities of the crystalline, nematic and liquid phases which takes the form

$$\left(\frac{1}{\rho}\frac{n^2-1}{n^2+2}\right)_{\text{cryst}} = \left(\frac{1}{\rho}\frac{n^2-1}{n^2+2}\right)_{\text{nem}} = \left(\frac{1}{\rho}\frac{n^2-1}{n^2+2}\right)_{\text{liq}} = \frac{4\pi}{3}\frac{N}{M}\bar{\gamma}, \qquad (3)$$

where ρ is the density, $\bar{\gamma}$ the average molecular polarizability, N the Avogadro number and M the molecular weight. The only available density data in the nematic and liquid phases are the early measurements of Conrat[4] recalibrated by Porter and Johnson.[5] Since some interpolation and extrapolation of the values in the nematic phase were required for the calculations, it was found convenient to fit the data with the following empirical relation

$$\rho_{\text{nem}} = 1.04\,[1 + 1.895 \times 10^{-3}(T_c - T)^{0.8}].$$

The density of the crystal was calculated to be 1.23 from X-ray measurements of the lattice constants.[6] Substituting for ρ and n in (3), $\bar{\gamma}$ has been evaluated and shown in Table 3. The average molecular polarizability is indeed very nearly the same in all three phases.

TABLE 3   Average molecular polarizability $\bar{\gamma} \times 10^{24}$ cc

		λ5893 Å	λ5461 Å	λ4358 Å
Crystal,	Room Temp.	36.9	37.8	
Nematic,	$T_c - T = 0.5$	36.6		
	1.0	36.6	37.3	41.2
	2.5	36.7	37.3	41.2
	3.5	36.7	37.3	41.2
	4.8	36.7	37.3	41.3
	5.4	36.7	37.3	41.3
	6.6	36.7	37.3	41.3
	8.0	36.7	37.3	41.3
	9.2	36.7	37.4	41.3
	11.8	36.7	37.4	41.3
	13.8	36.7	37.4	41.4
	15.5	36.7	37.4	41.4
	17.4	36.7	37.4	41.4
	18.9	36.7	37.4	41.4
	20.6	36.7	37.4	41.3
	24.7			41.3
	26.7	36.6	37.3	41.3
Liquid,	$T_c + 0.5$	36.5	37.2	41.0

The principal molecular polarizabilities deduced from the crystal structure[6] and the three principal refractive indices are:

	$\lambda 5893\,\text{Å}$	$\lambda 5461\,\text{Å}$
$\gamma_{\parallel}(=\gamma_z)$	63.4	66.0×10^{-24}
$\gamma_{\perp}\left(=\dfrac{\gamma_x+\gamma_y}{2}\right)$	23.7	23.7×10^{-24}

The orientational order parameter was calculated from the molecular polarizabilities by making use of the relation

$$s = \frac{\alpha_e - \alpha_0}{\gamma_{\parallel} - \gamma_{\perp}},$$

where α_e, α_0 are the principal polarizabilities of the nematic medium obtained by substituting n_e and n_0 in Vuks formula. The values are tabulated below (Table 4). As the crystal refractive indices were not

TABLE 4   Orientational order parameter in nematic phase $T_c = 454\,^{\circ}\text{K}$

$T_c - T$	$\lambda 5893\,\text{Å}$	$\lambda 5461\,\text{Å}$	$\lambda 4358\,\text{Å}$	Average s
0.5	0.406			0.406
1.0	0.413	0.410	0.411	0.411
2.5	0.445	0.440	0.441	0.442
3.8	0.466	0.463	0.462	0.464
4.8	0.477	0.476	0.476	0.476
5.4	0.486	0.484	0.484	0.485
6.6	0.496	0.496	0.496	0.496
8.0	0.516	0.511	0.513	0.513
9.2	0.525	0.522	0.523	0.523
11.8	0.547	0.540	0.540	0.542
13.8	0.556	0.554	0.557	0.556
15.5	0.567	0.563	0.567	0.566
17.4	0.578	0.574	0.577	0.576
18.9	0.585	0.581	0.585	0.584
20.6	0.594	0.590	0.593	0.592
24.7			0.610	0.610
26.7	0.622	0.616	0.621	0.620

measured for $\lambda 4358\,\text{Å}$, s for this wavelength was brought to the same scale as for the other wavelengths by equating the values at one temperature ($T_c - T = 6.6$). We have also verified that s evaluated from n_e and n_0 separately (see Ref. 1) agree with those in Table 4

generally to 3–4%. This discrepancy is slightly greater than for
p-azoxyanisole and p-azoxyphenetole[1] possibly because the
absolute densities of the liquid crystal are not known as accurately
for anisaldazine as for the other two compounds.

Pellet and Chatelain[7] have measured the refractive indices of the
liquid crystal for $\lambda 5893$ Å at a few temperatures, but not those of the
crystal. We have evaluated the order parameters from their data
using our $\gamma_\parallel$ and $\gamma_\perp$. The results are in approximate agreement
with our values, the maximum discrepancy being about 4%.

The excellent agreement between the s values for the different
wavelengths in Table 4 indicates that this method of determining
the order parameter is a reliable one. Figure 1 shows the mean s

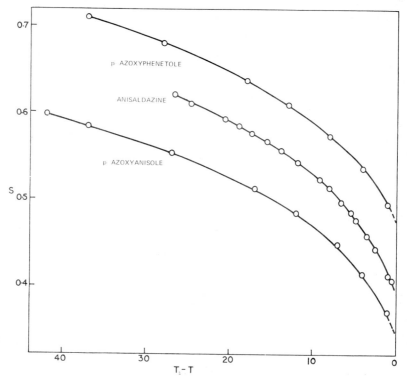

Figure 1. Orientational order parameter in p-azoxyphenetole, anisaldazine
and p-azoxyanisole.

plotted against $T_c - T$ together with the curves for p-azoxyanisole and p-azoxyphenetole also derived from optical data.[1]

Acknowledgements

Two of us (NVM and RS) are grateful to CSIR (India) for fellowships.

REFERENCES

1. Chandrasekhar, S. and Madhusudana, N. V., *Journal Phys. Radium* **30**, c4–24 (1969).
2. Vuks, M. F., *Optics and Spectroscopy* **20**, 361 (1966).
3. Born, M., *Sitz.d.Phys-math.* **25**, 614 (1916).
4. Conrat, F., *Physik. Z.* **10**, 202, (1909).
5. Porter, R. S. and Johnson, J. F., *J. Appl. Phys.* **34**, 51 (1963).
6. Galigne, J. L. and Falgueirettes, J., *Acta Cryst.* **B24**, 1523 (1968).
7. Pellet, O. and Chatelain, P., *Bull. Soc. franc. Miner. Crist.* **73**, 154 (1950).

Spatial Distribution of Light Scattered by p-Azoxyanisole in Applied Electric Field††

M. BERTOLOTTI, B. DAINO, F. SCUDIERI and D. SETTE

Fondazione Ugo Bordoni
Istituto Superiore P.T.
Roma, Italy

and

Istituto di Fisica-Facoltà di Ingegneria-Università di Roma, Roma-Italy

Received October 16, 1970; *in revised form January* 15, 1971

Abstract—Regular patterns of domain-like structure have been observed in the nematic range of p-azoxyanisole (PAA) when a transverse static electric field is applied.

The spatial distribution of scattered light has been studied using optical Fourier transform techniques.

In this way the relevant characteristics of the domain structure are particularly evident. The behaviour of this structure under different incident and scattered polarization conditions has been observed. A thermal hysteresis has been noted when the nematic range is reached from the liquid isotropic state. In this case, depending on how long the time spent and how high the temperature in the liquid state, the domain-like structure tends to be absent. This memory effect is cancelled out by a successive crystallization.

1. Introduction

It has been noted by many authors that the optical properties of p-azoxyanisole in the nematic mesophase are sensitive to an applied electric field.[1,2,3,4] We wish to report the results of some measurements performed on the light scattered by such a liquid crystal under static electric field. Our arrangement differs from the previously reported ones in that we have measured the scattering of the light normal to the applied electric field. The cell we used was a thin flat cell; a collimated coherent laser beam was directed normal to the flat surface of the cell. The liquid crystal was placed between two

---

† Partially supported by the National Research Council of Italy.

‡ Presented at the Third International Liquid Crystal Conference in Berlin, August 24–28, 1970.

123

glass plates separated by a mylar spacer. Two electrodes are evaporated on one of the plates and an electric field is applied across these electrodes. The electrodes are parallel and the measurements were performed with different spacings between 1 and 5 mm. The thickness of the cell is 25 μ. An external heater insured a temperature stability of 0.1 °C. The liquid crystal sample was purified by successive crystallizations. Its resistivity is of the order of 10^{10} Ωcm.

2. Experimental Results

The appearance of the liquid crystal film when a static electric field is applied is shown in Fig. 1(a). With a field of about 700 V/cm a periodic structure appears at the negative electrode, which is the upper one in the figure. As the field is increased this structure propagates until the whole cell is filled by this more or less regular pattern. With an electric field greater than 3.0 kV/cm, the periodicity disappears, giving rise to a fast moving threadlike pattern. In this condition the liquid crystal appears as a turbulent medium. This turbulent aspect is present also at lower voltages, but the movement is slower and confined near to the negative electrode. This movement is more evident where the field is inhomogeneous. The regular pattern shows slow random fluctuations, and the above pictures have been taken in a time shorter than the characteristic fluctuation time.

When observed in linearly polarized light the appearance of this structure depends on the direction of the polarization plane.

The experimental set-up is as follows. An Helium–Neon laser giving 5 mW in the red line was used. The beam was expanded and collimated. A polarization rotator was used to allow investigation of the effect of varying the direction of the incident polarization. The angular scanning of the scattered light field in the Fraunhofer range was performed with a photomultiplier whose output signal was directed, through an amplifier and a time-variable integrator, to a recorder. With this arrangement we investigated the behavior of a domain-like structure at different values of the applied electric field as a function of the temperature and of the optical polarization.

In Fig. 1(b) the scattered light distribution in the direction normal to the applied electric field at different values of this field is shown.

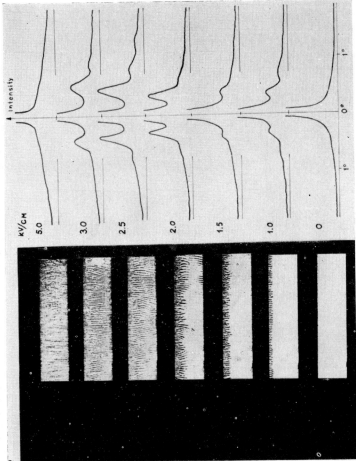

Figure 1. (a) Aspect of a PAA film for different values of the applied electric field. Electrode separation 1 mm, $T = 120.0\,°C$, Sample thickness 25 μ. Polarization vector $\mathbf{E}_i$ parallel to static electric field. (b) Angular distribution of scattered light intensity in a plane normal to the applied electric field.

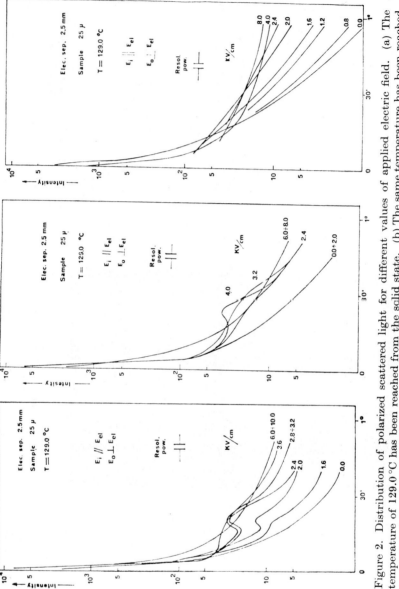

Figure 2. Distribution of polarized scattered light for different values of applied electric field. (a) The temperature of 129.0 °C has been reached from the solid state. (b) The same temperature has been reached by cooling from the isotropic liquid state. In (c) the same as in (b) but after a longer permanence in the isotropic state.

The incident light was polarized parallel to the applied field. It is possible to see that the periodicity of the domain-like structure gives two peaks in the scattered light at small angles. The position of the peaks is related to the spatial frequency of the structure; it is seen that it increases with the applied field. In the range in which all the cell is filled by the regular pattern, this dependence is linear. Together with the two main peaks, some other peaks are present, corresponding to higher harmonic frequencies. At applied field greater than 3.0 kV/cm, the peaks disappear according to the visually observed behavior of the structure, and the scattered distribution becomes smoother and broader. This behaviour is present in the nematic range, disappearing at the upper transition temperature. We have observed that when cooling the sample from the isotropic liquid to the nematic state, the periodic structure becomes less and less pronounced. This effect is more evident the longer the time the sample is maintained in the isotropic state, or the higher the temperature. Once the sample is cooled to the solid state, this memory effect is erased; when heated domains again appear. This effect is visible in Fig. 2.

In Fig. 2(a) the orthogonally polarized scattering is shown for different applied voltages, when the indicated temperature is reached from the solid state. Pronounced peaks are visible. In Fig. 2(b) and 2(c), the same temperature is reached after the liquid crystal was maintained in the isotropic liquid state for one and three hours, respectively. The polarization states are the same as before. In the parallel polarized scattering (not shown here), there are no peaks, and the curves are the same, whatever the thermal history of the sample.

In Fig. 2 the polarization of the incident light was parallel to the applied static field. In Fig. 3 the polarization is normal. In the two upper sets of curves the nematic phase is reached from the low temperature range. The periodic structure is observed in both the emerging polarization directions. In the lower sets the peaks disappear when the same temperature is reached after the liquid crystal was left in the isotropic liquid state some hours and then cooled.

Figure 4 shows the scattered intensity at spatial frequencies higher than the spatial characteristic frequencies of the domain-like structure. In this region the scattering has a spatial exponential

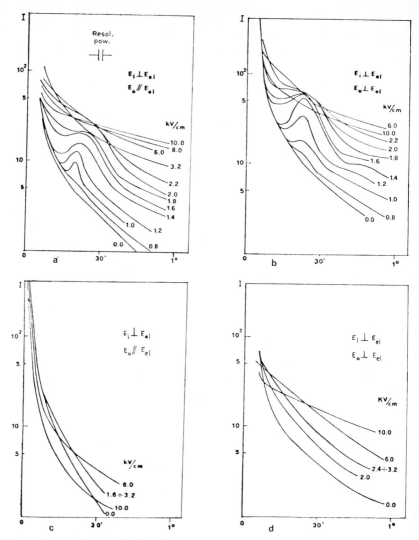

Figure 3.   (a, b) Angular distribution of the scattered light at different values of the static applied field.   Electrode separation 2.5 mm; Sample thickness 25 μ. $T = 129.0\,°\mathrm{C}$.   Polarization relations are shown in figures.   (c, d) The same as (a, b).   The temperature of observation has been reached after some hours of permanence in the isotropic liquid state.

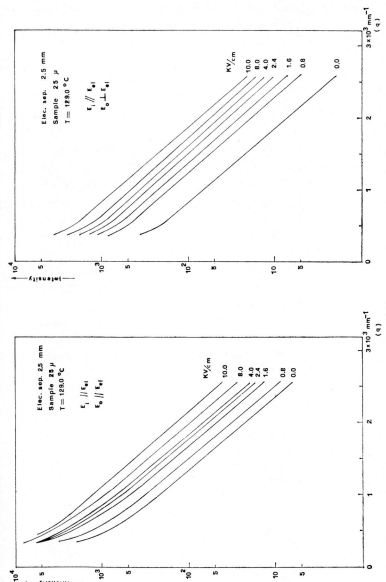

Figure 4.   Angular distribution of the scattered light at different values of the static electric field.   Plane polarized light.   The nematic phase has been reached from the solid state.

distribution, whose decay constant does not seem to depend on the applied voltage, neither on the polarization of incident and scattered light. The total scattered intensity depends on the thermal history of the sample.

3. Conclusions

The previously exposed measurements can be summarized as follows:

First, with an intermediate electric field, a periodic structure appears in p-azoxyanisole in the nematic range. This periodic structure is present in a plane parallel to the applied field. The observed results are in agreement with the hypothesis of a periodic orientation of the optical axis of the molecules. This arrangement gives rise to a phase and amplitude grating which acts differently with the two polarizations. The theory of this effect will be presented elsewhere. The exponential decay of the scattered intensity at high spatial frequencies allows the determination of the typical length of the scattering centers.

Another important observation which can be drawn from the measurements is the existence of a thermal hysteresis. A similar effect has been reported in cholesteric liquid crystal using different techniques[5] for measurement.

REFERENCES

1. Williams, R., *Nature* **199**, 273 (1963).
2. Williams, R., *J. Chem. Phys.* **39**, 384 (1963).
3. Elliot, G. and Gibson, J. G., *Nature* **205**, 995 (1965).
4. Heilmeier, G. H., *J. Chem. Phys.* **44**, 644 (1966).
5. Nordland, W. A., *J. Appl. Phys.* **39**, 5033 (1968).

Liquid Crystal Matrix Displays Using Additional Solid Layers for Suppression of Parasite Currents†

J. G. GRABMAIER, W. F. GREUBEL and H. H. KRÜGER

Forschungslaboratorium, Siemens AG
Munich, Germany

Received November 16, 1970; *and in revised form February* 2, 1971

Abstract—Because of their light-scattering behavior under the influence of an electric field, liquid-crystal layers are suitable as active layers in flat picture screens. In screens built up as conducting-line-matrixes the cross-talk arising from parasite currents has to be suppressed. Besides that a display unit with a large-volume picture needs the ability to store the information, since liquid crystals have a long rise-time.

It is shown that cross-talk is suppressed by combining a ferro-electric ceramic layer with the liquid-crystal layer in a liquid-crystal matrix using the non-linear properties of the ceramic, and that the necessary storage is obtained by the ceramic's ability to store polarization states.

Further on it is shown by examples, that liquid crystal screens based on this double layer can be practical in a wide range.

Introduction

Experiments described in the literature demonstrated, that by using liquid crystals, it is possible to display optical information with a versatility similar to that of the cathode ray tube. In these experiments liquid crystal displays operated at the full television rate. Essentially, this was done by scanning a liquid crystal film with an electron beam which impressed a locally variable electric field into the liquid crystal film.[1,2] Many recent efforts of realizing a universal display, of which the application of liquid crystals is only one example intend to avoid the disadvantages of the electron-beam-addressing (power-requirements, high voltage, large volume, limited display-area, vacuum-tube) and to use primarily matrix addressing for generation of the locally variable electric field. It is desired to

† Presented at the Third International Liquid Crystal Conference in Berlin, August 24–28, 1971.

131

construct in this way a flat solid state display, which can be operated by integrated circuits and which can be produced with a large area. On this basis, liquid crystal displays are also conceivable in principle.

Problems of the Liquid Crystal Matrix Display

If a voltage V is applied across one X- and one Y-conductor strip of the crossed-conductor-matrix shown in Fig. 1, the display element

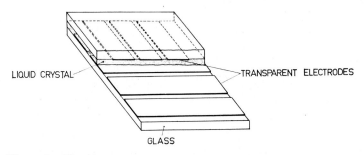

LIQUID CRYSTAL — TRANSPARENT ELECTRODES

GLASS

Figure 1.   Liquid crystal layer between crossed-conductor-matrix.

at the intersection of the electrode couple will receive the full voltage V, while at many other display-elements voltages equal to or less than $V/2$ will appear by a shunt effect. If the active layer between the electrodes consists of the nematic liquid crystal only, definite switching of a single display element into the dynamic scattering mode is not possible in this matrix. Generally, besides the excitation of the intersection element by the activated X–Y-conductor couple, the neighbouring elements of these conductors are, though weaker, also in the dynamic scattering mode. This is demonstrated in Fig. 2. For good visible and fast excitation of dynamic scattering with all presently known nematic liquid crystals, field strengths that amount to a multiple of the threshold field strength for dynamic scattering are necessary.

A first main problem existing with such a matrix is, therefore, to provide a sufficiently high electrical threshold. Another main problem stems from the relatively long rise times of the nematic LC's: If for example a display corresponding approximately to a TV frame with half a million elements is to be addressed 24 times per second, for excitation of dynamic scattering it is necessary that

Figure 2. Demonstration of the cross-talk arising from parasitic currents in the screen of Fig. 1.

the addressing pulses are applied longer than corresponds to the scanning time per element. This means: The elements must be able to store the electric signals that contain the brightness information.

Solutions

Both problems can be solved by combining a ferro-electric ceramic layer with a liquid crystal layer. In the following, proposals which have been tested on models are made in this direction. First a version A of a liquid crystal matrix display is discussed, where only the threshold problem is solved. This version is relatively simple in its technology and is practicable first for fast dynamic displays, which only need up to several thousand raster elements and secondly for displays having an arbitrary number of raster elements and only slow changes. In the second case the storage effect of nematic/ cholesteric liquid-crystal-mixtures is utilized. In version B, the problem of storing the electrical pulses containing the brightness pattern is also solved.

Version A

For an alternating voltage, a ferro-electric layer represents a capacity which varies with the amplitude of the applied voltage.

This can be seen from the familiar hysteresis loops, of which two specific cases are shown in **Fig. 3**: The large loop is traversed for an amplitude V, the small one for $V/2$.† The slopes of the broken lines are, as known, proportional to the effective dielectric constant, that is, to the capacity of the ferro-electric layer. If the ferro-electric ceramic possesses a sufficiently square hysteresis loop, below the saturation region the capacity increases very strongly with the amplitude of the applied voltage.

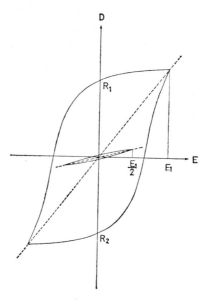

Figure 3. Hysteresis loops of a ferro-electric ceramic at a field strength of E_1 or $E_1/2$.

A double layer, consisting of a ferro-electric ceramic and a liquid crystal layer therefore represents for alternating voltage pulses, the series connection of a non-linear and a linear capacity. By suitably dimensioning the capacities of both layers, the voltage across the liquid crystal layer can be made to increase much stronger than linear with the total voltage applied across the double layer, as is

† If one polarizes the ferro-electric ceramic to the remanence state R_1 and if one then applies the $V/2$ amplitude then the small hysteresis loop in Fig. 3 is essentially displaced only parallel to the D-axis by the appropriate difference of remanence polarization.

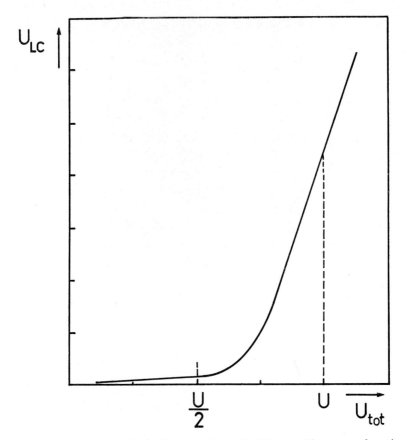

Figure 4. Voltage amplitude U_{LC} across the liquid crystal layer as a function of the total voltage (U_{tot}) across the double layer.

shown in Fig. 4. By this method the necessary electrical threshold voltage of the display elements in a liquid-crystal-matrix can be obtained. (This is demonstrated in Fig. 5, which shows that a single display element can be excited by matrix addressing using this method.) The double layer is provided on one side with the X-, and on the other side with the Y-conductors. Because of the great differences in the dielectric constants of the ferro-electric ceramic and the liquid crystal, it is necessary among other things to match the capacity by using different breadths of the X- and Y-conductor strips. This can be realized for example in a setup shown in Fig. 6a and Fig. 6b.

Figure 5. Laboratory model of a liquid crystal matrix display (version A). One display element (ca. 0.1 in × 0.1 in) is excited.

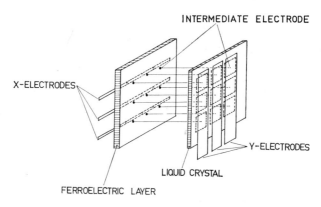

Figure 6a. Principle of a matrix display of version A.

The ferro-electric ceramic elements of the matrix display must be polarized by the addressing pulses alternately in positive and negative field directions. This can be done in practice for example by writing one frame with positive pulses and then applying across all elements at the same time one negative pulse, which is so short, that the liquid crystal will not be excited, but all ceramic elements will be polarized

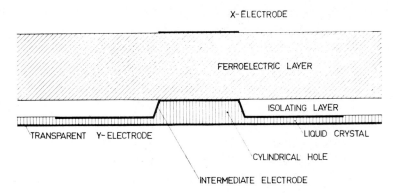

Figure 6b.   Integrated setup of the matrix display in Fig. 6a realized in the laboratory model.   Transverse section of one display element.

inversely.†   Then again, the next frame is written with positive pulses, etc.   The degree of brightness of the display elements is controlled by the amplitude of the write-pulses.

Since the resistivity of the ferro-electric ceramic is substantially greater than that of the liquid crystal, the ferro-electric layer can also be provided with a bias voltage.

Version B

In this version the video signals are stored as polarization states in the ferro-electric ceramic whereby for example, on a display consisting of 1 million elements, 24 frames per second can be displayed in spite of the long rise-times of the liquid-crystals.   The principle is explained with the aid of Fig. 7a.   One side of the ferro-electric layer carries the X-, the other the Y-conductors.   At each intersection of an X- and Y-conductor, on the side of the Y-conductors, a very small electrode spot (called readout-electrode) is isolated from the corresponding Y-conductor but is capacitively coupled to the Y-conductor by the ferro-electric ceramic between them.   Opposite to these readout electrodes, correspondingly larger electrode spots are on the backface of the liquid crystal layer.   On the frontface of the

† The polarization charges brought onto the liquid crystal capacitors by the reset pulse are shorted out by simple electronic measures during the switching off of the reset pulse.

liquid crystal is a uniform transparent front electrode. In Fig. 7b it is shown how these two electrode rasters are connected.

In the initial state, let all ceramic elements be in the upper remanence point R_1 of the hysteresis loop (Fig. 3). By applying

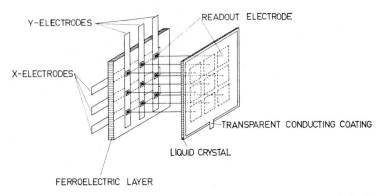

Figure 7a. Principle of a matrix display of version B for high speed displays.

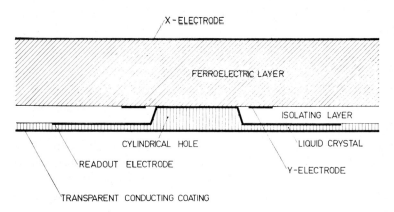

Figure 7b. Integrated setup of the matrix display in Fig. 7a. Transverse section of one display element.

negative direct voltage pulses across the conductor matrix (X- and Y-conductors), the individual elements are polarized inversely, for example, into the lower remanence state R_2. The polarization process takes about $1\ \mu\text{sec}$. The image information is thus first converted into a polarization pattern stored in the ferro-electric ceramic. Now, this polarization pattern can be converted at the same moment into a visible image on the liquid crystal film by applying a single positive pulse (a readout pulse) of about 1 msec across all X-conductors together, and the uniform front electrode. This readout pulse causes all ferro-electric elements to return to the initial state R_1. During this flipping back of the ferro-electric domains, polarization charges corresponding to the magnitude of the preceding polarization will flow to the respective liquid crystal capacitor elements, thus exciting the liquid crystal. After that, the next frame can be written into the ceramic, etc.

Remarks about the Ceramic and the Liquid Crystals

In our experiments, ceramic materials consisting of lead zirconate/lead titanate mixtures proved to be very suitable. They have relatively square hysteresis loops and can be prepared in large thin plates. The thickness of the ceramic layer was of the order of 100μ, that of the liquid crystal about 10μ. With a thickness of about 50μ these mixtures have a sufficient transparency, so that a matrix which also operates in transmitted light can be realized.

The addressing voltage pulses had an amplitude of about 100 V. The rise-times of the nematic liquid crystals used were several msec and the decay times were of the order of 100 msec.

In order that the liquid crystal capacitor elements, charged by polarization of the ceramic, do not discharge substantially within the rise-time of the liquid crystal, the liquid crystal should have high resistivity. With liquid crystals having a resistivity of about $10^{10}\,\Omega$-cm, very satisfactory results were achieved. The liquid crystals used were supplied by the firms Hoechst, Merck and LCI. Though the concept ferroelectric plus liquid crystal layer is similar to the well-known concept ferroelectric plus electroluminescent layer, especially the very low power requirements of the liquid crystals, and their specific rise and decay times, make possible the described solutions which we think to be practicable for a liquid crystal matrix display.

Acknowledgement

The authors wish to thank Professor Dr. Heywang for providing us with the ferro-electric ceramic, used in our experiments, and Dr. D. Röß and Dr. F. Schreiber for valuable discussions.

REFERENCES

1. Hansen, J. R. and Schneeberger, R. J., " Liquid Crystal Media for Electron Beam Recording ", *IEEE Trans. on Electron. Dev.* ED–**15**, 896–906 (1968).
2. van Raalte, J., " Reflective Liquid Crystal Television Display ", *Proc. IEEE*, **56**, 2146 (1968).

Thermal Radiography Utilizing Liquid Crystals†

R. D. ENNULAT

U.S. Army Electronics Command
Night Vision Laboratories
Fort Belvoir, Virginia

and

J. L. FERGASON‡

Liquid Crystal Institute
Kent State University
Kent, Ohio

Abstract—A thermal imaging system using cholesteric liquid crystals has been designed and built which utilizes the extreme temperature sensitivity of cholesteryl oleyl carbonate. Theoretical considerations for the design and the operating conditions of the device are given. The experimental results indicate that the limitations on such a device are primarily due to the finite film thickness required for scattering by the cholesteric liquid (on the order of ten micrometers). This system was able to image 0.2 °C with a limiting resolution of one line pair per millimeter. Improved lighting for direct viewing of the liquid crystal film should result in a sensitivity of about 0.02°C.

Introduction

Thermal radiography deals with the registration of radiation inherently emitted by physical objects due to differences in emissivity and/or temperature.[1] Thermal imaging systems are the most useful and versatile radiographic devices because they convert the invisible image formed by this infrared radiation into a visible replica. Thus the observer is able, for example, to see at night without extraneous illumination, to find certain structural faults in work pieces indicated by small temperature differences, to detect overheated components in electronic circuitry, and to test the blood circulation at the surface

† Presented at the Third International Liquid Crystal Conference in Berlin, August 24–28, 1970.
‡ Work performed while employed at the Westinghouse Research Laboratories, Pittsburgh, Pennsylvania.

of the human body and the malignancy of tumors. To date, wide-spread application of this powerful technique is restricted by the high cost of present infrared imaging devices. In the following we will describe and discuss a relatively simple, inexpensive thermal imaging device invented by Fergason, Garbuny and Vogl,[2] using as a transducer a thin film of a cholesteric liquid crystal.

Concept of Thermal Imaging Device

This thermal imaging device utilizes the temperature dependence of the light selectively reflected by the plane texture of a cholesteric liquid crystal. Figure 1 shows the spectral profiles of the light selectively reflected by regions of temperature T_A and T_B of the cholesteric film. If this film is illuminated with monochromatic light of wavelength λ_0, the region of temperature T_A has a much lower reflected intensity for light of wavelength λ_0 than the surrounding region of temperature T_B. Thus the observer perceives regions of different temperatures as regions of different brightness.

Figure 2 shows the schematics of a thermal imaging device based on this conversion principle. The infrared image of the scene is focused on the absorbing side of a membrane and converted by absorption into the corresponding heat pattern. Thermal conduction

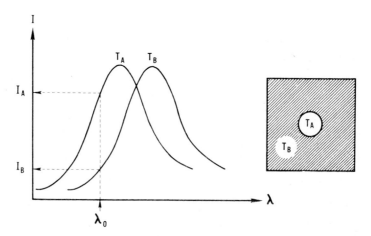

Figure 1.   Conversion Principle.

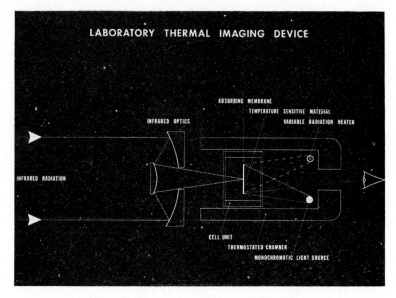

Figure 2.   Laboratory Thermal Imaging Device.

establishes an equivalent temperature pattern in the cholesteric liquid crystal, deposited on the other side of the membrane. Because of the temperature dependent selective reflectivity of the liquid crystal, this temperature image—and thus the original infrared image—is made visible by illumination with monochromatic light. To keep the liquid crystal at the proper operating temperature the sensing layer is enclosed in a coarsely temperature controlled chamber. A radiation heater provides fine control of the operating temperature. By varying the output of the radiation heater desired temperature levels of the temperature image in the liquid crystal can be brought into the selective reflection region and can thus be made visible. This capability and the extreme non-linearity of the temperature dependence of the selective reflection (i.e. its cut-off characteristics) are essential to suppress the unwanted effect of high background radiance of the scene without reducing the effect of the radiance coming from objects of interest. As we will see temperature differences of 0.2 °K in the scene can be detected against a background of 300 °K. It is very difficult to achieve such a performance with other non-scanning infrared to visible image converters.

Theoretical Consideration

To assess the potential of this thermal imaging principle we determine the minimum observable temperature difference as a function of a parameter characterizing resolution.

Figure 3 shows the parameters responsible for the radiation balance of the transducer. The radiation, emanating from background of temperature T_S and object of temperature $T_S + \Delta T_T$, is attenuated by a factor $t_A(\lambda)$ due to atmospheric absorption and focused by an

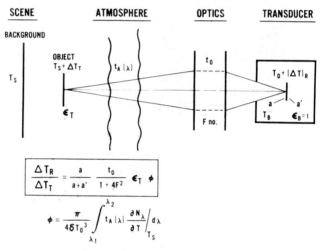

Figure 3.   Radiation Balance of Transducer.

optics, characterized by an attenuation factor t_0 and an f/number F, onto the transducer film. The latter is contained in a totally absorbing box admitting external radiation only through the optics. In the following we will treat ϵ_T, t_0, a, and a' as constants. This will simplify the problem significantly and still cover most of the practical cases.† For uniform background of temperature T_S the sensing layer assumes a "reference temperature" T_0. For an object of temperature $T_S + \Delta T_T$ in the scene, we obtain a corresponding pattern

† We assume in particular that the emissivities a and a' of the sensing layer are practically independent of the angle of incidence. The problem can be readily solved without those assumptions but the outcome will not contribute to the general understanding.

of temperature $T_0 + \Delta T_R$ on the membrane. If no lateral heat conduction occurs in the transducer film, we obtain according to Weihe[3] the relation†

$$\Delta T_R = \frac{a}{a+a'} \frac{t_0}{1+4F^2} \epsilon_T \phi \Delta T_T$$

$$\phi = \frac{\pi}{4\sigma T_0^3} \int_{\lambda_1}^{\lambda_2} t_A \frac{\partial N_\lambda}{\partial T}\bigg|_{T_S} d\lambda \qquad (1)$$

where $N_\lambda(T)$ is the spectral radiance, σ the Stefan–Boltzmann constant.

ϕ, a quantity strongly dependent on the water content, can be determined from tabulated data.[4] For example, for the 8 to $14\,\mu m$ wavelength region, a most suitable "atmospheric window" for our device, ϕ is approximately $\frac{1}{2}$ if the airpath contains 0.7 mm precipitable water and about $\frac{1}{3}$ if the airpath contains 17 mm precipitable water[3].

Next we address the influence of lateral heat conduction on the temperature distribution of the membrane. This problem can be solved in general for all radiance patterns imposed on the membrane if the heat conduction equation is linear, that is if the superposition principle is valid. We estimate that this is the case with sufficient approximation if the temperatures in the scene and of the transducer membrane and its inclosure differ by less than twenty percent. It is practical from the theoretical point of view to construct solutions of the heat conduction equation by superposition of temperature distributions obtained for sinusoidal radiance input. Since we did not have sources of sinusoidal radiance, we tested the thermal imaging device with bar pattern images (Fig. 4, upper curve). By reducing the temperature amplitude to the minimum observable level, we actually observe only the radiance contribution of the fundamental (Fig. 4, lower curve) as the following expression[5] shows:

$$\Delta T_{pp} = \frac{4}{\pi} \Delta T_R \sum \frac{(-1)^n}{(2n+1)[1+(2n+1)^2\, 4\pi^2(L_0/L)^2]} \approx$$

$$\frac{4}{\pi} \Delta T_R \frac{1}{1+4\pi^2(L_0/L)^2} \qquad L_0 = \sqrt{\frac{k_1 h_1 + k_2 h_2}{4(a+a^1)\sigma T_0^3}} \qquad (2)$$

† Since the distance of the objects from the optics is always more than 10 times the focal length, the effect of the magnification was neglected.

The characteristic length L_0 governing the resolution of the layer, depends on the thicknesses h_1, h_2 and the thermal conductivities k_1, k_2 of membrane and liquid crystalline film respectively.

Finally we have to relate the temperature differences in the liquid crystal film to the corresponding perceivable brightness differences. Figure 5 shows the membrane brightness as a function of temperature. The brightness level consists of a constant background brightness αI_{max} caused by specular reflections and scattering of the illuminating light and of the temperature dependent contribution I

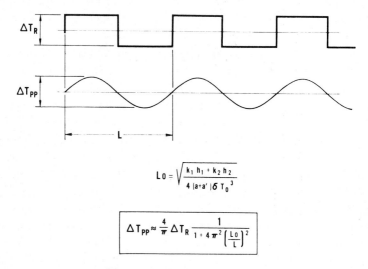

$$L_0 = \sqrt{\frac{k_1 h_1 + k_2 h_2}{4 |a+a'| \delta T_0^3}}$$

$$\Delta T_{PP} \approx \frac{4}{\pi} \Delta T_R \frac{1}{1 + 4\pi^2 \left(\frac{L_0}{L}\right)^2}$$

Figure 4.　Bar Pattern Image.

due to selective reflection. For a bar pattern image of amplitude $\Delta T/2$ we obtain a corresponding spacial brightness variation $\Delta I/2$ superimposed on the average brightness level $\alpha I_{max} + I$. Since the human eye responds to the contrast $\Delta I/I$ rather than to the brightness differences ΔI itself, we need to know the threshold contrast K_{min} for the determination of the minimum observable temperature difference. Considering that ΔI is equal to $I\Delta TC$, where C is the temperature coefficient of the brightness and considering that the maximum temperature coefficient occurs at the inflection points of the spectral response curve of cholesteryl oleyl carbonate at approxi-

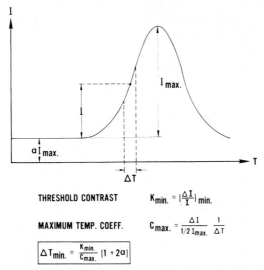

Figure 5.   Minimum Detectable Temperature Difference.

mately $I = \frac{1}{2}I_{\max}$,[6] we obtain for the minimum observable temperature difference

$$\Delta T_{\min} = \frac{K_{\min}}{C_{\max}}(1 + 2\alpha) \tag{3}$$

Notice the degrading influence of the background brightness $I_{\max}$ on this quantity. By combining the Eqs. (1), (2) and (3) we obtain for the minimum observable temperature difference $(\Delta T_T)_{\min}$ in the scene

$$(\Delta T_T)_{\min} = A\left(1 + 4\pi^2\left(\frac{L_0}{L}\right)^2\right) \tag{4}$$

$$A = \frac{\pi}{4}\frac{\Delta T_T}{\Delta T_R}\frac{K_{\min}}{C_{\max}}(1 + 2\alpha) \tag{4a}$$

where the pattern wavelength L is measured on the membrane. In the following we will utilize this relation to appraise experimentally the potential of this thermal imaging approach.

Experimental Studies

The experimental studies were conducted with a device designed to demonstrate the feasibility of the thermal imaging approach and

to permit studies of cholesteric liquid crystals, having widely differing operating temperatures. This test device, designed by Hansen
and Fergason of the Westinghouse Corporation, is shown in Fig. 6.
It consists of a reflective optics, a thermoelectric thermostat and of a
thermostated chamber containing illuminator, radiation heater and
the evacuated cell unit enclosing the transducer film. The optics,
originally designed for a different purpose, has five reflective elements.
Its optical axis in the image space is at right angles to that of the
object space and its long back focal length permits the focusing of
the image about 5 cm inside the thermostated enclosure. The
thermostat generates thermostated water heated or cooled by a
thermoelectric converter and pumps it through groves of the chamber.
A contact thermometer mounted in a water reservoir permits
adjustment and control of the water temperature. A circular shaped

Figure 6.   Laboratory System.

He gas discharge lamp and a radiation heater, consisting of a ring of 8 lightbulbs, blackened to eliminate visible light, are mounted in the plate closing the chamber towards the observer. The cell unit, shown in Fig. 7, is a blackened brass cylinder closed on one side by a germanium window for the infrared input and on the other side by an ordinary glass window to admit viewing light and heater radiation. The transducer membrane is suspended in the inside with the infrared absorber directed towards the germanium window. The cell unit is evacuated by a mechanical pump to prevent the degradation of the image resolution due to heat conduction through the surrounding air. A liquid nitrogen cold trap prevents the contamination of the liquid crystal film due to backstreaming pump oil.

Preparation of Transducer Membranes

To obtain the highest resolution (i.e. the smallest characteristic length L_0) and the smallest observable temperature difference ΔT_{min} the transducer film must be as thin as possible and the selective reflection of the liquid crystal must be large in intensity and narrow

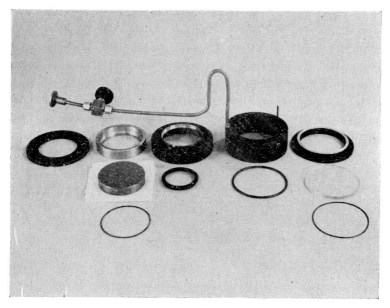

Figure 7.   Cell Unit.

in its spectral response. This requires almost complete alignment of the plane texture and a certain optimum thickness so that the light can interfere with a sufficient number of repeat distances of the liquid crystal structure. We found that liquid crystal films thinner than 5μm (i.e., roughly 10 times the wavelength of light) yield insufficient intensity of selectively reflected light while layers thicker than 20μm exhibit selective reflection against a high background of diffuse light. (The latter is apparently caused by the scattering of light on small unaligned regions of the plane texture.) Thus the optimum thickness must be somewhere between 5 and 20μm. The exact value depends on the particular liquid crystal and on the properties of the supporting substrate. The latter should be thin as compared to the liquid crystal film and should induce a well aligned plane texture spontaneously. Furthermore, to obtain a stable film the liquid crystal should wet the support sufficiently. Since the problem associated with these requirements can only be solved with considerable effort, we had to restrict ourself to an empirical selection of substrates. We found that Mylar† membranes of about 6μm thickness provided the best substrates‡ and that the optimum thickness of liquid crystal must be between 10 and 15μm.

Preparation of Transducer Films

To obtain uniform aligned liquid crystal films the membrane must be very clean and in particular free of grease and dust. Therefore the Mylar, stretched over the supporting ring, is first rinsed in running tap water. Then a dab of detergent is applied to both sides, rubbed thoroughly but gently (to avoid stretching) on both surfaces with a moist cotton swab and rinsed off with tap water and subsequently with distilled water. Afterwards the residual water is removed by thorough rinsing with hexane, containing 30% chloroform, benzene or methanol, and by drying in an oven at a temperature between 80 and 100 °C. Then one side of the membrane is sprayed with infrared absorbing paint consisting of carbon granules

† Mylar, Dupont trademark.

‡ Mylar, thinner than 6μm did not align the plane texture sufficiently apparently because the proper polar surface regions were not as well developed as for 6μm material. However, no effort was made to develop extremely thin Mylar membranes specifically for this application.

(average size about $2\,\mu$m) and of an organic binder. To obtain favorable thermal properties the amount of binder is reduced to the minimum.

The liquid crystal film can be applied by spreading or by spraying. In the spreading method about 0.1 ml of a 10 to 20% solution of liquid crystal is deposited with an eye dropper in the center of a horizontal membrane. The liquid rapidly spreads and evaporates leaving a thin, uniform area of liquid crystal behind, surrounded by an enclosing thicker rim. The latter is caused by the gradual increase of concentration and by the reduction of speed of spreading of the solution. The uniform center part is used as the sensing layer. Depending on the particular liquid crystal and on the ambient temperature a proper solvent mixture must be selected to adjust solubility and speed of spreading. For example petroleum ether or pentane should be used for temperatures of 25 °C or below, while ligroin is a better solvent for higher temperatures. To obtain the proper film thickness the solvent should contain between 10 and 20% liquid crystal.

Better control of thickness and uniformity is obtained by a spraying method, suggested by F. M. Schaer. Using an ordinary artist air brush with the finest nozzle, a mixture of 20% liquid crystal and 80% chloroform is sprayed on the membrane using as a carrier gas dry nitrogen at a pressure of 50 p.s.i. By spraying at a distance of about 30 cm a skilful operator can obtain very uniform membranes. Better results requiring less operator skill are obtained with a Zicon Spray Gun (Chemtronic, Mount Vernon, New York) which uses as a carrier gas superheated freon at a pressure of about 50 p.s.i. A mixture of 10% liquid crystal and cyclohexane (chloroform evaporates too fast) is sprayed with the finest nozzle at a distance of 15 to 20 cm.†

The spraying methods and to a lesser extent the spreading method have to be applied in a dry atmosphere, since the gas expanding from the nozzle‡ and the solvent evaporating from the film lower the temperature. If the temperature of the liquid crystal drops below the dew point the moisture of the atmosphere percipitates on the

† According to the manufacturer this gun can deposit films as thin as 0.5 μm with a thickness variation of less than ±10%.

‡ The temperature of the expanding gas at the nozzle can be as low as 0 °C !

sensing layer and appears as a veil of little droplets. This gives the layer the appearance of an orange peel. To avoid this undesirable non-uniformity and the deposition of dust particles, all critical operations such as final cleaning of the membrane, application of liquid crystal, and assemblage of the cell unit are performed in a bag of dry, ultra clean air.

The uniformity of the cholesteric film was qualitatively assessed in the thermal imaging system by capping the entrance stop of the optics with a metal plate of ambient temperature. By changing the average temperature of the membrane with the radiation heater and by rotating the whole cell unit one obtains a qualitative impression of uniformity. If the pattern of the selectively reflected light is invariant against rotation at various temperature levels, the centrosymmetric pattern is caused by the radiation field of the optical system (which has rotational symmetry) and not by non-uniformities of the membrane.

Experimental Tests

To assess this thermal imaging approach we have to distinguish between the limiting factors inherent of our particular device and those characteristic of the liquid crystal sensing layer. We made this distinction by directly determining the temperature difference on the membrane caused by a given temperature difference in the scene and by determining the minimum observable temperature differences of bar pattern images in dependence of pattern wavelength.

Two large black plates of equal emissivity ($\epsilon \approx 1$) but differing in temperature by ΔT_T were placed in the scene and imaged onto the sensing layer. Since the lateral dimensions of the associated images were large as compared to the characteristic length L_0 of the sensing layer, their temperature difference ΔT_R in the center was not noticeably affected by the lateral heat conduction. We adjusted the temperature difference T_T in the scene so that these images exhibited maximum selective reflection at the He lines 501.5 mμ and 587.5 mμ. This event was precisely determined with a spectrophotometer of 0.6 mμ resolution. Then we placed a piece of this sensing layer in a thermostated oven and determined with the aid of a photometer the temperature associated with the respective wavelengths. Thus we found that a temperature difference of $\Delta T_T = 11.5\,°C$ in the scene corresponds to a temperature difference $\Delta T_R = 0.17 \pm 0.02\,°C$ on the membrane.

This result indicates that the obscuration of the optics and the losses caused by the five reflective elements and by the germanium window reduce the received radiation by 85%!

The resolution test was made with the following set-up. A comb-shaped bar pattern cut out of a 0.6 cm thick aluminum plate was placed in front of a thick copper plate (0.6 cm thick), the temperature of which was adjustable. Both pattern and background plate were thermally insulated from each other and their front faces were coated with paint of emissivity close of one. The temperature difference between those two plates was determined with a copper-constantan thermocouple within $\pm 0.02\,°C$. To facilitate the tests the copper plate and the attached electrical heater were heat sinked.† By increasing or reducing the heater current we could impart a temperature drift slow enough to prevent thermal lags and yet fast enough to reduce testing time. Furthermore, we could adjust the background temperature level below and above the bar pattern temperature, which was always approximately at room temperature. The tests were conducted by two persons, one of them adjusting and measuring the temperature and the other one viewing the bar pattern image and indicating its appearance or disappearance. By changing the temperature in one direction one obtained the minimum observable temperature difference for, say, a background hotter than the bar pattern and subsequently for the reverse case. As expected for negligible thermal lags both minimum observable temperatures were equal within the uncertainties of this subjective measurement of approximately $\pm 20\%$.

Figure 8 presents the results of this test and the closest fit of the theoretical curve (Eq. (4)), which determined the characteristic length $L_0 = 0.41$ mm and the factor $A = 0.22\ (°C)$. Substituting into Eq. (2) for L_0 the known values $k_1 = 8.96 \times 10^{-5}$ cal/sec cm °C and $h_1 = 6\,\mu$m for Mylar, $k_2 = 2.9 \times 10^{-4}$ cal/sec cm °C for the liquid

† We used a 0.5 cm thick layer of transformer oil as a thermal barrier between the copper plate and the aluminum tank containing ice and water. Because of leaks we replaced the oil by silicon rubber.

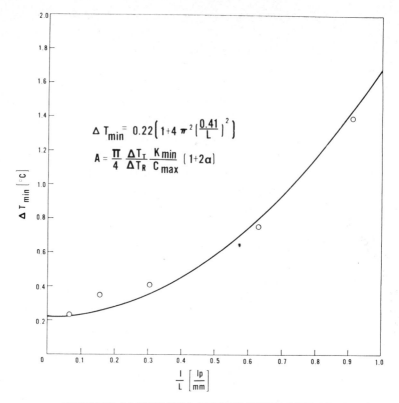

$$\Delta T_{min} = 0.22\left(1+4\,\pi^2\left(\frac{0.41}{L}\right)^2\right)$$

$$A = \frac{\pi}{4}\,\frac{\Delta T_T}{\Delta T_R}\,\frac{K_{min}}{C_{max}}\,(1+2a)$$

**MINIMUM OBSERVABLE TEMPERATURE DIFFERENCE
IN DEPENDENCE OF RESOLUTION**

Figure 8.   Limit of Resolution.

crystal,† and setting $T_0 = 300\,°K$ we obtain for the thickness h_2 of the liquid crystal $10\,\mu m$, i.e., a value within the expected range of thickness.   According to Eq. (4a), the value of A permits the determination of the magnitude of the threshold contrast K_{min}.   By considering that $\Delta T_T/\Delta T_R = 68$, $C_{max} = 100$ (/°C) for cholesteryl oleyl carbonate[6], and $\alpha = 3$ (as determined by a simple photometric test) we obtain $K_{min} = 0.06$.   This value deviates by a factor of 3 from the literature value[7] reported for 0.05 linepairs per millimeter, i.e. for the resolution at which $\Delta T_{min} \approx A$.   However, this discrepancy is not large if one considers that K_{min} depends strongly

† We measured k_2 by determining the heat current through and the temperature drop across a liquid crystal film.

on the human observer, the state of adaptation of the eye, and of other quantities not controlled in our experiment.

Figure 9 shows the thermal image of a person taken at a distance of about 4 m against a room temperature background. Since we could not fix the slowly drifting temperature of the membrane during the exposure time, the image quality of these photographs is quite inferior to that of the directly observed image. The features of a hand suddenly raised are sharp within about 4 to 5 seconds. This indicates a thermal time constant of the order of a few seconds, which is typical for radiation cooled transducers.

These experiments show that the performance of this thermal imaging device is severely limited by the high background luminance $(\alpha + \frac{1}{2})I_{\max}$ of the viewing light and by the efficiency of the optics. If α would be reduced from 3 to 0.1—and this can be done by using collimated, linear polarized viewing light—and if the optics would transmit at least 30% (instead of 15%) of the received radiation,

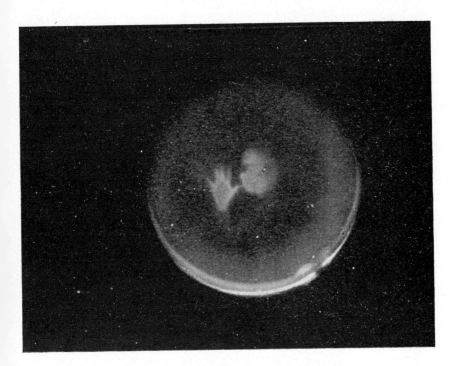

Figure 9.   Thermal Image of a Person.

the minimum observable temperature difference in the scene would drop from 0.2 °C to less than 0.02 °C.

It can be concluded that this thermal imaging approach is capable of detecting temperature differences as small as 0.02 °C. However, for fundamental reasons it is severely limited in spacial resolution to the order of a line pair per millimeter and to a time constant of the order of a second, because the thickness of liquid crystalline layers cannot be reduced substantially below 10 μm without adversely affecting the selective reflectivity.

REFERENCES

1. See for example, Infrared Imaging Issue, Applied Optics, Vol. 7, September 1968.
2. Fergason, J. L., Vogl, Th. and Garbuny, M., Patent 3,114,836 (U.S.).
3. Weihe, W. K., *Proc. IRE*, **47**, No. 9, p. 1593 (1959).
4. Taylor, J. H. and Yates, H. W., Naval Research Report No. 4759, May 11 (1956).
5. Jones, R. C., Polaroid Corp., Cambridge, Mass., Interim Tech. Report No. 188, Contract DA-44-009-ENG-1727.
6. Ennulat, R. D., to be published in Proceed. Third Liq. Cryst. Conf., 1970.
7. DePalman, J. J. and Lawry, E. M., *Journal Opt. Soc. Am.* **52**, No. 3, p. 328 (1962).

The Selective Light Reflection by Plane Textures[†]

R. D. ENNULAT

U.S. Army Electronics Command
Night Vision Laboratory
Fort Belvoir, Virginia 22060

Received October 31, 1970; *in revised form December* 11, 1970

Abstract—The dependence of the selective reflection on wavelength and temperature is determined for cholesteryl nonanoate (CN), cholesteryl oleyl carbonate (COC), cholesteryl erucyl carbonate (CEC) containing five weight percent of cholesteryl chloride, and a 1 : 1 mixture of COC and CEC. In addition the wavelength at peak selective reflection is measured as a function of temperature. For each of the materials both the half-width of the spectral response curve and the maximum temperature coefficient of selective reflection of monochromatic light increase with wavelength. COC exhibits the highest temperature coefficient of 13,000 percent intensity change per degree centigrade (at a wavelength of 700 mμ), which may also be the highest temperature coefficient observed for any optical effect. A brief discussion deals with the scientific and technological significance of the results.

Selective reflection of visible light by cholesteric mesophases may not only be the most spectacular optical effect exhibited by liquid crystals but also the most promising phenomenon that could be utilized for displays,[1] thermal mapping,[2] thermal radiography[3] and detection of microwave energy.[4] Therefore it is surprising that relatively few investigations deal with the temperature dependence and the theory of this effect.[5] However, the recent extension of the theoretical work, begun by Oseen[6] in 1921 and advanced by de Vries[7] in 1951, resulted in a phenomenological theory of selective reflection, which agrees very well with the experimental results.[8]

This investigation is concerned with the determination of the extremely large temperature coefficient of selective reflection exhibited by: cholesteryl nonanoate (CN), cholesteryl oleyl carbonate (COC), cholesteryl erucyl carbonate (CEC) containing 5% cholesteryl chloride, and a 1 : 1 mixture of COC and CEC. The measurements

† Presented at the Third International Liquid Crystal Conference in Berlin, August 24–28, 1970.

157

were performed with monochromatic light incident and selectively reflected within a fourteen degree cone which was perpendicular to the sample surface. The schematic overview shown in Fig. 1 indicates the results of the measurements performed: wavelength at peak selective reflection versus temperature; intensity versus wavelength at constant temperature; intensity versus temperature at constant wavelength.

Experimental Set-up

The experimental scheme shown in Fig. 2 consists of a thermostated miscroscope stage (Leitz, Model 350) containing the sample and a metallurgic microscope (Leitz, Ortholux) using a grating monochromator (Bausch & Lomb, Type 33–86–44) for illumination, a binocular eyepiece for observation, and a photomultiplier mounted on the third microscope tube for the measurement of the light intensity. The light coming from the sample can either be measured by the photometer (El Dorado, Model PH-200) or by simply flipping in a mirror (dashed lines), viewed through the eyepiece. This feature is essential because it enables the operator to frequently inspect the texture of the sample. Two copper constantan thermocouples are imbedded in the liquid crystal outside of the field of view. One is connected to a potentiometer (Rubicon, Type B-1) and measures the sample temperature within $\pm 0.01\,°C$. The other is connected over a bucking circuit with a microvolt amplifier (Keithly, Model 190) to measure temperature differences of the order of millidegrees

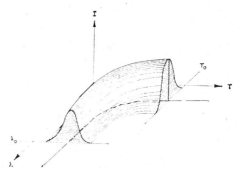

Figure 1.   The intensity of light selectively reflected by the plane texture of the cholesteric mesophase as a function of wavelength and temperature.

against a chosen temperature level.   The output of this amplifier drives the x axis of the xy recorder while the intensity of the photometer drives the y axis.

The sample temperature is stabilized by a circulator (Haake, Type Fe) pumping constant temperature water through the jacket of the microscope stage.   To achieve higher temperature stability, the electrical on-off control of the water temperature was replaced by an on-partial-off control.   In the partial off mode a constant heater current compensates for the minimum heat loss of the system, while in the on-control mode heat is added to counter temporary additional heat losses which are reduced by careful insulation.   Since the ambient temperature usually changed by less than one degree during the day, these measures resulted in a temperature reproducibility and reversibility of $\pm$ 0.002 °C over the test period (5 to 10 minutes).

Sample Preparation and Handling

To obtain a sufficient amount of selectively reflected light for the measurement, the sample had to be illuminated over an area of

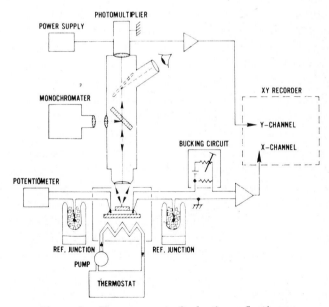

Figure 2.   Measurement of selective reflection.

about 0.5 mm diameter.   This requires a plane texture uniform over this extension.   However, known methods of sample preparation yielded only a mosaic of uniform texture elements, the latter ranging in dimensions from 10 to 50 μm.   These non-uniformities could be caused by impurities and as indicated by the angular dependence of selective reflection by deviations of the helical symmetry axis of the elements from the normal of the sample surface.   Since the degree of non-uniformities depends on purity, unknown interactions at interfaces, and on thermal history, we developed empirical procedures yielding reproducible results for a given sample by controlling these factors.

COC and CEC were carefully prepared in-house to avoid the formation of hard to remove impurities,[9] while reasonably pure CN was obtained from commercial sources.   After purification of these materials by column chromatography, the total amount of known impurities was reduced below the detection limit of thin layer chromatography, which is about one mole percent.

To avoid effects due to surface structures and to electrostatic and chemical interactions, the liquid crystal was supported and covered by clean, degreased glass slides.   Manipulation of the melted material on a glass slide usually resulted in a smooth coherent liquid crystal film, which was then covered by a thin heated cover slip. Care was taken to avoid trapping of dust and air bubbles.   Only CEC causes severe difficulties because it does not wet the glass surface. The addition of 5% cholesteryl chloride eliminated this problem but at the cost of obtaining data not characteristic of the pure CEC. Since perfect alignment of the plane texture could not be achieved, we did not measure the absolute magnitude of the selective reflectivity and therefore did not need to know the thickness of the liquid crystal film.   We adjusted the thickness by simply squeezing the assembly until bright and relatively pure spectral colors appeared for incident white light.†   This procedure allowed the experimenter to apply a variety of mechanical disturbances in order to eliminate undesirable textures and to obtain plane textures with a high degree of alignment.   The thermal history of the sample has a pronounced

---

† This occurred for sample thicknesses between 10 to 20 μ. Thicker samples had a milky appearance which may be due to light scattering by strongly misaligned plane texture elements.

influence on the texture. For example, fast cooling of CN from above the clearing point results in spherulites formed by elliptical focal conics, the long axis of which are radially oriented. The rapidly growing spherulites finally displace all other textures. At the transition from the cholesteric to the smectic mesophase the spherulites maintain their diameter while the focal conics convert into segments of fan-shaped textures. The latter are arranged in concentric rings with the ribs of the fan-shaped texture aligned approximately parallel to concentric circles. Subsequent heating reverses the changes of the textures. On the other hand, slow cooling from above the clearing point induces a grayish texture, which readily exhibits the colorful selective reflection in the appropriate temperature interval. All the investigated materials favor the plane texture on slow cooling (about 1 °C per minute and less) once the few persistent focal conic bands are eliminated by mechanical manipulation of the sample. To start with a well defined thermal history, all experiments were conducted on samples cooled from above the clearing point. As expected, the experimental results indicate that prior thermal history is annealed out at temperatures above the clearing point.

Experimental Results

The experimental results were obtained under the following conditions:

1. The polarizers of the microscope were always crossed to reduce the background level of light caused by specular reflection.

2. The field stop of the microscope illuminator limited the investigated sample area to circular disc of 0.75 mm.^{2}

3. The microscope objective illuminated and received the selectively reflected light within a cone of fourteen degrees.

4. The monochromator slit was set to a 1 mm opening in order to obtain monochromatic light with a spectral half-width of 1.2 mμ.

5. All intensity data were corrected for the spectral response of the apparatus.

Wavelength at Peak Selective Reflection versus Temperature

The temperature dependence of the wavelength at peak intensity was measured by adjusting the monochromator to a desired wave-length and by changing the temperature in one direction. When the photometer indicated the intensity peak, the temperature was determined with the thermocouple connected to the potentiometer. Figure 3 shows the results with the error bars indicating the $\pm$ 0.01 °C uncertainty of the temperatures. Clearly CEC exhibits the narrowest color band. Also notice the cross-over of the 1 : 1 mixture of COC and CEC at 550 mμ which indicates that the mixture apparently approaches the behavior of CEC for longer wavelengths. Measurements repeated on successive days revealed that except for CN these curves shifted by about 0.1 degree centigrade per day towards lower temperatures without change of shape and that samples not covered by a glass slide exhibited even a larger effect. Apparently oxygen, which was adsorbed on the coverslip in the first case and which was more readily available in the second case, must have reacted with the liquid crystal and formed products which depressed

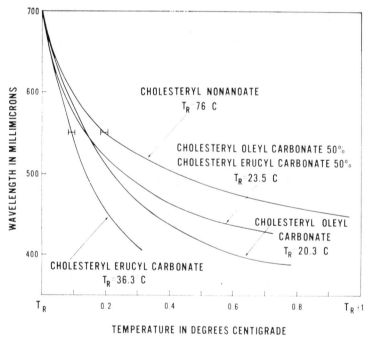

Figure 3. Wavelength of maximum selective reflection as a function of temperature.

the temperature range of the selective reflection.[10] This was confirmed by the fact that unknown impurities were detected by thin layer chromatography after the test and that the initial test results were repeated after their removal.†

Intensity versus Wavelength at Constant Temperature

The spectral response of the selective reflection was measured at constant temperature for increasing and subsequently for decreasing wavelength. Since the same wavelengths were used in either case, intensity differences at a given wavelength indicated changes in sample temperature. We rejected data associated with temperature variations larger than ± 0.002 degree centigrade. The error bars in Figs. 5 to 6 show the remaining uncertainties of the measurements. Considering the fact that the half-width of the spectral response curves approach that of customary interference filters (7mμ to 25 mμ), we conclude that our samples were reasonably well aligned.

Intensity versus Temperature at Constant Wavelength

The temperature dependence of the selective reflection of monochromatic light was measured by imparting a temperature drift on

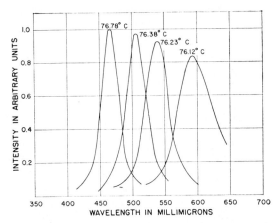

Figure 4.   Intensity of selectively reflected light as a function of wavelength.
Material: Cholesteryl nonanoate.

† This impurity effect is utilized to detect the presence of certain gases with the aid of liquid crystals.[11]

the sample and by plotting intensity versus temperature with the set-up shown in Fig. 2.   Errors caused by time lags in the recording channels were avoided by keeping the drift rate below 0.05 degree centigrade per minute.   The capability of the equipment is best demonstrated by the trace of a typical recording shown in Fig. 7. The superimposed spikes mark the calibration points, independently determined with the thermocouple connected to the potentiometer.

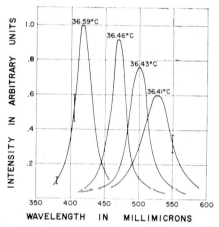

Figure 5.   Intensity of selectively reflected light as a function of wavelength. Material: Cholesteryl erucyl carbonate with 5% cholesteryl chloride.

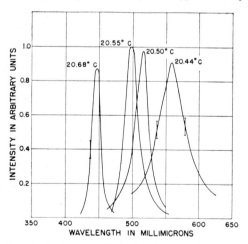

Figure 6.   Intensity of selectively reflected light as a function of wavelength. Material: Cholesteryl oleyl carbonate.

Smoothness and shape of this curve indicate that the sample was well aligned and uniformly heated. This is based on the fact that drastic changes in alignment, the appearance of birefringent textures, and non-uniformities of the temperature travelling across the sample strongly modulate the recorded light intensity in a way not systematically related to the temperature. To interpret more subtle distortions of the measurements it is necessary to inspect the sample with the microscope at the beginning and at the end of each run.

After cooling a sample from above the clearing point, we determined the intensities obtained for heating and cooling within a narrow temperature interval. We found that the intensities of the heating curves were consistently lower by 10 to 20% than those of the cooling curves. The temperatures of peak intensity are

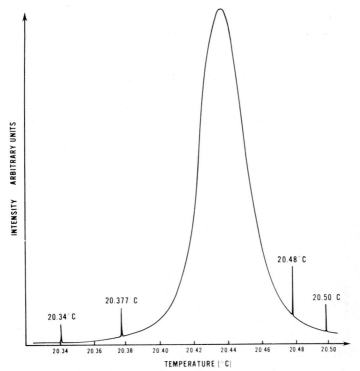

Figure 7.   Intensity of selectively reflected light in dependence of temperature as plotted by XY recorder.

Material: Cholesteryl oleyl carbonate.

Wavelength: 575 mμ.

reproducible within ± 0.002 degree centigrade for heating and cooling regardless of the magnitude of the temperature interval. This indicates that the alignment variations of the plane texture were only minor. But samples containing detectable amounts of oxidation products exhibited a temperature shift of the cooling curve. Since the selective reflection occurs only a fraction of a degree above the cholesteric to smectic phase transition, this hysteresis may be linked with the undercooling of the phase transition due to impurities.

Figures 8 through 10 show the temperature dependence of selective reflection determined for the various materials at the same wavelengths. These results indicate that neither peak height nor half-width exhibit a simple dependence on the temperature T_p at peak intensity. The latter can be better recognized on the normalized presentations of the data in Figs. 11 and 12. Notice that the half-width generally decreases with wavelength and that COC exhibits the smallest width of 0.024 degree centrigade.

The Temperature Coefficients

In Figs. 13 through 16 the temperature coefficients of the selectively reflected light intensity are plotted as a function of the temperature

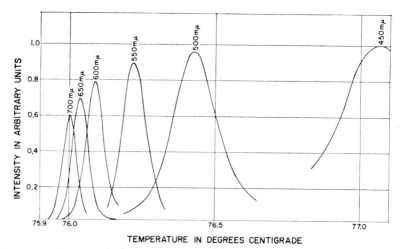

Figure 8.   Intensity of selectively reflected light in dependence of temperature.

Material: Cholesteryl nonanoate.

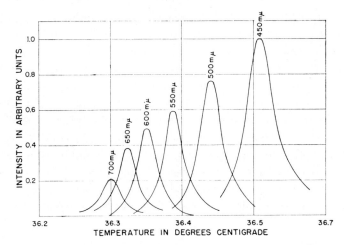

Figure 9. Intensity of selectively reflected light in dependence of temperature.

Material: Cholesteryl erucyl carbonate with 5% cholesteryl chloride.

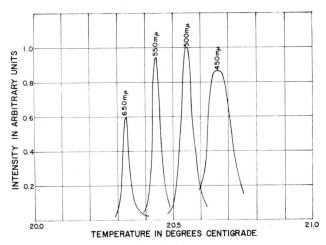

Figure 10. Intensity of selectively reflected light in dependence of temperature.

Material: Cholesteryl oleyl carbonate.

relative to the temperature T_p of peak intensity. For a given wavelength these coefficients have a relative maximum on either side of temperature T_p and decrease rapidly within a few hundredths of a degree. Depending on material and wavelenth these maxima occur at intensities ranging from 10 to 60% of peak intensity. The high magnitude of the coefficients underlines the importance of obtaining a slow but definite temperature drift and of ascertaining the calibration of a temperature interval at the beginning and at the end of each test run. The sensitivity and the high short time stability of the temperature measurement (see Fig. 7) made it possible to determine the temperature coefficients within ± 10 to ± 25%. This estimate is based on numerous test runs and on thermostated samples. For example, using a sample of COC in the most temperature sensitive region, we observed that a galvanometer deflection, indicating a

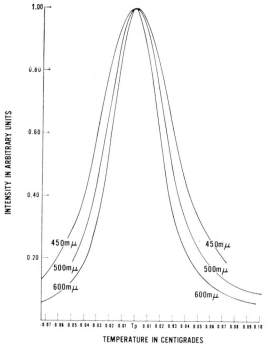

Figure 11. Normalized intensity of selectively reflected light versus temperature.
Material: 1 : 1 mixture of cholesteryl erucyl carbonate and cholesteryl oleyl carbonate.

control oscillation of ± 0.001 °C, was concurrent with a brightness oscillation of ± 10% displayed by the photometer. This effect could be observed for many minutes until an adjustment was required to compensate for drifts.

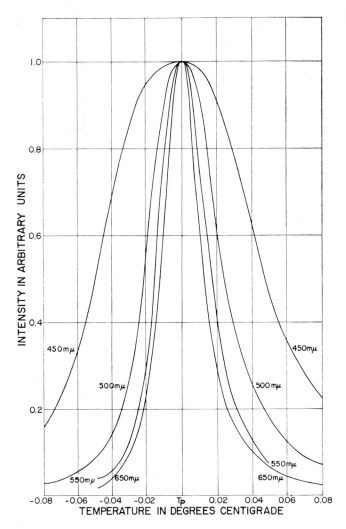

Figure 12. Normalized intensity of selectively reflected light versus temperature.

Material: Cholesteryl oleyl carbonate.

Discussion

The scientific assessment of the experimental results is restricted to a few speculative statements primarily because the degree of alignment of the plane texture is not known quantitatively. However, the narrowness of the half-width of the spectral response and the high degree of the temperature reproducibility of the wavelength at peak intensity both indicate that our experimental results may differ only slightly from those obtained on perfectly aligned textures. The curves in Fig. 3 suggest an interesting analogy to a Curie-Weiss law dependence. This view is supported by our experience that a material exhibits a steeper initial slope of the peak wavelength versus

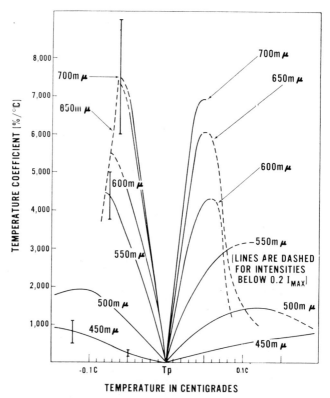

Figure 13.   Temperature coefficient of selective reflection versus temperature.
Material: Cholesteryl nonanoate.
T_p: Temperature of peak intensity.

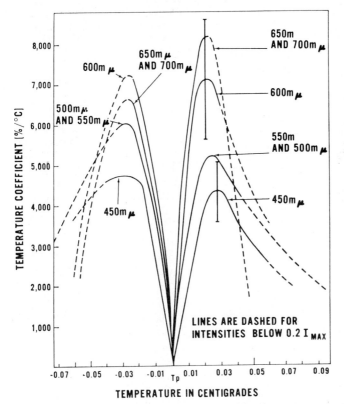

Figure 14. Temperature coefficient of selective reflection versus temperature.
Material: Cholesteryl erucyl carbonate with 5% cholesteryl chloride.
T_p: Temperature of peak intensity.

temperature curve (see Fig. 3) the smaller the difference is between
the reference temperature T_R (i.e. the arbitrarily chosen point on the
curve at 700 mμ) and the cholesteric to smectic transition temperature.   However, cholesteric-smectic phase transitions are of first
order, while phase transitions in the vicinity of the Curie points of magnetic and certain ferroelectric materials are of second order.   Furthermore, the curves in Fig. 3 are not hyperbolas required by the Curie-
Weiss law.   But the latter discrepancy could be explained as follows:
Assume a hyperbolic dependence for a plane texture element of
given orientation with respect to incident parallel light and with
respect to the angle of observation; in addition assume that hyperbolas associated with different angles of incidence and observation

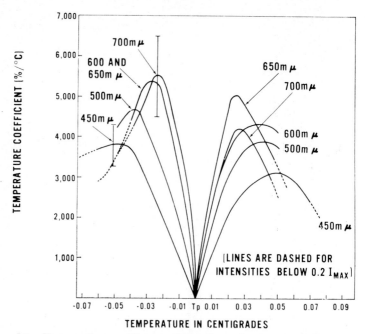

Figure 15.   Temperature coefficient of selective reflection versus temperature.
Material: 1 : 1 mixture of cholesteryl erucyl carbonate and cholesteryl oleyl carbonate.
T_p: Temperature of peak intensity.

are equal in shape but shifted against each other along the temperature axis.† Since our experimental set-up illuminates and observes the mosaic of slightly misaligned plane texture elements within a cone of fourteen degrees, a hyperbolic dependence of the peak wavelength cannot be expected. Thus we can conclude that our results do not contradict the theoretical consideration,[12] which predicts a hyperbolic dependence of peak wavelength versus temperature.

The experimental results show that liquid crystals have great technological potential as temperature indicators and as extremely sensitive detectors of temperature differences. In the former application the wavelength at peak selective reflection is calibrated with respect to temperature. If the liquid crystal is kept in a chemically inert environment and if it is shielded from radiation (such as

† The angular dependence of selective reflection[5] indicates such a possibility.

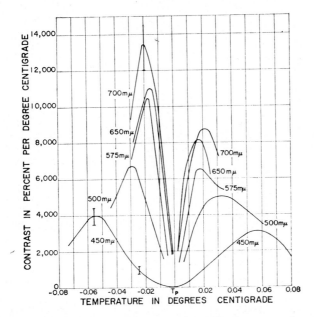

Figure 16.   Temperature coefficient of selective reflection versus temperature.
Material: Cholesteryl oleyl carbonate.
T_p: Temperature of peak intensity.

UV) that causes chemical reactions, the temperature calibration should be maintainable within the order of a few hundredths of a degree centigrade. The latter application relies on the high temperature sensitivity of the selective reflection of monochromatic light. The maximum temperature coefficients of this effect are shown in Fig. 17 for CN, COC, and CEC containing 5% cholesteryl chloride. It should be pointed out that the presence of cholesteryl chloride may have substantially decreased the temperature sensitivity of CEC. Notice that all coefficients increase with wavelength and that, except for CEC, they are generally higher on the low than on the high temperature flank of the selective reflection curve. We conclude that the temperature coefficient of 13,000 percent per degree centigrade exhibited by COC is the highest one in our investigation and may be the highest one observed for any optical effect. This material is capable of indicating temperature differences of less than a millidegree directly to the human eye.

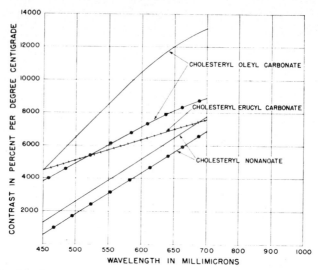

Figure 17. Maximum temperature coefficients of selective reflection versus wavelength.

——— Low temperature side   —·—·— High temperature side
        of intensity curve at constant wavelength.

Acknowledgements

I am ingratiated to Drs. W. Elser and J. L. W. Pohlmann for the preparation of the compounds and to our former co-workers Messrs. F. M. Schaer and R. Sherman for their work during 1963 and 1964 when most of the experiments were conducted.

REFERENCES

1. Fergason, J. L., Fr. Pat. Nr. 1 527 311 (1968).
2. Fergason, J. L., *Scientific American* **211**, 77 (1964); Selawry, O. S. and H. S., Holland, J. F., *Mol. Cryst.*, **1**, 495 (1966); Lukianoff, G. V., *Mol. Cryst. and Liq. Cryst.*, **8**, 389 (1969).
3. Ennulat, R. D. and Fergason, J., *Mol. Cryst. and Liq. Cryst.*, to be published.
4. Dev. of Liq. Cryst. Microwave Power Density Meter, U.S. Dept. of Health, Education, and Welfare, Public Health Service, Division of Electronic Products, BRH/DEP 70–8.
5. Fergason, J. L., *Mol. Cryst.*, **1**, 293 (1966).
   Ittner, G., Böttcher, B., *Mol. Cryst. and Liq. Cryst.*, to be published.
6. Oseen, C. W., Fortschritte der Chemie, Physik and Physikalischen Chemie, Band 20, Heft 2, Serie B, Verlag von Gebr. Borntraeger, Berlin (1929).
7. DeVries. Hl., *Acta. Cryst.*, **4**, 219 (1951).

8. Chandrasekhar, S., Prasad, J. S., *Mol. Cryst. and Liq. Cryst.*, to be published.

Berreman, D. W., Scheffer, T. J., *Mol. Cryst. and Liq. Cryst.*, to be published.

Dreher, R., Meier, G., Saupe, A. O., *Mol. Cryst. and Liq. Cryst.*, to be published.

9. Elser, W., to be published.

10. Scala, L. C. and Dixon, G. D., *Mol. Cryst. and Liq. Cryst.*, **7**, 443 (1969).
Scala, L. C. and Dixon, G. D., *Mol. Cryst. and Liq. Cryst.*, **10**, 411 (1970).

11. Fergason, J. L., Willey, D., and Sharpless, E., Private Communication.

12. Keating, P. N., *Mol. Cryst. and Liq. Cryst.*, **8**, 315 (1969).

Selective Reflection by Cholesteric Liquid Crystals†

R. DREHER and G. MEIER

Institut für Angewandte Festkörperphysik der Fraunhofer-Gesellschaft
78 Freiburg, Germany

and

A. SAUPE

Liquid Crystal Institute, Kent State University, Kent, Ohio, U.S.A.

Received November, 4, 1970

Abstract—Selective light reflection at the plane structure of a cholesteric liquid crystal is treated by the theory of de Vries[1] for normal incidence only. A more general approach is outlined for arbitrary angles of incidence. Conditions for the borders of the reflection bands are given. Also the cases of ordinary total reflection are included. Using the derived formula, the two principal dielectric constants are determined from the angles of total reflection measured with a refractometer. Their values are used to calculate the reflection spectrum of a layer of finite thickness at normal incidence which is compared with an experimental spectrum. In agreement with the experimental curve the calculated spectrum shows a central band with a nearly rectangular shape flanked by a series of maxima and minima due to interferences, the positions of which depend strongly on the dielectric constants.

General Theory

The optical properties of cholesteric liquid crystals are described very well by the theory of de Vries[1] but only for light normally incident on a plane structure. Recently Taupin[2] and Berreman and Scheffer[3] treated the case of oblique incidence and calculated by numerical techniques reflected and transmitted intensities. The latter two authors were able to calculate for a given sample practically exact intensity curves as a function of wavelength. The angle of incidence was assumed to be 45° and two cases of different polarizations of the incident light were considered. In the first part of this paper we outline a different approach which allows a direct calculation of the

---

† Presented at the Third International Liquid Crystal Conference in Berlin, August 24–28, 1970.

177

borders of the reflection bands as a function of the angle of incidence.

We adopt Oseen's[4] model and assume the cholesteric liquid crystal to have a uniformely twisted nematic structure, the helical axis being perpendicular to the nematic symmetry axis. Accordingly we describe the dielectric properties by a tensor of rotational symmetry that changes the orientation with the twist.

For the treatment of light propagation in this system it is convenient to use two coordinate systems (Fig. 1): the laboratory system x, y, z with the z-axis along the helical axis and a local coordinate system ξ, η, ζ with the ζ-axis parallel to the z-axis. The other two axes are positioned in such a way that the dielectric tensor is diagonal in it with principal values ϵ_1, ϵ_2, ϵ_3 along the axes ξ, η, ζ. Thus, the electric field $\mathbf{E}$ and the dielectric displacement $\mathbf{D}$ are connected by the relations

$$D_\xi = \epsilon_1 E_\xi$$
$$D_\eta = \epsilon_2 E_\eta \tag{1}$$
$$D_\zeta = \epsilon_3 E_\zeta.$$

We introduce a unit vector $\mathbf{L}$ parallel to the nematic symmetry axis. Because of the uniform twist its components in the laboratory system are given by

$$\mathbf{L} = \{\cos\alpha,\ \sin\alpha,\ 0\} \tag{2}$$

where $\alpha = 2\pi\, z/p$ and p the pitch of the helix.

The problem of wave propagation consists in solving the Maxwell equations or the correspondent wave equation

$$\frac{1}{c^2} \frac{\partial^2 \mathbf{D}}{\partial t^2} = \varDelta \mathbf{E} - \operatorname{grad} \operatorname{div} \mathbf{E}. \tag{3}$$

We assume that light passes from an isotropic medium of refractive index n into the liquid crystal (Fig. 2). Let the angle of incidence be ψ. The helix axis is taken to be normal to the interface.

Without loss of generality we confine ourselves to waves propagating in the (x, z)-plane and try to find solutions of the form

$$\mathbf{E} = \mathbf{F}(z) \exp\left[i\omega\left(t - \frac{m}{c} x \right) \right] \tag{4}$$

with $m = n \sin\psi$ and $F(z)$ an unknown vectorfunction. The components of $F(z)$ are given in the laboratory system by

$$\mathbf{F}_{lab}(z) = \{F_x,\ F_y,\ F_z\} \tag{5}$$

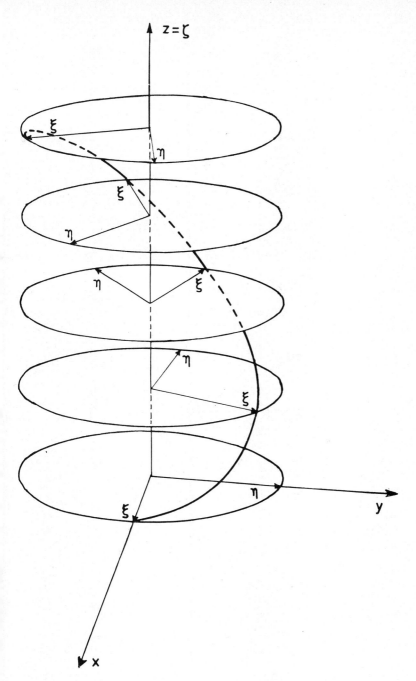

Figure 1.   Definition of the laboratory and local coordinate systems.

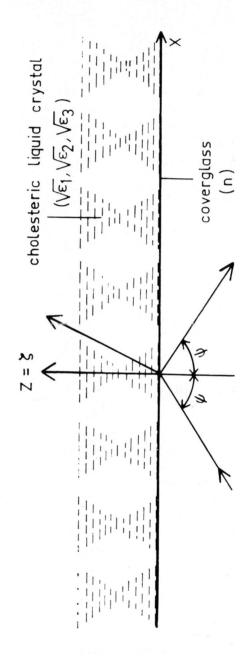

Figure 2.   Light propagates in the (x, z)-plane from an isotropic medium of refractive index n into the liquid crystal.

and in the local system by

$$\mathbf{F}_{loc}(z) = \{\phi, \chi, F_z\}. \tag{6}$$

We chose the ξ axis parallel to $\mathbf{L}$ and have because of the nematic symmetry

$$\epsilon_2 = \epsilon_3. \tag{7}$$

We obtain for ϕ and χ a system of second order differential equations with periodic coefficients:

$$\frac{d^2\phi}{d\alpha_2} - 2\frac{d\chi}{d\alpha} + (a_1 + a_2\cos 2\alpha)\phi = 0$$

$$\frac{d^2\chi}{d\alpha^2} + 2\frac{d\phi}{d\alpha} + b_1\chi - a_2\sin 2\alpha \cdot \phi = 0. \tag{8}$$

For the third component we obtain

$$F_z - i\frac{\lambda}{p}\frac{m}{\epsilon_2 - m^2}\frac{dF_x}{d\alpha} = 0 \tag{8'}$$

where $\alpha = 2\pi z/p$, and

$$a_1 = \left(\frac{p}{\lambda}\right)^2\left[\epsilon_1 - \frac{m^2}{2}\left(\frac{\epsilon_1}{\epsilon_2} + 1\right)\right] - 1$$

$$a_2 = \left(\frac{p}{\lambda}\right)^2\frac{m^2}{2}\left(1 - \frac{\epsilon_1}{\epsilon_2}\right)$$

$$b_1 = \left(\frac{p}{\lambda}\right)^2[\epsilon_2 - m^2] - 1.$$

We can also consider instead of the system (8) a single fourth order differential equation with periodic coefficients:

$$\frac{d^4\phi}{d\alpha_4} + (a + a_2\cos 2\alpha)\frac{d^2\phi}{d\alpha^2} - 6a_2\sin 2\alpha\frac{d\phi}{d\alpha} + (b + da_2\cos 2\alpha)\phi = 0 \tag{9}$$

where $a = 4 + a_1 + b_1$

$$b = a_1 b_1$$

$$d = b_1 - 8.$$

According to Floquet's Theorem we expect solutions of the form

$$\phi(\alpha) = e^{i\mu\alpha}P_1(\alpha); \qquad \chi = e^{i\mu\alpha}P_2(\alpha). \tag{10}$$

P_i is a periodic function with period π. μ is the characteristic exponent. Since P_i is periodic and therefore bounded, the characteristic exponent decides if wave propagation is allowed or forbidden depending on a real or complex value. It can be shown that on the borders of the reflection bands μ is an integer:

$$\mu(\lambda, \psi) = \nu, \qquad \nu = 0, \pm 1, \pm 2, \ldots. \tag{11}$$

The characteristic curves defined by Eq. (11) can be calculated relatively easily.

They describe the shift and splitting of the main reflection band with increasing angle of incidence and the occurence of higher order bands. This will be shown in detail in a later paper.

One characteristic curve is given by the simple equation

$$\lambda = p\sqrt{\epsilon_2 - m^2}, \qquad m = n \cdot \sin\psi. \tag{12}$$

It corresponds to the solution $\phi = 0$, $\chi = \text{const}$, $F_z = -i(P/\lambda)m\chi\cos\alpha$. An equation similar to (12) has been used by Fergason[5] for the center of the reflection band. He derived his equation treating the reflection like a simple Bragg reflection.

Determination of the Dielectric Constants

The characteristic curves give the conditions for the selective reflection as well as for the ordinary total reflection. For ordinary total reflection the following two relations were derived:

$$m_1^2 = \epsilon_3$$

$$m_2^2 = \epsilon + \frac{\delta^2}{32(\lambda^2/p^2)}\left(1 - \frac{\delta}{\epsilon}\right) + o\left[\left(\frac{\delta}{\epsilon}\right)^4\right] \tag{13}$$

$m_1 = n\sin\psi_1$ and $m_2 = n\sin\psi_2$, where ψ_1, ψ_2 are the angles of total reflection as measured with a refractometer, $\epsilon = \frac{1}{2}(\epsilon_1 + \epsilon_2)$, $\delta = \frac{1}{2}(\epsilon_1 - \epsilon_2)$.

The first relation shows that m_1 is identical with one of the dielectric constants, ϵ_3. This relation remains valid for cases of lower symmetry where $\epsilon_3 = \epsilon_2$. It is assumed for the second Eq. (13) that $\lambda^2 > p^2\epsilon/8$. In most cases m_2 gives in a good approximation the mean value ϵ and does not correspond directly to a principle dielectric constant. This fact was not realized by earlier workers (see for instance Ref. (6)).

Figure 3 shows a plot of the two dielectric constants versus wavelength determined using Eq. (13) for a mixture of cholesteryl nonanoate, cholesteryl chloride and cholesteryl acetate in weight ratios of 20:15:6 at room temperature (24 °C).

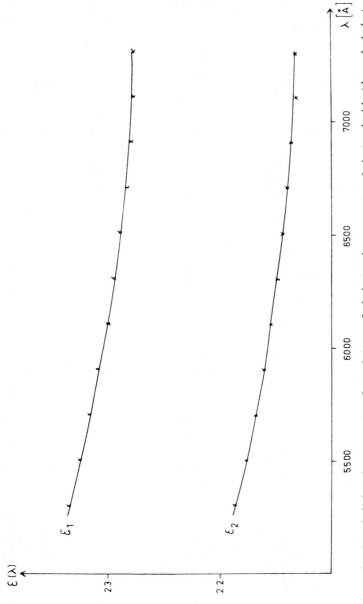

Figure 3. Local dielectric constants of a mixture of cholesteryl nonanoate, cholesteryl chloride and cholesteryl acetate in weight ratios of 20 : 15 : 6 at 24 °C.

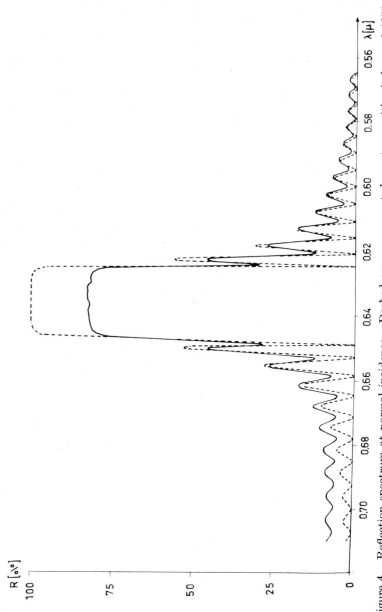

Figure 4.   Reflection spectrum at normal incidence.   Dashed curve: computed spectrum with pitch $p = 0.4273\mu$ and thickness of layer 21.0μ.   Solid curve: experimental spectrum (intensity in arbitrary units).

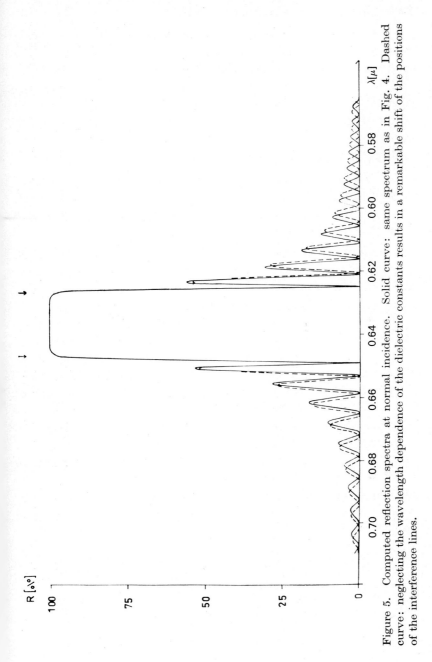

Figure 5. Computed reflection spectra at normal incidence. Solid curve: same spectrum as in Fig. 4. Dashed curve: neglecting the wavelength dependence of the dielectric constants results in a remarkable shift of the positions of the interference lines.

Reflection Spectrum at Normal Incidence

Figure 4 shows the reflection spectrum of the above mentioned mixture at room temperature for normally incident light. The solid curve gives the experimental result in arbitrary units. The dashed curve was calculated using the values of the dielectric constants shown in Fig. 3. The pitch was determined from the center of the reflection band using de Vries' formula $\lambda_0 = n_0 p$ with $n_0 = \frac{1}{2}(\sqrt{\epsilon_1} + \sqrt{\epsilon_2})$.

Both curves are in agreement concerning:

(i) the nearly rectangular shape of the central band,
(ii) the decreasing amplitude of the secondary minima and maxima with increasing distance from the region of reflection and
(iii) the position of the minima and maxima.

The positions of the minima and maxima depend strongly on the values of the dielectric constants used. Thus, the comparison of the measured and calculated spectrum represents a test of our method of determining the dielectric constants.

The strong dependence of the positions of the interference lines on the dielectric constants is demonstrated in Fig. 5. Here constant values of the dielectric constants were used neglecting their weak wavelength dependence. There results a remarkable discrepancy. Fitting the curves by varying other parameters, e.g. the thickness of the layer is not possible. There is also another point of interest. The dielectric constants that can be determined by total reflection in a refractometer are ϵ_3 and approximately ϵ. With these values and assuming $\epsilon_2 = \epsilon_3$ we calculated the reflection spectrum for normally incident light which depends on ϵ_1 and ϵ_2 only. We consider the good agreement of the theoretical and experimental curves as a strong confirmation of the assumption that the local dielectric properties are uniaxial.

REFERENCES

1. De Vries, Hl., *Acta Cryst.* **4**, 219 (1951).
2. Taupin, D., *Journal de Physique* **30**, C4–32 (1969).
3. Berreman, D. W. and Scheffer, T. J., *Phys. Rev. Letters* **25**, 577 (1970).
4. Oseen, C. W., *Trans. Faraday Soc.* **29**, 833 (1933).
5. Fergason, J. L., *Mol. Cryst.* **1**, 293 (1966).
6. Landolt-Börnstein, Zahlenwerte und Funktionen, II, 8, p. 4–553, Springer-Verlag, Berlin, 1962.

Doppelbrechung an dünnen Schichten cholesterinischer Flüssigkeiten†

B. BÖTTCHER and G. GRABER

Bundesanstadt für Materialprüfung
I Berlin 45
Unter den Eichen 87, Germany

Received October 19, 1970; *and in revised form December* 22, 1970

Abstract—The knowledge of birefringence gives a better insight, especially to the optical scattering properties of cholesteric liquid crystal films.

We therefore evaluated the mean refractive indices of about 16 aliphatic and mono- e.g. di-alkyl-cholesteric esters as functions of temperature and wavelength.

We first ensured that the cholesteric liquids were nearly oriented between carefully cleaned plane glass surfaces. In a conoscopic arrangement of a polarizing microscope the probes showed a darker, blurred cross of principal isogyres.

To get the mean refractive indices, we used an experimental set up existing of a monochromator (400–750 mm) and a temperature controlled Abbe-refractometer.

With some substances and mixtures clearing points and temperatures of disappearing birefringence disagreed. Phase transitions, e.g. from smectic to cholesteric phases, were marked by a sudden change in birefringence and optical character. We always found normal dispersion within the visible part of the spectrum. There are some relations between birefringence properties and chemical constitution.

1. Einleitung

Zur Erklärung der optischen Eigenschaften cholesterinischer Flüssigkeiten ist die Kenntnis der Hauptbrechungsindizes erforderlich. Die älteste uns bekannte Arbeit zur Messung der Hauptbrechungsindizes von p-Cyanbenzalaminozimtsäure-akt-amylester stammt von F. Stumpf.[1] Er benutzte eine optische Anordnung, bestehend aus zwei drehbaren Flintglasprismen, wie sie in älteren Ausführungen des bekannten Abbe-Refraktometers verwendet wurde. F. Stumpf konnte die Hauptbrechungsindizes der cholesterinischen und den

† Presented at the Third International Liquid Crystal Conference in Berlin, August 24–28, 1970.

Brechungsindex der flüssig-isotropen Phase als Funktion von Wellenlänge und Temperatur messen. Später hat P. Chatelain[2] an den beiden Substanzen mit nematischer Zwischenphase p-Azoxyanisol und p-Azoxyphenetol die Hauptbrechungsindizes nach dem Verfahren der Newtonschen Ringe gemessen. Hierbei befindet sich die Substanz zwischen zwei teildurchlässigen Flächen, wobei die eine eben ist und die andere eine bekannte Krümmung hat. Aus den Radien der auftretenden Interferenzringe können die Hauptbrechungsindizes bestimmt werden. Die Messungen wurden später[3,4] mit der bekannten Prismenmethode wiederholt. Hierbei befindet sich die Substanz in einem Hohlprisma, an dessen brechender Kante der eintretende Lichtstrahl eine Ablenkung erfährt. Die Messung erfolgt nach dem bekannten Verfahren der minimalen Strahlablenkung. L. Kopf[5] hat diese Meßmethode auch bei einer Substanz mit cholesterinischer Zwischenphase angewendet.

Cholesterinische Flüssigkeiten weisen für links- und rechtszirkular polarisiertes Licht unterschiedlich große Phasengeschwindigkeiten auf, was zu unterschiedlichen Brechungsindizes führt. Die Brechunsindizes für links- und rechtszirkulares Licht konnten als Funktion von Wellenlänge und Temperatur an einer Mischung aus Cholesterin-Benzoat und p-Azoxyanisol von P. Chatelain und J. C. Martin[6] nach der eben beschriebenen Prismenmethode gemessen werden. Ueber weitere Ergebnisse von Brechzahlmessungen berichten H. Sackmann, D. Demus[7] und M. A. Jeppensen, W. T. Hughes.[8] Letztere benutzen das Verfahren der Newtonschen Ringe. Eine zusammenfassende Darstellung der Brechzahlmessungen an Substanzen mit nematischer und cholesterinischer Zwischenphase findet sich bei W. Maier.[9]

In der BAM werden cholesterinische Flüssigkeiten als Temperaturindikatoren in der zerstörungsfreien Materialprüfung mit Wärmeflußverfahren eingesetzt. Hierbei werden die optischen Eigenschaften—insbesondere das spektrale Reflexionsvermögen—ausgenutzt.

Zur Erklärung der optischen Erscheinungen cholesterinischer Flüssigkeiten—und damit ihrer Wirkungsweise als Temperaturindikatoren—müssen die Hauptbrechungsindizes als Funktion von Wellenlänge und Temperatur bekannt sein. Messungen hierzu werden diskutiert.

2. Zur Meßanordnung

Die Schwierigkeiten bei der Messung der Hauptbrechungsindizes kristalliner Flüssigkeiten werden vor allem dadurch verursacht, daß bei allen bisherigen Meßverfahren die Orientierung der Flüssigkeit durch Randeinwirkung gegeben ist. Dies wiederum bedingt eine sehr sorgfältige Reinigung der Glasoberflächen, die anschliessend z. B. mit Linsenpapier einsinnig gerieben werden müssen, um eine einheitliche Orientierung der Flüssigkeit zu erzielen. Da auf diese Weise nur ca. $20\,\mu$ dicke, quasi orientierte Flüssigkeitsschichten erzielt werden können, sollte ohne weitere Hilfsmittel (elektrische und magnetische Felder) eine Schichtdicke von ca. $20\,\mu$ nach Möglichkeit nicht überschritten werden. Um dabei eine einheitliche Orientierung zu erhalten, sind parallele Flüssigkeitsschichten zu bevorzugen. Nach Möglichkeit sollte bei dem Einsatz der Prismenmethode der brechende Winkel des verwendeten Hohlprismas möglichst klein sein. Ein Winkel von $30°$ [5] ist möglicherweise schon zu groß. Wir haben uns aus diesem Grunde für das Verfahren nach Abbe entschieden, bei dem aus den Grenzwinkeln der Totalreflexion für ordentlichen und außerordentlichen Strahl auf die Hauptbrechungsindizes geschlossen werden kann. [10] Ein entscheidender Unterschied des gewählten Meßverfahrens gegenüber den von P. Chatelain u. a. gewählten Verfahren der Newtonschen Ringe und der Prismenmethode besteht darin, daß einmal das reflektierte, zum anderen das durchgehende Licht untersucht wird. Infolge der komplizierten schraubenförmigen Anordnung der Moleküle in cholesterinischen Flüssigkeiten [11] muß geklärt werden, wie der Zusammenhang zwischen den Dielektrizitätskonstanten einer monomolekularen Schicht $\epsilon_1, \epsilon_2, \epsilon_3 = \epsilon_1$ und den makroskopisch gemessenen Hauptbrechungsindizes ist. G. H. Conners [12] gibt eine Transformationsformel des Dielektrizitäts-Tensors an, wobei eine Koordinatentransformation vom ortsfesten Meßsystem in das mit der molekularen Anordnung umlaufende " Molekülsystem " durchgeführt wird.

Da bei der Messung des Grenzwinkels der Totalreflexion das einfallende Licht größenordnungsmäßig einige Wellenlängen tief in die cholesterinische Flüssigkeit eindringt, darf in den Gleichungen (1) und (2) über den Drehwinkel Θ integriert werden, wobei die

Matrix (3) entsteht. Das heißt: Parallel und senkrecht zur Schrau-
benachse liegt einmal die kleinere Dielektrizitätskonstante, zum
anderen das arithmetische Mittel der Dielektrizitätskonstanten
einer mono-molekularen Schicht vor. Ueber die bekannte
Maxwellsche Relation: $n = \sqrt{\epsilon}$ ist in Verbindung mit (3) die Bezie-
hung zwischen "mikroskopischen" und "makroskopischen" Hauptbrechungsindizes gegeben.

Wir mußten zunächst prüfen, ob die von uns untersuchten Substanzen sich in ihrer cholesterinischen Phase zwischen Glasoberflächen orientieren ließen. Hierzu wurden dünne Schichten der
cholesterinischen Flüssigkeiten zwischen sehr gut gesäuberten, mit

$$
\begin{bmatrix} D_\xi \\ D_\eta \\ D_\zeta \end{bmatrix} = \begin{bmatrix} \epsilon_1 & 0 & 0 \\ 0 & \epsilon_1 & 0 \\ 0 & 0 & \epsilon_1 \end{bmatrix} \cdot \begin{bmatrix} E_\xi \\ E_\eta \\ E_\zeta \end{bmatrix}
$$

D = dielektrische Verschiebung   (1)
E = elektrische Feldstärke
ξ, η, ζ = Molekülsystem
$\epsilon_1, \epsilon_2, \epsilon_3 = \epsilon_1$ = Hauptdielektrizitätskon-
stanten einer monomolekularen Schicht.

$$
\begin{bmatrix} D_x \\ D_y \\ D_z \end{bmatrix} = \begin{bmatrix} \left\{ \frac{\epsilon_1+\epsilon_2}{2}\left[1 + \frac{\epsilon_1-\epsilon_2}{\epsilon_1+\epsilon_2}\cos 2\varphi\right]\right\} ; & \left\{ \frac{\epsilon_1-\epsilon_2}{2}\sin 2\varphi\right\} & ; 0 \\ \left\{\frac{\epsilon_1-\epsilon_2}{2}\sin 2\varphi\right\} & ; \left\{\frac{\epsilon_1+\epsilon_2}{2}\left[1 - \frac{\epsilon_1-\epsilon_2}{\epsilon_1+\epsilon_2}\cos 2\varphi\right]\right\} ; 0 \\ 0 & ; 0 & ; \epsilon_1 \end{bmatrix} \cdot \begin{bmatrix} E_x \\ E_y \\ E_z \end{bmatrix}
$$

(2)

$$
\begin{bmatrix} \bar{D}_x \\ \bar{D}_y \\ \bar{D}_z \end{bmatrix} = \begin{bmatrix} \frac{\epsilon_1+\epsilon_2}{2} & 0 & 0 \\ 0 & \frac{\epsilon_1+\epsilon_2}{2} & 0 \\ 0 & 0 & \epsilon_1 \end{bmatrix} \cdot \begin{bmatrix} \bar{E}_x \\ \bar{E}_y \\ \bar{E}_z \end{bmatrix}
$$

$\bar{D}$ = Mittelwert der
    diel. Versch.   (3)

$\bar{E}$ = Mittelwert der
    elekt. Feldst.

x, y, z = Meßsystem

Linsenpapier in einer Richtung geriebenen Objektträgern im cono-
skopischen Strahlengang eines Polarisationsmikroskopes untersucht.

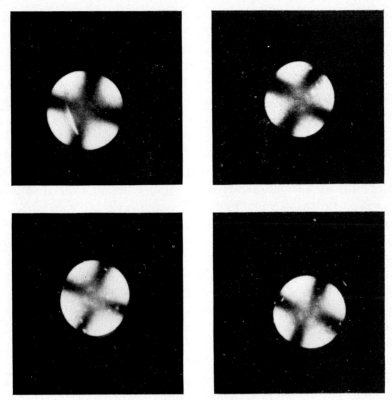

Bild 1. Isogyrenkreuze verschiedener Cholesterinester:
Cholesterin-β-2-Butoxy-Propionat,
Cholesterin-Aethoxy-Aethoxy-Propionat,
Cholesterin-Methoxy-Aethoxy-Propionat,
Cholesterin-Decanoat.

Wie in[13] näher beschrieben, wurde in allen Fällen ein Isogyrenkreuz beobachtet, woraus geschlossen werden konnte, daß das Präparat sich wie ein optischeinachsiger Kristall verhielt. Weitere Untersuchungen zeigten, daß die Präparate einen optisch-negativ-einachsigen Charakter hatten (Abb. 1). Nach Abschluß der Voruntersuchungen wurde eine Apparatur zur Messung der Hauptbrechungsindizes als Funktion von Wellenlänge und Temperatur aufgebaut. Die Anordnung bestand aus einem .lichtstarken Projektor mit Halogenlampe sowie einem Prismen-Monochromator und Abbe-Refraktometer nach Zeiss. Der Meßvorgang und die dabei beobachteten Phänomene wurden schon in[13] ausführlich beschrieben.

Infolge unterschiedlicher Hauptbrechungsindizes und daraus fol-
gender unterschiedlicher Winkel der Totalreflexion wird das Gesichtsfeld in drei Anteile unterschiedlicher Helligkeit unterteilt. Es läßt
sich zeigen, daß ordentlicher und außerordentlicher Strahl zueinander
senkrecht polarisiert sind, daß die untersuchte cholesterinische
Flüssigkeit optisch-negativen Charakter hat und das Auftreten einer
smektischen Phase mit einer Umkehr des optischen Charakters bei
sprunghafter Aenderung der Hauptbrechungsindizes verknüpft ist[13].
Die Messungen waren gut reproduzierbar. Die Oberflächenbehand-
lung der Meßprismen, die vor jeder Messung mit Methylenchlorid
gut gesäubert und mit Linsenpapier und Watte in einer Richtung
gerieben wurden, beeinflußte die Messung durch die Wahl anderer
Lösungsmittel nicht.

Es wurde beobachtet, daß bei einigen Substanzen durch Zusam-
menpressen der Glasprismen die beiden Meßkanten im Gesichtsfeld
des Refraktometers schärfer wurden. Offenbar hängt die Deutlich-
keit der Anzeige vom Ordnungsgrad der cholesterinischen Flüssigkeiten zwischen den Glasprismen ab. Um zu prüfen, ob die gemessenen Hauptbrechungsindizes von der Schichtdicke abhängen, wurde
bei der Messung an einer cholesterinischen sowie einer flüssig-isotropen
Flüssigkeit mit vergleichbarem Brechungsindex (Glyzerin) ein $20\,\mu$
dicker Draht zwischen die Glasprismen gebracht. Die Messungen
mit und ohne Drahtzwischenlage wurden miteinander verglichen.
Bei der cholesterinischen Substanz wurden die beiden Meßkanten
unschärfer, veränderten aber nicht ihre Lage, während beim Glyzerin
die Meßkante scharf blieb und sich um ca. zwei Einheiten der vierten
Dezimale verschob. Die Reproduzierbarkeit der Messungen lag in
derselben Größenordnung, während die Absolutgenauigkeit ca.
± 0,0002 betrug.

3. Meßergebnisse

Die untersuchten Mono- und Iso-Alkyl-Propionsäure-Cholesterin-
Ester wurden selbst hergestellt[13] und auf ihre Reinheit nach ver-
schiedenen Verfahren überprüft. Die aliphatischen Cholesterin-
Ester dagegen wurden im Handel bezogen.†

In Abb. 2 sind die am Cholesterin-Propionat gemessenen Haupt-

† F. A. Schuchardt.

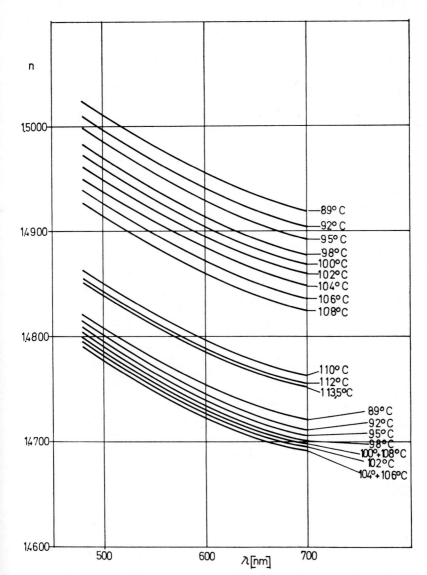

Bild 2.   Messung der Hauptbrechungsindizes der cholesterinischen und des Brechungsindex der flüssig-isotropen Phase von Cholesterin-Propionat als Funktion der Wellenlänge.   Parameter: Probentemperatur.

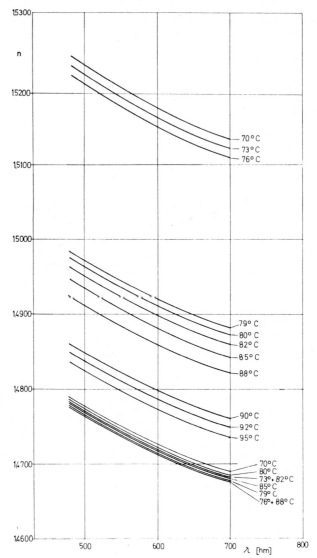

Bild 3. Brechungsindizes als Funktion der Wellenlänge, gemessen am Cholesterin-Decanoat. Parameter: Temperatur.

Brechungsindizes als' Funktion der Wellenlänge aufgetragen sind. Parameter ist die Probentemperatur. Wegen des optisch negativen Charakters der untersuchten Cholesterin-Ester in der cholesterinischen Zwischenphase wird ad. def der kleinere Brechungsindex dem ordentlichen, der größere dem außerordentlichen Strahl zugeordnet.

Alle von uns untersuchten Cholesterin-Ester zeigten eine normale Dispersion, d. h. die Brechungsindizes nehmen mit zunehmender Wellenlänge ab. Wie auch aus Abb. 4 links oben zu erkennen, verschwindet die Doppelbrechung bei ca. 109 °C. Unabhängig von der jeweils vorliegenden Temperatur bzw. Zwischenphase haben die $n(\lambda)$-Kurven den gleichen Verlauf. Abb. 3 zeigt die am Cholesterin-Decanoat gemessenen Kurvenscharen. Bei ca. 79 °C reduziert sich die anfangs sehr große Doppelbrechung auf einen wesentlich kleineren Wert, mit zunehmender Erwärmung verschwindet die Doppelbrechung schließlich bei ca. 89 °C. Diese auch von Pelzl[7] beobachtete Erscheinung ist damit zu erklären, daß zuerst eine smektische Phase vorliegt, die bei ca. 79 °C verschwindet und durch eine cholesterinische Zwischenphase abgelöst wird. Mit zunehmender

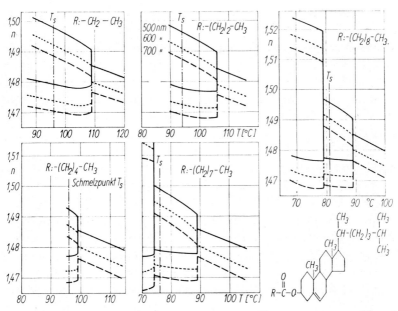

Bild 4. Zusammenstellung der an aliphatischen Estern gemessenen Hauptbrechungsindizes als Funktion der Temperatur. Parameter: Meßwellenlänge.

Temperatur findet schließlich bei 89 °C die Umwandlung der cholesterinischen in die flüssig-isotrope Phase statt.   In Abb. 4 sind die an
verschiedenen aliphatischen Estern gemessenen Brechzahlen als
Funktion der Temperatur zusammengestellt.   Parameter ist
jeweils die Wellenlänge.

Um die Uebersicht zu wahren, haben wir aus jeder Gruppe der
untersuchten Cholesterin-Ester nur eine Substanz ausgewählt und
die hierfür gemessenen Hauptbrechungsindizes als Funktion von
Wellenlänge und Temperatur in den Abb. 5 bis 10 zusammengestellt.
Hierbei ist zu beachten, daß die Abhängigkeit der Hauptbrechungsindizes des ß-2-Butoxy als Funktion der Temperatur (Parameter:
Wellenlänge) schon in Abb. 8 angegeben wurden.   Wie eine genauere
Auswertung aller Messungen ergeben hat, lassen sich die Brechzahlen der anderen Substanzen als Funktion von Wellenlänge und
Temperatur recht gut interpolieren, wenn die Temperatur bei
zusammenfallender Doppelbrechung bekannt ist.

4. Isotropiepunkt, Klärpunkt, Schmelzpunkt

Angeregt durch die Arbeit von Sackmann, Demus, Pelzl[7] die den
Hinweis enthält, daß die Temperatur zusammenfallender Doppel-
brechung bei cholesterinischen Flüssigkeiten oftmals nicht mit der
Temperatur des Klärpunktes identisch ist, haben wir selbst einige
Untersuchungen in dieser Richtung an Alkoxypropionaten des
Cholesterins[13] und aliphatischen Estern durchgeführt und diese
Aussage teilweise bestätigen können.   Eine Erklärung hierfür steht
noch aus.

Um Mißverständnisse zu vermeiden, sollen Isotropiepunkt, Klärpunkt und Schmelzpunkt definiert werden.   Der Isotropiepunkt
wurde refraktometrisch als die Temperature bestimmt, bei der die
Doppelbrechung aufhört.

Zur Ermittlung des Klärpunktes wurde ein automatisch registrie-
rendes Schmelzpunktgerät der Firma Mettler—FP1—verwendet.
Das auf einem Objektträger befindliche Präparat, z. B. ein Cholesterin-Ester mit enantiotroper cholesterinischer Zwischenphase,
konnte im Innern eines Mikroheiztisches mit einer linearen Aufheiz-
rate von 2°/min erwärmt werden.   Der Heiztisch war dabei auf dem
Tisch eines Stereomikroskopes angebracht, wobei sich die Probe

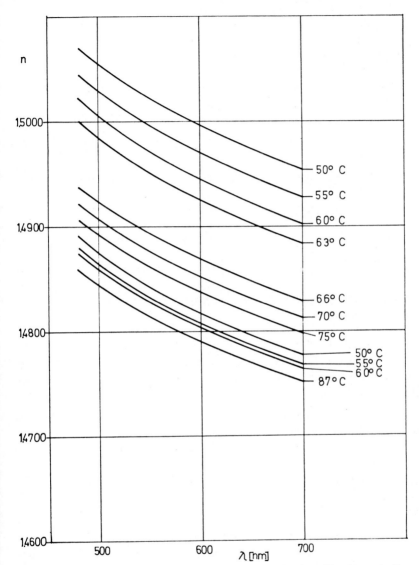

Bild 5. Am Cholesterin-β-n-Pentoxy-Propionat gefundene Brechungsindizes als Funktion der Wellenlänge.

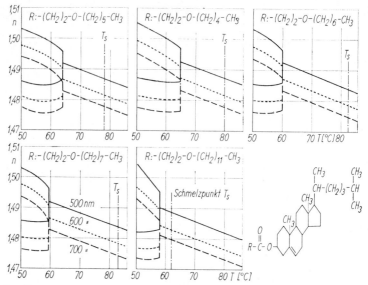

Bild 6. Zusammenstellung der an Mono-Alkoxy-Propionsäure-Cholesterin-Estern ermittelten Brechungsindizes als Funktion der Temperatur. Parameter: Meßwellenlänge.

zwischen zwei gekreuzten Polarisationsfiltern befand. Wird die cholesterinische Zwischenphase durchlaufen, so ist das Gesichtsfeld infolge der Rotationsdispersion des Präparates aufgehellt. Beim Uebergang von der cholesterinischen zur flüssig-isotropen Phase verschwindet die optische Aktivität, das Gesichtsfeld wird dunkel. Diese Temperatur soll Klärpunkt heißen.

Der Schmelzpunkt—in allen Diagrammen mit T_s bezeichnet— wurde mit derselben Apparatur bestimmt. Er ist visuell erkennbar an dem Abrunden der Kristallkanten mit anschließendem Zerfließen der Kristallite. Der so definierte Schmelzvorgang erstreckte sich über einen Temperaturbereich von 1 bis 2 °C.

Die gemessenen Schmelzpunkte wurden mit Literaturwerten[9] u. a. verglichen. Dabei ergaben sich nur unwesentliche Abweichungen, was den Schluß zuläßt, daß die verwendeten Substanzen hinreichend rein waren. Die so definierten Temperaturen konnten mit einer Genauigkeit von ca. ± 1 °C bestimmt werden.

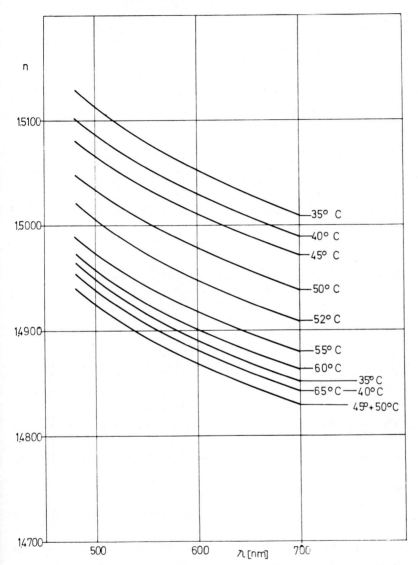

Bild 7. Brechungsindizes als Funktion der Wellenlänge für verschiedene Probentemperaturen, gemessen am Cholesterin-Aethoxy-Aethoxy-Propionat.

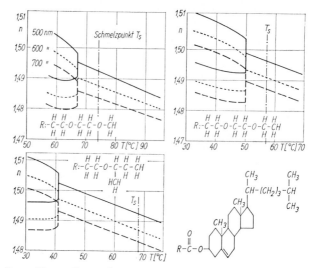

Bild 8. Gegenüberstellung der an zwei Di-Alkoxy-Propionaten und einem Iso-Alkoxypropionat gemessenen Brechungsindizes als Funktion der Temperatur. Parameter: Meßwellenlänge.

5. Diskussion und Auswertung der Meßergebnisse

Bei Betrachtung der Meßwerte am Isotropiepunkt fällt—besonders bei den aliphatischen Estern—auf, daß für alle Substanzen bei ein und derselben Wellenlänge die Brechzahlen der verschwindenden cholesterinischen und der Brechungsindex der gerade beginnenden flüssig-isotropen Phase sowie auch die Steigungen, d. h. die Aenderung des Brechungsindex mit der Temperatur jeweils fast dieselben Werte haben (Abb. 4). Die gewonnen Meßergebnisse können qualitativ wie folgt interpretiert werden:

1. Die Brechungsindizes nehmen mit zunehmender Temperatur ab.

2. Alle Brechzahlen zeigen normale Dispersion, d. h. sie nehmen mit zunehmender Wellenlänge ab.

3. Von den Brechungsindizes für außerordentlichen und ordentlichen Strahl weist der erstere eine größere Temperaturabhängigkeit auf.

4. Mit zunehmender Kettenlänge der substituierten Säure verschiebt sich der Isotropiepunkt zu niedrigeren Temperaturen.

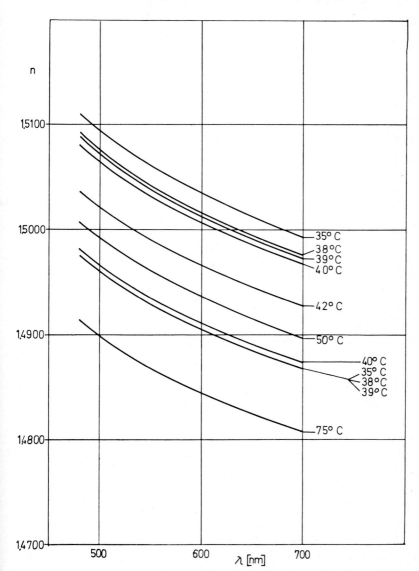

Bild 9. Messungen am β-2-Butoxy-Cholesterin-Propionat, Brechungsindizes als Funktion der Wellenlänge. Parameter: Probentemperatur.

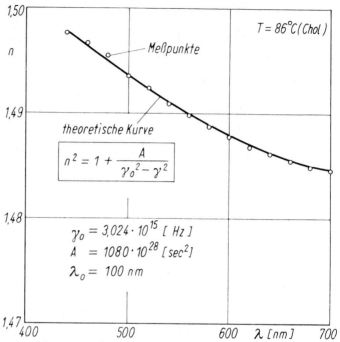

Bild 10. Nach der Dispersionstheorie berechnete Hauptbrechungsindizes als Funktion der Wellenlänge.

5. Für Substanzen einer bestimmten Stoffklasse von Cholesterin-Estern stimmen die am Isotropiepunkt gemessenen Werte nahezu überein.

In Tafel 1 sind die an verschiedenen Cholesterin-Estern am Isotropiepunkt gemessenen Werte zusammengestellt. In den einzelnen Spalten sind von links nach rechts die Stoffklasse der untersuchten Cholesterin-Ester, die einzelnen Substanzen, die Meßwellenlänge, die Temperatur am Isotropiepunkt, die Brechzahl der eben beginnenden flüssig-isotropen Phase und die Doppelbrechung der endenden cholesterinischen Phase sowie der Temperaturkoeffizient der Brechzahl der isotropen Phase angegeben. Die Meßwerte in den Spalten 5, 6 und 7 bestätigen die unter 5. gemachte Aussage.

Ausgehend von den aliphatischen zu den Mono-Di- und Iso-Alkoxypropionaten nimmt der mittlere Brechungsindex der isotropen Phase monoton zu. Das kann ebenso wie die monotone Zunahme mit zunehmender Kettenlänge für Substanzen innerhalb

TAFEL 1   Zur Auswertung der Brechzahlmessungen an Cholesterin-Estern: Der Isotropiepunkt—definiert durch verschwindende Doppelbrechung—nimmt mit größer werdender Esterkette allgemein ab.   Innerhalb einer Stoffklasse von Cholesterin-Estern bleibt der Brechungsindex der isotropen Phase näherungsweise konstant.   Die Doppelbrechung steigt mit zunehmender Kettenlänge monoton an

Stoffklasse	Substanz	λ/nm	$T_{isotrop}$/°C	$n_{T-isotrop}$	$\Delta n_{T-isotrop}$	$\Delta n/\Delta T_{isotrop}/(°C)^{-1}$
	Acetat	500	113	1.4843	≈ 0.0118	≈ 0.00030
	Propionat	500	109	1.4850	0.0120	0.00034
Aliphatische	Butyrat	500	106	1.4847	0.0123	0.00040
Cholesterin-	Capronat	500	99	1.4855	0.0126	0.00043
Ester	Nonanoat	500	89	1.4859	0.0126	0.00044
	Caprinat	500	89	1.4868	0.0134	0.00048
Mono-	β-Butoxy	500	65	1.4923	0.0102	0.00037
Alkyl-	β-Hexoxy	500	62	1.4920	0.0103	0.00037
Propionsäure-	β-Heptoxy	500	58	1.4924	0.0107	0.00038
Cholesterin-	β-Octoxy	500	59.5	1.4918	0.0115	0.00036
Ester	β-Dodecoxy	500	58	1.4910	0.0120	0.00036
Dialkyl-	Methoxy-Änthoxy	500	50	1.4954	0.0076	0.00036
Propionsäure-	Äthoxy-Äthoxy	500	66	1.4990	0.0112	0.00038
Cholesterin-						
Ester						
Iso-						
Alkyl						
Propionsäure-	β-2-Butoxy	500	41	1.5024	0.0083	0.00035
Cholesterin-						
Ester						

einer Stoffklasse durch die Additivität der Atomrefraktionen zur Molrefraktion verstanden werden. Wie aus der Dispersionstheorie bekannt, bestimmt der Brechungsindex die Molrefraktion. Dadurch ist z. B. der Brechungsindex für Substanzen einer Stoffklasse von Cholesterin-Estern eine charakteristische Größe.

Nach dem heute allgemein akzeptierten Modell für eine cholesterinische Flüssigkeit[11] ordnen sich die Moleküle des Cholesterin-Esters so an, daß die quasi flachen Cholesteringerüste innerhalb der monomolekularen Ebenen liegen, während die substituierten Säureketten aus den Ebenen herausragen. Dies hat zur Folge, daß die Raumerfüllung innerhalb einer cholesterinischen Flüssigkeit richtungsabhängig ist, und zwar ist die Raumerfüllung innerhalb einer monomolekularen Schicht größer als senkrecht dazu. Mit zunehmender Kettenlänge der substituierten Säure sollte daher die Doppelbrechung zunehmen, was in der Tat beobachtet wird. Interessant ist die unterschiedliche Temperaturabhängigkeit der Brechungsindizes für ordentlichen und außerordentlichen Strahl. Wie aus der Dispersionstheorie[14] allgemein bekannt, sollte die Molrefraktion temperaturunabhängig sein. Da in erster Näherung die für eine Elektronenbindung verantwortlichen Kräfte temperaturunabhängig sind, sollte der Brechungsindex nur insofern von der Temperatur beeinflußt werden können, als die Dichte hiervon abhängt. Da der Brechungsindex für den außerordentlichen Strahl sehr viel stärker mit der Temperatur abnimmt als der für den ordentlichen, sollte die thermische Ausdehnung in cholesterinischen Flüssigkeiten parallel zu den monomolekularen Ebenen größer sein als senkrecht dazu, was auf unterschiedliche Beweglichkeiten der Moleküle schließen läßt.

Die Abhängigkeit des Brechungsindex von der Wellenlänge läßt sich für alle untersuchten Cholesterin-Ester erstaunlich gut mit der Dispersionstheorie erklären.[14,15] Für den reellen Brechungsindex ergibt sich in Gebieten ohne Absorption:

$$n^2 = 1 + \frac{A}{\nu_0{}^2 - \nu^2} \tag{4}$$

n: Brechungsindex
A: Konstante
ν_0: Elektronen-Resonanzfrequenz
ν: Frequenz der einfallenden Lichtwelle

In[14] wird die angegebene Gleichung, insbesondere die Konstante A näher diskutiert; ebenso wird eine Umrechnung in die übliche Gleichung für die Molrefraktion angegeben. Die in der Formel angegebenen Konstanten A und ν_0 können aus jeweils zwei gemessenen Brechzahlen ermittelt werden. Die Mittelwerte der so gefundenen Konstanten wie ν_0 und A bzw. λ_0 sind in Abb. 10 angegeben. Die zuerst an Cholesterin-Decanoat ermittelten Konstanten ergaben eine Wellenlängenabhängigkeit des Brechungsindex, die innerhalb einer Genauigkeit von zehn Einheiten der vierten Dezimale auf alle anderen vermessenen Substanzen übertragen werden konnte. Hieraus folgt, daß insbesondere die Resonanzwellenlänge von λ_0 ungefähr 100 nm nur von dem Cholesteringerüst, nicht aber von der substituierten Säurekette abhängig ist. Abweichungen von der gefundenen Dispersionskurve treten erst dann auf, wenn in der Säurekette Doppelbindungen, womöglich in konjugierter Stellung, vorhanden sind. Die höhere Beweglichkeit der π-Elektronen verursacht niedrigere Resonanzfrequenzen, die in der Gleichung (4) durch entsprechende Zusatztherme berücksichtigt werden müssen. Hierdurch entstehen steilere Dispersionskurven, wie sie z. B. am Cholesterin-Oleat gefunden wurden (Abb. 11).

6. Zusammenfassung

Es wurden an verschiedenen Substanzen unterschiedlicher Typen von Cholesterin-Estern die Hauptbrechungsindizes als Funktion von Wellenlänge und Temperatur gemessen. Die hierbei gefundenen Ergebnisse lassen sich wie folgt zusammenfassen:

1. Der Brechungsindex nimmt mit zunehmender Temperatur ab.
2. Alle vermessenen Brechungsindizes zeigen normale Dispersion.
3. Ordentlicher und außerordentlicher Brechungsindex zeigen unterschiedliches Temperaturverhalten.
4. Mit zunehmender Kettenlänge der an das Cholesteringerüst substituierten Säurekette nimmt die Doppelbrechung zu und der Isotropiepunkt—definiert durch verschwindende Doppelbrechung—verschiebt sich zu niedrigeren Temperaturen.
5. Die am Isotropiepunkt gemessenen Daten stimmen für Substanzen innerhalb einer Gruppe von Cholesterin-Estern etwa überein.

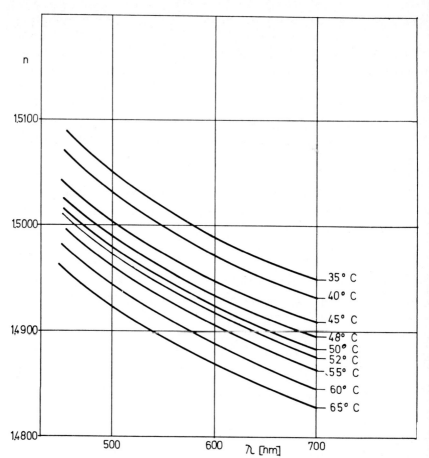

Bild 11. Am Cholesterinoleat gemessene Dispersionskurven. Parameter: Temperatur.

Die Ergebnisse der Brechzahlmessungen lassen sich qualitativ mit dem von De Vries vorgeschlagenen Modell einer cholesterinischen Flüssigkeit erklären. Die Abhängigkeit der Brechungsindizes von der Wellenlänge konnte quantitativ mit der Dispersionstheorie erklärt werden.

LITERATURZUSAMMENSTELLUNG

1. Stumpf, F., *Annalen der Physik* **37**, S. 351, Diss. (1912).
2. Chatelain, P., *Bull. Soc. franç. Minér. Crist.* **60**, S. 280 (1937).
3. Chatelain, P., Pellet, O., *Bull. Soc. franç. Minér. Crist.* **73**, S. 154 (1950).

4. Chatelain, P., Germain, M., *C. R. Acad. Sc. Paris, t.* **259**, Gr. 7, S. 127 (1964).
5. Kopf, L., *J. Opt. Soc. Am.* Vol. 58, No. 2, S. 269 (1968).
6. Chatelain, P., Martin, J. C., *C. R. Acad. Sc. Paris, t.* **268**, S. C., S. 758 (1969).
7. Sackmann, H., Demus, D., *Fortschritte der chemischen Forschung* **12**, Nr. 2, S. 349 (1969).
8. Jeppensen, M. A., Hughes, W. T., *Amer. J. Phys.* Vol. 38, No. 2, S. 199 (1970).
9. Maier, W., In Landolt-Börnstein, Zahlenwerte und Funktionen aus Physik, Chemie, Astronomie, Geophysik und Technik, 6. Auflage, II. Bd., 8. Teil, S. 553, Berlin–Göttingen–Heidelberg: Springer (1962).
10. Kohlrausch, F., *Praktische Physik Bd.* **1**, Leipzig–Berlin: B. G. Teubner (1944).
11. De Vries, H. L., *Acta Cryst.* **4**, S. 219 (1951).
12. Conners, G. H., *Journ. Opt. Soc. Am.* Vol. 58, No. 7, S. 875 (1968).
13. Groß, D., Böttcher, B., *erscheint in Zeitschrift f. Naturforschung*, im Druck.
14. Wolf, K. L., Herzfeld, K. F., *In Handbuch der Physik, Bd.* **20**, S. 480 ff., Berlin, Springer (1928).
15. Macke, W., Wellen, 2. Auflage, S. 294 ff., Leipzig, Akad. Verlagsges. Geest und Portig (1961).

Theory of Rotatory Dispersion of Cholesteric Liquid Crystals†

S. CHANDRASEKHAR and J. SHASHIDHARA PRASAD

Received October 12, 1970; and in revised form November 30, 1970

Abstract—A theory is developed of the circular dichroism and rotatory power of thin films of cholesteric liquid crystals. It is an extension of the treatment for infinitely thick specimens discussed in a previous paper. The theory predicts that the circular dichroism of a thin film plotted as a function of wavelength should exhibit a principal maximum accompanied by subsidiary maxima, and that the rotatory dispersion should be anomalous. Experimental circular dichroism and rotatory dispersion curves are presented for cholesteric cinnamate, cholesteryl-2-propyn-1-yl carbonate and spectratherm. The results are in qualitative agreement with the theory both inside and outside the region of reflexion. The rotatory dispersion curves are also in accord with the de Vries equation outside the region of reflexion.

1. Introduction

The first theory to be proposed of the very high rotatory power of cholesteric liquid crystals and its relation to the reflexion of circularly polarized light was by de Vries.[1] According to this theory, the spectral width of total reflexion of circularly polarized light incident along the optic axis of an infinitely thick specimen is $P\Delta\mu$, and the rotatory power outside the region of reflexion is

$$\rho = -\frac{\pi(\Delta\mu)^2 P}{4\lambda^2[1-(\lambda/\lambda_0)^2]}, \tag{1}$$

where P is the pitch of the helical structure, $\Delta\mu$ the layer birefringence, λ the wavelength in vacuum and $\lambda_0 = \mu P$, μ being the mean refractive index. The predictions of the theory are in qualitative agreement with observations. When $\lambda \ll P$, (1) reduces to

$$\rho = -\frac{\pi(\Delta\mu)^2 P}{4\lambda^2}, \tag{2}$$

---

† Presented at the Third International Liquid Crystal Conference in Berlin, August 24–28, 1970.

a relation first derived by Mauguin,[2] which has been verified quantitatively by Robinson[3] and by Cano and Chatelain.[4,5]

Another somewhat simpler and more direct explanation of the reflexion and rotatory power was put forward by us[6] making use of a modified form of Darwin's dynamical theory of X-ray diffraction.[7,8] This theory leads to a spectral width of total reflexion from an infinitely thick specimen equal to $Q\lambda/\pi$ and the following formulae for the rotatory dispersion:

outside the region of reflexion ($\lambda < \lambda_0 - Q\lambda/2\pi$ or $\lambda > \lambda_0 + Q\lambda/2\pi$),

$$\rho = -\frac{\pi(\Delta\mu)^2 P}{4\lambda^2} + \frac{\pi(\lambda - \lambda_0)}{P\lambda}\left[1 - \left(1 - \frac{Q^2}{\epsilon^2}\right)^{1/2}\right]; \qquad (3)$$

inside the region of reflexion ($\lambda_0 - Q\lambda/2\pi < \lambda < \lambda_0 + Q\lambda/2\pi$),

$$\rho = -\frac{\pi(\Delta\mu)^2 P}{4\lambda^2} + \frac{\pi(\lambda - \lambda_0)}{P\lambda}, \qquad (4)$$

where $\epsilon = -2\pi(\lambda - \lambda_0)/\lambda$ and Q is the reflexion coefficient per pitch of the cholesteric structure.

Strictly, the rotatory power cannot be measured for an infinitely thick specimen inside the reflexion band since one of the circular components is completely attenuated. Nevertheless, (4) is theoretically significant in that it shows how the phase difference between the two opposite circular waves (or, equivalently, the azimuth of the major axis of the elliptically polarized wave) varies with wavelength within the reflexion band. Far away from the region of reflexion on either side, the second term in (3) becomes small and the rotatory power approaches the normal value given by (2).

In discussing the form of the rotatory dispersion curve in the previous paper,[6] the dependence of Q and $\Delta\mu$ on each other and on λ were neglected. In the present paper, we shall show that inclusion of these factors modifies the rotatory dispersion curve slightly so that it now bears a close resemblance to that derived from the de Vries equation outside the reflexion band. We shall also extend the theory to films of finite thickness and compare the results with detailed observations on some cholesteric materials.

2. Theory of Reflexion

We assume the cholesteric structure to be built up of a large number of thin birefringent layers with the principal axes of the successive layers turned through a small angle β. By the application of the Jones calculus, it was shown[6] that when reflexion is negligible the optical rotatory power is given by (2), the negative sign indicating that the sign of the rotation is opposite to that of the helical twist of the structure.

Let us suppose that the structure is right handed. Right circular light incident along the optic axis of such a structure is reflected without change of sense of circular polarization when $\lambda_0 = \mu_d P$, where μ_d is the refractive index for right circular light. Left circular light, on the other hand, is not reflected.

The reflexion coefficient at the boundary between the vth and $(v+1)$th layers is

$$|q| = \frac{\mu'_{v+1} - \mu'_v}{\mu'_{v+1} + \mu'_v},\tag{5}$$

where μ'_{v+1} and μ'_v are the refractive indices of the $(v+1)$th and vth layers for a given direction of the electric vector. If we assume that $\mu'_{v+1} - \mu'_v \simeq \beta \Delta\mu$,

$$|q| \simeq \frac{\beta \Delta\mu}{2\mu},$$

where $\mu = \frac{1}{2}(\mu_1 + \mu_2)$, $\Delta\mu = \mu_1 - \mu_2$, μ_1 and μ_2 being the principal refractive indices of a layer. The reflexion coefficient per thickness P of the liquid crystal is then

$$Q_0 = n|q| \simeq \frac{\pi \Delta\mu}{\mu},\tag{6}$$

since $n\beta = 2\pi$, where n is the number of molecular layers per pitch of the helix.

The general expression for the variation of the refractive index with direction is

$$\frac{1}{\mu'^2} = \frac{\cos^2 \alpha}{\mu_1^2} + \frac{\sin^2 \alpha}{\mu_2^2},\tag{7}$$

which for the present calculation may be represented quite well by the relation[9]

$$\mu'_v = \mu - \frac{1}{2}\Delta\mu \sin 2v\beta.\tag{8}$$

Substituting (8) in (7) and averaging over the different layers,

$$|q| \simeq \frac{\beta \Delta\mu}{\pi\mu}$$

and

$$Q_0 \simeq \frac{2\Delta\mu}{\mu}, \tag{9}$$

which is a slightly better approximation than (6).

The effect of multiple reflexions may be calculated by setting up difference equations similar to those formulated by Darwin.[7,8] Such a procedure is valid because circularly polarized light is propagated along the optic axis without change of form, and the interference of multiply reflected waves with one another and with the primary wave can be evaluated directly. For the convenience of development of this theory, we shall regard the liquid crystal as consisting of a set of parallel planes spaced P apart and ascribe a reflexion coefficient $-iQ$ to each plane for right circularly polarized light at normal incidence. (The relation between Q and Q_0 will be discussed presently.) Let T_r and S_r be the complex amplitudes of the primary and reflected waves at a point just above the rth plane, the topmost plane being designated by the serial number zero. Neglecting the normal absorption coefficient, which is in fact extremely small in the visible spectrum for most of these compounds,[10] the difference equations may then be written as

$$S_r = -iQT_r + \exp(-i\emptyset)S_{r+1}, \tag{10}$$

$$T_{r+1} = \exp(-i\emptyset)T_r - iQ\exp(-2i\emptyset)S_{r+1}, \tag{11}$$

where $\emptyset = 2\pi\mu_d P/\lambda$. The reflexion coefficient is here taken to be the same on both sides of the plane. Replacing r by $(r-1)$ in (10) and (11), substituting and simplifying, we obtain

$$T_{r+1} + T_{r-1} = yT_r \tag{12}$$

$$S_{r+1} + S_{r-1} = yS_r \tag{13}$$

where $y = \exp(i\emptyset) + \exp(-i\emptyset) + Q^2\exp(-i\emptyset)$.

Suppose that the film consists of m planes. Putting $S_m = 0$, we have from (13)

$$S_{m-2} = yS_{m-1},$$

$$S_{m-3} = yS_{m-2} - S_{m-1} = (y^2 - 1)S_{m-1},$$

$$S_{m-4} = (y^3 - 2y)S_{m-1}, \text{ etc.,}$$

and $\quad S_0 = \left[y^{m-1} - \dfrac{(m-2)}{1!} y^{m-3} + \dfrac{(m-4)(m-3)}{2!} y^{m-5} - \cdots \right] S_{m-1}$

$$= f_m(y) S_{m-1} \quad \text{(say)}. \tag{14}$$

Similarly, from (11) and (12),

$$T_{m-1} = \exp(i\emptyset) T_m$$

$$T_{m-2} = [y \exp(i\emptyset) - 1] T_m,$$

$$T_{m-3} = [(y^2 - 1) \exp(-i\emptyset) - y] T_m, \text{ etc.},$$

and $\qquad T_0 = [f_m(y) \exp(i\emptyset) - f_{m-1}(y)] T_m. \tag{15}$

Since from (10),

$$S_{m-1} = -iQ T_{m-1} = -iQ \exp(i\emptyset) T_m,$$

the ratio of the reflected to the incident amplitudes is

$$\frac{S_0}{T_0} = -\frac{iQ f_m(y) \exp(i\emptyset)}{f_m(y) \exp(i\emptyset) - f_{m-1}(y)} \tag{16}$$

Let us assume a relation in the form $T_{r+1} = x T_r$, so that x satisfies

$$x + \frac{1}{x} = y = \exp(i\emptyset) + \exp(-i\emptyset) + Q^2 \exp(-i\emptyset). \tag{17}$$

We have seen that the reflexion condition is $\mu_d P = \lambda_0$ or $\emptyset_0 = 2\pi$. Accordingly we may write

$$\emptyset = 2\pi \lambda_0/\lambda = \emptyset_0 + \epsilon, \tag{18}$$

where $\qquad \epsilon = -2\pi(\lambda - \lambda_0)/\lambda, \tag{19}$

which is a small quantity in the neighbourhood of the reflexion. Therefore, from (17)

$$x + \frac{1}{x} = \exp(i\epsilon) + \exp(-i\epsilon) + Q^2 \exp(-i\epsilon). \tag{20}$$

This suggests that in the neighbourhood of the reflexion we may put

$$x = \exp(-\xi) \exp(-i\emptyset_0) = \exp(-\xi), \tag{21}$$

where ξ is small and may be complex. From (20) and (21),

$$\xi \simeq \pm (Q^2 - \epsilon^2)^{1/2}. \tag{22}$$

When

$$y = \exp(\xi) + \exp(-\xi) = 2 \cosh \xi,$$

the series in (14) is summable (see, e.g., Ref. 11) and is given by

$$f_m(y) = \frac{\sinh m\xi}{\sinh \xi}. \tag{23}$$

Substituting in (16) and simplifying

$$\frac{S_0}{T_0} \simeq \frac{-iQ \exp(i\epsilon)}{i\epsilon + \xi \coth m\xi}, \tag{24}$$

or

$$R = \left| \frac{S_0}{T_0} \right|^2 = \frac{Q^2}{\epsilon^2 + \xi^2 \coth^2 m\xi}. \tag{25}$$

For an infinitely thick specimen,[6]

$$\frac{S_0}{T_0} = -\frac{Q}{\epsilon \pm i\xi} = \frac{Q}{\epsilon \pm i(Q^2 - \epsilon^2)^{1/2}} \tag{26}$$

When $-Q < \epsilon < Q$, ξ is real and

$$R_{\text{inf}} = |S_0/T_0|^2 = 1.$$

The reflexion is therefore total within this range. The spectral width $\Delta\lambda$ of total reflexion is $Q\lambda/\pi \simeq Q_0\lambda_0/\pi$. If we use (6), $\Delta\lambda = P\Delta\mu$, in exact agreement with the de Vries theory. The slightly better approximation (9) gives $\Delta\lambda = 2P\Delta\mu/\pi$. Outside this range, ξ is imaginary and the reflexion falls off rapidly on either side. When $\lambda > \lambda_0$, ϵ is negative and hence the negative value of the square root in the denominator of (26) has to be taken because R_{inf} can never exceed unity; when $\lambda < \lambda_0$, the positive root has to be taken.

So far, we have regarded the liquid crystal as consisting of a set of parallel planes, each with a reflexion coefficient $-iQ$. Clearly $-iQ$ represents the over-all effect of the reflexions from n molecular layers and is related to $-iq$ the reflexion coefficient of a single molecular layer as follows:

$$Q = q[1 + \exp(-2i\delta) + \exp(-4i\delta) + \cdots \exp(-2ni\delta)]$$

$$= \frac{q[1 - \exp(-2ni\delta)]}{[1 - \exp(-2i\delta)]},$$

where $\delta = 2\pi\mu_d P/n\lambda = \emptyset/n$.   Therefore

$$|Q|^2 = \frac{q^2 \sin^2 n\,\delta}{\sin^2 \delta} = n^2 q^2 \left(\frac{\sin \emptyset}{\emptyset}\right)^2.$$

In the neighbourhood of the reflexion,

$$Q^2 = Q_0^2\left(\frac{\sin \epsilon}{\epsilon}\right)^2. \tag{27}$$

Using (25), (26) and (27), theoretical reflexion curves have been drawn with $Q_0 = 0.1$ (or $\Delta\mu = 0.075$) and $\lambda_0 = 6000 \times 10^{-8}$ cm for various values of m; these are shown in Fig. 1.   With increasing film thickness the peak intensity of the principal maximum increases while its width decreases; at the same time the subsidiary maxima increase in number and get closer together, until for the very thick film the principal and subsidiary maxima merge to give a single flat-topped maximum.   The width of total reflexion for the very thick specimen is $2P\Delta\mu/\pi$.

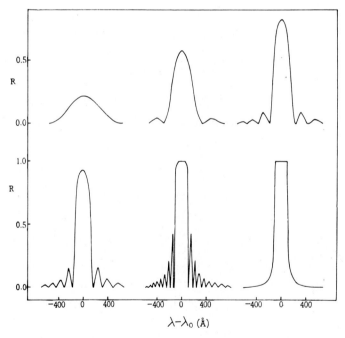

Figure 1.   Theoretical reflexion curves for films of thickness mP; $m = 5, 10, 15$ (top row), 20, 40 and ∞ (2nd row).

3. Circular Dichroism

From (15) and (23),

$$\frac{T_m}{T_0} = \left[\exp{(i\epsilon)} \frac{\sinh m\xi}{\sinh \xi} - \frac{\sinh (m-1)\xi}{\sinh \xi} \right]^{-1}$$

$$\simeq \frac{\xi \operatorname{cosech} m\xi}{i\epsilon + \xi \coth m\xi}. \tag{28}$$

It is easily verified that

$$\left| \frac{T_m}{T_0} \right|^2 + \left| \frac{S_0}{T_0} \right|^2 = 1.$$

The circular dichroism is therefore

$$D = \frac{R}{2-R}. \tag{29}$$

D plotted as a function of wavelength should exhibit primary and secondary maxima similar to the reflexion curve *except that the peaks will be less pronounced.*

4. Anomalous Rotatory Dispersion

In the region of normal dispersion, the optical rotation per thickness P of the liquid crystal is $\frac{1}{2}(\theta_d - \theta_l)$ and the rotatory power in radians per cm

$$\rho = \frac{1}{2P}(\theta_d - \theta_l) = -\frac{\pi(\varDelta\mu)^2 P}{4\lambda^2},$$

where θ_d, θ_l are the phase retardations for right and left circular light. Here a clockwise rotation as seen along the direction of propagation of light is taken as positive.

Near the region of reflexion, the dynamical theory predicts that the right circular component suffers anomalous phase retardation. Left circular light, on the other hand, exhibits normal behavior throughout and, as a consequence, the rotatory dispersion is anomalous in the vicinity of the reflexion.

The phase of the right circular wave can be evaluated from (28). The ratio of the transmitted to the incident amplitudes may be expressed as

$$\frac{T_m}{T_0} = A \exp\{-im\,(\emptyset_0 + \psi)\} = A \exp(-im\,\psi),$$

where

$$\tan m\,\psi = \frac{\epsilon}{\xi \coth m\xi}.$$

The optical rotation per thickness P is

$$\tfrac{1}{2}(\emptyset_0 + \psi - \emptyset_l) = \tfrac{1}{2}[(\emptyset_a - \emptyset_l) + (\psi - \epsilon)],$$

from (18). Hence the rotatory power in radians per cm

$$\rho = -\frac{\pi(\Delta\mu)^2 P}{4\lambda^2} + \frac{(\psi - \epsilon)}{2P}. \tag{30}$$

Far away from the region of reflexion *on either side*, i.e., when $\epsilon^2 \gg (Q_0^2 \sin^2 \epsilon/\epsilon^2)$, $\xi \simeq i\epsilon$ from (22), $\psi \simeq \epsilon$ and the rotatory power reduces to the normal value.

The theoretical rotatory dispersion curve is illustrated in Fig. 2 for $m = 10$, $\lambda_0 = 6000 \times 10^{-8}$ cm, $P = 4000 \times 10^{-8}$ cm (or $\mu_d = 1.5$), $Q_0 = 0.1$ (or $\Delta\mu = 0.075$ at λ_0). The layer birefringence $\Delta\mu$ was assumed to vary linearly from 0.1 at $\lambda4000$ Å to 0.075 at $\lambda6000$ Å and extrapolated to longer wavelengths. The curve gives the rotatory power (in degrees/mm) of a right-handed structure using the standard sign convention according to which a clockwise rotation as seen by an observer looking at the source of light is taken as positive.

The corresponding curve for the very thick specimen given by (3) and (4) is shown as a broken curve in Fig. 2. As mentioned earlier, the curves drawn in the previous paper[6] had neglected the relation between Q_0 and $\Delta\mu$; Q_0 was taken as 0.05 and $\Delta\mu$ as 0.15, whereas according to (9) $\Delta\mu$ should have been 0.0375 at λ_0. Moreover, the variation of $\Delta\mu$ with λ had been ignored. Consequently, the shape of the curve was somewhat distorted and the theory seemed to show a zero of rotatory power close to the reflexion band on the long wavelength side. In fact, when these factors are properly taken into account, the curve tends to be almost asymptotic with the zero rotatory power line as can be seen in Fig. 2. It is interesting to note that the curve is now closely similar to what is expected from the de Vries equation (1).

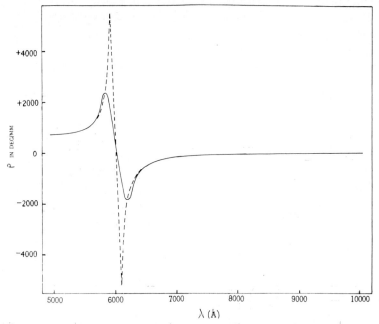

Figure 2.   Theoretical rotatory dispersion curves; $m = 10$ (full curve), $m = \infty$ (broken curve).

5. Comparison with Experiment

Circular dichroism and anomalous rotatory dispersion curves right through the reflexion band have been reported by Mathieu[12] for cholesteric cinnamate and by Fergason[10] for a mixture of cholesteryl benzoate, acetate and palmitate. Their data are in broad agreement with the predictions of our theory both inside and outside the reflexion band.

We have carried out somewhat more detailed measurements on cholesteric cinnamate, cholesteryl-2-propyn-1-yl carbonate (CPC) and a sample of spectratherm supplied by Westinghouse Electric Corporation, Pittsburgh, Penna. (When the spectratherm was supplied five years ago it had a temperature response of 20°–60 °C from red to violet, but in course of time the temperature range changed gradually. At present the reflexion occurs at about 4500 Å at room temperature. The composition of the sample is not known.) The measurements were made on 'plane texture' preparations[13] between microscope slides. No spacers were used. The polarimetric arrangement consisted of a Perkin-Elmer-Hitachi (model 139) monochromator, linear polarizer and analyzer, and a sensitive photo-transistor detector. The relative rotations could be determined to $\pm 4'$ of arc from 4000–10000 Å. Small areas of the film, about 2×2 mm², were used for the experiments. That the areas were optically homogeneous were checked by the uniformity and per-fection of the extinction for wavelengths outside the reflecting region. The film thickness was measured by forming interference fringes between the glass surfaces in air gaps. Since no spacers were used, the thickness measurements are not expected to be accurate to better than $\pm 15\%$.

The circular dichroism was obtained by measuring the intensity of the transmitted light for right and left circular polarizations and applying the formula

$$ D = \frac{I_l - I_r}{I_l + I_r}. $$

This procedure eliminates errors arising from reflexions from glass surfaces, spectral variations of the source and of the sensitivity of the detector, etc. However it suffers from the limitation that the quarter wave plate has to be achromatic for the measurements to be quantitatively precise. Since D involves the difference of two intensity measurements, which is quite small for the subsidiary maxima, the error in the heights of the maxima may be expected to be appreciable. Moreover this error will vary with wavelength. No correction has been applied for this in our measurements and thus the circular dichroism curves presented here are intended for quali-tative comparison with the theory.

Observations were made on a number of specimens of cholesteric cinnamate, CPC and spectratherm. Typical results are shown in Figs. 3–5, and as can be seen they reproduce the features predicted by theory. The rotatory dispersion curves are also in qualitative agreement with the de Vries equation outside the region of reflexion.

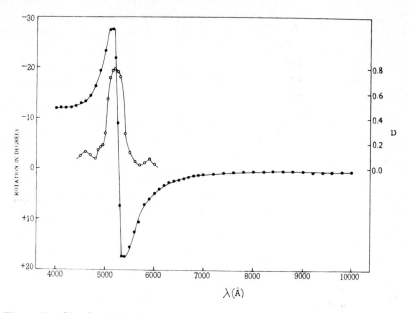

Figure 3.   Circular dichroism and rotatory dispersion of cholesteric cinnamate at 177 °C.   Thickness ∼3μ.

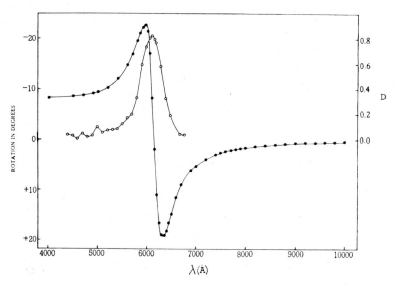

Figure 4.   Circular dichroism and rotatory dispersion of cholesteryl-2-propyn-1-yl carbonate at room temperature (supercooled).   Thickness ∼4 μ.

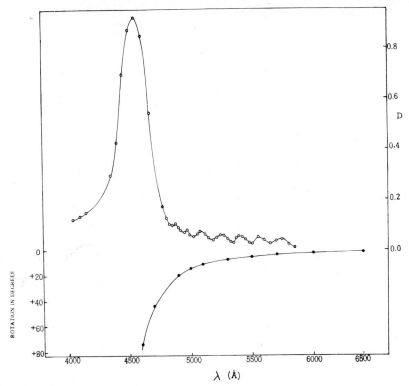

Figure 5. Circular dichroism and rotatory dispersion of spectratherm at room temperature. Thickness $\sim 18\,\mu$.

6. Concluding Remarks

Since the derivation of the Mauguin formula (either by the use of the Poincare sphere[2] or the Jones calculus[6]) would appear to be valid irrespective of whether λ is greater than or less than P, the rotatory power may be expected to reduce to the normal value when reflexion is negligible. Thus, in addition to the reversal of sign of rotation inside the reflexion band, there should be a second reversal of sign on the long wavelength side of the band. Such a behavior is not predicted by the de Vries equation in its present form. However, since $(\varDelta\mu/\lambda)^2$ decreases very rapidly with increase of λ, the curve tends to be nearly asymptotic with the zero rotatory power line (Fig. 2). This was indeed found to be the case experimentally up to

10000 Å for all the specimens examined. Nevertheless, in principle, a change of sign of rotation should be observable under favourable circumstances. Neville and Caveney[14] have recently reported such a behavior in the rotatory dispersion curves of some beetle ⌐xocuticles which form helical structures similar to cholesteric liquid crystals.† It would be of interest to confirm these observations in other liquid crystalline systems.

Acknowledgements

We are grateful to the Director, National Aeronautical Laboratory, Bangalore, for the use of the facilities of the Materials Science Division. We are particularly indebted to Dr. S. Ramaseshan and Dr. S. Rajagopalan for their valuable help and advice in setting up the spectro-polarimeter. Our thanks are due to Vari-Light Corporation, Cincinnati, Ohio, for the samples of CPC and cholesteric cinnamate. The award of a UGC scholarship to one of us (JSP) is gratefully acknowledged.

† These authors have wrongly stated that there is a numerical error in our formulae for the rotatory power.[6] The confusion has arisen because they have used different units for P and λ.

REFERENCES

1. Vries, H. de, *Acta Cryst.* **4**, 219 (1951).
2. Mauguin, M. C., *Bull. Soc. franç. Minér. Crist.* **34**, 71 (1911).
3. Robinson, C., *Tetrahedron* **13**, 219 (1961).
4. Cano, R. and Chatelain, P., C.R. *Acad. Sci. Paris* **259**, 352 (1964).
5. Cano, R., *J. de Physique* **30**, c4–28 (1969).
6. Chandrasekhar, S. and Srinivasa Rao, K. N., *Acta. Cryst.* **A24**, 445 (1968).
7. Darwin, C. G., *Phil. Mag.* **27**, 315, 675 (1914).
8. Darwin, C. G., *Phil. Mag.* **43**, 800 (1922).
9. Chandrasekhar, S. and Shashidhara Prasad, J., in *Physics of the Solid State* Academic Press, London and New York, p. 77 (1969).
10. Fergason, J. L., in *Liquid Crystals.* Gordon and Breach, New York-London-Paris, edited by Brown, G. H., Dienes, G. J. and Labes, M. M., p. 89 (1967).
11. Gradshteyn, I. S., and Ryzhik, I. M., *Tables of Integrals, Series and Products* (Academic Press, London and New York) p. 27 (1965).
12. Mathieu, J. P., *Bull. Soc. franç. Minér. Crist.* **61**, 174 (1938).
13. Gray, G. W., *Molecular Structure and the Properties of Liquid Crystals,* Academic Press, London and New York (1962).
14. Neville, A. C. and Caveney, S., Biol. Rev. **44**, 531 (1969).

Reflection and Transmission by Single-Domain Cholesteric Liquid Crystal Films: Theory and Verification†

DWIGHT W. BERREMAN and TERRY J. SCHEFFER

Bell Telephone Laboratories, Incorporated
Murray Hill, New Jersey

Received October 19, 1970

Abstract—We have developed a fast and essentially exact numerical technique for computing propagation, reflection and transmission of light by a flat layer of any linear optical medium in which the dielectric tensor varies only in a direction normal to the surfaces. Using this technique with Oseen's spiraling-dielectric-tensor model of a single domain in a cholesteric liquid crystal, we predicted triplet Bragg reflection bands of both first and higher orders for light incident obliquely on thin films, similar to the triplet bands that Taupin predicted by a different technique for semi-infinite samples. We have observed the first and second order Bragg reflection bands for light incident at 45 degrees on single-domain cholesteric films between two glass prisms. The films used were mixtures of 4,4'-Bis(n-hexyloxy)azoxybenzene, which is nematic at about 100 °C, and dextro-4,4'-Bis(2-methylbutoxy)azoxybenzene which is asymmetric and causes the cholesteric spiral twist in the mixture. Adjustment of parameters in a general spiraling ellipsoid model to fit the data shows that the dielectric ellipsoids of such films are approximately prolate spheroids with the major axis normal to the spiral axis, as hypothesized by Oseen and Taupin. In mixtures having a pitch of 0.764 microns, for example, the two unlike principal values of the dielectric tensor are approximately 3.060 and 2.430 for blue light around the second order triplet. Additional Bragg reflection bands, which we predicted if no major axis of the dielectric ellipsoid were parallel to the spiral axis, were not observed.

1. Mathematical Technique

We have used a 4×4 matrix formulation of the electromagnetic wave equations in stratified media to compute the reflectance and transmittance of single-domain cholesteric liquid crystal films.[1] Our technique is basically equivalent to the 4×4 matrix technique first described by Teitler and Henvis,[2] and applied by them to

† Presented at the Third International Liquid Crystal Conference, Berlin, August 24–28, 1970.

finite layers of homogeneous anisotropic media. We have found that the method can easily be extended to the numerical solution of problems involving media with continuously varying anisotropic dielectric properties.

Prior to our publication,[1] Taupin[3] found an entirely different technique for computing some of the optical properties of certain models of single domain cholesteric liquid crystals with obliquely incident light using truncated infinite matrices. Recently Dreher et al.[4] have found propagation eigenvalues for oblique rays in such crystals using a single fourth-order differential equation. We believe the generality and simplicity of the 4×4 matrix technique makes it a useful alternative to Taupin's method or the method of Dreher et al. for computing optical properties of cholesteric liquid crystals.

2. Propagation in Stratified Media

When stratified, nonmagnetic, dielectric media carry electromagnetic waves of the form

$$\psi(z) \exp\left(ikx - i\omega t\right),$$

Maxwell's equations can be reduced to the matrix form

$$\frac{\partial}{\partial z}
\begin{bmatrix} E_x \\ iH_y \\ E_y \\ -iH_x \end{bmatrix}
= \frac{\omega}{c}
\begin{bmatrix}
\left(-i\frac{kc\epsilon_{xz}}{\omega\epsilon_{zz}}\right) & \left[1 - \frac{1}{\epsilon_{zz}}\left(\frac{kc}{\omega}\right)^2\right] & \left(-i\frac{kc\,\epsilon_{yz}}{\omega\,\epsilon_{zz}}\right) & 0 \\
\left(-\epsilon_{xx} + \frac{\epsilon_{xz}^2}{\epsilon_{zz}}\right) & \left(-i\frac{kc\,\epsilon_{xz}}{\omega\,\epsilon_{zz}}\right) & \left(\frac{\epsilon_{xz}\epsilon_{yz}}{\epsilon_{zz}} - \epsilon_{xy}\right) & 0 \\
0 & 0 & 0 & 1 \\
\left(\frac{\epsilon_{xz}\epsilon_{yz}}{\epsilon_{zz}} - \epsilon_{xy}\right) & \left(-i\frac{kc\,\epsilon_{yz}}{\omega\,\epsilon_{zz}}\right) & \left[\frac{\epsilon_{yz}^2}{\epsilon_{zz}} - \epsilon_{yy} + \left(\frac{kc}{\omega}\right)^2\right] & 0
\end{bmatrix}
\begin{bmatrix} E \\ iH \\ E \\ -i \end{bmatrix}$$

or

$$\frac{\partial}{\partial z}\psi(z) = \frac{\omega}{c}\,\mathscr{D}(z)\psi(z).$$

We shall call $\mathscr{D}(z)$ the differential propagation matrix. When $\mathscr{D}(z)$ does not vary appreciably over an interval h, an integral of this equation is

$$\psi(z + h) = \mathbf{P}(z, h)\psi(z) = \exp\left[\mathscr{D}(z)(h\omega/c)\right]\psi(z)$$
$$= \left[\mathbf{1} + \mathscr{D}(z)(h\omega/c) + \mathscr{D}(z) : \mathscr{D}(z)(h\omega/c)^2/2! + \ldots\right]\psi(z).$$

We shall call $\mathbf{P}(z, h)$ the local propagation matrix.

Now consider larger intervals of length $l = mh$, where the total variation of $\mathscr{D}(z)$ is large over l, but small over each of the m sub-intervals, h. We may write a general propagation matrix $\mathbf{F}(z, l)$ such that

$$\psi(z + l) = \mathbf{F}(z, l)\psi(z).$$

An obvious approximation for $\mathbf{F}(z, l)$ is

$$\mathbf{F}(z, l) \approx \mathbf{P}(z + l - h, h) : \mathbf{P}(z + l - 2h, h) : \ldots \mathbf{P}(z + h, h) : \mathbf{P}(z, h).$$

However, for most practical problems another approximation for $\mathbf{F}(z, l)$ converges faster. From the symmetry of the physical problem we know that

$$\mathbf{P}(z, h) = \mathbf{P}^{-1}(z, -h) \approx \mathbf{P}^{-1}(z + h, -h).$$

If this expression is substituted for alternate terms in the preceding product series for $\mathbf{F}(z, l)$, we obtain the following more symmetrical expansion, assuming the number of subintervals, m, is even.

$$\mathbf{F}(z, l) \approx \mathbf{P}(z + l - h, h) : \mathbf{P}^{-1}(z + l - h, -h) : \ldots \mathbf{P}(z + h, h) :$$
$$\mathbf{P}^{-1}(z + h, -h).$$

If ϵ is periodic with period l, then

$$\mathscr{D}(z + l) = \mathscr{D}(z),$$

$$\mathbf{P}(z + l, h) = \mathbf{P}(z, h)$$

and

$$\psi(z + Nl) = \mathbf{F}(Nl)\psi(z).$$
$$=: \mathbf{F}^{N}(l)\psi(z)$$

3. Computing Reflectance and Transmittance

Let the subscript i denote incident, r reflected and t transmitted field components for beams in isotropic media separated by a flat stratified layer of thickness T. Let the first medium, which contains the incident and reflected rays, have optical dielectric constant ϵ_1, and let the last medium have optical dielectric constant ϵ_2. Let the angle of incidence within the first medium be θ_1 (see Fig. 1). Snell's law gives

$$\epsilon_1^{1/2} \sin \theta_1 = \epsilon_2^{1/2} \sin \theta_2.$$

The following 6 relations are easily obtained from Maxwell's equations

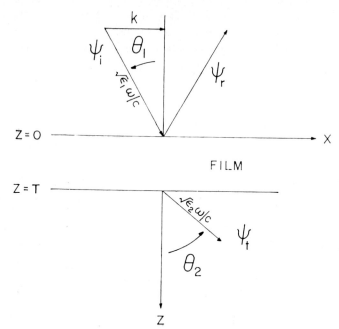

Figure 1. Illustration of variables used in computing the reflectance and transmittance of a stratified film of thickness T.

in isotropic media

$$(H_y/E_x)_i = -(H_y/E_x)_r = \epsilon_1^{1/2}/\cos\theta_1$$
$$(H_x/E_y)_i = -(H_x/E_y)_r = \epsilon_1^{1/2}\cos\theta_1$$
$$(H_y/E_x)_t = \epsilon_2^{1/2}/\cos\theta_2$$
$$(H_x/E_y)_t = \epsilon_2^{1/2}\cos\theta_2$$

Matching fields at the layer surfaces gives the matrix equation

$$\psi_t(T) = \mathbf{F}(T)\,(\psi_i(0) + \psi_r(0))$$

which can now be expressed as 4 linear equations in 6 field variables, such as E_{xi}, E_{yi}, E_{xr}, E_{yr}, E_{xt} and E_{yt}. Given E_{xi} and E_{yi}, we can compute the remaining 4, which give reflectance and transmittance of the combined layer and two interfaces.

4. Optical Model of a Cholesteric Liquid Crystal

A very simple optical model of a perfectly ordered cholesteric liquid crystal was first studied by Oseen[5] and later by Hl. de

Vries.[6] They only investigated light propagated normal to the x, y plane. A slight generalization of their model, which appears to describe correctly the samples of real liquid crystals that we studied, is given by the following dielectric tensor.

$$\varepsilon = \begin{bmatrix} \bar{\epsilon} + \delta \cos 2\beta z & \delta \sin 2\beta z & 0 \\ \delta \sin 2\beta z & \bar{\epsilon} - \delta \cos 2\beta z & 0 \\ 0 & 0 & \epsilon_3 \end{bmatrix}$$

The value of ϵ_3 was irrelevant to Oseen and de Vries' investigations because they only found solutions for normally incident light. Taupin[3] recently described theoretical solutions for light obliquely incident on semi-infinite samples, assuming that $\epsilon_3 = \bar{\epsilon} - \delta$, which appears to be at least approximately the correct relationship for our samples.

Our model gives a differential propagation matrix

$$\mathscr{D}(z) = \mathscr{D}_0 + \mathscr{D}_2(z),$$

where

$$\mathscr{D}_0 = \begin{bmatrix} 0 & 1 - (kc/\omega)^2/\epsilon_3 & 0 & 0 \\ -\bar{\epsilon} & 0 & 0 & 0 \\ 0 & 0 & 0 & 1 \\ 0 & 0 & -\bar{\epsilon} + (kc/\omega)^2 & 0 \end{bmatrix}$$

and

$$\mathscr{D}_2(z) = \begin{bmatrix} 0 & 0 & 0 & 0 \\ -\delta \cos 2\beta z & 0 & -\delta \sin 2\beta z & 0 \\ 0 & 0 & 0 & 0 \\ -\delta \sin 2\beta z & 0 & +\delta \cos 2\beta z & 0 \end{bmatrix}$$

In this model, dielectric ellipsoids spiral about the z axis with pitch $2\pi/\beta$, but the period of the periodic $\mathscr{D}(z)$ matrix is $l = \pi/\beta$ (see Fig. 2). If the ellipsoids were tilted, ε would have no zeros and $\mathscr{D}$ would contain $\sin(\beta z)$ and $\cos(\beta z)$ terms, so that the period would be $l = 2\pi/\beta$. We found solutions for this case. Additional strong Bragg reflection bands corresponding to the longer fundamental period appear in this case. These additional bands were not observed

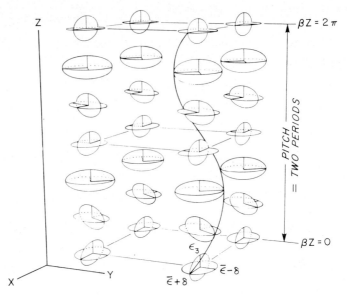

Figure 2. Spiraling dielectric ellipsoids in Oseen's optical model of a cholesteric liquid crystal.

experimentally. Hence the dielectric ellipsoids must not be tilted in our sample.

If the alternating product series expression is used to compute $\mathbf{F}(l)$, a rather rough approximation for $\mathbf{P}(z, h)$ may be used without introducing excessive cumulative errors in $\mathbf{F}$. With the generalized Oseen model, a satisfactory approximation is

$$\mathbf{P}(z, h) \approx \mathbf{P}_0(h) + (h\omega/c)\, \mathscr{D}_2(z).$$

The z-independent term $\mathbf{P}_0(h)$ is the propagation matrix corresponding to the invariant part, $\mathscr{D}_0$, of the differential propagation matrix. It may be written in the following exact, closed form.

$$\mathbf{P}_0(h) = \begin{bmatrix} \cos(abh\omega/c) & (a/b)\sin(abh\omega/c) & 0 & 0 \\ (-b/a)\sin(abh\omega/c) & \cos(abh\omega/c) & 0 & 0 \\ 0 & 0 & \cos(vh\omega/c) & (1/v)\sin(vh\omega/c) \\ 0 & 0 & (-v)\sin(vh\omega/c) & \cos(vh\omega/c) \end{bmatrix}$$

where
$$a = [1 - (kc/\omega)^2/\epsilon_3]^{1/2}$$
$$b = (\bar{\epsilon})^{1/2}$$
and
$$v = [\bar{\epsilon} - (kc/\omega)^2]^{1/2}$$

We computed the reflectance spectrum for obliquely incident plane wave radiation interacting with a system obeying Oseen's optical model. Figure 3 (bottom) shows the first and second order Bragg reflection bands that we predicted for certain principal values of the dielectric tensor.

5. Experiment

A straightforward experiment to verify our calculations would be to measure the reflectivity of a single domain in a cholesteric liquid crystal where the helicoidal axis is uniformly perpendicular to the film surface over the whole area of the light beam. To our knowledge, there have been no prior reflectivity studies made on single-domain cholesteric liquid crystal systems.

The cholesteric films that Fergason[7] and Adams, Haas, and Wysocki[8] used in their optical experiments were not single domain systems. To explain the reflectivity of these films Fergason[7] assumed a distribution in orientation of small Bragg scattering domains embedded in a matrix of constant refractive index. Experiments of Adams, Haas, and Wysocki[8] have shown that there is also a variation in the Bragg spacing, making it impractical to measure the distribution in orientation of these domains. Without knowledge of this orientational distribution, only qualitative comparison of experiments with the single-domain optical theories of Oseen,[5] de Vries,[6] and others[3,4,9] can be made.

We have used a single-domain cholesteric film in which the helicoidal axis is uniformly perpendicular to the film surface over regions of a square centimeter or more. Our cholesteric film is a binary mixture of non-mesomorphic dextro-4,4'-Bis(2-methylbutoxy)azoxy-benzene (2 MBAB) and nematic 4-4'-Bis(n-hexyloxy)azoxy-benzene.[10] We can vary the pitch of the resulting cholesteric mesophase from infinity to $0.24\ \mu$ by increasing the mole fraction of 2 MBAB in the mixture from 0 to 85%, which is the upper limit for

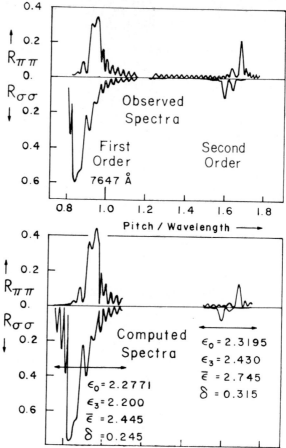

Figure 3.   First and second order reflectance spectra of a cholesteric liquid crystal film 15 pitch lengths or 11.47 μ thick, confined between two glass prisms of optical dielectric constant ϵ_0. Light beam is incident at 45 degrees. Polarizer and analyzer were parallel to the plane of incidence for $R_{\pi\pi}$ and normal to it for $R_{\sigma\sigma}$ measurements. Mole fraction of 2 MBAB is 0.45 and temperature is 88 °C. Small oscillations are interference fringes from the two film-prism interfaces.

the existence of a pure cholesteric phase. The pitch shows only a small temperature dependence, decreasing only a few tenths of a percent for each centigrade degree increase in temperature. The mesomorphic range depends upon the fraction of 2 MBAB in the mixture, but all ranges fall between 42 and 130 °C.

The experimental arrangement that we used for measuring Bragg reflection from this cholesteric film is shown in Fig. 4. We directed an obliquely incident, plane-polarized, monochromatic beam of parallel light at the liquid crystal film contained between the faces of two $36 \times 25 \times 25$ mm right angle glass prisms. We observed that the reflected light from the film always emerged at the specular angle. The reflected beam passed through an analyzer and was focused on a photomultiplier detector. We measured the reflected intensities for both sigma and pi polarized radiation. For pi polarized radiation both the polarizer and analyzer were oriented so that the electric field vector of the radiation passing through them would be in the plane defined by the incident and reflected beam. The polarizer and analyzer were rotated 90 degrees from this position for sigma polarized radiation. The analyzer was needed because it eliminated the dependence of detector sensitivity on polarization. We compared the reflected intensities with 100% reflection values that we measured in a separate experiment by using only the lower prism so the light beam would be totally internally reflected.

We made permanent spacers for the sample by evaporating chromium at three spots on the lower prism face, electroplating a thicker layer of gold on them and then polishing the gold to the desired thickness. The sample thickness was determined at the time of the experiment by measuring the wavelengths of a series of interference minima observed at normal incidence within an air bubble trapped in the film. We calculated the cholesteric pitch by measuring the spacing of the Grandjean-Cano[11,12] discontinuities produced by placing some of the sample between a convex lens surface of known curvature and a flat glass plate, both of which had been rubbed in one direction with lens tissue to insure a well-oriented sample.

We defined the molecular orientation at the surfaces of the liquid crystal film by rubbing the prisms on lens tissue in the x-direction. (See Fig. 4.) We introduced the sample in its isotropic phase between the heated glass prisms and then allowed the system to cool until the sample passed to its cholesteric phase. The desired temperature was held within a degree centigrade or so by means of a simple thermostatic oven arrangement. Before starting the reflection measurements we sheared the film by moving the upper prism back and forth several times in the x direction to obtain the Grandjean plane texture.

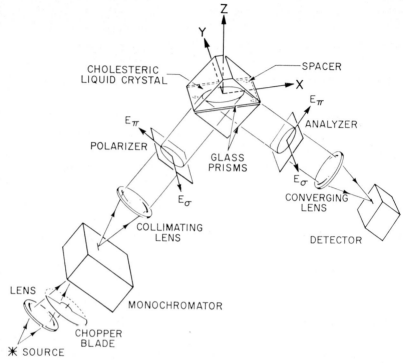

Figure 4.   Apparatus for measuring reflectance of oblique rays by a liquid crystal film.

Our sample contained two or three parallel Grandjean discontinuities about 1 cm apart because it was slightly wedge-shaped. We took reflectivity measurements over a single domain region of uniform pitch by positioning a mask so that only light reflected from a $2 \times \frac{1}{2}$ mm rectangular area half way between two discontinuities and parallel to them was allowed to strike the detector.

The measured reflectivity curves for our cholesteric system are shown in Fig. 3 (top).

6. Conclusions

The mathematical method outlined here was used to generate reflectance spectra for liquid crystal films having the known thickness and pitch of our samples. By adjusting $\bar{\epsilon}$, δ and ϵ_3 we were able to fit frequencies of variations in reflectance quite closely. (See Fig. 3, top.) The method can easily be used for models with dielectric tensors that vary in a more complicated way. Our experimental data did not show additional Bragg reflection bands or other spectral features that we predicted if the principal axis ϵ_3 were not parallel to the z axis. We found that $\epsilon_3 \approx \bar{\epsilon} - \delta$; that is, that the dielectric tensor ellipsoid is (at least approximately) a prolate spheroid, as assumed by Taupin.[3] Our computations show that the second order Bragg reflection band for an oblate spheroid would be much less symmetric about the central component of the band (which is common to both π and σ polarized radiation) than that computed for a prolate spheroid.

We are in doubt as to whether the discrepancy between the computed and the measured intensities shown in Fig. 3 is significant. The first order Bragg reflection band appears to be somewhat weaker and the second somewhat stronger than predicted. Altering the initial and final azimuth of the dielectric ellipsoid or its principal values only made the fit worse. Assuming an error in pitch measurement did not help either. Thin regions near the surfaces with anomalous dielectric properties might account for the discrepancy. However, there might have been an experimental error due to difficulty in getting the same alignment of the sample and reference beams.

Acknowledgement

We wish to acknowledge the capable assistance of F. C. Unterwald in the optical measurements.

REFERENCES

1. Berreman, D. W. and Scheffer, T. J., *Phys. Rev. Lett.* **25**, 577 (1970).
2. Teitler, S. and Henvis, B. W., *J. Opt. Soc. Amer.* **60**, 830 (1970).
3. Taupin, D., *J. Phys.* (*France*) **30**, C4–32 (1969).
4. Dreher, R., Meier, G. and Saupe, A. O., *Third Internat. Liq. Cryst. Conf.*, Berlin, 1970 (to be published).
5. Oseen, C. W., *Trans. Faraday Soc.* (GB) **29**, 833 (1933).
6. de Vries, Hl., *Acta Cryst.* (Internat.) **4**, 219 (1951).
7. Fergason, J. L., *Mol. Cryst. and Liq. Cryst.* **1**, 293 (1966).
8. Adams, J. E., Haas, W., and Wysocki, J., *J. Chem. Phys.* **50**, 2458 (1969).
9. Conners, G. H., *J. Opt. Soc. Amer.* **58**, 875 (1968).
10. Sackmann, E., Meiboom, S. and Snyder, L. C., *J. Amer. Chem. Soc.* **89**, 5981 (1967).
11. Grandjean, F., *CR Acad. Sci.* (*France*) **172**, 71 (1921).
12. Cano, R., *Bull. Soc. Franc. Mineral. Crist.* **91**, 20 (1968).

Birefringence of Smectic Modifications of the Homologous Thallium Soaps†

G. PELZL and H. SACKMANN

Martin-Luther-Universität
402 Halle/Saale Sektion Chemie
German Democratic Republic

Received November 6, 1970; in revised form January 14, 1971

Abstract—The birefringence has been studied of the smectic high temperature modification (neat phase) of the anhydrous thallium soaps in dependence on temperature and at different wavelength. The measurements were carried out on uniaxially orientated liquid crystalline layers on the principle of Abbé's double prism. The lower homologues exhibit negative double refraction which decreases with increasing chain length and decreasing temperature. In the middle members of the homologous series a change in the sign of double refraction is observed. The higher members exhibit positive birefringence, which increases with increasing alkyl chain length and with decreasing temperature. An attempt will be made to explain this behaviour on the basis of the structure of the smectic modification of the thallium salts.

1. Introduction

As part of the extensive investigations of the double refraction of liquid crystalline smectic modifications[1,2] we have also studied the double refraction of the neat phases of anhydrous thallium soaps. The morphological connections of the neat phase with the smectic modifications of aromatic compounds have recently been described.[3] The knowledge of the structure of these phases especially through the works of Luzzati, Skoulios and coworkers[4,5,6,7] allows a more detailed discussion of the results. The thallium salts were selected for measurement because of the favourable temperature range of the liquid crystalline state.

2. Substances

The anhydrous thallium salts of n-fatty acids were synthesized according to the formula of Holde and Selim.[8] The microscopically

† Presented by title only at the Third International Liquid Crystal Conference in Berlin, August 24–28, 1970.

determined transition temperatures are to be found in Table 1
together with the values of Walter, who first investigated the liquid
crystalline behavior of these compounds.[9]

The smectic high temperature modification of the thallium salts
between slide and cover slip appears mostly as an optically uniaxial
pseudoisotropic texture.   Under suitable conditions a well-formed,
fan-shaped texture is also obtained.[11]

TABLE 1   Transition Temperatures of Thallium Salts

n†	Transition into the neat phase		Clearing point	
	This work	Walter	This work	Walter
5	181.0	175.0	215.5	212.0
6	149.0	152.0	229.5	224.0
7	142.8	143.0	227.5	227.0
8	135.7	136.0	222.5	220.0
9	138.6	130.0	217.0	215.0
10	131.0	127.0	209.5	207.0
11	130.4	126.0	203.5	201.0
12	124.7	123.0	197.0	197.0
14	120.2	119.5	185.0	181.5
16	118.2	116.0	175.5	172.0
18	119.0	118.0	167.0	163.0

† n = number of C-atoms.

3. Method of Measurement

Measurements of refractive indices were carried out on optically
uniaxial layers on the principle of Abbé's double prism.   Further
details about the refractometer used and the measuring method are
reported in another place.[1,2]   Measurements were carried out at
four wavelengths: 436, 546, 589, 644 nm.   The average error of the
measured refractive indices amounts to about $\pm 1.10^{-3}$.   At higher
temperatures the average error of measurements is larger because
substances decompose a little.   Some of the lower homologues begin
to sublime at about 180 °C which renders measurement more
difficult.

4. Results of Measurements

A summary of the measured results are given in Tables 2–12. The refractive indices at the temperatures listed are taken from the refractive index-temperature-curves obtained by the graph-balancing method from the single values.[1] Since the temperature dependence in most cases is exactly linear it is in general sufficient to list only a few values. In what follows the refractive index of the extraordinary ray (electric vector parallel to the optical axis) and the index of the ordinary ray (electric vector normal to the optical axis) are designated with n_e and n_o respectively ; n_i is the refractive index of isotropic liquid.

The most important results of the measurements can be seen from Fig. 1. This gives the temperature dependence of refractive indices for five homologous thallium soaps ($\lambda = 589$ nm). It is clear that both indices n_e and n_o decrease with the number of C-atoms in the

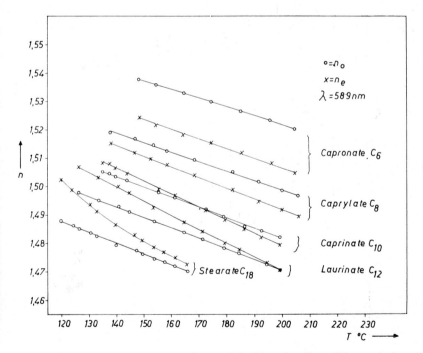

Figure 1. The temperature dependence of double refraction of the neat phase for five homologous thallium soaps ($\lambda = 589$ nm).

TABLE 2   Refractive Indices for Thallium Pentanoate

Phase	T °C	436 nm		546 nm		589 nm		644 nm	
		n_e	n_o	n_e	n_o	n_e	n_o	n_e	n_o
Smectic	207.5	1.5370	1.5670	1.5203	1.5434	1.5165	1.5381	1.5128	1.5333
	195.0	1.5404	1.5708	1.5239	1.5470	1.5203	1.5419	1.5168	1.5367
	180.3	1.5447	1.5751	1.5284	1.5511	1.5247	1.5460	1.5209	1.5408
Plastic modification	176.5	1.5734	1.5764	1.5567	1.5545	1.5523	1.5495	1.5480	1.5445
	125.0	1.5835	1.5844	1.5663	1.5627	1.5621	1.5574	1.5580	1.5524
	85.0	1.5912	1.5908	1.5738	1.5688	1.5698	1.5639	1.5657	1.5588

TABLE 3   Refractive Indices for Thallium Hexanoate

Phase	T °C	436 nm		546 nm		589 nm		644 nm	
		n_e	n_o	n_e	n_o	n_e	n_o	n_e	n_o
Smectic	204.0	1.5242	1.5466	1.5087	1.5250	1.5047	1.5205	1.5020	1.5161
	175.0	1.5337	1.5560	1.5185	1.5342	1.5150	1.5298	1.5118	1.5248
	148.3	1.5426	1.5649	1.5278	1.5428	1.5241	1.5378	1.5207	1.5330
Plastic modification	144.0	1.5558	1.5600	1.5400	1.5393	1.5370	1.5346	1.5322	1.5300
	139.0	1.5572	1.5602	1.5420	1.5397	1.5384	1.5349	1.5346	1.5302

TABLE 4   Refractive Indices for Thallium Heptanoate

Phase	T °C	436 nm		546 nm		589 nm		644 nm	
		n_e	n_o	n_e	n_o	n_e	n_o	n_e	n_o
Smectic	207.5	1.5146	1.5323	1.4995	1.5118	1.4961	1.5073	1.4934	1.5029
	170.0	1.5270	1.5436	1.5130	1.5237	1.5097	1.5190	1.5062	1.5145
	144.0	1.5359	1.5519	1.5220	1.5318	1.5188	1.5270	1.5148	1.5224

TABLE 5   Refractive Indices for Thallium Octanoate

Smectic	205.0	1.5070	1.5200	1.4930	1.5012	1.4897	1.4971	1.4862	1.4926
	170.0	1.5205	1.5320	1.5062	1.5128	1.5030	1.5086	1.4998	1.5042
	139.0	1.5321	1.5426	1.5180	1.5231	1.5150	1.5190	1.5117	1.5143

TABLE 6   Refractive Indices for Thallium Nonanoate

Smectic	207.5	1.4964	1.5067	1.4835	1.4900	1.4804	1.4854	1.4772	1.4820
	170.0	1.5130	1.5212	1.5000	1.5034	1.4971	1.4995	1.4938	1.4954
	136.7	1.5274	1.5337	1.5144	1.5154	1.5112	1.5117	1.5080	1.5071

TABLE 7   Refractive Indices for Thallium Decanoate

Smectic	199.0	1.4950	1.5021	1.4825	1.4859	1.4795	1.4823	1.4760	1.4782
	172.5	1.5073	1.5124	1.4946	1.4957	1.4918	1.4920	1.4883	1.4879
	135.0	1.5247	1.5265	1.5120	1.5094	1.5087	1.5052	1.5055	1.5017

TABLE 8   Refractive Indices for Thallium Undecanoate

Smectic	199.0	1.4880	1.4942	1.4763	1.4789	1.4734	1.4751	1.4704	1.4715
	165.0	1.5056	1.5080	1.4930	1.4920	1.4902	1.4880	1.4874	1.4846
	131.0	1.5225	1.5217	1.5098	1.5049	1.5070	1.5011	1.5042	1.4973

TABLE 9   Refractive Indices for Thallium Laurate

Smectic	200.0	1.4850	1.4894	1.4730	1.4738	1.4703	1.4703	1.4676	1.4674
	165.0	1.5023	1.5028	1.4903	1.4872	1.4874	1.4834	1.4845	1.4800
	126.0	1.5223	1.5179	1.5100	1.5016	1.5072	1.4980	1.5041	1.4942

TABLE 10   Refractive Indices for Thallium Myristate

Phase	T°C	436 nm n_i	436 nm n_e	436 nm n_o	546 nm n_i	546 nm n_e	546 nm n_o	589 nm n_i	589 nm n_e	589 nm n_o	644 nm n_i	644 nm n_e	644 nm n_o
Isotr.	197.5	1.4766			1.4638			1.4604			1.4580		
	187.0	1.4810			1.4683			1.4647			1.4619		
Smectic	185.0		1.4827	1.4838		1.4710	1.4700		1.4682	1.4667		1.4652	1.4636
	170.0		1.4902	1.4899		1.4784	1.4755		1.4759	1.4723		1.4730	1.4690
	145.0		1.5042	1.5000		1.4922	1.4851		1.4897	1.4817		1.4868	1.4781
	125.8		1.5150	1.5077		1.5035	1.4926		1.5008	1.4890		1.4980	1.4855

TABLE 11   Refractive Indices for Thallium Palmitate

Phase	T°C	436 nm n_i	436 nm n_e	436 nm n_o	546 nm n_i	546 nm n_e	546 nm n_o	589 nm n_i	589 nm n_e	589 nm n_o	644 nm n_i	644 nm n_e	644 nm n_o
Isotr.	195.5	1.4722			1.4600			1.4569			1.4540		
	178.0	1.4788			1.4667			1.4635			1.4605		
Smectic	176.0		1.4814	1.4809		1.4700	1.4678		1.4674	1.4648		1.4647	1.4617
	165.0		1.4870	1.4852		1.4750	1.4720		1.4728	1.4690		1.4703	1.4654
	145.0		1.4980	1.4932		1.4870	1.4796		1.4841	1.4762		1.4816	1.4728
	120.0		1.5150	1.5030		1.5042	1.4888		1.5015	1.4858		1.4987	1.4824

TABLE 12   Refractive Indices for Thallium Stearate

Phase	T°C	436 nm n_i	436 nm n_e	436 nm n_o	546 nm n_i	546 nm n_e	546 nm n_o	589 nm n_i	589 nm n_e	589 nm n_o	644 nm n_i	644 nm n_e	644 nm n_o
Isotr.	185.0	1.4722			1.4595			1.4565			1.4537		
	166.7	1.4786			1.4660			1.4631			1.4603		
Smectic	166.0		1.4810	1.4701		1.4694	1.4669		1.4667	1.4638		1.4640	1.4610
	150.0		1.4893	1.4861		1.4778	1.4728		1.4754	1.4698		1.4725	1.4667
	135.0		1.4985	1.4920		1.4870	1.4784		1.4848	1.4755		1.4816	1.4723
	120.0		1.5105	1.4979		1.4990	1.4840		1.4960	1.4810		1.4938	1.4778

alkyl chain and with rising temperature. The temperature co-efficient of n_e is always larger than that of n_o and is especially clear in the case of the homologues with long chains.

The lower homologues (for instance for $\lambda = 589$ nm the members C_5 to C_9) show negative double refraction ($n_0 > n_e$). This diminishes with decreasing temperature, a phenomenon not observed in the crystalline liquid phases of other substances. With increasing chain length n_o decreases more than n_e. Therefore the negative double refraction diminishes with the chain length. In the middle members of the homologous series (C_{10} to C_{12} for $\lambda = 589$ nm), this behavior causes a point of intersection of the n_e- and n_o-curves at a definite temperature, which varies with the wavelength. Above this temperature the smectic phases exhibit negative double refraction, below this isotropic point positive double refraction. In contrast to the negative double refraction the positive double refraction increases with decreasing temperature. With further lengthening of the chain length the n_o-curve has fully " overtaken " the n_e-curve over the entire range of the liquid crystalline phase. The homologues with longer chains (C_{14}–C_{18}) therefore show only positive double refraction.

The dispersion of double refraction is indicated by the example of thallium undecanoate (Fig. 2). For this substance the neat phase possesses an isotropic point of double refraction at all wavelengths investigated. This shifts with increasing wavelength at higher temperatures. The negative double refraction diminishes with increasing wavelength, the positive double refraction on the other hand increases with wavelength. This is also clear from Fig. 3, which shows the dispersion curves of n_e and n_o at constant temperature ($T_{\text{clearing point}} - 40\,^\circ\text{C}$) for three members of the homologous series. It is further clear, that the dispersion of n_e and n_o decreases with increasing chain length.

5. Discussion

The behavior represented by the double refraction of the neat phase of thallium soaps differs from the smectic phases of aromatic compounds.[1,2] For this the structure of the smectic modification of these salts is responsible.

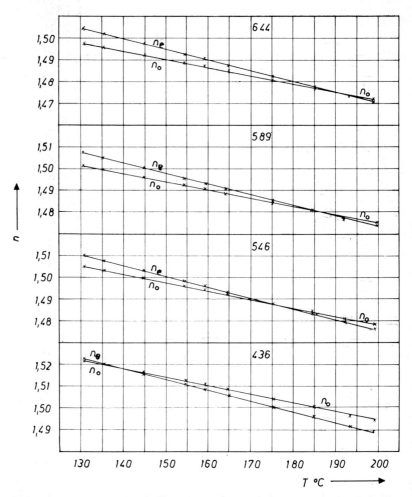

Figure 2.   The refractive indices (n_e and n_o) of the neat phase of thallium undecanoate as a function of the temperature for four different wavelengths: 436, 546, 589, 644 nm.

According to Baum *et al.*[3] this structure should be identical with the " structure lamellaire labile " of the neat phases of alkali soaps.[4] In this structure the polar groups of the molecules are arranged in equidistant planes separated by the double layers of paraffin chains (Fig. 4).   The alignment of polar groups in the planes is random similar to a two-dimensional liquid.   The alkyl chains are not stretched, but more or less bunched together.   A shift of layers is

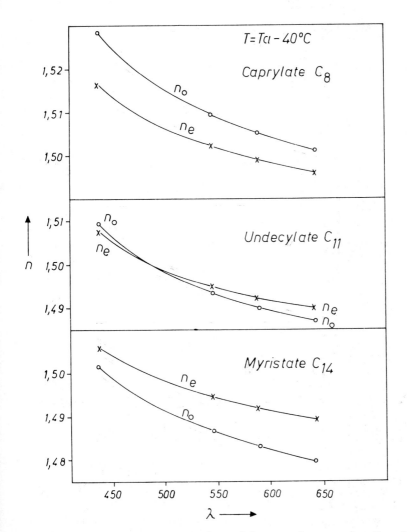

Figure 3. The refractive indices (n_e and n_o) of the neat phase as a function of wavelength and at constant temperature ($T = T_{\text{clearing}} - 40\ °C$) for thallium octanoate, undecanoate and myristate.

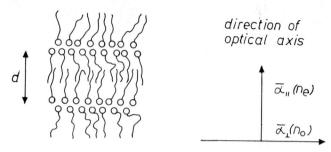

Figure 4. The arrangement of molecules in the " structure lamellaire labile " (schematic).

possible as in the smectic liquids of aromatic compounds. With a rise of temperature the distance of the layers d decreases and the average lateral packing area of each carboxyl group increases. The contraction of chains caused through the temperature mobility of chains is larger the longer the chains.[6] In the homologous series the layer distance and the lateral packing area for each polar group increases with increasing chain length.

In the following discussion we proceed from the Lorenz-Lorentz-formula. According to this the refractive index is dependent on the molar volume V and the polarizability α:

$$\frac{n^2 - 1}{n^2 + 2} = \frac{1}{V} \cdot \tfrac{4}{3}\pi \cdot N_L \cdot \alpha$$

n_e is determined by the temporal mean value of polarizability parallel to the optical axis $(\bar{\alpha}_\parallel)$, n_o by the mean polarizability perpendicular to the optical axis $(\bar{\alpha}_\perp)$ (Fig. 4). The generally diminution of n_e and n_o with increasing chain length (Fig. 1) is obviously caused by the increase of molar volume with increasing chain length.

Presumably two counteracting specific structural factors determine the polarizability anisotropy $\bar{\alpha}_\parallel - \bar{\alpha}_\perp$ and consequently the quantity and sign of the double refraction of the orientated crystalline liquid. These are the uniaxial layer arrangement of polar groups and the more or less bunched configuration of hydrocarbon chains between planes. The layer arrangement of the polar groups will give an amount of negative polarizability anisotropy, since the optically uniaxial layer structures usually show negative double refraction.[10]

This amount should diminish with increasing chain length because of the increasing distances between the planes and the increase of the average lateral packing areas of polar groups. The paraffin chains should yield some of positive polarizability anisotropy (respectively, double refraction) because despite bunching, the C—C-bonds should lie generally in the direction normal to the planes (that is the direction of the optical axis) which correspond on the average with a larger longitudinal arrangement of the molecules and a comparatively small cross section.

For the lower homologues the influence of paraffin chains on the sign of double refraction is obviously small and therefore the double refraction is negative. With increasing chain length the influence of positive polarizability anisotropy of paraffin chains increasingly becomes apparent and causes a diminution of negative double refraction with chain length. The competition of the two counter-acting influences—the influence of layer arrangement of polar groups and the influence of paraffin chains—can explain the discovered zero position of double refraction in the middle members of the homologous series. For the homologues with longer alkyl chains the amount of positive double refraction of paraffin chains predominates.

On this basis it is possible to explain the different temperature dependence of n_e and n_o. The general decrease of n_e and n_o with increasing temperature is undoubtedly caused by a decrease of density. The increased bunching of the paraffin chains should be responsible for the different temperature coefficients. This implies a decrease of $\bar{\alpha}_\parallel$ and an increase of $\bar{\alpha}_\perp$. Therefore, n_e increases more with increasing temperature than n_o. The greater temperature coefficients of n_e and n_o in the long chain homologues are convincing because the contraction of chains in consequence of the temperature for long paraffin chains is larger than for short chains.

For those middle members of the homologous series for which the differences between n_e and n_o of the neat phase are very small, the n_e- and n_o-functions intersect because of the different temperature coefficients.

This concept can also be applied to the optical behavior of plastic (possibly likewise liquid crystalline) modifications of thallium-pentanoate (and -hexanoate) which arise by the cooling of the neat

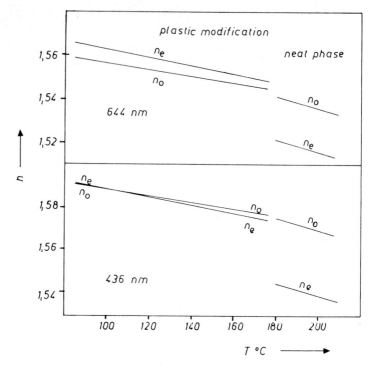

Figure 5. The double refraction of the plastic modification and of the neat phase of thallium pentanoate on dependence of temperature for $\lambda = 436$ nm and $\lambda = 644$ nm.

modification (Fig. 5). The structure of the plastic modification is unknown. We can suppose that, compared with the neat phase, the mobility of the paraffin chains is restricted and the arrangement of polar groups is more compact. The larger stretch of paraffinic chains causes a rise of $\bar{\alpha}_{\parallel}$ as opposed to $\bar{\alpha}_{\perp}$. This could well be the main reason for the fact that compared with the neat phase the n_e-values are much greater. Therefore in longer wavelengths the double refraction becomes positive or is only slightly negative in shorter wavelengths (at higher temperatures).

Moreover the dispersion of double refraction of the plastic modification is similar to that of the neat phase, i.e. with increasing wavelength and decreasing temperature the negative double refraction diminishes and the positive double refraction increases.

This concept about the double refraction of the neat phase of thallium soaps should also be valid for the same modifications of alkali metal soaps. Indeed Oberländer[12] has found in the smectic high temperature modification of three sodium soaps a similar temperature dependence and dispersion of (always slightly positive) double refraction.

For a quantitative discussion, the Lorenz-Lorentz-formula is, of course, not sufficient. For a further separation of the individual influences mentioned, a determination of density-temperature functions is necessary.

An interpretation of the different dispersion of n_e and n_o and the regular change of dispersion of double refraction with the chain length requires an exact knowledge of UV absorption or UV dichroism of orientated liquid crystalline phases.

Acknowledgement

We thank Dr Demus for many helpful discussions.

REFERENCES

1. Pelzl, G., Dissertation, Halle-Saale (1969).
2. Pelzl, G. and Sackmann, H., in preparation.
3. Baum, E., Demus, D. and Sackmann, H., *Wiss. Z. d. Univ. Halle* **XIX**, M, H5, 37 (1970).
4. Skoulios, A. and Luzzati, V., *Acta. Cryst.* **14**, 278 (1961).
5. Gallot, B. and Skoulios, A., *Kolloid-Z. u. Z. Polymere* **210**, 143 (1966).
6. Gallot, B. and Skoulios, A., *Kolloid-Z. u. Z. Polymere* **213**, 143 (1966).
7. Gallot, B. and Skoulios, A., *Mol. Cryst.* **1**, 263 (1966).
8. Holde, D. and Selim, M., *Ber. dtsch. chem. Ges.* **38**, 523 (1925).
9. Walter, R., *Ber. dtsch. chem. Ges.* **59**, 963 (1926).
10. Wooster, W. A., *Z. Kristallogr. Mineral. Petrogr. Abt.* **A80**, 495 (1931).
11. Sackmann, H. and Demus, D., *Mol. Cryst.* **2**, 81 (1966).
12. Oberländer, L., Dissertation, Halle-Saale (1914).

2 Theory (Statistical or Continuum)

Molecular Theory of Nematic Liquid Crystals†

S. CHANDRASEKHAR and N. V. MADHUSUDANA‡

Department of Physics
University of Mysore
Mysore, India

Received October, 1970; *in revised form August* 25, 1971

Abstract—The thermodynamic conditions of nematic stability are discussed on the basis of the molecular statistical theory of orientational order developed in previous papers. Theoretical calculations of the order parameter in the nematic phase and the volume change at the nematic–isotropic transition point are presented for 2-4-nonadienic acid, 2-4-undecadienic acid, *p*-azoxyanisole, *p*-azoxyphenetole and anisaldazine. The significance of the results are discussed briefly.

1. Introduction

Since the high geometrical anisotropy of the molecule appears to be a necessary condition for the occurrence of the nematic mesophase, it is to be expected that repulsion forces play a significant role in determining orientational order. Recent theoretical studies[1,2] have shown that when repulsion and dispersion interactions are taken into account the orientational potential energy of a molecule in a nematic assembly is expressible as a power series in $\cos^2 \theta_i$, where θ_i is the angle which the long axis of the molecule makes with the uniaxial direction of the medium. In these calculations the repulsion energy was worked out by replacing the rod-like molecules by $(2n + 1)$ centres of repulsion, and the dipole–dipole and dipole–quadrupole contributions to the dispersion energy were evaluated in terms of the anisotropic oscillator model of van der Merwe.[3,4] Assuming an average volume dependence of V^{-3} for the sum of the repulsion and dispersion energies,§ using a mean field approximation and imposing

---

† Presented at the Third International Liquid Crystal Conference in Berlin, Germany, August 24–28, 1970.

‡ Present address: Raman Research Institute, Bangalore 6, India.

§ The theory of melting[5,6] which treats the crystal–nematic and nematic–isotropic transitions as order–disorder phenomena supports the assumption that the volume dependence of the orientational energy is V^{-3}.

the condition that the orientational energy vanishes in the isotropic phase, the potential function reduces to the form

$$U_i = -V^{-3}\left[Bs_1\left(\frac{3\cos^2\theta_i - 1}{2}\right) + D\left(s_1\frac{5\cos^4\theta_i - 1}{4} + s_2\frac{3\cos^2\theta_i - 1}{2}\right)\right],$$

(1)

where B and D are constants, V is the molar volume,

$$s_1 = \frac{\overline{3\cos^2\theta} - 1}{2} \quad \text{and} \quad s_2 = \frac{\overline{5\cos^4\theta} - 1}{4}.$$

Based on (1) a statistical theory of orientational order was developed which led to a quantitative explanation of many of the properties of p-azoxyanisole and p-azoxyphenetole.

When $D = 0$ and the volume dependence is taken to be V^{-2}, (1) reduces to the potential function of the form used by Maier and Saupe.[7] The theory then gives a universal curve for the order parameter as a function of the reduced temperature.

In the present communication, we shall discuss in detail an aspect of the theory which was touched upon only briefly in previous papers[1,2] viz., the stability of the nematic phase. We shall also apply the theory to evaluate the order parameter and the volume change at the nematic-isotropic transition point for a few compounds.

2. Stability of the Nematic Phase

The potential energy function (1) may be conveniently written as

$$U_i = -V^{-3}(a'x_i^4 + b'x_i^2 + c'),$$

(2)

where $x = \cos\theta$, $x_i = \cos\theta_i$,

$a' = \frac{5}{4}Ds_1,$

$b' = \frac{3}{2}(Bs_1 + Ds_2)$

and $c' = -\frac{1}{4}[2Bs_1 + D(s_1 + 2s_2)].$

The component of the Helmholtz free energy due to orientational order is

$$F_s = NkT\left[\tfrac{1}{2}(a\overline{x_i^4} + b\overline{x_i^2} - c) - \log\int_0^1 \exp\left(ax_i^4 + bx_i^2\right)dx_i\right].$$

(3)

For a stable equilibrium of the ordered system

$$\left(\frac{\partial F_s}{\partial s_1}\right)_{V,T} = \left(\frac{\partial F_s}{\partial s_2}\right)_{V,T} = 0 \tag{4}$$

and

$$\left(\frac{\partial^2 F_s}{\partial s_1^2}\right)_{V,T} > 0, \qquad \left(\frac{\partial^2 F_s}{\partial s_2^2}\right)_{V,T} > 0. \tag{5}$$

It has been shown[1,2] that (4) is satisfied when

and

$$\left.\begin{aligned}
\overline{x_i^2} &= \overline{x^2} \\[2mm]
\overline{x_i^4} &= \overline{x^4}
\end{aligned}\right\} \tag{6}$$

Figures 1–3 illustrate that the free energy is also a minimum under these circumstances. The integrals involved in the theory were evaluated to an accuracy of 1 in 10^5 by the use of a computer for a range of values of a and b (see Refs. 1 and 2). From these data, the free energies for a representative set of values of a, b, B and D have been plotted in the figures. In each figure there is a family of curves connecting F_s/NkT versus s_1 for a given value of a/b and various values of $(B/kTV^3, D/kTV^3)$. The minimum of the free energy in every curve occurs at a particular value of s_1 (and therefore of s_2) satisfying the equilibrium conditions (6). The broken curve shows the variation of the free energy with the stable value of s_1. The point of intersection of this curve with the zero line, which represents the free energy of the completely disordered system or isotropic phase, fixes the order parameters s_1 and s_2 at the transition point. (Strictly speaking, it is the Gibbs free energy which is equalized at the transition (see Ref. 1 and 2), but the volume change is so small that the error in the order parameters so determined is only of the order of 1–2%). Figure 4 shows how the order parameters at the transition point should vary for a range of materials with different a/b. The Maier–Saupe case corresponds to $a/b = 0$.

Currently used experimental methods of determining the order parameter lead to a measure of s_1 only and not of s_2. An approximate estimate of s_2 has been made recently[8] in p-azoxyanisole from the polarized light scattering intensity data of Chatelain.[9,10]

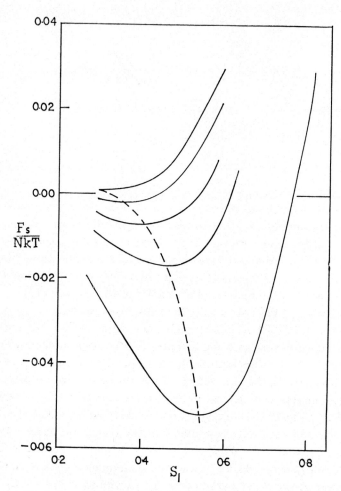

Figure 1.   Variation of F_s/NkT with s_1 for $a/b = -\frac{1}{5}$. The values of $(B/kTV^3,$ $D/kTV^3)$ for the curves from top to bottom are $(6.6132, -1.3435)$, $(6.6745,$ $-1.3530)$, $(6.7794, -1.3714)$, $(6.9244, -1.3979)$ and $(7.3192, -1.4721)$ respectively.

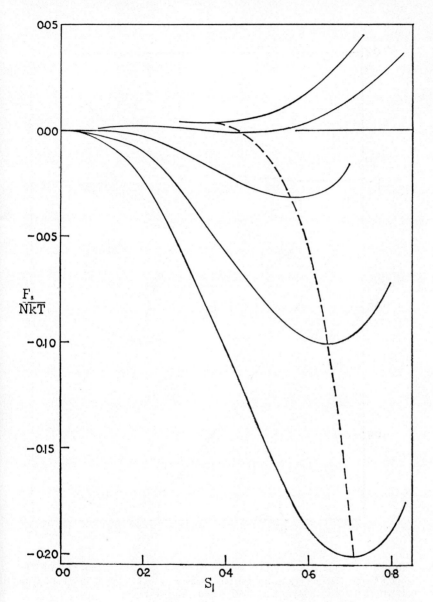

Figure 2. Variation of F_s/NkT with s_1 for $a/b = 0$. The values of B/kTV^3 for the curves from top to bottom are 4.4932, 4.5517, 4.7880, 5.1643 and 5.5982 respectively.

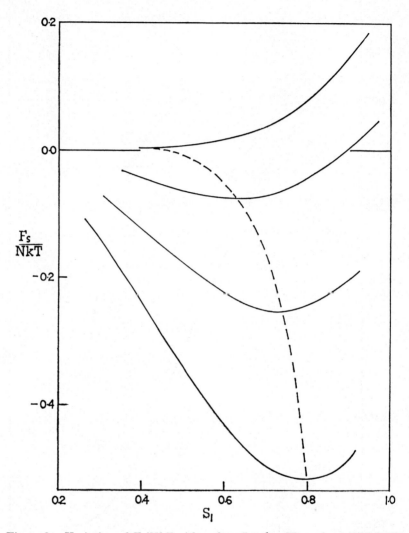

Figure 3.   Variation of F_s/NkT with s_1 for $a/b = \frac{1}{15}$.   The values of $(B/kTV^3,$ $D/kTV^3)$ for the curves from top to bottom are (3.9539, 0.3377), (4.4044, 0.3778), (5.0406, 0.4334) and (5.8080, 0.5003) respectively.

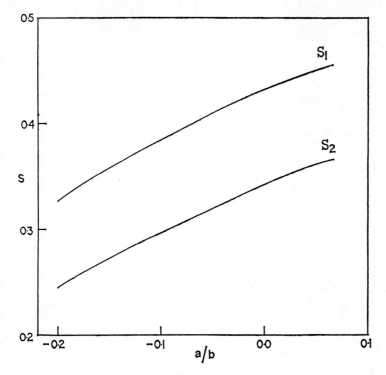

Figure 4.   Order parameters at the nematic-isotropic transition point versus a/b.

3. Application of the theory to a few compounds

A theoretical calculation of the order parameter s_1 and its variation with temperature requires a knowledge of the thermal expansion of the liquid crystal.   As far as we are aware, data on s_1 and V in the nematic range and on $\Delta V/V$ at T_c are available for only five compounds: p-azoxyphenetole (PAP),[11-13] 2-4-nonadienic acid,[14] 2-4-undecadienic acid,[14] anisaldazine[15-17] and p-azoxyanisole (PAA).[7,12,13,18]   We have applied the theory to all these compounds.   Figure 5 presents the theoretical curves for s_1 versus $T_c - T$ along with the available experimental data.   (The magnetic resonance measurements of Rowell *et al.*[19] on deuterated PAA and PAP have not been included in the diagram as the values seem to be slightly higher than those reported by other authors;   however, these

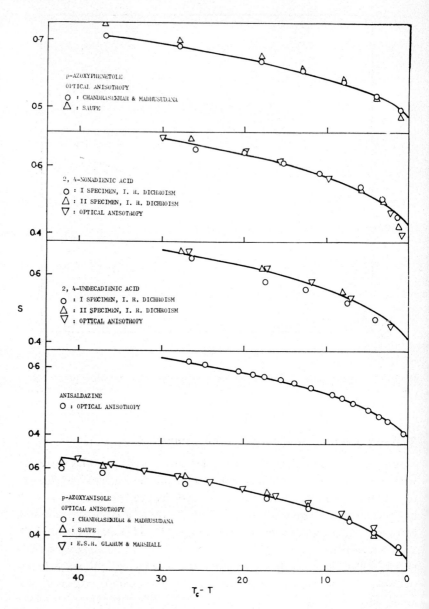

Figure 5.   Orientational order parameter s_1 in some compounds.   Curves represent the variations derived from theory.

measurements do confirm that s_1 of PAA is relatively much lower than that of PAP.) The constants B and D of the potential function, the calculated and observed $\Delta V/V$ are given in Table 1. From a

TABLE 1

	T_c in °K	$B \cdot 10^6$ erg·cm⁹	$D \cdot 10^6$ erg·cm⁹	$(\Delta V/V)$ (theor)	$(\Delta V/V)$ (expt)
2–4-nonadienic acid	326.5	1.0285	− 0.0882	0.0047	0.0047
2–4-undecadienic acid	335.5	1.9840	− 0.2079	0.0039	0.0039
p-azoxyanisole	407	4.5448	− 1.0460	0.0035	0.0035
p-azoxyphenetole	438	5.2502	0.0675	0.0061	0.0060
anisaldazine	454	6.4578	− 0.9738	0.0054	0.0054

preliminary study of these results, the following conclusions may be drawn:

(i) B, which makes the predominant contribution to the potential energy, increases with increasing nematic-isotropic transition temperature T_c. The nematic-isotropic transition temperature is generally regarded as a measure of the " thermal stability " of the nematic phase, as evidenced by studies on a large number of homologous series of compounds (see, e.g., Ref. 20). The relation between B and T_c shows that the strength of the orientational barrier is directly related to the thermal stability. An important point to be noted is that the degree of orientational order does not follow this relationship.

(ii) B and D are of opposite signs for all the compounds except for PAP. The significance of this result is explained by the fact that PAP is the only compound in which the anisotropy of the end group coincides with that of the molecule as a whole. The end group is known to play a significant role in the stability of the nematic phase, as evidenced, for example, by the " odd–even " effect. The asymmetry of the end group may be expected to influence D to a greater extent than B, since D depends on the dipole–quadrupole part of the dispersion forces[4] and on the repulsion forces. Thus in PAP, D adds to the total anisotropy. In the other compounds, D has the effect of reducing the anisotropy of the potential energy. We are investigating these points in greater detail with a view of finding a relation between B and D and the molecular structure.

Of the five compounds, relevant data are available for only two, PAA and PAP, for calculating the heat of transition H, specific heat and compressibility. These two cases have been discussed in detail in previous papers.[1,2] The theory also leads to a relation between the elastic coefficients and the order parameters, and yields values in very good quantitative agreement with the experimental data for these two compounds.[21]

Alben[22] has expressed the view that the excellent agreement obtained by us for the pre-transition effects in specific heat is not a proof of the validity of the theory. According to him, we have ignored an additional condition, viz.

$$\frac{\Delta V}{V} = \beta_l \left(\frac{\partial F_s}{\partial V}\right)_{T_c} \tag{7}$$

where β_l is the isothermal compressibility of the disordered system (liquid phase), thus enabling the volume change to be fitted without the use of a cluster parameter (to allow for short range order). This condition has in fact been used by us in deriving the expression for $\Delta V/V$ (see Eqs. (17) and (18) of Ref. 1). It is true that (7) can be utilized to provide an independent estimate of the cluster parameter, but we find that such an estimate only confirms the validity of our calculations. To illustrate this point we give below the theoretical heats of transition of PAA and PAP obtained by substituting the cluster parameter derived from (7).

TABLE 2

| | H in joules/mole | |
	theoretical	experimental
PAA	760	690[23]
		740[24]
		780[25]
		760[26]
PAP	1500	1500[23]

These values of H differ slightly from our previous values, for, as explained clearly in our papers, we chose the cluster parameter to give the best over-all fit for H, C_p and β. This was necessary because of the wide scatter in the experimental values reported by the different authors, particularly for H and β. It is easily verified that the agreement for the pre-transition effect in the specific heat remains just as satisfactory.

Acknowledgement

We are grateful to the referee for his suggestions.

REFERENCES

1. Chandrasekhar, S. and Madhusudana, N. V., *Mol. Cryst. and Liq. Cryst.* **10**, 151 (1970).
2. Chandrasekhar, S. and Madhusudana, N. V. *Acta Cryst.* **27**A, 303 (1971).
3. van der Merwe, A. J., *Z. Physik.* **196**, 212 (1966).
4. van der Merwe, A. J., *Z. Physik.* **196**, 332 (1966).
5. Chandrasekhar, S., Shashidhar, R. and Tara, N., *Mol. Cryst. and Liq. Cryst.* **10**, 337 (1970).
6. Chandrasekhar, S. and Shashidhar, R., *Mol. Cryst. and Liq. Cryst.* (in press).
7. Maier, W. and Saupe, A., *Z. Naturforsch.* **15a**, 287 (1960).
8. Krishnamurti, D. and Subramhanyam, H. S., presented at the 3rd International Liquid Crystal Conference, West Berlin (1970) (to be published in *Mol. Cryst. and Liq. Cryst.*).
9. Chatelain, P., *Acta Cryst.* **1**, 315 (1948).
10. Chatelain, P., *Bull. Soc. franc. Miner. et Crist.* **77**, 353 (1954).
11. Bauer, E. and Bernamont, J., *J. Phys. Radium.* **7**, 19 (1936).
12. Saupe, A., *Angew. Chem. Internat. Edit.* **7**, 97 (1968).
13. Chandrasekhar, S. and Madhusudana, N. V., *J. Phys. Radium.* **30**, c4–24 (1969).
14. Maier, W. and Markau, K., *Zeit. fur Physik. Chem.* **28**, 190 (1961).
15. Conrat, F., *Physik Z.* **10**, 202 (1909).
16. Porter, R. S. and Johnson, J. F., *J. Appl. Phys.* **34**, 51 (1963).
17. Madhusudana, N. V., Shashidhar, R. and Chandrasekhar, S., *Mol. Cryst. and Liq. Cryst.* **13**, 61 (1971).
18. Glarum, S. H. and Marshall, J. H., *J. Chem. Phys.* **44**, 2884 (1966).
19. Rowell, J. C., Phillips, W. D., Melby, L. R. and Panar, M., *J. Chem. Phys.* **43**, 3442 (1965).
20. Gray, G. W., *Molecular Structure and the Properties of Liquid Crystals*, Academic Press, London and New York (1962).
21. Chandrasekhar, S., Madhusudana, N. V. and Shubha, K., *Acta Cryst.* (in press).
22. Alben, R., *Mol. Cryst. and Liq. Cryst.* **13**, 193 (1971).
23. Arnold, H., *Z. Phys. Chem.* **226**, 146 (1964).
24. Barrall, E. M., Porter, R. S. and Johnson, J. F., *J. Phys. Chem.* **71**, 895 (1967).
25. Sakevich, N. M., *Izz. Vyssh. Ucheb. Zavedi Fiz.* **10**, 52 (1967).
26. Chow, L. C. and Martire, D. E., *J. Phys. Chem.* **73**, 1127 (1969).

On the Validity of the Maier-Saupe Theory of the Nematic Transition†

THEODORE D. SCHULTZ

IBM Thomas J. Watson Research Center
Yorktown Heights
New York

Abstract—The Maier–Saupe theory of the nematic phase transition can be viewed as arising from two basic assumptions: a kind of induced–dipole induced–dipole interaction and the neglect of the effect of orientational interactions on positional correlations. The theory makes the further assumption of the validity of the molecular field approximation for the orientational interactions. We have asked if the first-order transition predicted by Maier and Saupe is just an artificial consequence of the molecular field approximation. To answer this question, we have constructed a model based on the same two assumptions. These are augmented by the further assumptions of discretization of space and discretization of molecular orientations and by the replacement of a rotationally invariant interaction with one having a preferred axis. The latter replacement is analogous to replacing the Heisenberg model for spin systems with the Ising model. By imbedding the present model and the Maier–Saupe theory within the same sequence of variational bounds on the grand potential, it is argued that the present model is superior. It is shown that this model has no first-order phase transition, although the molecular field approximation, when applied to this model, again gives such a transition. It is therefore proposed that the failure to find a first-order transition points to a breakdown in one of the two basic assumptions.

1. Introduction

Maier and Saupe[1] (MS) have described the nematic transition with a theory involving two basic assumptions and one further approximation:

(A) the assumption of an induced–dipole induced–dipole interaction between molecules of the liquid as the sole source of the transition;

(B) the assumption that the probability of any configuration of centers of mass is not affected by the interaction between molecular orientations;

† Presented at the Third International Liquid Crystal Conference in Berlin, August 24–28, 1970.

(**C**) the molecular field approximation to treat the resulting problem of interacting orientations.

The MS theory has often been quoted both regarding its description of the order vs. T and the prediction of a first-order phase transition.

In this paper, we wish to argue that the first-order transition found by Maier and Saupe may be a result of the crudity of the molecular field approximation. We shall argue that a better theory (one still based on **A** and **B** but avoiding the molecular field approximation) would not show a first-order transition. Since such a transition is observed, we believe that it probably comes either from longer range forces than assumed or from detailed correlations of center of mass motions to molecular orientations. The correlations seem more likely because the important forces that have been neglected are, if anything, the shorter range hard-core forces.

In Section 2, we shall formulate a model that we believe incorporates some of the essential features of MS's first and second assumptions but which has the one drawback of breaking rotational symmetry. In Section 3, the model will be exactly solved and shown to give no phase transition for forces as short ranged as those assumed by Maier and Saupe. By contrast, when the same model is solved in the molecular field approximation, a first-order transition is predicted.

In Section 4, we attempt to compare the MS theory with the model presented here with some rigor. To this end, we formulate a systematic series of successively cruder approximations to the grand potential of a liquid crystal. The approximations that lead specifically to the MS theory and to our present model are deferred as long as possible to get the best possible direct comparison. Neither model falls into this series rigorously, but the suggestion is strong that the MS theory gives the poorer upper bound to the exact grand potential.

The possibility that the symmetry-breaking character of the soluble model is a crucial defect is not, however, excluded.

2. Formulation of Model

The Maier–Saupe theory would result if the molecular field approximation were applied to a system of distinguishable molecules interacting with one another through an interaction of the form

$$u_{ij} = -4K(\mathbf{r}_i - \mathbf{r}_j)(\cos^2 \theta_i - \tfrac{1}{3})(\cos^2 \theta_j - \tfrac{1}{3}), \qquad (2.1)$$

where θ_i and θ_j are the angles made by the molecular axes of the ith and jth molecules with some preferred direction. In the molecular field approximation, the details of K_{ij} are not needed because the sum over pairwise interactions (2.1) is replaced by a sum of terms, each one describing a molecule in a molecular field:

$$-4 \sum_i (\cos^2 \theta_i - \tfrac{1}{3}) \sum_{j \neq i} K_{ij} \langle \cos^2 \theta_j - \tfrac{1}{3} \rangle. \qquad (2.2)$$

Only $K = \sum_i K_{ij}$ appears, because $\langle \cos^2 \theta_j \rangle$ is independent of j.

Maier and Saupe, of course, do not start with an interaction of the form (2.1) but with an induced–dipole induced–dipole interaction for which there is no preferred direction in space and in which the dependence on the relative position vector $\mathbf{r}_i - \mathbf{r}_j$ and on the orientations of the two molecules can not be written as a product of independent factors. Thus, although the two interactions are " consistent " in that they yield the same result in the molecular field approximation, a consideration of (2.1) is not equivalent to considering the Maier–Saupe interaction.

We defer to Section 4 a detailed attempt at rigorously formulating the MS model so that it can be compared with a model like (2.1). In this and the next sections, we wish only to formulate a model suggested by (2.1) and to solve it exactly, showing how the molecular field approximation is able to predict a first-order transition when in fact no transition at all occurs.

We consider first N particles whose positions are characterized by $\{\mathbf{r}_i\}$ and whose orientations are given by $\{\theta_i, \phi_i\} \equiv \{\Omega_i\}$. We further assume pairwise interactions of the form (2.1).

Our task is to calculate the partition function

$$(N!)^{-1} \int (d\Omega) \int (dr) \exp\left[2\beta \sum_{i,j} K(\mathbf{r}_i, \mathbf{r}_j)(\cos^2 \theta_i - \tfrac{1}{3})(\cos^2 \theta_j - \tfrac{1}{3}) \right], \qquad (2.3)$$

where $\int (d\Omega)$ denotes $\int \cdots \int \prod_i \sin \theta_i \, d\theta_i \, d\phi_i$, etc.

We now suppose 3-space is replaced by a perfect lattice with mesh points $\mathbf{R}_\alpha$, $\alpha = 1, \cdots, \mathcal{N}$ and that the particle positions $\mathbf{r}_i$ are confined to be at the lattice points. For $\mathcal{N}$ sufficiently large compared with N, this could be as accurate as we wish. We shall, however, go to the other extreme and assume that $\mathcal{N} = N$, i.e., the fluid is completely dense. In this case, particles are still free to " move " in the sense that we sum over the $N!$ possible configurations, but the local density cannot vary with the degree of local orientational order.

The partition function is then

$$(N!)^{-1} \int (d\Omega) \sum_{\mathscr{P}} \exp \left[2\beta \sum_{\alpha,\gamma} K_{\alpha\gamma}(\cos^2 \theta_\alpha - \tfrac{1}{3})(\cos^2 \theta_\gamma - \tfrac{1}{3}) \right], \quad (2.4)$$

where

$$K_{\alpha,\gamma} = K(\mathbf{R}_\alpha, \mathbf{R}_\gamma), \quad (2.5)$$

and $\mathscr{P}$ ranges over the $N!$ permutations of $(1, 2, 3, \cdots N)$. In a particular configuration characterized by $\mathscr{P}$, the $\mathscr{P}\alpha$th particle is at the position $\mathbf{R}_\alpha$, etc.

Because the variables $\Omega_1, \cdots, \Omega_N$ are just dummy variables, they can be renamed appropriately in each term of (2.4), giving for the partition function Z' and the free energy F'

$$e^{-\beta F'} = Z'$$

$$= \int (d\Omega) \exp \left[2\beta \sum_{\alpha,\gamma} K_{\alpha\gamma}(\cos^2 \theta_\alpha - \tfrac{1}{3})(\cos^2 \theta_\gamma - \tfrac{1}{3}) \right], \quad (2.6)$$

i.e., the problem reduces exactly to that of molecules fixed on a lattice. This illustrates that once the assumption has been made that relative orientations don't affect configurational probabilities, the motion of the molecules is irrelevant.

The integration in (2.6) over all the polar angles ϕ_i can be performed immediately, leaving for the free energy the N-dimensional integral

$$\exp(-\beta F') = \int \cdots \int \prod_\alpha (\sin \theta_\alpha \, d\theta_\alpha)$$

$$\cdot \exp \left[2\beta \sum_{\alpha,\gamma} K_{\alpha\gamma}(\cos^1 \theta_\alpha - \tfrac{1}{3})(\cos^2 \theta_\gamma - \tfrac{1}{3}) \right]. \quad (2.7)$$

The variable $\cos^2 \theta_\alpha$ is a random variable ranging over $(0, 1)$ with an *a priori* weight $\tfrac{1}{2} \sin \theta_\alpha \, d\theta_\alpha$, i.e.,

$$\text{Prob}\ (y < \cos^2 \theta_\alpha < y + dy) = \tfrac{1}{2} y^{-1/2} \, dy \quad (2.8)$$

at infinite temperature.

At this point we " discretize " the model by making the replacement

$$\cos^2 \theta_\alpha \to 1 - \sigma_\alpha, \quad \sigma_\alpha = 0, 1 \quad (2.9)$$

attaching *a priori* weights of $\frac{2}{3}$ to $\sigma_\alpha = 1$ and $\frac{1}{3}$ to $\sigma_\alpha = 0$, so that

$$\langle 1 - \sigma_\alpha \rangle_{T \to \infty} = \langle \cos^2 \theta_\alpha \rangle_{T \to \infty} = \tfrac{1}{3}. \tag{2.10}$$

This model problem[2] defines a free energy F and partition function Z:

$$\exp\left(-\beta F\right) = Z$$

$$= \sum_{\sigma_1=0}^{1} \cdots \sum_{\sigma_N=0}^{1} 2^{\Sigma \sigma_\alpha} \exp\left[2\beta \sum_{\alpha,\gamma} K_{\alpha\gamma}(\sigma_\alpha - \tfrac{2}{3})(\sigma_\gamma - \tfrac{2}{3})\right]. \tag{2.11}$$

This discretization assumption is the first we have made that is not consistent with the MS theory, i.e. (2.11) in the molecular field approximation does not agree with the results of MS theory. In some sense this assumption is like replacing an infinite-spin Ising model by a spin-$\frac{1}{2}$ model. It can be expected to affect the qualitative behavior very near a second-order transition, when there is one, and the detailed behavior elsewhere, so we shall have to see what the molecular field approximation would give for this discretized model.

3. Solution of Model

The partition sum Z is essentially that of a spin-$\frac{1}{2}$ Ising model in a special temperature-dependent magnetic field. To see this, we introduce variables τ_α,

$$\tau_\alpha = 2\sigma_\alpha - 1 \tag{3.1}$$

which take on the values -1 and 1. Then the partition function is

$$Z = \sum_{\tau_1} \cdots \sum_{\tau_N} \exp\left[-\beta(H_{\mathrm{I}} + \tfrac{1}{2}NkT \ln 2 + N \sum_\gamma K_{\alpha\gamma}/18)\right], \tag{3.2}$$

where

$$H_{\mathrm{I}} = -\tfrac{1}{2} \sum_{\alpha,\gamma} K_{\alpha\gamma} \tau_\alpha \tau_\gamma + \sum_\alpha h(\tau) \tau_\alpha \tag{3.3}$$

and $h(T)$ is the " field "

$$h(T) = \tfrac{1}{3} \sum_\gamma K_{\alpha\gamma} - \tfrac{1}{2}kT \ln 2. \tag{3.4}$$

The second term in $h(T)$ comes from the weighting factor $2^{\Sigma \sigma_\alpha}$.

The free energy per molecule is just

$$f(T) = -(kT/N) \ln Z$$

$$= \tfrac{1}{2} \ln 2 + (\beta/18) \sum_\gamma K_{\alpha\gamma} + f_{\mathrm{I}}(T, h(T)), \tag{3.5}$$

where $f_I(T, h)$ is the free energy of the spin-$\frac{1}{2}$ Ising model at temperature T in the field h.

Let us recall two properties[3] of the spin-$\frac{1}{2}$ model in the thermodynamic limit ($N \to \infty$).

(1) In the limit of vanishing magnetic field, and below a certain temperature T_I, the system manifests spontaneous magnetization, i.e.

$$\lim_{h \to 0\pm} \lim_{N \to \infty} \left\langle \frac{1}{N} \sum_1^N \tau_i \right\rangle_{h,T} \equiv \pm M_s(T) = \lim_{h \to 0\pm} \left(-\frac{\partial}{\partial h} f_I \right)_{T_I},$$
$$T < T_I.$$

Thus, the limiting free energy per particle f_I is nonanalytic along the $h = 0$ line in the interval $0 < T \leqslant T_I$. T_I is the critical temperature or Curie temperature for this Ising model.

(2) In a finite magnetic field, the free energy f_I is analytic for all positive temperatures.

Thus, if a first-order transition is to occur for $f(T)$, it can only occur for $h = 0$ and at a temperature below T_I, i.e. it occurs at a temperature T_h defined by

$$h(T_h) = 0 \tag{3.6}$$

and then only if T_h is below T_I. The criterion for a first-order transition is therefore

$$T_h < T_I. \tag{3.7}$$

If this condition is satisfied, the latent heat per molecule is $\frac{1}{2}kT_h M_s(T_h)$, where $M_s(T)$ is the spontaneous magnetization for the Ising model in zero field.

We also remark that if a transition occurs, the discontinuity in $\langle \tau \rangle$ must be symmetric around zero, since the spontaneous magnetization just changes sign as $h(T)$ goes through zero. In terms of the order parameter $S = \langle 1 - \frac{3}{2}\sigma \rangle = \frac{1}{4}\langle 1 - 3\tau \rangle$, this implies that the jump in the order must be symmetric around $S = \frac{1}{4}$, and that there is order at all finite temperatures. We discuss this at the end of this section.

Is the inequality (3.7) satisfied? To give a precise answer, we would have to know how K_{xy} varies with $|\mathbf{R}_x - \mathbf{R}_y|$, and we would need to know T_I for such a non-nearest-neighbor Ising model. Lacking this information precisely, we have used the calculations of Domb and Dalton[4] to get an estimate of T_I. Domb and Dalton studied Ising models on various two- and three-dimensional lattices with a constant interaction J out to a certain shell of neighbors and zero beyond.

If q is the total number of molecules interacting with a given one, and $K = qJ$, then

$$kT_h = 0.953K, \tag{3.8}$$

while for the Ising critical temperature, using series methods, Domb and Dalton made the following estimates:

$$kT_I = 0.794K \qquad \text{b.c.c., nearest neighbors}$$
$$= 0.816K \qquad \text{f.c.c., nearest neighbors} \tag{3.9}$$
$$\sim \left(\frac{q}{3.5 + q}\right)K, \text{ as } q \to \infty, K \text{ fixed.}$$

We see that a first-order transition is predicted only if $q \gtrsim 71$, i.e. with a constant interaction, it must extend to third nearest neighbors in a face-centered cubic lattice. In fact, the interaction we are considering falls off far more rapidly than that, so there would be no first-order transition.

What would we have predicted had we applied the molecular field approximation to the discretized model (2.13)? To answer this question, we could, of course, carry out a calculation exactly analogous to Maier and Saupe's. But for this model, there is a simpler way. We simply use the fact that the molecular field approximation is exact for interactions of infinite range and zero strength (the limit being taken so that $qK = $ constant as $q \to \infty$). Thus if the discretized model were calculated in the molecular field approximation, we would conclude that a first-order transition always occurs at a temperature T_h defined by (3.8). This is in sharp contrast to the exact results for reasonably short-ranged interactions.

We conclude that the molecular field approximation can seriously overestimate the circumstances under which a first-order transition will occur. In the next section, we shall discuss the relation of our model to that of Maier and Saupe and the implications of this conclusion for the validity of the MS theory.

Let us discuss briefly the existence, found for our discretized model, of a non-vanishing order parameter at all temperatures. It is easy to see that the order parameter is non-vanishing for the continuous model (2.6) as well. The non-vanishing of the order parameter is a detailed consequence of the way the two models have broken full rotational symmetry. To see this, we compare with the classical Heisenberg and Ising models for interacting spins, where the pairwise interactions occur between spin vectors of fixed length but arbitrary direction and are, respectively, $-K_{ij}\mathbf{S}_i \cdot \mathbf{S}_j$ and $-K_{ij}S_i{}^z S_j{}^z$. In the Heisenberg model, the reduced probability density for the ith spin is $\rho(\Omega_i) = \int \cdots \int \prod_{j \neq i} d\Omega_j \exp [\beta \sum_{j \neq i} K_{ij}\mathbf{S}_i \cdot \mathbf{S}_j]$. This is independent of the direction Ω_i of $\mathbf{S}_i$, because $\mathbf{S}_i \cdot \mathbf{S}_j$ is invariant under rotations of the coordinate axes in spin space. Thus $\langle \mathbf{S}_i \rangle \propto \int d\Omega_i \rho(\Omega_i)\mathbf{S}_i = 0$. In the Ising model, the reduced probability density is not independent of $S_i{}^z$ but it is still an even function of $S_i{}^z$, because $S_i{}^z S_j{}^z$ is invariant under inversion of the coordinate axes in spin space. This is enough to insure that $\langle S_i{}^z \rangle = 0$.

The model (2.6) can be considered as an Ising-like approximation to a Heisenberg-like interaction $-\frac{4}{3}K_{\alpha\gamma}(\cos^2 \theta_{\alpha\gamma} - \frac{1}{3})$ where $\theta_{\alpha\gamma}$ is the angle between Ω_α and Ω_γ. Because this Heisenberg-like interaction is rotationally invariant, we find that $\langle \cos^2 \theta_\alpha - \frac{1}{3} \rangle = 0$, the function $\cos^2 \theta - \frac{1}{3} \propto P_2 (\cos \theta)$ being orthogonal to a constant $(P_0(\cos \theta))$. However, in passing to the Ising-like model, the fact that the reduced probability density is still invariant under inversion is of no help, because the order parameter is now the average of an even function, $\cos^2 \theta_\alpha - \frac{1}{3}$, which is not orthogonal to all even functions but only to a constant.

The order calculated above the transition temperature (if there is one) is therefore an artificial consequence of the model, although the description of short-range correlations may be good. This is just complementary to the situation with the molecular field approximation where, in order to predict correctly the absence of all long-range order at high temperatures, one must foresake the description of all short-range correlations.

Let us now turn to the relation of the present model to that of Maier and Saupe.

4. Variational Comparison of Various Models

Of the three cornerstones of the Maier–Saupe theory mentioned in Section 1, the second and third are crucial and merit restatement:

B. It is assumed that the probability of any configuration of molecular centers of mass is not affected by the interaction between molecular orientations. In the language of Maier and Saupe, time averages are performed over the orbit of a particle on the assumption that the orbits are not affected by the orientations of the particular particle or of the particles near which it passes. In the language of phase-space averages, dependence of the two-body, three-body, etc. correlation functions on position variables is not affected by the orientations of the particles involved. An effective statistical two-body interaction between orientations is thus heuristically derived from the fundamental interaction.

C. This effective interaction between orientations is treated in the approximation of a uniform " mean field " or " molecular field ".

In the original work of Maier and Saupe, these ideas are implemented in an *ad hoc* manner, rather than systematically within the framework of an otherwise rigorous statistical mechanical calculation. It is therefore not clear where **B** ends and **C** begins. We first present an attempt at putting the Maier–Saupe theory within a more rigorous context.

For a given configuration of centers of mass and a given set of orientations, the full interaction energy will be assumed to have the form

$$W(\mathbf{r}_1 \Omega_1, \cdots, \mathbf{r}_N \Omega_N) = V(\mathbf{r}_1, \cdots, \mathbf{r}_N) + \sum_{(i,j)} u_{ij}, \qquad (4.1)$$

where we do not assume (2.1) but only that

$$u_{ij} = u(\mathbf{r}_i \Omega_i, \mathbf{r}_j \Omega_j) \qquad (4.2)$$

is symmetric in i and j. The summation goes only over distinct pairs. The only assumption we have made other than to neglect internal deformations of the molecules is that the interaction between orientations is a symmetric *two*-body interaction, i.e., we are not making assumption **B**. The decomposition (4.1) is of course not unique, since any function of the form $\sum_{(i,j)} v(\mathbf{r}_i, \mathbf{r}_j)$ could be added to $V(\mathbf{r}_1, \cdots, \mathbf{r}_N)$ and subtracted from $\sum_{(i,j)} u_{ij}$. It is made unique by the requirement that $\int d\Omega_j\, u_{ij} = 0$ for all $(\mathbf{r}_i, \mathbf{r}_j)$.

We must now calculate the configuration integral Q_N and Helmholtz free energy F_N defined by[5]

$$\exp\left(-\beta F_N\right) = Q_N$$
$$= (N!)^{-1} \int \cdots \int (dr)(d\Omega) \exp\left[-\beta\left(V + \sum_{(i,j)} u_{ij}\right)\right]. \tag{4.3}$$

Assumption **B** is equivalent to the assumption that the interaction term $V(\mathbf{r}_1 \cdots \mathbf{r}_N)$ alone determines the probability of any configuration $(\mathbf{r}_1 \cdots \mathbf{r}_N)$. We have tried to express this idea in some rigorous mathematical development. One relatively crude way to do this is to use a multidimensional version of a well-known inequality. For single integrals with real functions $a(x)$ and $b(x)$, this inequality[6] is just

$$\int_L dx\, e^{a(x)+b(x)} \geqslant \int_L dx\, e^{a(x)}e^{\bar{b}}, \tag{4.4a}$$

where

$$\bar{b} = \int_L dx\, b(x) e^{a(x)} \Big/ \int_L dx\, e^{a(x)}, \tag{4.4b}$$

and L is any domain on the real axis for which the integrals all exist. When generalized to the integral over the $3N$-dimensional configuration space, this inequality yields

$$Q_N \geqslant Q_N{}^c Q_N{}^{\text{or}}, \tag{4.5}$$

where

$$Q_N{}^c = (N!)^{-1} \int \cdots \int (dr) \exp\left[-\beta V(\mathbf{r}_1, \cdots, \mathbf{r}_N)\right], \tag{4.6a}$$

and

$$Q_N{}^{\text{or}} = \int \cdots \int (d\Omega) \exp\left(-\beta \sum_{(i,j)} \bar{u}_{ij}\right) \tag{4.6b}$$

is the configuration integral, neglecting orientational interactions, and

$$\bar{u}_{ij} = \bar{u}(\Omega_i, \Omega_j) = \int \cdots \int (dr)\, e^{-\beta V} u_{ij} \Big/ \int \cdots \int (dr)\, e^{-\beta V} \tag{4.7}$$

is the average interaction between the ith and jth orientations, the average being taken over all configurations $(\mathbf{r}_1 \cdots \mathbf{r}_N)$ with weight $e^{-\beta V}$. Now if the probability that the ith and jth molecules are in unit volumes at $\mathbf{r}_i$ and $\mathbf{r}_j$ is called $f(\mathbf{r}_i, \mathbf{r}_j)$, so that

$$f(\mathbf{r}_i, \mathbf{r}_j) = \int \cdots \int \prod_{k \neq i,j} d^3 r_k\, e^{-\beta V} \Big/ \int \cdots \int (dr)\, e^{-\beta V}, \tag{4.8}$$

then

$$\bar{u}_{ij} = \int \int \mathrm{d}^3r_i \, \mathrm{d}^3r_j \, u(\mathbf{r}_i \Omega_i, \mathbf{r}_j \Omega_j) f(\mathbf{r}_i, \mathbf{r}_j). \qquad (4.9)$$

The function $f(\mathbf{r}_i, \mathbf{r}_j)$, being normalized by $\int\int \mathrm{d}^3r_i \, \mathrm{d}^3r_j f(\mathbf{r}_i, \mathbf{r}_j) = 1$, approaches ρ^2/N^2 as $|\mathbf{r}_i - \mathbf{r}_j| \to \infty$ and is $O(N^{-2})$ for all i and j. Since u_{ij} is of finite range, we conclude that $\bar{u}_{ij} = O(N^{-1})$.

Expression (4.5) gives an approximation to the free energy F_N which is an upper bound:

$$F_N \leqslant F_N{}^c + F_N{}^{\mathrm{or}} = -kT(\ln Q_N{}^c + \ln Q_N{}^{\mathrm{or}}). \qquad (4.10)$$

$F_N{}^c$ is the pure configurational contribution to the free energy (i.e., neglecting the orientational contribution). $F_N{}^{\mathrm{or}}$ is a purely orientational free energy. In evaluating $F_N{}^{\mathrm{or}}$, each molecular orientation interacts with every other one, but with a strength that is averaged over all relative positions. This effective, two-body, orientational interaction $\bar{u}_{ij}$ is therefore of essentially infinite range and infinitesimal strength.

Because of the infinite range of $\bar{u}_{ij}$, the molecular field approximation should be exact[7] to leading order in N, in evaluating $F_N{}^{\mathrm{or}}$. Thus, if approximation **B** is implemented in the crude manner of (4.5)–(4.10), then approximation **C** is not an additional approximation.

But, of course, this implementation of approximation **B** is too crude. While each particle will have interacted with every other particle after a sufficiently long period of time, most of these interactions will not have occurred before equilibrium is established. It is therefore unnecessarily crude to replace the strong but very occasional and short-lived orientational interaction between any pair of particles by an extremely weak but infinitely long-lived interaction. Yet this is what is done in (4.5)–(4.10), albeit in the language of phase space averages rather than time averages.

Let us turn to a different but equivalent formulation of the liquid crystal problem in which we can again assume that the configurational probability is independent of the molecular orientations, but in which the orientational interactions extend only to the immediate environment. Such an implementation of **B** is intuitively better than the previous one. We shall also show that it is mathematically superior in the sense of giving a better upper bound to the exact free energy (or, in this case, grand potential).

We consider 3-space to be replaced by the mesh introduced in Section 2 and further assume that the number of mesh points $\mathcal{N}$ is extremely large compared with the number of particles. We shall now describe a configuration of the molecules by assigning to each mesh point an occupation number n_R which can be zero or one, and an orientation Ω_R which gives the orientation of the molecule centered at $\mathbf{R}$ when $n_R = 1$ and is arbitrary when $n_R = 0$.

We propose to sum over all configurations for which $\sum_R n_R = N$ and for each configuration to integrate over all orientations at sites where there is a particle ($n_R = 1$). To avoid the constraint on particle number, we go to the grand canonical ensemble. Also, it is convenient to integrate over orientations at *all* sites, introducing an extra factor $(4\pi)^{\mathcal{N} - \Sigma_R n_R}$ which must then be divided out. Thus

$$Q\mu = \int \cdots \int \prod_R (d\Omega_R/4\pi) \sum_{\{n_R\}} (4\pi)^{\Sigma n_R} \exp\left[-\beta \sum_{R,R'} V_2(\mathbf{R}, \mathbf{R}')n_R n_{R'} \right]$$

$$\cdot \exp\left[-\beta \sum_{R,R',R''} V_3(\mathbf{R}, \mathbf{R}', \mathbf{R}'')n_R n_{R'} n_{R''} + \cdots \right]$$

$$\cdot \exp\left[-\beta\mu \sum_R n_R \right] \exp\left[-\beta \sum_{R,R'} u(\mathbf{R}, \Omega_R; \mathbf{R}', \Omega_{R'})n_R n_{R'} \right]. \quad (4.11)$$

Here V_2, V_3 etc. are the two-body, three-body, etc. contributions to the interaction $V(\mathbf{R}_1, \cdots, \mathbf{R}_N)$ and μ is determined so that

$$\left\langle \sum_R n_R \right\rangle = N \quad (4.12)$$

where $\langle \cdots \rangle$ denotes an average with the weighting factor

$$\exp\left[-\beta \sum_{RR'} V_2 n_R n_{R'} - \beta\mu \sum_R n_R \right].$$

For simplicity let us neglect V_3, V_4, $\cdots$.

If we neglect all interactions, then

$$\left\langle \sum_R n_R \right\rangle = \mathcal{N}(1 + e^{-\beta\mu})^{-1} = N \quad (4.13)$$

so that as $\mathcal{N} \to \infty$, we require that

$$e^{\beta\mu} \to \mathcal{N}/N \quad \text{or} \quad \mu \to -\infty. \quad (4.14)$$

Even when the interactions are turned on, this behavior of μ is substantially unchanged.

Now we can make an analogous approximation to that of (4.5),

$$Q_\mu \geq (4\pi)^N Q_\mu{}^c \int \cdots \int \prod_R (d\Omega_R/4\pi)$$

$$\cdot \exp\left[-\tfrac{1}{2}\beta \sum_{R,R'} u(\mathbf{R}, \Omega_R; \mathbf{R}', \Omega_{R'})\langle n_R n_{R'}\rangle \right] \qquad (4.15)$$

where $Q_\mu{}^c$ is now the grand partition function neglecting orientational effects. If we let the mesh size shrink to zero, Eq. (4.15) can be replaced by one involving a functional integral over the functions $\Omega(\mathbf{R})$:

$$Q_\mu \geq Q_\mu{}^c Q_\mu{}^{(\theta,\phi)} \qquad (4.16)$$

where

$$Q_\mu{}^{(\theta,\phi)} = (4\pi)^N \int \mathscr{D}[\Omega]$$

$$\cdot \exp\left[-\tfrac{1}{2}n^2\beta \int\int d^3R\, d^3R'\, u(\mathbf{R}, \Omega(\mathbf{R})\,;\, \mathbf{R}'\Omega(\mathbf{R}')) f(\mathbf{R} - \mathbf{R}') \right]$$
$$(4.17)$$

and $n = N/\mathscr{V}$ is the average particle density.

To simplify the further approximations, we shall assume that the basic two-body interaction is what we have called a " Heisenberg-like " interaction:

$$u(\mathbf{R}, \Omega(\mathbf{R}); \mathbf{R}', \Omega(\mathbf{R}')) = -(8/3)K(\mathbf{R} - \mathbf{R}')(\cos^2 \Theta_{RR'} - \tfrac{1}{3}) \quad (4.18)$$

where $\Theta_{RR'}$ is the angle between $\Omega(\mathbf{R})$ and $\Omega(\mathbf{R}')$. This interaction is, of course, not the induced–dipole induced–dipole interaction, but it is invariant under rotations of orientation space and, with a proper choice of $K(\mathbf{R} - \mathbf{R}')$, it has all the properties of the induced–dipole induced–dipole interaction used by Maier and Saupe, and will give identical results in the molecular field approximation. There is no *a priori* reason for thinking that if the molecular field approximation is valid for the induced–dipole induced–dipole interaction, it won't work equally well on this interaction. Conversely, if the molecular field fails for the interaction (4.17), it should fail for the induced–dipole induced–dipole interaction.

Now we get a further bound on $Q_\mu{}^{(\theta,\phi)}$ if we avoid the difficulties associated with the functional integration over the functions $\phi(\mathbf{R})$ by making an approximation analogous to (4.5). Using a uniform weight for all functions $\phi(\mathbf{R})$, we get a lower bound to $Q_\mu{}^{(\theta,\phi)}$:

$$Q_\mu{}^{(\theta,\phi)} \geqslant Q_\mu{}^{(\theta)} \equiv \int \mathscr{D}[\theta]$$

$$\cdot \exp\left[-\tfrac{1}{2}\beta n^2 \int\int \mathrm{d}^3R\,\mathrm{d}^3R'\,\bar{u}(\mathbf{R},\theta(\mathbf{R});\,\mathbf{R}',\theta(\mathbf{R}'))f(\mathbf{R}-\mathbf{R}') \right],$$

$$(4.19)$$

where

$$\mathscr{D}[\theta] = \lim_{\mathcal{N}\to\infty} \int \cdots \int \prod_R (\tfrac{1}{2}\sin\theta_R\,\mathrm{d}\theta_R)$$

and

$$\bar{u}(\mathbf{R},\theta(\mathbf{R});\,\mathbf{R}',\theta(\mathbf{R}')) = \int \mathscr{D}[\phi]u(\mathbf{R},\Omega(\mathbf{R});\,\mathbf{R}',\Omega(\mathbf{R}')). \qquad (4.20)$$

Using the expansion

$$P_2(\cos\Theta)$$

$$= P_2(\cos\theta)P_2(\cos\theta') + \sum_{m=1}^{2} A_m P_2{}^m(\cos\theta)P_2{}^m(\cos\theta')\cos m(\phi-\phi'),$$

$$(4.21)$$

we find that

$$\bar{u}(\mathbf{R},\theta(\mathbf{R});\,\mathbf{R}',\theta(\mathbf{R}'))$$

$$= -4K(\mathbf{R}-\mathbf{R}')(\cos^2\theta(\mathbf{R}) - \tfrac{1}{3})(\cos^2\theta(\mathbf{R}') - \tfrac{1}{3}). \qquad (4.22)$$

From the point of view of bounds on the grand partition function, the bounds $Q_\mu{}^c Q_\mu{}^{(\theta,\phi)}$ and $Q_\mu{}^c Q_\mu{}^{(\theta)}$ are progressively poorer estimates of the exact grand partition function Q_μ. The orientational function $Q_\mu{}^{(\theta)}$ can be further approximated in two ways: On way leads to the approximate grand potential that Maier and Saupe would have found had they considered the interaction (4.18); the other way leads to the exactly soluble model investigated in Sections 2 and 3.

Let us first show that a certain lower bound on $Q_\mu{}^{(\theta)}$ (or upper bound on the corresponding grand potential $\varXi_\mu{}^{(\theta)}$) is equivalent to the molecular field approximation of Maier and Saupe. We start by formulating the most general molecular field approximation as a further application of the multidimensional version of (4.4). Specifically, we approximate the weight function

$$\exp\left[-2\beta n^2 \int\int \mathrm{d}^3R\,\mathrm{d}^3R'\,K(\mathbf{R}-\mathbf{R}')f(\mathbf{R}-\mathbf{R}') \right.$$

$$\left. \cdot (\cos^2\theta(\mathbf{R}) - \tfrac{1}{3})(\cos^2\theta(\mathbf{R}') - \tfrac{1}{3}) \right] \qquad (4.23)$$

in the functional integral over $\theta(\mathbf{R})$ by a factorized density

$$\rho[w(\theta)] = \exp\left[-\beta n \int d^3R w(\theta(\mathbf{R})) \right], \qquad (4.24)$$

i.e. the orientations $\theta(\mathbf{R})$ and $\theta(\mathbf{R}')$ are assumed independent for all pairs of points $\mathbf{R}$ and $\mathbf{R}'$ and we have used the translational symmetry in assuming that $w(\theta(\mathbf{R}))$ does not depend explicitly on $\mathbf{R}$. Then, using the generalization of (4.4) once again, we have an upper bound on the grand potential $\mathcal{Z}_\mu^{(\theta)}$:

$$\mathcal{Z}_\mu^{(\theta)} \equiv -kT \ln Q\mu^{(\theta)}$$

$$\leqslant \mathcal{Z}_\mu[w] + 2n^2 \iint d^3R\, d^3R'\, K(\mathbf{R} - \mathbf{R}')f(\mathbf{R} - \mathbf{R}')\langle\cos^2\theta(\mathbf{R}) - \tfrac{1}{3}\rangle_w$$

$$\cdot\langle\cos^2\theta(\mathbf{R}') - \tfrac{1}{3}\rangle_w \qquad (4.25)$$

where

$$\mathcal{Z}_\mu[w] = -kT \ln \int \mathcal{D}[\theta]\rho[w(\theta)] \qquad (4.26)$$

and

$$\langle\cos^2\theta(\mathbf{R}) - \tfrac{1}{3}\rangle_w = \frac{\int \mathcal{D}[\theta](\cos^2\theta(\mathbf{R}) - \tfrac{1}{3})\rho[w(\theta)]}{\int \mathcal{D}[\theta]\rho[w(\theta)]}$$

$$= \frac{\int d\theta \sin\theta(\cos^2\theta - \tfrac{1}{3})e^{-\beta w(\theta)}}{\int d\theta \sin\theta e^{-\beta w(\theta)}}. \qquad (4.27)$$

If we take the functional derivative of this bound with respect to the " effective potential " $w(\theta)$, we obtain a self-consistent equation for the best function, $w_{sc}(\theta)$:

$$w_{sc}(\theta(\mathbf{R}))$$

$$= \frac{4\int \mathcal{D}_R[\theta](\cos^2\theta(\mathbf{R}) - \tfrac{1}{3})\int d^3R\, K(\mathbf{R} - \mathbf{R}')f(\mathbf{R} - \mathbf{R}')(\cos^2\theta(\mathbf{R}') - \tfrac{1}{3})}{\int \mathcal{D}_R[\theta] \exp[-\beta\int d^3R''w_{sc}(\theta(\mathbf{R}''))]} ,$$

$$\qquad (4.28)$$

where $\int \mathcal{D}_R[\theta]$ denotes integration over all functions θ having a fixed value $\theta(\mathbf{R})$ at $\mathbf{R}$. Interchanging $\int d^3R'$ and $\int \mathcal{D}_R[\theta]$ in the numerator of (4.28), we have the simpler self-consistent equation for the molecular field:

$$w_{sc}(\theta(\mathbf{R})) = 4(\cos^2\theta(\mathbf{R}) - \tfrac{1}{3}) \int d^3R'\, K(\mathbf{R} - \mathbf{R}')f(\mathbf{R} - \mathbf{R}')\langle\cos^2\theta - \tfrac{1}{3}\rangle_{w_{sc}},$$

$$\qquad (4.29)$$

the theory of Maier and Saupe. When this best $w_{sc}(\theta)$: is substituted in (4.25), we have what we shall call $\Xi_\mu{}^{mf}$, an upper bound on $\Xi_\mu{}^{(\theta)}$, (" mf " for " molecular field " or " mean field ").

Before leaving the development of the Maier–Saupe theory for the interaction (4.18), we should comment on the role of rotational invariance. The approximation leading from $\Xi_\mu{}^{(\theta,\phi)}$ to $\Xi_\mu{}^{(\theta)}$ destroys the invariance of the problem under rotations in orientation space, but the subsequent molecular field approximation leading to $\Xi_\mu{}^{mf}$ effectively restores this invariance above the transition (the molecular field being zero). Thus while the molecular field approximation gives a still higher (hence worse) upper bound to the grand potential, it could be argued that $\Xi_\mu{}^{mf}$ is nevertheless better than $\Xi_\mu{}^{(\theta)}$ because it occurs in a rotationally invariant theory, i.e., although $\Xi_\mu{}^{mf}$ is worse than $\Xi_\mu{}^{(\theta)}$ in the sense of leading to a poorer variational estimate of $\Xi_\mu = -kT \ln Q_\mu$ for all T, its analytic properties as a function of T (existence and nature of a phase transition) could conceivably be better. This is a universal drawback of any variational approach, but it seems to us that the burden of proof lies with the method giving the poorer variational bound to the grand potential.

The alternative way to proceed from $\Xi_\mu{}^{(\theta)}$ leads to the model we have presented in Sections 2 and 3. What we have done there is to try to avoid the molecular field approximation in (4.18) by discretizing $\cos\theta$ and replacing the continuous 3-space by a lattice. The statistical mechanical problem remains non-trivial after these approximations, in contrast to what results from the molecular field approximation.

We have already discussed the effects of the discretization of $\cos\theta$. Similar comments apply to the discretization of 3-space: Since we know of no estimates of T_I for Ising models on a continuum, rather than a lattice, we can only repeat the observation that the molecular field approximation on the lattice predicts the first-order transition that an exact theory shows to be absent.

5. Conclusion

We have attempted to avoid the molecular field approximation that is fundamental to the Maier–Saupe theory, in order to see if the first-order phase transition is a consequence of the molecular field or is a real consequence of assumptions **A** and **B** stated in the Introduction.

We have constructed a model which we believe to be closely related but superior to the Maier–Saupe model. In this model, no first-order transition occurs. Since such a transition occurs in nature, the failure to predict it could arise from several sources:

(1) The discretizations of space and $\cos \theta$ could make our model inferior to the MS theory, but this seems unlikely in view of the fact that the molecular field approximation incorrectly predicts a first-order transition for our model.

(2) The averaging over ϕ could conceivably make the grand potential $\varXi_\mu^{(\theta)}$ have less accurate analytic properties than $\varXi_\mu^{\mathrm{mf}}$ even though, in magnitude, $\varXi_\mu^{(\theta)}$ is the better bound on the exact grand potential.

These two possibilities suggest the need for a more detailed study of the interaction $J_{ij}(\cos^2 \theta_{ij} - \frac{1}{3})$ on a lattice:—can it ever show no phase transition, as the present paper suggests?

Two other possible sources of the failure to predict a phase transition are these:

(3) The assumption of an interaction of the form (4.18). Consideration of interactions that depend on the direction of $\mathbf{R}_i - \mathbf{R}_j$ relative to Ω_i and Ω_j and which involve higher harmonics in Ω_i and Ω_j could conceivably restore the first-order transition, although we think it unlikely.

(4) The neglect of correlations of spatial positions with orientational interactions. This approximation, which underlies both the Maier–Saupe theory and the present model, seems to us the most serious approximation. It suggests that further work be specifically oriented toward studying the interplay of orientational and positional correlations.

Note Added in Proof

The model solved in Section 3 has also been solved by R. G. Priest in a paper that has just appeared, *Phys. Rev. Letters.* **26**, 423 (1971). Priest takes the point of view, in contrast to ours, that the persistence of the long-range order at high temperatures and the lack of a first-order transition invalidate this model as a qualitative guide to models with rotationally invariant interactions.

Acknowledgements

It is a pleasure to thank Dr. Marvin Freiser, for bringing this problem to my attention and for many elucidating conversations, and to thank Dr. Gordon Lasher, for some provocative comments on the significance of breaking rotational symmetry.

REFERENCES

1. Maier, W. and Saupe, A., Z. Naturforsch. **14A**, 882 (1959) and **15A**, 287 (1960).
2. We have also applied this model to the problem of solid orthohydrogen (unpublished) only to find that a similar analysis of solid orthohydrogen had been done independently by G. M. Bell and W. M. Fairbairn, *Mol. Phys.* **4**, 481 (1961) and A. Brooks Harris, *Sol. State Comm.* **6**, 149 (1968). In solid orthohydrogen, the two "discretization approximations" are very good, the system consisting essentially of three-level subsystems on a lattice.
3. The limiting procedures in the first of these properties are discussed by T. Schultz, D. Mattis and E. Lieb, *Revs. Mod. Phys.* **36**, 856 (1964). The second of these properties was proved by T. D. Lee and C. N. Yang, *Phys. Rev.* **87**, 410 (1952).
4. Domb, C. and Dalton, N. W., *Proc. Phys. Soc.* **89**, 859 (1966), Table 4 and Eq. 5.
5. We have neglected the contributions to the Helmholtz free energy of the kinetic energy and internal molecular degrees of freedom.
6. This inequality is readily proved. If we let

$$\rho(y)\, \mathrm{d}y \;=\; \int_{y<b(x)<y+\mathrm{d}y} \mathrm{d}x\, e^{a(x)} \Big/ \int \mathrm{d}x\, e^{a(x)}$$

$$\int \mathrm{d}x\, e^{a(x)+b(x)} \;=\; \int \mathrm{d}x\, e^{a(x)} \times \int \mathrm{d}b\, e^{b}\rho(b).$$

Expanding e^{b} around $\bar{b} \equiv \int \mathrm{d}b\, b\rho(b)$ to first order, and using the upward concavity of the exponential function,

$$e^{b} > e^{\bar{b}} + (b - \bar{b})e^{\bar{b}},$$

we obtain (4.4) when this lower bound to e^{b} is substituted in $\int \mathrm{d}b\, e^{b}\, \rho(b)$.
7. In some problems where the molecular field approximation is made, such as for short-range antiferromagnetic interactions, the molecular field that minimizes the free energy is a symmetry-breaking field. In the present case, where every particle interacts with every other particle with the same interaction, this cannot be so. To see this, consider the molecular fields seen by two different particles, say, the ith and j^{th}. Each of the two particles sees a field resulting from the average orientations of *all* the other particles. Even if we assume that the average orientations of these two particles are more than infinitesimally different, the fields that the two particles see are identical except for the negligible difference between $\bar{u}(\Omega_i, \langle\Omega_j\rangle)$ and $\bar{u}(\Omega_j, \langle\Omega_i\rangle)$. Thus the molecular field is the same for all particles, and hence so are the average orientations.

Successive Transitions in a Nematic Liquid†

M. J. FREISER

IBM Thomas J. Watson Research Center
Yorktown Heights,
New York 10598

Received October 19, 1970; *in revised form January* 11, 1971

Abstract—The general form of the energy of interaction between two asymmetric molecules is considered. This leads to a generalization of the Maier–Saupe model of a nematic liquid. The exact state of minimum internal energy of the system is found to be biaxial. In the molecular field approximation the consistency relations yield two distinct ordered states, a uniaxial state and a biaxial state. It is shown that with decreasing temperature the fluid will have two successive transitions according to the scheme: isotropic→ uniaxial order→biaxial order.

Introduction

The prevailing picture of a nematic liquid is that of an optically uniaxial fluid. The corresponding one-particle orientational distribution function is then axially symmetric. The structures of the individual molecules are far from possessing axial symmetry and are often lath-like.[1] It would therefore seem that nematic liquid might possess a biaxial state. Such a structure has been hypothesized by Williams[2] to account for his observations of optical activity in PAA. The ordered states of nematic liquid may therefore be richer in possible symmetries than had been imagined.

The fullest existing statistical mechanical theory of the nematic state, a molecular field treatment by Maier and Saupe,[3] gives a description of the uniaxial state. In their work the orientational interaction between two molecules is taken proportional to $P_2(\cos \theta)$ where θ is the angle between the long axes of the molecules, and P_2 is the Legendre polynomial of second degree. This is the form of the

† Presented at the Third International Liquid Conference in Berlin, August 24–28, 1970.

281

interaction between two axially symmetric quadrupoles. The states derived from this interaction necessarily have axial symmetry.

In the following we shall discuss the possible forms of the orientational interaction between two asymmetric molecules and shall then specialize it to the simplest generalization of the P_2 interaction, namely, a more general quadrupole–quadrupole type of coupling, which we then treat in the molecular field approximation. It will be shown that the orientational ground state is one in which all of the molecules have identical orientations, and is therefore biaxial. The clearpoint is nonetheless associated with a first-order transition between the isotropic state and a uniaxial state. At some temperature below the clearpoint the liquid, if it remains liquid, will undergo a second transition to the biaxial state.

The Orientational Interaction Energy

We shall assume that the orientational interaction energy of the liquid is a sum of pair-wise interactions among the molecules. We shall further assume that an effective pair interaction between the molecules can be obtained by averaging the energy of two molecules of fixed orientation over all directions of the intermolecular vector, $\mathbf{r}_{ij}$. This latter assumption, which is the same as that used by Maier and Saupe, is a severe limitation. One is treating the two-particle distribution function as if it were separable into a spherically symmetric radial part and an orientationally dependent part. This is transparently not true in the smectic type of order but is a more suitable approximation for nematic and cholesteric states and should give qualitatively reasonable results.

No assumption will be made concerning the physical origin of the inter-molecular potential. Whether the liquid crystal state arises because of the hard-core repulsive forces or the longer range dispersion forces is a matter of indifference in the following since it is only the angular form of the interaction that will play a role.†

---

† Maier and Saupe[3] derived the orientational interaction from the lowest order dispersion force. Their intermolecular potential therefore has a v^{-2} dependence where v is the specific volume. This, however, cannot be taken literally. For a first-order transition one can derive the thermodynamic relation

$$(\mathrm{d}/\mathrm{d}T_k)\ln v = \alpha - \beta\, \mathrm{d}p/\mathrm{d}T$$

We shall expand the intermolecular potential in a complete set of functions of the Euler angles which specify the orientations of the molecules with respect to a fixed set of axes, and functions of the direction of the vector joining the centers of gravity of the two molecules, $\mathbf{r}_{ij}$. This expansion introduces coefficients which are, in their transformation properties under rotation, analogs of the multipole moments of a charge distribution. They are parameters that characterize the molecule. When referred to a coordinate system fixed in the molecule, they are constant parameters, the same for all molecules in the system. When referred to a coordinate system fixed in space, they depend on the orientation of the molecule. In a spherical representation these quasi-multipole moments will be denoted by $Q_{lm}(\alpha, \beta, \gamma)$ where α, β, γ are the Euler angles of the rotation that carries the space-fixed axes into the molecular axes.[5] In a cartesian representation the parameters are denoted $Q_{ij \ldots k}(\alpha, \beta, \gamma)$ where $i, j, \cdots k$ take the values 1, 2, 3 (or x, y, z). The Q_{lm} transform under rotations of the molecule just as do the spherical harmonics. Thus if Q_{lm}, without specification of an angular argument, denotes the parameters referred to axes fixed in the molecule, then:

$$Q_{lm}(\alpha, \beta, \gamma) = \sum_{m'} D^{(l)}_{m'm}(\alpha, \beta, \gamma)\, Q_{lm'}. \tag{1}$$

The $D^{(l)}_{m'm}$ are the elements of the representations of the rotation group. Their properties are discussed in Ref. 5, and are briefly summarized in the Appendix.

The most general orientational interaction between molecules i and j is:

$$\sum_{l_1 l_2 l_3} a_{l_1 l_2 l_3} \sum_{m_1 m_2 m_3} \begin{pmatrix} l_1 l_2 l_3 \\ m_1 m_2 m_3 \end{pmatrix} Q_{l_1 m_1}(\alpha_i, \beta_i, \gamma_i)\, Q_{l_2 m_2}(\alpha_j, \beta_j, \gamma_j)\, Y_{l_3 m_3}(\theta, \phi), \tag{2}$$

where θ, ϕ are the polar and azimuthal angles of $\mathbf{r}_{ij}$, and the first factor in the sum on m_1, m_2, m_3 is a 3j-symbol. The coefficients

where T_k is the transition temperature, dp/dT is the slope of the coexistence curve, and α, β, v are respectively the limiting values of the thermal expansion coefficient, the isothermal compressibility and the specific volume of one of the two phases at the transition. If the interaction has the form $v^{-n} f(\theta_{ij})$, then $(d/dT_k) \ln v = -1/nT_k$. Available data for PAA yield a value of n $\approx$ 13 (see Ref. 4).

$a_{l_1 l_2 l_3}$ are functions of the magnitude $\mathbf{r}_{ij}$. The transformation properties of the Q_{lm} and Y_{lm} ensure that such a sum is invariant to rotations of the spatial frame of reference. Dipole–dipole forces are given by terms with $(l_1, l_2, l_3) = (1, 1, 2)$, whereas induced dipole-induced dipole dispersion forces (as well as quadrupole–quadrupole forces) are given by a combination of terms with $l_1 = 2$, $l_2 = 2$, and $l_3 = 0, 2, 4$. Terms with odd values of l_1 and l_2 would rigorously be zero for centrosymmetric molecules. Such odd-parity terms can occur in the cholesteric state, and if Williams's[2] hypothesis is correct they may also be present in PAA.

If Eq. (2) is averaged over all orientations of $\mathbf{r}_{ij}$, then all terms vanish except those with $l_3 = m_3 = 0$. The $3j$-symbols in the surviving terms of the sum are:

$$\begin{pmatrix} l_1 l_2 & 0 \\ m_1 m_2 & 0 \end{pmatrix} = \delta_{l_1 l_2} \, \delta_{m_1 m_2} (-1)^{l_1 - m_1} \, (2l_1 + 1)^{-1/2}, \tag{3}$$

and so Eq. (2) becomes:

$$\sum_l a_l \sum_m (-1)^{-m} \, Q_{lm}(\alpha_i, \beta_i, \gamma_i) \, Q_{l-m}(\alpha_j, \beta_j, \gamma_j). \tag{4}$$

This is the effective orientational interaction between two molecules in the fluid. With the use of Eq. (1) this can be written:

$$\sum_l a_l \sum_{mm'm''} (-1)^m \, D_{m'm}^{(l)}(R_i) \, D_{m''-m}^{(l)}(R_j) \, Q_{lm'} \, Q_{lm''}, \tag{5}$$

where R has been used to denote the rotation (α, β, γ) that carries the space axes into the molecular axes. An alternative form of Eq. (5) is:

$$\sum_l a_l \sum_{m'm''} (-1)^{m'} \, D_{m''-m'}^{(l)}(R_{ij}) \, Q_{lm'} \, Q_{lm''}, \tag{6}$$

where $R_{ij} = R_i R_j^{-1}$. This form makes explicit the fact that the energy depends only on the relative orientations of the two molecules, and hence is clearly invariant to rotations of the space axes.

Which terms in Eq. (6) will play a significant role in nematic liquids? It is plausible that terms will decrease in importance with increasing l if only because orientational oscillations will tend to wash out terms of higher values of l. Thus we will restrict our attention to the first few terms in Eq. (6). Furthermore, since nematic liquids do exist which are made up of centrosymmetric molecules,[1] the odd-parity terms do not play an essential role in the existence of the nematic state. We shall therefore restrict attention to terms with $l = 2$ and, indeed, the qualitative success of the Maier–Saupe theory does indicate that these are the most important terms. Terms with $l = 1$ can be introduced as a perturbation in order to obtain the kind of state pictured by Williams or a cholesteric state. We shall therefore assume an effective interaction energy between molecules i and j given by:

$$w_{ij} = - \sum_{mm'm''} (-1)^m D^{(2)}_{m'm}(R_i) \, D^{(2)}_{m''m}(R_j) \, Q_{2m'} \, Q_{2m''}. \qquad (7)$$

The sign has been chosen so as to yield a stable state of parallel orientation, as will be seen shortly.

Nothing has been said thus far about the range of the interaction. If our assumed interaction is the anisotropic part of the London interaction, then it falls off at least as fast as $1/r^6$ at large separations. The repulsive forces are of much shorter range. The material is, however, a liquid and the diffusion of the molecules through the liquid will increase the effective range of the interaction. Each molecule will then have the same interaction with a large number of other molecules. For each molecule, therefore, we shall take Eq. (7) as its interaction with each of z neighbors, z being an effective co-ordination number in the liquid. We shall, for convenience, drop the index $l = 2$ henceforth.

For axially symmetric molecules, the interaction (7) reduces to the P_2 interaction of Maier and Saupe. With such symmetry the only nonzero quadrupole tensor component is Q_{20} (denoted simply Q_0 in the following), so that:

$$Q_m = Q_0 \, \delta_{m0}. \qquad (8)$$

Then, with

$$D^{(2)}_{0m}(\alpha, \beta, \gamma) = (4\pi/2l+1)^{1/2} \, Y_{2m}(\beta, \gamma), \qquad (9)$$

we find:

$$w_{ij} = - (4\pi/2l+1) \, Q_0^2 \sum_m (-1)^m \, Y_{2m}(\beta_i, \gamma_i) \, Y_{2-m}(\beta_j, \gamma_j)$$
$$= - Q_0^2 \, P_2(\cos \beta_{ij}) \qquad (10)$$

from the addition theorem for spherical harmonics. (Alternatively (6) can be used to get the same result.)

In a cartesian representation Eq. (7) is:

$$w_{ij} = - \text{Trace} \, (\mathbf{R}^{-1} \, \mathbf{QRQ}) \qquad (11)$$

where $\mathbf{R}$ is the orthogonal matrix for the rotation of the axes of molecule i into those of molecule j, and $\mathbf{Q}$ is the quasi-quadrupole tensor. Its components form a real symmetric matrix with zero trace. Thus, one can choose the molecular axes so that $\mathbf{Q}$ is diagonal. These diagonal elements are real and their sum is zero, and so only two can be independent. In terms of the spherical components of the tensor, this means that $Q_{\pm 1} = 0$ and $Q_{+2} = Q_{-2}$ is real. We shall choose as the molecular z-axis that axis for which the magnitude of the corresponding diagonal element of $\mathbf{Q}$ is largest. The relation between the spherical and cartesian representation of $\mathbf{Q}$ is given by:

$$Q_{xx} = -(2/3)^{1/2} Q_0 + 2Q_2, \qquad Q_{yy} = -(2/3)^{1/2} Q_0 - 2Q_2,$$
$$Q_{zz} = 2(2/3)^{1/2} Q_0. \tag{12}$$

We shall in the following denote these spherical components by:

$$Q_0 = Q, \qquad Q_2 = q. \tag{13}$$

Our choice of the molecular z-axis means that:

$$|Q| \geqslant 6^{1/2} |q|. \tag{14}$$

For a molecular orientation R relative to the space axes, each $Q_m(R)$ is a two-parameter linear combination of the $D_{m'm}(R)$. Thus, from Eq. (1) and the symmetry properties of the D's given in the Appendix:

$$Q_2(R) = Q\, D_{02}(R) + q[D_{22}(R) + D_{-22}(R)]$$
$$= Q^*_{-2}(R). \tag{15a}$$
$$Q_0(R) = Q\, D_{00}(R) + q[D_{20}(R) + D_{-20}(R)]$$
$$= Q^*_0(R). \tag{15b}$$

The State of Minimum Orientational Energy

The state of minimum orientational energy for the assumed inter-action is easily obtained through the use of the form in Eq. (11). The Schwartz inequality yields immediately

$$|w_{ij}|^2 \leqslant [\mathrm{Tr}\,(R^{-1}\,QR)^2]\,[\mathrm{Tr}\,Q^2]$$

with equality holding when R is the identity. The invariance of the trace to a similarity transformation then yields:

$$|w_{ij}|^2 \leqslant [\mathrm{Tr}\,Q^2]^2. \tag{16}$$

Thus $|w_{ij}|$ attains its absolute maximum when the molecules have identical orientations, and w_{ij} then attains its absolute minimum value. The state of minimum energy of this system is therefore optically biaxial.

Molecular Field Approximation

We assume an orientational distribution function,

$$f(R) = f(\alpha, \beta, \gamma), \tag{17}$$

where

$$\int dR\, f(R) = \int_0^{2\pi} d\alpha \int_0^\pi d\beta \sin\beta \int_0^{2\pi} d\gamma\, f(\alpha, \beta, \gamma) = 1. \tag{18}$$

The expectation value of any function of α, β, γ will be denoted by a bar, as for example:

$$\bar{D}_{m'm} = \int dR\, D_{m'm}(R)\, f(R), \tag{19}$$

$$\bar{Q}_m = \int dR\, Q_m(R)\, f(R)$$

$$= \sum_{m'} \bar{D}_{m'm}\, Q_{m'}. \tag{20}$$

It is readily seen that the barred quantities obey the relations:

$$\bar{D}_{-m'-m} = (-1)^{m'+m}\, \bar{D}^*_{m'm}, \tag{21a}$$

$$\bar{Q}_{-m} = (-1)^m\, \bar{Q}^*_m. \tag{21b}$$

The energy of interaction of a molecule with its z neighbors, averaged over the orientations of the neighbors, is then:

$$\bar{W}_i(R_i) = -z \sum_{mm'm''} (-1)^m\, D_{m'm}(R_i)\, \bar{D}_{m''-m}\, Q_{m'}\, Q_{m''}, \tag{22a}$$

$$= -z \sum_{mm'} (-1)^m\, D_{m'm}(R_i)\, \bar{Q}_{-m}\, Q_{m'}. \tag{22b}$$

The orientational distribution function, in the molecular field approximation, is then:

$$f(R) = \frac{1}{Z} \cdot \exp\{-\beta\, \bar{W}_i(R)\}, \tag{23}$$

where:

$$Z = \int dR\, \exp\{-\beta\, \bar{W}_i(R)\}. \tag{24}$$

The self-consistency of the approximation is assured by the requirement that the $\bar{Q}_m$ satisfy:

$$\bar{Q}_m = \frac{1}{Z} \sum_{m'} Q_{m'} \int dR \, D_{m'm}{}^{(R)} \exp\left\{\beta z \sum_{n'n} (-1)^n \, D_{n'n}(R) \, \bar{Q}_{-n} \, Q_{n'}\right\}. \quad (25)$$

The self-consistency condition can also be written as:

$$\bar{Q}_m = \frac{1}{\beta z} (-1)^m \frac{\partial}{\partial \bar{Q}_{-m}} \ln Z. \quad (26)$$

There may, in general, be more than one solution of Eq. (25). The physically stable solution is the one that minimizes the free energy. With the assumed distribution function, the internal energy and the entropy are, respectively:

$$U = -\frac{Nz}{2} \sum_m (-1)^m \, \bar{Q}_{-m} \, \bar{Q}_m, \quad (27)$$

$$S = -Nk \int dR \, f(R) \ln f(R)$$
$$= -Nk \, \beta z \sum_m (-1)^m \, \bar{Q}_{-m} \, \bar{Q}_n + Nk \ln Z, \quad (28)$$

so that the free energy per molecule is:

$$F/N = +\frac{z}{2} \sum_m (-1)^m \, \bar{Q}_{-m} \, \bar{Q}_m - \frac{1}{\beta} \ln Z. \quad (29)$$

It can be seen that the consistency equations (26) are the conditions for the free energy to be an extremum with respect to the order parameters, $\bar{Q}_m$.

Because we have chosen to work within a spherical representation, one feature of the consistency conditions (25) is obscured, that is, that every solution, by means of an appropriate choice of the laboratory frame of reference, will have the form:

$$\bar{Q}_{\pm 1} = 0; \qquad \bar{Q}_0, \ \bar{Q}_{+2} = \bar{Q}_{-2}, \text{ real.} \quad (30)$$

Had we worked with a cartesian representation, it would have been evident that $\bar{\mathbf{Q}}$ for any solution would be a real, symmetric matrix, hence diagonalizable by proper choice of the frame of reference. If it is then expressed in spherical representation, its components would obey (30). In seeking solutions of (25), we can therefore limit ourselves to those satisfying (30). Therefore all indices m, m', etc., in the consistency equation can be taken to assume even values only.

On the Solutions of the Consistency Conditions

In this section we shall show that with decreasing temperature the system undergoes a first-order transition to a state possessing axial symmetry. At some lower temperature, however, another ordered state will arise having a lower symmetry, consistent with the biaxial symmetry of the ground state.

We first note that (25) will, at all temperatures, admit the trivial solution, corresponding to the isotropic state,

$$\bar{Q}_m = 0. \tag{31}$$

For this isotropic state,

$$Z_I = 8\pi^2. \tag{32}$$

$$(F/N)_I = -\frac{1}{\beta} \ln 8\pi^2. \tag{33}$$

We next consider the existence of an axially symmetric solution of (25), that is, a solution of the form:

$$\bar{Q}_m = \delta_{m0}\, \bar{Q}_0. \tag{34}$$

With this assumption (25) becomes:

$$\delta_{m0}\, \bar{Q}_0 = \frac{1}{Z} \sum_{m'} Q_{m'} \int dR\, D_{m'm}(R) \exp\left\{ \beta z \bar{Q}_0 \sum_{n'} D_{n'0}(R)\, Q_{n'} \right\}. \tag{35}$$

The exponential is then a function of the Euler angles α, β, but not of γ. Hence the integration over γ in (33) yields zero unless the $D_{m'm}(R)$ factor is also independent of γ, that is, $m = 0$. The equation then reduces to that of Maier and Saupe for axially symmetric molecules, and a self-consistent solution exists.

In order to see what changes are introduced by the more general interaction, we first sketch the results of the Maier–Saupe theory. Figure 1 shows the free energy as a function of the order parameter $S = \bar{Q}_0/Q$. (In the case of nematic liquids we are concerned only with positive values of S). Above a temperature T^*, the only extremum occurs at the origin, $S = 0$. When $T \leqslant T^*$ a pair of extrema at finite values of S develop in the curve, coalescing when $T = T^*$. The local minimum is unstable relative to the isotropic state until $T = T_k$. For $T < T_k$ the local minimum becomes the

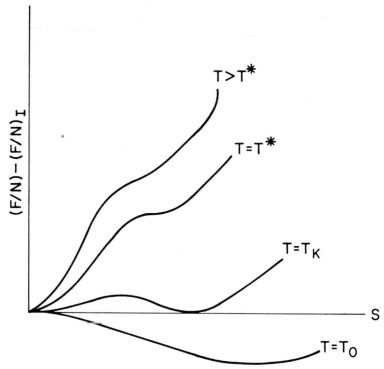

Figure 1.   Free energy in the Maier–Saupe theory as a function of the order parameter S at the clearpoint, T_K, and at temperatures above and below T_K.

stable solution.   At a still lower temperature, T_0, the local maximum coalesces with the extremum at the origin.   The values S_k and T_k/T_0 are independent of the strength of the interaction and are consequences of its form alone.   Maier and Saupe obtain the accurate values:

$$T_k/T_0 = 1.101, \qquad S_k = .4292. \tag{36}$$

In the axially symmetric case there is only a single angular variable and in fact the integral in the expression for Z can be evaluated in terms of a tabulated function, Dawson's integral.[6] Here we shall rely on an expansion of the integrand, which does not seem encouraging in view of the fact that the order parameter at the transition has so large a value.   In order to gauge the feasibility of using such an expression, we consider the axially symmetric case.

With $q = 0$, $\bar{Q}_{\pm 2} = 0$, and the free energy given by (29), we obtain:

$$\Delta(F/N) = F/N - (F/N)_I$$

$$= \frac{1}{\beta}\left\{\left(\frac{1}{2\beta z Q^2} - \frac{1}{10}\right)(\beta z Q^2 S)^2 - \frac{1}{105}(\beta z Q^2 S)^3\right.$$

$$\left. + \frac{1}{700}(\beta z Q^2 S)^4 + \frac{1}{1925}(\beta z Q^2 S)^5 + \cdots\right\}. \qquad (37)$$

If only the first two terms are retained, one gets a second-order transition at a temperature T_0 given by:

$$\frac{1}{\beta_0 z Q^2} = \frac{kT_0}{zQ^2} = \frac{1}{5}. \qquad (38)$$

With retention of the fourth degree term there is a first-order transition (determined by $\Delta(F/N) = 0$ and $\partial(\Delta F/N)/\partial S = 0$) at a temperature T_k, with order parameter S_k where:

$$\frac{T_k}{T_0} = 1.16, \qquad S_k = .77, \qquad (39)$$

which do not compare well with (36). If terms through S^5 are kept, then for the first-order transition one obtains:

$$\frac{T'_k}{T'_0} = 1.095, \qquad S_k = .377, \qquad (40)$$

in fair agreement with (36). We therefore expect that terms up to fifth degree in the order parameter are adequate for obtaining the essential results of a more detailed calculation of the molecular field free energy.

Returning to the more general case expressed by (22) and (24), by expansion one obtains:

$$Z = \int dr \left\{1 + \beta z \sum_{mm'}(-1)^m D_{m'm}(R) \bar{Q}_{-m} Q_{m'}\right.$$

$$\left. + \cdots + \frac{1}{n!}(\beta z)^n \left[\sum_{mm'}(-1)^m D_{m'm}(R) \bar{Q}_{-m} Q_{m'}\right]^n + \cdots\right\}. \qquad (41)$$

The first few terms in (41) are easily evaluated with the use of

$$\int dR = 8\pi^2 \qquad (42a)$$

$$\int dR\, D_{m'm}(R) = 0, \qquad (42b)$$

$$\int dR\, D_{m'_1 m_1}(R)\, D_{m'_2 m_2}(R) = \frac{8\pi^2}{5}\, \delta_{m_1,m_2}\, \delta_{m'_1,-m'_2}(-1)^{m_1+m'_1} \qquad (42c)$$

so that:

$$Z = 8\pi^2 \left\{ 1 + \frac{(\beta z)^2}{10} \left(\sum_m (-1)^m\, Q_{-m}\, Q_m \right) \left(\sum_m (-1)^m\, \bar{Q}_{-m}\, \bar{Q}_m \right) + \cdots \right\}. \qquad (43)$$

We note that the second degree term is the product of a rotationally invariant function of the Q_m and the same rotationally invariant function of the $\bar{Q}_m$, with a numerical coefficient. A simple physical argument proves that every term in the expansion (41) must have such a structure. Since there are no external fields in the problem, the laboratory axes, with respect to which the $\bar{Q}_m$ are defined, can be chosen freely. Similarly the molecular axes can be freely chosen. (We had earlier made a specific choice for the sake of algebraic simplicity, but (41) is quite general and in no way dependent on that choice.) The free energy, and therefore Z, must consequently be invariant to rotations of the laboratory axes as well as to rotations of the molecular axes. Thus Z must be a sum of products of invariants. Furthermore, the symmetry of (41) with respect to Q_m and $\bar{Q}_m$ means that each term is a product of the same invariant for the $\bar{Q}_m$ as for the Q_m. (The result can be obtained by a more formal mathematical argument based on the transformation properties of the Q_m, $\bar{Q}_m$, and $D_{m'm}$.) Thus the general term in (41) has the form:

$$\frac{1}{n!}\,(\beta z)^n \sum_p c_p^{(n)}\, F_p^{(n)}(Q_m)\, F_p^{(n)}(\bar{Q}_m), \qquad (44)$$

where $F_p^{(n)}$ is a rotationally invariant function of nth degree and $c_p^{(n)}$ is a numerical coefficient. For $n \geq 6$ there will be more than one invariant, and so the index p is necessary for the general term.

Now all of the invariants of a second rank spherical tensor can be decomposed into a product of powers of two fundamental invariants, namely:

$$F_\alpha(Q_m) = \sum_{m_1 m_2} \left(\begin{smallmatrix} 2 & 2 & 0 \\ m_1 & m_2 & 0 \end{smallmatrix} \right) Q_{m_1}\, Q_{m_2}, \qquad (45a)$$

$$F_\beta(Q_m) = \sum_{m_1 m_2 m_3} \left(\begin{smallmatrix} 2 & 2 & 2 \\ m_1 & m_2 & m_3 \end{smallmatrix} \right) Q_{m_1}\, Q_{m_2}\, Q_{m_3}. \qquad (45b)$$

In a cartesian representation these are proportional to the trace of the square of $\mathbf{Q}$ and the determinant of $\mathbf{Q}$, respectively.[7] In the case of interest, with the axes chosen so as to make $Q_{\pm 1} = 0$, these are:

$$F_\alpha(Q_m) = \frac{1}{\sqrt{5}}\,(Q^2 + 2q^2), \tag{46a}$$

$$F_\beta(Q_m) = -\sqrt{\frac{2}{35}}\,Q\,(Q^2 - 6q^2). \tag{46b}$$

It is clear now that there is just one invariant of $\mathbf{Q}$ of degree 2, 3, 4, and 5, namely, F_α, F_β, F_α^2, $F_\alpha F_\beta$, respectively. There are however two independent invariants of degree 6, F_α^3 and F_β^2. So long as there is only one invariant, the coefficient in (44) can be found easily. These coefficients are independent of the Q_m and $\bar{Q}_m$. Consequently, if we put q and $\bar{Q}_2$ equal to zero, thereby reducing the problem to that of Maier and Saupe, then the c_p can be found by comparison of (44) with the corresponding terms in the easily evaluated expansion of:

$$\int dR \exp\left[\beta z\, Q\, \bar{Q}_0\, P_2(\cos\theta)\right]. \tag{47}$$

Thus, the terms up to the fifth degree in the expansion of the free energy in the present case can be obtained from the expansion (37) which gives:

$$\begin{aligned}
\Delta(F/N) = \frac{1}{\beta}\Big\{&\big[(2\beta z(Q^2+2q^2)^{-1} - 1/10\big](\beta z)^2(Q^2+2q^2)(\bar{Q}_0^2+2\bar{Q}_2^2) \\
&- (1/105)(\beta z)^3 Q(Q^2-6q^2)\bar{Q}_0(\bar{Q}_0^2-6\bar{Q}_2^2) \\
&+ (1/700)(\beta z)^4(Q^2+2q^2)^2(\bar{Q}_0^2+2\bar{Q}_2^2)^2 \\
&+ (1/1925)(\beta z)^5 Q(Q^2-6q^2)(Q^2+6q^2)\cdot\bar{Q}_0(\bar{Q}_0^2-6\bar{Q}_2^2) \\
&\qquad\qquad\qquad\qquad\qquad\qquad \cdot(\bar{Q}_0^2+2\bar{Q}_2^2)\cdots\Big\}.
\end{aligned} \tag{48}$$

To determine where the free energy has its minimum, it is convenient to introduce polar coordinates in the parameter space of $\bar{Q}_0$, $\bar{Q}_2$. Thus we put:

$$\bar{Q}_0 = r\cos\theta, \qquad \bar{Q}_2 = 2^{-1/2}\,r\sin\theta$$
$$\bar{Q}_0^2 + 2\bar{Q}_2^2 = r^2, \qquad \bar{Q}_0(\bar{Q}_0^2 - 6\bar{Q}_2^2) = r^3\cos 3\,\theta. \tag{49}$$

and also:

$$Q = R\cos\Theta, \qquad q = 2^{-1/2}\,R\sin\Theta$$
$$Q^2 + 2q^2 = R^2, \qquad Q(Q^2 - 6q^2) = R^3\cos 3\,\Theta. \tag{50}$$

Equation (48) then becomes:

$$\Delta(F/N) = \frac{1}{\beta} \{[(2\beta z R^2)^{-1} - 1/10](\beta z R r)^2 + (\beta z R r)^4/700$$

$$- (\beta z R r)^3 [55/3 - (\beta z R r)^2] \cos 3\,\Theta \cos 3\,\theta (1/7 \cdot 11 \cdot 25)$$

$$+ \cdots\}. \tag{51}$$

We can, without loss of generality, assume Q and q positive. Then condition (14) implies that $-\pi/6 \leqslant \Theta \leqslant \pi/6$. The spatial frame of reference can be chosen so that $\bar{Q}_0$ and $\bar{Q}_2$ satisfy condition (14), that is $|\bar{Q}_0| \geqslant 6^{1/2} |\bar{Q}_2|$. There are then two physically distinct regions for θ, namely $-\pi/6 \leqslant \theta \leqslant \pi/6$ and $5\pi/6 \leqslant \theta \leqslant 7\pi/6$. The second region, with $\bar{Q}_0 = 0$, corresponds to a state in which the molecular z-axes lie in the spatial x, y-plane. In the axially symmetric case of Maier and Saupe such a state is never stable relative to the isotropic state. This is also true for the free energy given by Eq. (51), at least for values of the order parameter for which the approximation is valid. We need consider, therefore, only the first region in order to discuss the transition from the isotropic state to an ordered state.

Since the ground state of the system is a biaxial state, there appear to be two possibilities: (1) with decreasing temperature the system makes a transition directly from the isotropic to the biaxial state; (2) the system first undergoes a transition to the uniaxial state and then at lower temperature will make the transition to the biaxial state. Examination of Eq. (51) shows that this depends on the sign of $[55/3 - (\beta z R r)^2]$. If this quantity is positive for given values of $1/kT$ and r, then the free energy as a function of θ has its minimum at $\theta = 0$; if it is negative, then the minimum of the free energy occurs for $\theta \neq 0$. Now, at the Maier–Saupe clearpoint, we have from Eq. (36), in our notation,

$$\frac{\beta_0 z R^2}{\beta_K z R^2} = \frac{T_K}{T_0} = 1.101, \quad \frac{r_K}{R} = S_K = .4292.$$

Then

$$[55/3 - (\beta_K z r_K R)^2] = [55/3 - 25(T_0/T_K)S_K] = 6.31 > 0,$$

and the system will therefore go from the isotropic to the uniaxial state. The transition is of first order and, since $\bar{Q}_2$ remains zero and q plays no role, the transition is identical with that of the Maier–Saupe theory.

As the temperature is lowered further, the free energy minimum as a function of r moves out to higher values of r and becomes deeper, as is indicated in Fig. 1. As a function of θ, however, the free energy minimum becomes shallower with increasing r and β, and eventually $\theta = 0$ becomes a maximum with respect to θ with minima developing at either side of the $\theta = 0$ axis, as shown schematically in Fig. 2. This change in the curvature of the free energy surface occurs as the coefficient of $\cos 3\,\theta$ in Eq. (51) becomes less positive, and eventually becomes negative. When the curvature changes sign, that is when the point for the minimum free energy of the uniaxial state becomes a saddle point, there then occurs a second order transition to the biaxial state which has the symmetry of the ground state.

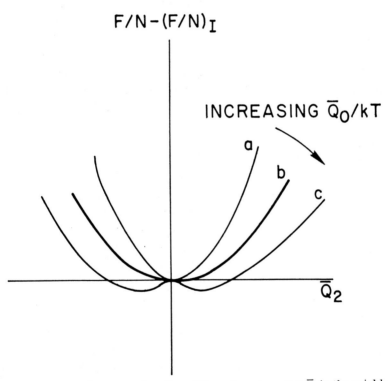

Figure 2.   Free energy as a function of the order parameter $\overline{Q}_2$ in the neighborhood of the free energy minimum for the uniaxial state.   Curve b shows the cross-section of the surface at the temperature at which a second order transition from the uniaxial to the biaxial state occurs; curves a and c show the sections at somewhat higher and lower temperatures, respectively.

There is an alternative possibility. At some temperature between T_K and the temperature at which the free energy develops a saddle point at the uniaxial state, there may develop a minimum off the $\theta = 0$ axis, that is, for finite values of $\bar{Q}_2$. There would then occur a first order transition to the biaxial state. The expansion yielding Eq. (51) is inadequate to rule out this possibility.

Discussion

We have shown that by allowing an interaction of more general angular form than that employed by Maier and Saupe, and which is consistent with the pronounced asymmetric form of nematogenic molecules, the application of the molecular field approximation yields a prediction of a sequence of transitions according to the scheme isotropic → uniaxial order → biaxial order. It is possible that the onset of crystallization, or of a smectic phase, would preclude the observation of the second transition in many nematic materials. If such a transition does occur, it should be manifested in the specific heat and in the optical properties of the material. We shall discuss the available evidence on these two points for PAA.

In PAA, which has a nematic range of 116–135 °C, an anomaly in the specific heat has been observed at 128 °C which may be associated with the symmetry change that we predict.[8-10] The anomaly is quite small but the authors of Reference 9 remark, " The portion of the nematic specific heat between 128° and 134.4° appears to be reproducible and stable." They go on to say of this anomaly that, " The only other evidence for existence other than the present work is given by Martin and Müller. Arnold observed a change in his values but discounted the data. Since this minor anomaly has been observed by at least three independent workers, it is apparently not a calorimetric artifact." They also note that no such anomaly was apparent in specific volume, viscosity, and surface tension measurements.

A particular difficulty arising in the optical observation of a biaxial phase is due to surface forces. If a thin film of nematic liquid is placed between solid substrates, the " accidental " orientation of the molecules on wetting the substrates could produce a mixture of small biaxial domains having only a single principal axis in common. With ordinary microscope resolution such a poly-crystalline sample would appear to be uniaxial. In Williams's[2] observations an attempt was made to avoid such effects. In his case one surface of the film was free and the other surface was in contact with a substrate which had been treated so as to minimize surface interactions. Williams interpreted his observations in terms of a biaxial structure but he did not remark on any abrupt change at 128 °C, the temperature at which the specific heat anomaly was seen to occur. It has been proposed[11] that deformation of the free surface accompanied by orientational distortion below the surface was responsible for the effects seen by Williams. However, Williams's published curve of optical rotary power vs wavelength of the light shows a $1/\lambda^2$ dependence which is consistent with a molecular mech-anism and the kind of structure proposed by Williams. The signifi-cance of Williams's experiment would therefore appear to be open to question.

Appendix

Some properties of the $D^{(l)}_{m'm}(\alpha, \beta, \gamma)$ (Taken from Ref. 5.).

The matrices $D^{(l)}(R) = D^{(l)}(\alpha, \beta, \gamma)$, with elements $D^{(l)}_{m'm}(R)$, form an irreducible representation of the rotation group in three dimen-sions. The matrix elements obey the following symmetry relations:

$$D^{(l)}_{m'm}(\alpha, \beta, \gamma) = D^{(l)}_{mm'}(-\gamma, -\beta, -\alpha)^*, \tag{A.1}$$

$$D^{(l)*}_{m'm}(\alpha, \beta, \gamma) = (-1)^{m'-m} D^{(l)}_{-m'-m}(\alpha, \beta, \gamma), \tag{A.2}$$

$$D^{(l)}_{m'm}(\alpha, \beta, \gamma) = (-1)^{l+m'} D^{(l)}_{-m'm}(-\alpha, \beta+\pi, \gamma). \tag{A.3}$$

Since $-\gamma, -\beta, -\alpha$ are the Euler angles of the rotation inverse to $R(\alpha, \beta, \gamma)$, Eq. (A.1) is merely a statement of the unitary property of $D^{(l)}(R)$. The group property of the $D^{(l)}(R)$ means that:

$$D^{(l)}_{m'm}(RS) = \sum_{m''} D^{(l)}_{m'm''}(R) D^{(l)}_{m''m}(S). \tag{A.4}$$

The central row and column of $D^{(l)}(R)$ has a particularly simple form, that is:

$$D^{(l)}_{m0}(\alpha, \beta, \gamma) = (-1)^m (4\pi/2l+1)^{1/2} Y_{lm}(\beta, \alpha), \tag{A.5}$$

$$D^{(l)}_{0m}(\alpha, \beta, \gamma) = (4\pi/2l+1)^{1/2} Y_{lm}(\beta, \gamma). \tag{A.6}$$

REFERENCES

1. Gray, G. W., *Molecular Structure and Properties of Liquid Crystals* (Academic Press, New York, 1962).
2. Williams, R., *J. Chem. Phys.* **50**, 1324 (1969).
3. Maier, W. and Saupe, A., *Z. Naturforsch.* **13a**, 564 (1958); **14a**, 882 (1959); **15a**, 287 (1960).
4. Alben, R., *Mol. Cryst. and Liq. Cryst.* **10**, 21 (1970).
5. Edmonds, A. R., *Angular Momentum in Quantum Mechanics* (Princeton University Press, Princeton, N. J., 1957). We shall follow this book in the definition of the Euler angles, the conventions with regard to phase of the spherical harmonics, and representations of the rotation group.
6. Abramowitz, M. and Stegun, F. A., Eds., *Handbook of Mathematical Functions* (National Bureau of Standards Applied Mathematics Series, Washington, D.C., 1964), No. 55.
7. Since any invariant of **Q** must be a symmetric function of the eigenvalues of **Q**, the statement that all of the invariants are expressible in terms of two fundamental ones (the trace of **Q** being zero) is an application of the fundamental theorem on symmetric polynomials. See, for example, S. Borofsky, "Elementary Theory of Equations," (The MacMillan Company, New York, 1950) p. 182.
8. Martin, H. and Muller, F. H., *Kolloid-Z.* **187**, 107 (1963).
9. Arnold, H., *Z. Physik. Chem.* **226**, 146 (1964).
10. Barrall, II, E. M., Porter, Roger S. and Johnson, Julian F., *J. Phys. Chem.* **71**, 895 (1967).
11. de Gennes, P. G., *Solid State Commun.* **8**, 213 (1970).

Fluid Phases of Highly Asymmetric Molecules: Plate-Shaped Molecules[†][‡]

L. K. RUNNELS and CAROLYN COLVIN

Department of Chemistry
Louisiana State University
Baton Rouge, Louisiana, USA

Received November 2, 1970

Abstract—We develop the theory of a fluid of thin plate-shaped molecules in parallel to existing theory of thin rod-shaped molecules. The molecular interactions (due to the hard core) are accounted for by a graphical expansion including 285 diagrams (through the seventh-order virial coefficients). Our simplified model envisions square tile-like molecules of vanishing thickness and only three allowed orientations. It is shown that the only irreducible diagrams of importance for this model are those for which the vertices may be colored with three (or two) colors without coloring adjacent vertices the same color. Padé analysis of the series generates a fairly stable sequence of predictions of a first-order phase transition between an isotropic low density phase and an anisotropic (but axially symmetric) higher density phase. Thermodynamic parameters characterizing the transition are remarkably similar to those characterizing the corresponding transition of a thin rod model—a similarity with some experimental reinforcement.

Introduction

There is currently a great deal of interest in the study of liquid crystals, from various points of view. Experimentally it is known that mesomorphic (liquid-crystal-forming) compounds are composed of rod-shaped, semirigid molecules.[1] And many theoretical treatments, beginning with that of Onsager,[2] have implicated high molecular asymmetry as the origin of a fluid–fluid transition.[3–8]

Strictly speaking, Onsager's analysis[2] dealt with solutions of highly asymmetric molecules in a structureless solvent. Hence the virial expansion he outlined was a series development of the osmotic

† Research supported in part by NSF Grant No. GP-17026 and based in part on a Thesis presented by Carolyn Colvin to the Graduate Faculty of Louisiana State University in partial fulfillment of the requirements for the degree of M.S., 1970.

‡ Presented at the Third International Liquid Crystal Conference in Berlin, August 24–28, 1970.

pressure of such solutions; he obtained the first nonideal term for rigid molecules of cylindrical shape. A limiting case, height much greater than diameter ("neddles"), was discussed in connection with aqueous solutions of tobacco mosaic virus—which solutions exhibit phase separation at remarkably low concentrations of tobacco virus (2% by volume).[9]

It was also pointed out that Langmuir's experiments[9] had revealed a similar phase separation, at similar concentrations, for sols of platelike particles (bentonite, iron oxide). Onsager's treatment of this limit ("pancakes"), together with Isihara's analysis of the corresponding ellipsoids,[3] suggested that theory *might* substantiate a macroscopic similarity between systems of needles and pancakes.

The whole comparison was clouded, however, by the fact that the *second* nonideal term (involving the third virial coefficient) differed greatly for the two. In fact, the third virial coefficient is vanishingly small in the needle limit, but of order one (with appropriate density units) in the pancake limit.

Zwanzig[4] patented a modification of Onsager's model which permitted the calculation of many more terms in the virial expansion of the hard rod system (now described as a "gas" rather than solution). The cylindrical needles became rectangular parallelepipeds which, moreover, could point in only three mutually perpendicular directions.

The hard rod transition signaled by the second virial coefficient treatment, is now rather completely documented as a first-order phase transformation from an isotropic (randomly oriented) phase to an anisotropic phase having axial symmetry. We present here the corresponding treatment of the related model of systems of platelike molecules. To obtain the simplicity necessary for calculation of several terms of the virial series, we also adopt here a parallelepiped model restricted in orientation to three perpendicular directions. (See Fig. 1.)

Method

In the general case, the thermodynamic properties would depend on the ratio d/l. To avoid this extra variable, the obvious model value

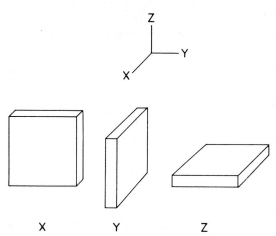

Figure 1. The model. The molecules are represented by rectangular parallelepipeds, with thickness d much less than the edge length l. Translational coordinates are continuous but orientations are limited to the three discrete perpendicular orientations shown.

is $d/l = 0$. Furthermore, setting $d = 0$ will result in additional integral simplifications, but we must be concerned with how the limit $d \to 0$ is to be taken. In our earlier treatment of rod-shaped molecules[7] the correct limiting prescription was obtained thermodynamically by showing that the ideal gas entropy of the hard rod gas contained the shape-dependent term $R \log(l^2 d)$; this arose from the moments, of inertia of the molecule. Consequently in that case the limit $d \to 0$ had to be approached with $l^2 d$ held constant.[4] It has been somewhat awkward that the hard rod molecules were thus required to be of infinite length. For the present problem, however, the ideal gas rotational entropy contains, in addition to molecular mass m and fundamental constants, the term $R \log(l^3)$. This again arises from the moments of inertia, assuming $l \gg d$. Hence, the limit $d \to 0$ should be achieved while holding l constant *and finite*. We shall take the constant to be one and employ dimensionless density units. Equivalently, the density could be regarded as having dimensions (molecules/(volume of l^3)).

We use the same general approach as before.[7] The gas is regarded as a three component system—the components being identified by the three possible orientations. The Helmholtz free energy A is calculated as a function of the three mole fractions X_i, and then

minimized with respect to variations in them.   The excess free
energy A_e, due to the molecular interactions, is defined by

$$A/NkT = \log\Lambda^3 - 1 + \log\rho + \sum_{i=1}^{3} X_i \log X_i + A_e/NkT, \qquad (1)$$

where $\Lambda = (h^2/2\pi mkT)^{1/2}$, A is the total free energy, ρ is the total
density, and the rest of the symbols have their usual meaning. A_e is
calculated by the expansion

$$A_e/NkT = -\sum_{\mathbf{n}}\mathbf{X}^{\mathbf{n}}B_{\mathbf{n}}\rho^{n-1}, \qquad (2)$$

where $\mathbf{X} = (X_1, X_2, X_3)$, $\mathbf{n} = (n_1, n_2, n_3)$ with $n_i =$ nonnegative integer
and $n = \sum n_i$, and $\mathbf{X}^{\mathbf{n}} = X_1^{n_1}X_2^{n_2}X_3^{n_3}$.

As usual, we use a graphical expansion of $B_{\mathbf{n}}$, whereby

$$B_{\mathbf{n}} = (V\prod n_i!)^{-1}\sum_{\alpha}S_{\mathbf{n}.\alpha} \qquad (3)$$

where α is a new suffix to label the irreducible (multiply connected
graphs $G_{\mathbf{n},\alpha}$ with n_1 distinguishable vertices of color (orientation) 1
n_2 of color 2 and n_3 of color 3.   The graph $G_{\mathbf{n},\alpha}$ stands for a function
of the $3n$ variables locating the centers of the n oriented molecules
and $S_{\mathbf{n},\alpha}$ is the integral of this function over all space.   The Mayer
integrand $G_{\mathbf{n},\alpha}$ vanishes for any configuration which does not produce
overlap of all pairs of molecules (vertices) joined by lines of the graph
Otherwise the integrand has value $(-1)L$, where L is the number of
lines in the graph.   In actual practice the summation in Eq. (3) is
over the various multiply connected graphs with unlabelled vertices
of three colors—since the labeling does not affect the value of the
integral.   We must, however, multiply each graph's integral by its
degeneracy: the number of distinguishable labeled, colored graphs
which become identical if the labels are removed (but the colors
retained).

There is, in the general case, one term in Eq. (3) for each distinguishable way of assigning three colors to the vertices of the star
graphs that occur in the virial expansion of a one component gas of
symmetric molecules.[10]   Many of these terms, however, do not
contribute to Eq. (3) in the limit $d \to 0$.   For suppose two adjacent
vertices (i.e., two vertices joined by a line) both have the same color.
This requires the intersection of two parallel molecules, which occurs
only in a " covolume " of order l^2d; two perpendicular molecules,

on the other hand, intersect in a covolume of order l^3. In the limit $d \to 0$, $l = 1$, the difference is three dimensional measure versus two dimensional measure. Hence we include only those graphs which may be colored with three vertex colors (or two) without matching of adjacent vertices. There are several ways some graphs may be tricolored, while in other cases there is only one, or none. (See Fig. 2 and Table 1.) It should be recalled that the rigid rod limit involved even fewer of the irreducible graphs—only those which could be bicolored.[4] (i.e., there are only two colors (orientations), which alternate.) Thus all of the graphs which contribute to the virial expansion of the hard rod gas contribute to that of the hard plate gas, plus many more.

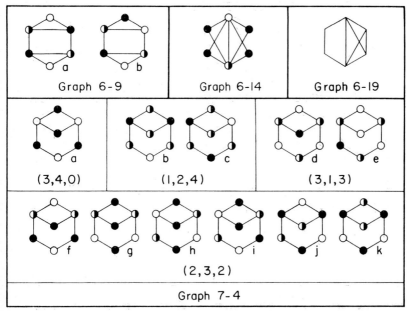

Figure 2. Examples of graph colorings. Graph 6–9 has two fundamentally different tricolorings, a and b, each employing 2 of each color. We use an open circle to denote an x-oriented molecule, a filled circle to denote a y-oriented molecule and a half-filled circle for a z-oriented molecule. The integers shown for each graph in Table 1 are the degeneracies (see Appendix) and the decimal figures are the integrals of these example graphs. Graph 6–14 allows only one tricoloring (apart from isomorphic colorings resulting from color permutations). It would require at least four colors for the vertices of graph 6–19, so it makes no contribution to the virial expansion. Graph 7–4 has a total of 11 distinct tricolorings (including the bicoloring a).

TABLE 1 Examples of Integrals and Degeneracies†

Graph	Integral	Degeneracy
6–9a	0.6815	12
6–9b	0.5602	24
6–14	– 0.4000	1
7–4a	3.9277	36
7–4b	3.1065‡	12
7–4c	2.3689	24
7–4d	3.1624	36
7–4e	3.1065‡	36
7–4f	2.5809	24
7–4g	2.7484	12
7–4h	1.9715‡	12
7–4i	1.9715‡	24
7–4j	2.6437	24
7–4k	3.3459	12

† See Fig. 2.
‡ The " accidental degeneracy " evidenced by colorings b and e and colorings h and i are a consequence of the form of the interaction (i.e., the molecular shape and orientations) assumed in the model.

In fact, with the natural density units, the contributions of the bicolored graphs are identical in the two cases *and* obtainable from the one-dimensional integrals tabulated by Hoover and DeRocco. [10] The complete integral $S_{n,\alpha}$ is a product of three factors—one arising from integrations over $x_1, x_2, x_3, \ldots$, one from integrations over $y_1, y_2, y_3, \ldots$, and a third from the z-coordinates. In the hard rod case each of these three factors is essentially the same as *the* integral for a one-dimensional hard " sphere " model of appropriate diameter. The appropriate diameter is $(l+d)/2$ in two cases and d in the third. The only difference for plate-shaped molecules is that the appropriate diameters are $(l+d)/2$ twice and l for the third direction, but the integrals still may be obtained from the work on the one-dimensional hard sphere model.

Such is not the case for the tricolored graphs, in which plates of all three orientations occur. It is still true that the total integral factors into three integrals, one for integrations along each of the three coordinate directions. But the three factors are not integrals from a one-dimensional model, since there is no single equivalent one-dimensional length which will generate the correct integrals. This is discussed further in the Appendix, where the integration technique is presented.

In minimizing the free energy with respect to variations in the three mole fractions X_i we have not forced axial symmetry by requiring two to be equal. Instead, as in our earlier study of the hard rod case, we allow any variation subject to the single restraint $X_1 + X_2 + X_3 = 1$. There are thus two independent variables; we have used an iterative, two-dimension version of the Newton–Raphson method to locate the extrema.

We have also (hopefully) improved our estimate of the excess free energy by replacing the truncated virial series Eq. (2) by its $[m, k]$ Padé approximant,[11] *before* minimizing with respect to the mole fractions. If the highest power of ρ in Eq (2) is the Kth, we take $m = k = K/2$ if K is even or $k = m + 1 = (K + 1)/2$ if K is odd. It was found with the hard rod problem that this Padé analysis improved the convergence of the transition parameters. Preliminary study of the present problem using only the truncated series, Eq. (2), produced results so erratic and peculiar that they were of little use.

Our procedure, once the virial coefficients have been determined, then consists of the following steps: (1) for fixed density ρ, determine the minimum (with respect to mole fractions X_i) of the Padé-approximant-modified free energy; (2) calculate thermodynamic properties such as p/kT and μ/kT at the equilibrium mole fractions (i.e., at the minimum); (3) repeat steps (1) and (2) for a series of densities; (4) in the event of a " van der Waals loop ", infer a phase transition along a tie line determined by the simultaneous (graphical) solution of $(p/kT)_{p_1} = (p/kT)_{p_2}$ and $(\mu/kT)_{p_1} = (\mu/kT)_{p_2}$. The same series of steps was initially executed without replacing the truncated series for the excess free energy by its Padé approximant.

Results

In Table 2 we show explicitly the contributions to Eq. (3) of all diagrams of five or fewer points. Table 3 shows the number of contributing diagrams of seven or fewer points and Table 4 summarizes all of the calculations in the form of the virial coefficients B_n.

Direct use of the truncated series, Eq. (2), provides very little

TABLE 2   Values of Diagrams of Five Points or Fewer

Graph No.†	Colors	Degeneracy	I_x	I_y	I_z	$S_{n,\alpha}$
2–1	xy	1	2	2	4	-2.0000
3–1	xyz	1	8	8	8	-1.0000
4–1	x^2y^2	1	32	32	256	2.3704
	xy^2z	1	80	32	80	1.8518
4–2	xy^2z	1	48	32	48	-0.6667
4–3‡						
5–1	x^2yz^2	4	352	1088	352	-2.3808
5–2	x^2yz^2	8	352	640	256	1.0185
	x^2yz^2	4	256	1088	256	1.2593
5–3	x^2y^3	1	192	192	3072	2.0000
	xy^3z	1	576	192	576	1.1250
	x^2yz	2	448	1088	192	1.6528
5–4	xy^3z	1	384	192	384	-0.5000
5–5	x^2yz^2	4	256	384	256	-0.4444
5–6	x^2yz^2	4	256	640	192	-0.5556
5–7‡						
5–8	x^2yz^2	1	192	384	192	0.2500
5–9‡						
5–10‡						

† As tabulated in Ref. (10). For graphs of five points or fewer, the colors used uniquely define the graph coloring except for graph 5–2; the colorings are defined uniquely by the degeneracies for that graph.
‡ No tricolored graphs.

TABLE 3   Numbers of Irreducible Graphs (Stars)

Number of points, n	Stars of n points	Bicolored stars of n points	Tricolored stars of n points†
2	1	1	1
3	1	0	1
4	3	1	2
5	10	1	7
6	56	5	35
7	468	8	239

† Includes every bicolored star, since a bicolored star may always be tricolored.

information, other than the qualitative indication that *something* happens at densities greater than about 1.5. At lower densities an isotropic fluid ($X_1 = X_2 = X_3 = \frac{1}{3}$) is the only extremum (minimum) of the free energy, as we would expect. The anticipated transition to an orientationally ordered fluid at higher densities cannot really be proclaimed on the basis of the truncated series work. It is true that (axially symmetric) minima do occur, but there is erratic change as the order of the approximation changes. And the "stable" phase (i.e., that associated with the minimum in A) is often quite unphysical. Besides occurring with "two-dimensional ordering" (such as $X_1 = X_2 = 0.45$, $X_3 = 0.1$, for example), the high density phases often have negative compressibility, and even negative pressure at high enough densities.

This wild behavior is not really so surprising if Table 4 is taken into account The coefficients B_n are not decreasing regularly as $n = n_1 + n_2 + n_3$ increases. Under such circumstances reliable estimates of the excess free energy at higher densities is hardly to be expected. It may be seen that the situation is considerably worse than for the hard rod case (coefficients with n of the form $(m, l, 0)$).

TABLE 4   Free Energy Coefficients B_n

$n = (j, k, l)$	B_n	
	Rational	Decimal
(1, 1, 0)	-2	-2.000
(1, 1, 1)	-1	-1.000
(1, 1, 2)	16/27	0.5926
(2, 2, 0)	16/27	0.5926
(2, 2, 1)	695/864	0.8044
(1, 1, 3)	5/48	0.1042
(2, 3, 0)	1/6	0.1667
(2, 2, 2)	51077/108000	0.4729
(1, 2, 3)	$-35839/216000$	-0.1659
(1, 1, 4)	2/125	0.0160
(3, 3, 0)	$-1352/6750$	-0.2003
(2, 4, 0)	16/375	0.0427
(2, 3, 2)	$-918787/2332800$	-0.3939
(3, 1, 3)	$-17517911/23328000$	-0.7509
(1, 2, 4)	$-62137/486000$	-0.1279
(3, 4, 0)	$-916/6075$	-0.1508
(1, 1, 5)	7/3240	0.0022
(2, 5, 0)	4/405	0.0099

TABLE 5   Transition Parameters†

Approximant (m, k)	p/kT	μ/kT	Isotropic Density	Mesophase Density	z‡
(1, 2)	2.22	0.75	1.21	1.72	0.91
(2, 2)§	...	...	...	...	...
(2, 3)	2.67	0.96	1.76	2.24	0.91
(3, 3)	2.58	0.92	1.60	2.02	0.88

† The corresponding estimates for the hard rod case, from the (3, 4) approximant, are $p/kT = 2.51$, $\mu/kT = 0.89$, densities = 1.45 and 1.93, and $z = 0.88$. All chemical potentials μ/kT in Ref. (7) are erroneously high by a constant term $\ln 3 = 1.0986$.

‡ The unique mole fraction in the mesophase. The other two are each $(1 - z)/2$.

§ "Two-dimensional ordering." That is, the unique mole fraction is less than 0.5. Furthermore, this mesophase has negative compressibility.

The situation seems to be improved considerably by Padé analysis. As shown in Table 5, a reasonably stable sequence of transition parameters is provided by the (m, k) Padé approximants. While these parameters are not determined to high accuracy, the existence of the transition and its general characteristics seem to be indicated fairly clearly. All extrema are axially symmetric—i.e., there are at least two equal mole fractions. Our best estimate of the equation state is shown in Fig. 3.

The comparisons between the transition parameters and those of the hard rod case are intriguingly close. In the simplest possible treatment of the two cases, i.e., the second virial approximation (0, 1), the transition parameters are identical. This is true because both expansions would involve only B_{110} (and B_{101} and B_{011}). The equations of state cannot be identical, however, since the third derivatives (of p/kT with respect to ρ) differ at $\rho = 0$. Nonetheless, it does appear that our more extended treatment preserves the macroscopic similarity of the two systems indicated earlier by experiment[9] and initial analyses.[2,3]

Appendix. The Integrals and Degeneracies

As discussed in the text we need to determine those star graphs (as tabulated by Hoover and DeRocco[10]) whose vertices may be colored

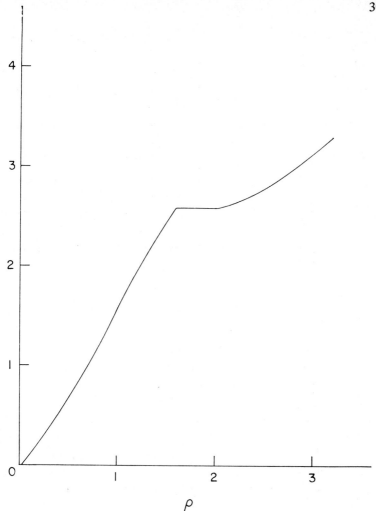

Figure 3.   Equation of state in the limit $d \to 0$.   The ordinate is actually Pl^3/kT and the abscissa is Nl^3/V.   We have set $l = 1$.   This curve is the one calculated from the (3, 3) approximant.

with three or two colors without matching colors of adjacent vertices. The bicolored graphs have previously been determined and evaluated, so we focus our attention on the tricolored graphs.

It is easy to characterize a graph which may be bicolored:[12] it contains no odd cycles. The corresponding characterization of tricolored graphs has not been discovered, so we have determined empirically (with a computer program) which of the stars of seven or fewer points may be tricolored (see Table 3). At least a subset of the nontricolored graphs may be characterized by the rule that such a graph contains a vertex which is adjacent to every vertex of an odd cycle. The simplest is the complete graph of four points (a tetrahedron). The next simplest is a pentagonal pyramid (or the Chrysler symbol). It is easy to see that these graphs cannot be tricolored, but whether or not all nontricolored graphs may be so characterized is not known. Empirically the rule is adequate for irreducible graphs of seven points or fewer.

The same computer program also determined the degeneracies of the permissible colorings. In the language of combinatorial analysis, our graph colorings correspond to ordered partitions (or compositions) of three parts. For a coloring n with no repeated parts, such as $(1, 2, 4)$ of graph 7–4, the degeneracy is given by

$$\frac{n_1! \, n_2! \, n_3!}{\sigma},$$

where σ is the number of color-preserving permutations of the vertices which are symmetry operations of the graph. Of course we determine only the contributions to the virial coefficient for $n = (1, 2, 4)$, since, for example, the coefficient for $(2, 4, 1)$ will clearly have the same value.

Another factor must be taken into account when the coloring contains repeated parts, such as $(3, 1, 3)$ of graph 7–14. If interchange of the equally numerous colors is not a symmetry operation of the colored graph, then the graph with the interchanged colors must be included also. But since the integrals would clearly be equal, it suffices simply to let the interchange contribute to the degeneracy of one representative form. Thus graph coloring 7–4d would have a degeneracy of only 18 if it did not also represent the graph with open and half-filled circles interchanged. Similarly the degeneracies of each $(2, 2, 2)$ coloring of graph 6–9 include a factor of 3 to provide for nonequivalent graphs produced by color permutations. (Half of the 6 possible permutations *are* symmetry operations.) It should be noticed, however, that no such factor is present in graph coloring 7–4j, for interchange of open and half-filled circles does not produce a distinguishable graph coloring.

Turning now to the actual evaluation of the integrals, we have used basically the integration scheme previously employed in connection with the hard rod gas.[7] There are, however, some modifications required by the presence of three molecular orientations. Since each Mayer f-factor represented by the lines in the diagrams may be written as the product $f = f_x f_y f_z (= 0$ or $-1)$, the entire integrand still factors into a product of three integrals, one arising from integrations along each of the three coordinate axes.

For an example we consider graph 7–4 with coloring b, numbering the vertices clockwise beginning at the top and numbering the central vertex seven. The essence of the Mayer factor for hard parallelepiped molecules is that two molecules intersect only if their projections intersect on *each* of the three coordinate axes. This is the origin of the factoring of the integral. The projections of the molecules, however, differ in the three directions. For the x-integrations we may imagine the molecules all projected onto the x-axis—whereby (in the limit $d \to 0$, $l = 1$) an x-oriented molecule becomes a point, while a y- or z-oriented molecule becomes a line of length one. To view. the required intersections we may transcribe the lines of 7–4b into " long bonds " and " short bonds ", the former occurring between molecule projections which are both of length one and the latter representing the case of a line and a point. Thus short bonds emanate from vertices whose color (orientation) is the same as the coordinate axis of the current integrations. Figure 4 shows the three projection diagrams for graph coloring 7–4b. Only in a " homogeneous " case such as for the z-projection of 7–4b, where all bonds have the same length, may the integral be obtained from the one-dimensional hard rod integrals tabulated by Hoover and DeRocco.[10]

The " short bond " between molecules 3 and 4 in the x-projection means, for example, the requirement that $|x_3 - x_4| \leqslant \frac{1}{2}$. The "long bond " between molecules 1 and 2 means $|x_1 - x_2| \leqslant 1$. For convenience, however, we have doubled all lengths and later we divide the entire integral by $2^{3(n-1)}$. The integrals are also divided by the total volume V (see Eq. (3)), which is equivalent to confining one molecule (number n) to the origin and measuring the other molecular centers relative to it.

Each of the integrals represented by diagrams such as in Fig. 4 are thus related to the " volume " of a six-dimensional region

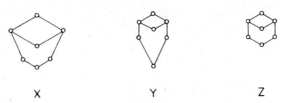

X   Y   Z

Figure 4. Diagrams depicting the three factor integrals arising from graph coloring 7–4b of Fig. 2. A " short bond " between two vertices indicates that the integrand vanishes unless the centers of the corresponding projected molecules are no more distant than one; the " long bond " allows the molecules to be twice as far apart.

(molecule 7 fixed) in which all required inequalities of the form $|x_3 - x_4| \leqslant 1$ and $|x_1 - x_2| \leqslant 2$ are satisfied. This region is thus bounded by hyperplanes (with equations such as $x_3 = x_4 + 1$, etc.) and its " volume " is best determined by our procedure described earlier.[7] This scheme divides 6-space into unit 6-cubes and determines for each the content of the region enclosed by the bounding hyperplanes —these contents must necessarily be integral multiples of $(\frac{1}{5}!)$, and we denote these integers by I_x, I_y, I_z. (See Table 2.) The more general statement is that for a tricolored diagram of n points, one of them stationary, the integral is of the form

$$S_{n, \alpha} = \frac{I_x \cdot I_y \cdot I_z}{2^{3n-3}[(n-1)!]^3} \tag{4}$$

In the case of 7–4b, the numerator is 303 953 996 677 120.

Since we have determined all integrals as rational numbers, their summations to give the virial coefficients are also obtainable as rationals (Table 4). It was only for the minimization of the free energy that the decimal equivalents were introduced (as double precision floating point numbers).

REFERENCES

1. Gray, G. W.. *Molecular Structure and the Properties of Liquid Crystals* (Academic Press, New York, 1962).
2. Onsager, L., *Ann. N.Y. Acad. Sci.* **51**, 627 (1949).
3. Isihara, A., *J. Chem. Phys.* **19**, 1142 (1951).
4. Zwanzig, R., *J. Chem. Phys.* **39**, 1714 (1963).
5. Wulf, A. and DeRocco, A. G., in Johnson, J. F. and Porter, R. S. (Eds.), *Liquid Crystals and Ordered Fluids* (Plenum Press, New York, 1970), p. 227.

6. Cotter, M. A. and Martire, D. E., *J. Chem. Phys.* **52**, 1902, 1909 (1970).
7. Runnels, L. K. and Colvin, Carolyn, *J. Chem. Phys.*, to be published.
8. Hubbard, J. B. and Runnels, L. K., to be published.
9. Langmuir, I., *J. Chem. Phys.* **6**, 873 (1938).
10. Hoover, W. G. and DeRocco, A. G., *J. Chem. Phys.* **36**, 3141 (1962).
11. Baker, G., Jr., *Advan. Theoret. Phys.* **1**, 1 (1965).
12. Busacker, R. G. and Saaty, T. L., *Finite Graphs and Networks* (McGraw-Hill Book Company, New York, 1965), p. 86.

A Molecular Theory of the Cholesteric Phase and of the Twisting Power of Optically Active Molecules in a Nematic Liquid Crystal†

W. J. A. GOOSSENS

Philips Research Laboratories
N. V. Philips' Gloeilampenfabrieken
Eindhoven, Netherlands

Received October 16, 1970

Abstract—The molecular properties of optically active molecules are used to extend the molecular statistical theory of the nematic phase in order to explain the helical structure of the cholesteric phase. In order to account for these properties the dispersion energy between two molecules is calculated taking into account not only the dipole–dipole interaction but also the dipole–quadrupole interaction. The calculated twist has the right order of magnitude. The theory moreover explains the twisting power of optically active solute molecules in a nematic solvent and also the concentration dependence of the induced twist angle.

A consequence of this theory is that the helical structure only exists, if the distribution of orientations around the long molecular axes is not rotationally symmetric; one may expect this to be the case for e.g. planar molecules.

The cholesteric phase can be considered as a special case of the nematic phase.[1,2] The long axes of the anisotropic molecules are on the average aligned parallel to each other within planes; the direction of this alignment rotates smoothly as one proceeds in a direction perpendicular to the parallel planes. The pitch of this helical structure is of the order of $10^{3[4]}$ Å, corresponding to a twist angle between the planes of the order of minutes of an arc. The cholesteric phase occurs only with optically active molecules. It seems therefore reasonable to conclude that those molecular properties that are responsible for the optical activity also give rise to the helical structure. In order to account for these molecular properties we make an extension of the molecular statistical theory of

† Presented at the Third International Liquid Crystal Conference, Berlin, August 24–28, 1970.

315

Maier and Saupe[3] for the nematic ordering. We calculate the dispersion interaction energy between two anisotropic optically active molecules i and j taking into account not only the dipole–dipole interaction but also the spatial variation of the mutually induced dipole fields, which is in fact also considering the dipole–quadrupole interaction.

The dispersion interaction energy V_{ij} between two molecules i and j is the second order perturbation energy of the electrostatic interaction H_{ij} between these molecules, i.e.,

$$V_{ij} = \sum_\mu \frac{\langle 0|H_{ij}|\mu\rangle\langle\mu|H_{ij}|0\rangle}{E_{0,\mu}} \tag{1}$$

Considering the molecules as an assembly of point charges e^{ki} distributed in space at various points $\mathbf{r}^{ki}$, this electrostatic interaction is given by

$$H_{ij} = \sum_{ki} \frac{e^{ki} e^{lj}}{|\mathbf{r}^{ki} - \mathbf{r}^{lj}|} \tag{2}$$

It is convenient to define the position of the point charges with respect to the position $\mathbf{r}^i$ of the origin of a coordinate system ξ, η, ζ fixed to the molecule, i.e., $\mathbf{r}^{ki} = \mathbf{r}^i + \boldsymbol{\rho}^{ki}(\phi_i, \theta_i, \psi_i)$, where ϕ, θ and ψ are the Eulerian angles[4] that define the orientation of the molecular ξ, η, ζ coordinate system with respect to the fixed macroscopic x, y, z coordinate system.

By expanding $H_{ij}(\{\mathbf{r} + \{\boldsymbol{\rho}\}\})$ in a double Taylor series with respect to the $\boldsymbol{\rho}^{ki}$ and $\boldsymbol{\rho}^{lj}$, the electrostatic interaction can be written as an infinite sum of interactions between electric molecular multipoles, i.e.,

$$H_{ij} = (p_\alpha^i p_\beta^j) \frac{\partial}{\partial r_\alpha^i} \frac{\partial}{\partial r_\beta^j}\left(\frac{1}{r^{ij}}\right) + (p_\alpha^i q_{\beta\gamma}^j) \frac{\partial}{\partial r_\alpha^i} \frac{\partial}{\partial r_\beta^j} \frac{\partial}{\partial r_\gamma^j}\left(\frac{1}{r^{ij}}\right)$$

$$+ (q_{\alpha\beta}^i p_\gamma^j) \frac{\partial}{\partial r_\alpha^i} \frac{\partial}{\partial r_\beta^i} \frac{\partial}{\partial r_\gamma^j}\left(\frac{1}{r^{ij}}\right) + \dots \tag{3}$$

where the $p_\alpha^i = \sum_k e^{ki} \rho_\alpha^{ki}$, $q_{\alpha\beta}^i = \sum_k e^{ki} \rho_\alpha^{ki} \rho_\beta^{ki}$ are the components of the electric dipole, respectively electric quadrupole moment and $r^{ij} = |\mathbf{r}^i - \mathbf{r}^j|$ is the distance between the molecules; it is assumed that the molecules are neutral, $\sum_k e^{ki} = 0$. Repeated indices α, β, etc. which refer to the x, y, z components, have to be summed.

Substitution of this equation into Eq. (1) gives the dispersion energy as a sum of terms,

$$V_{ij} = V_{ij}^{pp} + V_{ij}^{pq} + V_{ij}^{qp} \tag{4}$$

where V_{ij}^{pp} is the second order perturbation energy of the dipole–dipole interaction, i.e. the London–Van der Waals energy, and V_{ij}^{pq} the second order perturbation energy due to the combination of the dipole–dipole and dipole–quadrupole interaction. For these different terms we find:

$$V_{ij}^{pp} = \sum_{\nu\nu'} \frac{(p_\alpha^i/p_{\alpha'}^i)_\nu \, (p_\beta^j/p_{\beta'}^j)_{\nu'}}{E_{\nu\nu',00}} \frac{C_{\alpha\beta}^{ij} C_{\alpha'\beta'}^{ij}}{(r^{ij})^6} \tag{5}$$

$$V_{ij}^{pq} = \sum_{\nu\nu'} \frac{(p_\alpha^i/p_{\beta'}^i)_\nu \, (p_\beta^j/q_{\alpha'\gamma'}^j)_{\nu'}}{E_{\nu\nu',00}} \frac{C_{\alpha\beta}^{ij} D_{\alpha'\beta'\gamma'}^{ij}}{(r^{ij})^7}$$

$$+ \sum_{\nu\nu'} \frac{(p_\alpha^i/p_{\alpha'}^i)_\nu \, (p_\beta^j/q_{\gamma\gamma}^j)_{\nu'}}{E_{\nu\nu',00}} \frac{C_{\alpha\beta}^{ij}(r_{\alpha'}^{ij}/r^{ij})}{(r^{ij})^7} + \text{c.c.} \tag{6}$$

where $(p_\alpha^i/p_\beta^i)_\nu = \langle 0 | p_\alpha^i | \nu \rangle \langle \nu | p_\beta^i | 0 \rangle$ etc., $C_{\alpha\beta}^{ij} = \delta_{\alpha\beta} - 3r_\alpha^{ij} r_\beta^{ij}/(r^{ij})^2$ and $D_{\alpha\beta\gamma}^{ij} = (3r_\alpha^{ij}/2r^{ij})(2\delta_{\beta\gamma} - 5r_\beta^{ij} r_\gamma^{ij}/(r^{ij})^2)$.

In order to show that the terms V_{ij}^{pq} can give rise to the twist we use the above pairpotential for an internal field approximation in which the precise interaction $V_i = \sum_j V_{ij}$ of one molecule with all the others will be approximated by a suitable averaged interaction V, i.e.

$$V = \sum_i \overline{V_{ij}^{pp}} + \sum_j (\overline{V_{ij}^{pq} + V_{ij}^{qp}}) \tag{7}$$

For the calculation of this averaged interaction energy one has to make some assumptions on the distribution of the molecular orientations, consistent with the symmetry of the cholesteric phase. A simple model compatible with this symmetry is one in which for a given nematic ordering in parallel planes, which we consider to be parallel with the x–z plane, the molecules can have, independently of their position, only four distinct orientations with equal probability of occurrence, described by the possible combinations out of the set of Eulerian angles, $\phi_i = 0$, $\theta_i = \theta$, $\theta \pm \pi$, $\psi_i = 0$, $\pm \pi$; θ is the angle between the long (ζ) axes, which all lie in planes parallel with the x–z plane, and the z-axis. The calculation of V is now in principle reduced to the calculation of the dispersion energy V_{ab} between a molecule in a plane (a) and a molecule in a plane (b) averaged over all orientations and positions of these in the planes as described above; the quite formal summation, necessary to obtain V from V_{ab}

will be discussed only in connection with the concentration dependence of the twist induced in a nematic solvent by optically active solute molecules. To calculate V_{ab} from Eqs. (5) and (6), we express the components of $\mathbf{p}$ and $\mathbf{q}$ into components defined in the molecular ξ, η, ζ coordinate system by means of the standard transformation[4] $p_\alpha = T_{\alpha\xi}(\phi, \theta, \psi) p_\xi$ etc., and use for the description of the relative position of the molecules cylindrical coordinates with the normal to the planes as polar axis. The averaging is now straightforward; the expression obtained contains terms even in θ_{ab} and odd in θ_{ab} where $\theta_{ab} = -\theta_{ba}$ is the angle between the directions of alignment of the long axes in the respective planes. It is clear that the odd term will give rise to the twist. For this θ-dependent part we find:

$$- V_{ab} = \left(\alpha \cos 2\theta_{ab} + \frac{2\beta}{r_y^{ab}} \sin 2\theta_{ab} \right) \frac{3}{16(r_y^{ab})^4} \qquad (8)$$

where $r_y^{ab} = r_y^a - r_y^b = -r_y^{ba}$ is the distance between the planes and where the molecular quantities α and β involve matrix elements expressed in the molecular ξ, η, ζ coordinate system:

$$\alpha = \sum_{v,v'} \frac{[(p_\zeta/p_\zeta)_v - (p_\xi/p_\xi)_v][(p_\zeta/p_\zeta)_{v'} - (p_\xi/p_\xi)_{v'}]}{4E_{vv',00}} \qquad (9)$$

$$\beta = \sum_{v,v'} \frac{[(p_\zeta/p_\zeta)_v - (p_\xi/p_\xi)_v][(p_\zeta/q_{\xi\eta})_{v'} + (p_\xi/q_{\eta\zeta})_{v'} - (p_\eta/q_{\zeta\xi})_{v'} + c.c.]}{2E_{vv',00}} \qquad (10)$$

α is related to the anisotropy of the molecular polarizability. A non vanishing β requires anisotropy of the molecule as well as non vanishing matrix elements of the form $(\xi/\eta\zeta)_{cycl}$. These matrix elements are non zero only if the molecules have no center or plane of symmetry. Whereas the optical activity of such molecules in random orientation is determined by electric dipole–magnetic dipole transitions, the present " asymmetric part " of the dispersion energy is determined by electric dipole–electric quadrupole transitions. Since the leavo and dextro modifications are the mirror image of each other, β and therefore the twist have opposite sign for these modifications; a racemic mixture will be nematic. Moreover, there is no direct correlation between the sign and magnitude of the optical activity and the sign and magnitude of the twist. By minimalizing V with respect to θ it follows that the magnitude of the twist is determined by the ratio of the coefficients of the odd and even terms in θ, i.e.,

$$2\theta_{ab} \cong tg\ 2\theta_{ab} = \frac{2\beta}{\alpha r_y^{ab}} \tag{11}$$

To estimate the order of magnitude of β/α we may state that β/α will be of the order of the fourth power of an atomic length divided by the molecular volume; we then find that β/α is of the order of $10^{-2 (3)}$ Å. Another possibility is to state that β/α will be of the order of γ_0/Δ where γ_0 is the "optical rotary parameter" of the polarizability theory of Kirkwood[5,6]† and Δ the anisotropy of the molecular polarizability. Since typical values of γ_0 are of the order of 10^{-2} Å^4, this estimate gives the same order of magnitude for β/α. So we may conclude that the calculated twist angle has the right order of magnitude. One could hope to find also the correct temperature dependence of the twist by applying Boltzmann statistics within this molecular field approximation. Doing so one finds that the twist-angle is proportional to the two dimensional ordering parameter $S = \overline{\cos 2(\theta - \theta_0)}$, $\theta_0 = \bar{\theta}$, which is determined self consistently as a function of temperature by an equation quite analogous to that for the three dimensional ordering parameter.[3] Since S is a weakly decaying function of temperature, the twist should show the same behaviour. In general this is not the case; it is known that especially near the transition to the solid or smectic phase the twist angle falls off very steeply to zero with decreasing temperature. To calculate this temperature dependence one should go beyond the molecular field approximation; this has formally been done by Keating.[7] As to our model with only four orientations we like to remark that a more general assumption on the ordered distribution of orientations leads to essentially the same conclusions as to the necessary conditions for the occurrence of the "asymmetric part" of the dispersion energy and the order of magnitude of the twist.

It is known that a nematic liquid crystal can be converted into the cholesteric phase by an admixture of optically active solute molecules.

This twisting power of optically active solute molecules in a nematic solvent and the concentration dependence of the induced twist follow directly from our theory. In Eq. (7) for the internal field,

† In the notation of Ref. 6 γ_0 is $\beta^{(0)}$

$\overline{V_{ij}^{pq}}$ is, as shown above, non zero only if j refer to an anisotropic, optically active molecule, while i may refer to any anisotropic (nematic) molecule; in a mixture therefore only the optically active molecules contribute to the " asymmetric part " of the internal field V, obtained by summation of V_{ab}; this " asymmetric part " is now proportional to the number density n of the optically active solute molecules. If roughly spoken the structure of these solute molecules differs from that of the nematic solvent molecules only with respect to their optical activity then they contribute equally to the nematic ordering, determined by the first term on the right hand side of Eq. (7); this symmetric part of V is then proportional to the total number density N. The induced twist angle, determined by the ratio of the coefficients of the odd and even terms in θ, is in this case proportional to n/N, i.e., it is a linear function of the concentration, molar or by weight, of the optically active solute molecules. This conclusion agrees with the experimental results of Cano and Chatelain[8] and of Baessler and Labes,[9] who found that the pitch of such mixtures was proportional to the inverse concentration, at least in the investigated concentration range. In connection with these experiments Aleksandrov and Chystiakow[10] have investigated the optical activity of mixtures especially at low concentrations of the optically active solute molecules. They found a saturation of the optical rotary power as a function of the inverse concentration. They conclude that " evidently the proportionality between the pitch and rotary power holds true, hence it follows that the relation between pitch and the reciprocal of the titer should be analogous to the relation for the optical activity "; the simple theory of dilution therefore should not apply to mixtures with small concentrations. However, we doubt the validity of their conclusions. Examination of the theory of de Vries[11] shows that the proportionality between the pitch p and rotary power ceases to be valid if the pitch becomes to large, to be specific, one should not only have $p > \lambda$, which is generally known, but also $p < \lambda/\delta$; λ is the wavelength of the light and δ the relative anisotropy of the dielectric constant of the liquid crystal. Since $p = p_0/c$ and typical values of p_0, λ and δ are $5 \cdot 10^3$ Å, $5 \cdot 10^3$ Å and $5 \cdot 10^{-2}$ respectively, one finds that the assumed proportionality ceases to be valid at concentrations smaller than 5%. The tendency of the rotary power to saturate with increasing pitch can be demonstrated by explicit calculations; moreover, it is easily shown that for $p \gg \lambda/\delta$ the optical rotary power is proportional to p^{-1}. A region of saturation in between is therefore almost necessary.

If the molecular structure of the optically active solute molecules differ greatly from that of the nematic solvent molecules, such that they do not form a cholesteric phase by themselves, the concentration dependence of the induced twist will be more complex. To illustrate this point we consider the case that the optically active solute molecules do not contribute to the nematic ordering but only are aligned, which will be the case for small, anisotropic, optically active molecules. The "asymmetric part" of V is still proportional to the number density n of the optically active solute molecules, whereas the "symmetric part" is now proportional to the number density $N–n$ of the nematic solvent molecules. The induced twist is for this case proportional to $(n/N–n)$; such solute molecules are more effective in producing a twist. One may expect that there is an optimum concentration of solute molecules with a maximum twist above which the nematic ordering and therefore the twist vanish.

As to the necessity of a planar structure of the optically active solute or cholesteric molecules it follows from our theory that if these molecules have a threefold or higher symmetry axis, which in general implies a rotational symmetric distribution of orientations around these axes, the "asymmetric part" of the potential and therefore the twist vanish. To show this one calculates the dispersion energy as a function of ψ which describes the rotation of the molecules around the long symmetry axis. The "asymmetric part" of the energy for these molecules is now proportional to $\cos 2\psi$; for a rotational symmetric distribution $\cos 2\psi$ has to be averaged giving zero. Baessler and Labes[9] have argued the necessity of a planar structure for steric reasons. They found experimentally that l- and d-mandelic acid did not have twisting power, which was attributed to the free rotation of the optically active groups. Buckingham and coworkers,[12] however, reported that d-tartaric acid converts the nematic phase of p-n-octyl-oxybenzoic acid into a cholesteric phase, which seems contradictory to the above results. The explanation, however, could be that free rotation is hindered by hydrogen bonds between the solvent and solute molecules. In connection with the above we like to remark that the ordered distribution of orientations of the optically active solute molecules need not necessarily be the same in different nematic solvents. In principle therefore it is possible that the magnitude and even the sign of the twist induced by the same optically active molecules in different nematic solvents are different.

REFERENCES

1. Gray, G. W., " Molecular Structure and the Properties of Liquid Crystals " (Academic Press, London, 1962).
2. Saupe, A., *Angew. Chem. Intern. Ed.* **7**, 97 (1968).
3. Maier, W. and Saupe, A., *Z. Naturforsch.* **14a**, 882 (1959).
4. Margenau, H. and Murphy, G., " The Mathematics of Physics and Chemistry " (D. van Nostrand Company Inc., New York, 1955) 273.
5. Mathieu, J. P., " Les Théories Moléculaires du Pouvoir Rotatoire Naturel " (Centre National de la Recherche Scientifique, Paris, 1946) 151, 189.
6. Kauzmann, W., Walter, J. and Eyring, H., *Chem. Revs.* **26**, 339 (1940).
7. Keating, P. N., *Mol. Cryst. and Liq. Cryst.* **8**, 315 (1969).
8. Cano, R. and Chatelain, P., *Compt. Rend.* **259B**, 252 (1964).
9. Baessler, H. and Labes, M., *J. Chem. Phys.* **52**, 631 (1970).
10. Alexandrow, V. N. and Crystyakov, I. G., *Mol. Cryst. and Liq. Cryst.* **8**, 8 (1969).
11. Vries de H., *Act. Cryst.* **4**, 219 (1951).
12. Buckingham, A. D., Ceasar, G. P. and Dunn, M. B., *Chem. Phys. Letters* **3**, 540 (1969).

3 NMR and EPR

An NMR Measurement of the Diffusion Anisotropy in a Nematic Liquid Crystal†‡

J. A. MURPHY and J. W. DOANE

Department of Physics and Liquid Crystal Institute
Kent State University
Kent, Ohio 44240

Received October 19, 1970; *in revised form December* 14, 1970

Abstract—We have measured the anisotropy of the diffusion constant for the solute molecule, tetramethylsilane, dissolved in the nematic liquid crystal, p-methoxybenzylidene-p'-n-butylaniline. We measure a diffusion constant of $D = 3.2 \pm 0.3 \times 10^{-5}$ cm²/sec for diffusion parallel to the preferred direction of alignment, while a value of $D = 0.8 \pm 0.3 \times 10^{-5}$ cm²/sec is obtained for diffusion perpendicular to the preferred direction.

Pulsed NMR techniques are well known for their use in diffusion studies in solids and liquids. In some cases, the diffusion constant can be determined directly. One such technique,[1] used primarily in the case of liquids, involves measuring the transverse nuclear polarization or intensity of the spin-echo from a sample placed in a linear magnetic field gradient. The translational movement of the nuclear spins into different regions of the sample and hence into different magnetic field strengths alters their phase relationship and destroys the transverse polarization. If one applies a 90° pulse followed by n 180° pulses appropriately phased[2] and spaced, the intensity of the resulting spin-echo, M_y, as a function of time follows

$$M_y(t) = M_0 \exp\left[-t/T_2 + \left(-\gamma^2 G^2 D t^3/12n^2 \right) \right] \qquad (1)$$

Where γ is the gyromagnetic ratio of the nuclear spin, G the linear field gradient, D the diffusion constant and T_2' the transverse relaxation time. It is readily seen from the above expression that if the

† This research was supported in part by the Air Force Office of Scientific Research, Office of Aerospace Research, U.S. Air Force under Contract No. F44620-69-C-0021.
‡ Presented at the Third International Liquid Crystal Conference, Berlin, August 24–28, 1970.

325

diffusion constant is to be measured, the condition $T_2^3 \gtrsim 12n^2/\gamma^2 G^2 D$ must be met. Further, if one applies a continuous field gradient across the sample, one must restrict the value of G to be less than ~ 1 gauss/cm in order that Eq. (1) be valid. This places severe restrictions on T_2. As a matter of fact, if one applies a continuous gradient, it completely precludes the measurement of D for a liquid crystal molecule as $T_2 \sim 10^{-4}$ sec for these partially ordered systems.

In order to circumvent this problem, we have dissolved a "spherical" molecule, tetramethylsilane (TMS), into the liquid crystal p-methoxybenzylidene-p'-n-butylaniline (MBBA). As this molecule is only slightly ordered[3] by the nematic matrix, it shows a large T_2 (0.30 sec at room temperature). This value is large enough for the measurement of the diffusion constant for diffusion rates typical of liquids. Because of the large disparity of times for T_2 between the solute and the liquid crystal, one sees only the proton spin-echo from the solute.

Using a Bruker Model No. B-KR-322s pulsed NMR system, we have measured $M_y(t)$ for TMS dissolved in MBBA at different magnitudes of G in a direction parallel to the nematic director $\mathbf{N}$ and for one value of G perpendicular to $\mathbf{N}$. The gradients were created by introducing opposing fields with a circuit placed in the magnet and with use of inhomogenieties inherent in the magnet itself. A check on the linearity as well as the magnitude of the gradient was determined by the use of two small capillaries inserted in the gradient and observing the resulting beats of the two echos. A further check on the gradient was made by measuring the diffusion constant of water.

The value of T_2 was determined in the usual manner of the Carr–Purcell sequence by making the number n, in Eq. (1), large. The diffusion constant was then obtained from the 90°–180° sequence and plotting $\ln M_y/M_0 + t/T_2$ vs t^3. A straight line was obtained and the slope of the line was used to determine D. The values measured were:

$$D_\parallel = 3.2 \pm 0.3 \times 10^{-5} \text{ cm}^2/\text{sec} \quad \text{and} \quad D_\perp = 0.8 \pm .03 \times 10^{-5} \text{ cm}^2/\text{sec}.$$

The value of the measured ratio, $D_\parallel/D_\perp = 4$, is not unreasonable in view of previous viscosity measurements. From simple considerations, one might expect $D_\parallel/D_\perp \sim n_\perp/n_\parallel$. It is interesting to note that measured values[4] of $\eta_\perp/\eta_\parallel$ for p-azoxyanisole give a value of

3.8 for this ratio. More significantly, the measured value of $D_\parallel / D_\perp$ has been found to be in accord with a more detailed calculation based upon a modified Kirkwood diffusion theory.[5]

Since the diffusion constants were measured for a solute molecule and not the liquid crystal solvent, their absolute values might be difficult to predict from theory. However, it is generally believed that the diffusion rate of an impurity in normal liquids is equal to that of the solvent provided the size of the impurity molecule is equal to or somewhat smaller than the solvent molecule.[6]

Finally, it should be noted that the mole fraction of solute TMS to the liquid crystal host was quite large, $\sim 5\%$. This large concentration was necessary in order to have sufficient signal strength to make the measurement.

REFERENCES

1. Carr, H. Y. and Purcell, E. M., *Phys. Rev.* **94**, 630 (1954).
2. Meiboom, S. and Gill, D., *Rev. Sci. Inst.* **29**, 688 (1958).
3. Snyder, L. C. and Meiboom, S., *J. Chem. Phys.* **44**, 4057 (1966).
4. Chistyakov, I. G., *Sov. Phys.—Usp.* **9**, 551 (1967).
5. Wilbur Franklin, in the Third International Liquid Crystal Conference, Berlin, 1970.
6. Cohen, M. H. and Turnbull, D., *J. Chem. Phys.* **31**, 1164 (1959).

Errata

A subsequent measurement of the diffusion constant of TMS dissolved in MBBA using pulsed gradient techniques gives a value of $D_\parallel = 1 \times 10^{-6} \, cm^2/sec$ for diffusion parallel to the preferred direction of alignment. A value of $D_\perp$ has not yet been accurately remeasured. However, because the value of $D_\parallel$ is significantly less than that previously reported, the ratio $D_\parallel / D_\perp$ given should not be taken seriously until a more accurate value of $D_\perp$ is obtained.

Quadrupole and Proton Spin-Lattice Relaxation in the Nematic Liquid Crystalline Phase†‡

J. J. VISINTAINER, J. W. DOANE

Department of Physics and Liquid Crystal Institute
Kent State University
Kent, Ohio 44240

and

D. L. FISHEL

Department of Chemistry and Liquid Crystal Institute
Kent State University
Kent, Ohio 44240

Received October 19, 1970; *in revised form December* 14, 1970

Abstract—Measurements of the quadrupole and proton spin-lattice relaxation times, T_1, in selectively deuterated terephthalbis-(4-amino-fluorobenzene) as well as proton relaxation in other compounds are compared with a calculation for T_1 which recognizes molecular reorientations in addition to the collective order fluctuations. Further, spin-lattice relaxation times in the rotating frame have been measured in p-methoxybenyzlidene-p'-butylaniline to determine the effect of an applied magnetic field on spin-lattice relaxation. These measurements, made at a constant spin-locking field strength, are found to be independent of the strength of the applied magnetic field up to 10 kG.

Introduction

The existence of long range order fluctuations[1,2] in liquid crystals is clearly established by the light scattering properties of these systems.[3,4] Nuclear spin-lattice relaxation is also sensitive to these collective modes,[5] but they are affected by a different regime of the fluctuation spectrum. That is, measurements of the spin-lattice relaxation time T_1, at normal NMR frequencies correspond to wave-

† This research was sponsored in part by the Air Force Office of Scientific Research, Office of Aerospace Research, U.S. Air Force, under Contract No. F44620-69-C-0021.

‡ Presented at the Third International Liquid Crystal Conference, Berlin, August 24–28, 1970.

329

lengths of these modes which are more than an order of magnitude shorter than the wavelength of light.

Nearly all of the T_1 measurements in liquid crystals to date have been on the proton spins.[6-9] While theory can, within reason, account for these measurements, the agreement between theory and experiment has not been as good as one would like. For example, the frequency dependence of T_1 for protons in p-azoxyanisole follows the expression $T_1 = A + B\omega^{1/2}$. A theory[10,5] of T_1 for protons based on order fluctuations gives the $\omega^{1/2}$ dependence but fails to account for the intercept A. The temperature dependence, however, appears to be in good agreement with the theory[5] if one recognizes the presence of molecular reorientations in addition to the long range order fluctuations.

There are two possible causes for the discrepancy in the frequency dependence. First, T_1 measurements for protons are sensitive to those fluctuation modes near their short wavelength limit. The quadratic dispersion relation which describes these collective modes would not be expected to hold in this short wavelength regime and would therefore affect the frequency dependence of T_1. A second and perhaps more realistic reason for the discrepancy is that the mechanism which has been used in calculating T_1 for protons has been too simple. In these calculations it has been assumed that the nuclear dipole–dipole interaction has been modulated by fluctuations in the orientation of the molecule. One might also expect the translational motion of neighboring molecules to modulate the interaction and also relax the spins.

In this paper we describe $T_{1\rho}$ measurements[11] in a nematic liquid crystal. These measurements are sensitive to those fluctuations where the quadratic dispersion relation is thought to be valid. Since magnetic field effects on the collective modes[2] are thought to be significant in this range we also present $T_{1\rho}$ measurements at different magnetic field strengths. To check the spin-lattice relaxation mechanism we have made measurements of the quadrupole spin-lattice relaxation times for a selectively deuterated liquid crystalline molecule. The proton spin-lattice relaxation in this system was measured as well. The spin-lattice relaxation measurements for deuterons should give better agreement with theory, as one would not expect the quadrupole interaction in these systems to be as strongly perturbed by the motion of neighboring molecules.   To compare the dipole with the quadrupole relaxation we have generalized the theory[5] for T_1.

Theory

A theory for the temperature dependence as well as the frequency dependence of T_1 in nematic liquid crystals has been described in an earlier paper.[5]   In that paper it was shown that a calculation of T_1 should be based not only for the collective order fluctuations but also the molecular reorientations which are characteristic of liquid crystals.   An expression for T_1 was calculated for the specific case where the internuclear vector responsible for spin-lattice relaxation was parallel to the molecular axis.   For the data presented in this paper it will be necessary to generalize that expression for T_1 to account for the case where the internuclear vector of the dominant dipole–dipole interaction is at some arbitrary angle with respect to the molecular axis.

The nuclear spin-lattice relaxation time for two like nuclei of spin $\frac{1}{2}$ having a constant separation distance may be expressed as[11]

$$T_1^{-1} = \tfrac{9}{8}\gamma^4 \hbar^2 r^{-6}[J_1(\omega) + J_2(2\omega)] \tag{1}$$

where γ is the nuclear gyromagnetic ratio and r is the internuclear separation distance.   The $J_h(\omega)$ are the Fourier intensities at the frequency ω of the correlation functions given by the expression

$$J_h(h\omega) = \int_{-\infty}^{\infty} \langle F_h(0)\, F_h^*(t) \rangle e^{ih\omega t}\, dt \tag{2}$$

for $h = 1, 2$ and where

$$\begin{aligned}
F_0(t) &= 1 - 3n^2 \\
F_1(t) &= (l + im)n \\
F_2(t) &= (l + im)^2
\end{aligned} \tag{3}$$

The direction cosines l, m and n describe the internuclear vector **r** in the laboratory coordinate system (x, y, z) with the z-axis in the direction of the magnetic field **H**.   It is the time dependence of l, m and n which must be described in order to determine T_1.

We visualize the molecules in nematic liquid crystals as reorienting about a nematic director **N** which is itself executing small fluctuations about the preferred direction of orientation which is the direction of the magnetic field $\mathbf{H}$. In order to describe the instantaneous orientation of $\mathbf{N}$ in $\mathbf{H}$ we follow the same prescription as used in an earlier paper[5] by making a transformation of the direction cosines to a frame (primed frame in Fig. 1) where the Z'-axis is parallel to $\mathbf{N}(\mathbf{r}, t)$. In order to account for the fact that the internuclear vector may not lie along the molecular axis we make a second transformation to a frame which is fixed to the molecule with the Z_0-axis parallel to the long axis of the molecule. The transformed direction cosines become

$$
\begin{bmatrix} (l+im)/\sqrt{2} \\ (l-im)/\sqrt{2} \\ n \end{bmatrix} = M^{-1}(\phi, \delta\theta, \Psi) M^{-1}(\alpha, \beta, \gamma) \begin{bmatrix} (l_0+im_0)/\sqrt{2} \\ (l_0-im_0)/\sqrt{2} \\ n_0 \end{bmatrix} \quad (4)
$$

where ϕ, $\delta\theta$, Ψ and α, β, γ are the appropriate Euler angles[12] for each successive transformation and the matrices M^{-1} are

$$
\begin{bmatrix} e^{i(\phi+\psi)} & 0 & \dfrac{-i}{\sqrt{2}} e^{i\phi}\, \delta\theta \\[2ex] 0 & e^{-(\phi+\psi)} & \dfrac{i}{\sqrt{2}} e^{-i\phi}\, \delta\theta \\[2ex] \dfrac{-i}{\sqrt{2}} e^{i\psi}\, \delta\theta & \dfrac{i}{\sqrt{2}} e^{-i\psi}\, \delta\theta & 1 \end{bmatrix}
$$

and

$$
\begin{bmatrix} e^{i(\alpha+\gamma)}\dfrac{(1+\cos\beta)}{2} & e^{i(\alpha-\gamma)}\dfrac{(1-\cos\beta)}{2} & \dfrac{-i}{\sqrt{2}} e^{i\alpha}\sin\beta \\[2ex] e^{i(-\alpha+\gamma)}\dfrac{(1-\cos\beta)}{2} & e^{-i(\alpha+\gamma)}\dfrac{(1+\cos\beta)}{2} & \dfrac{i}{\sqrt{2}} e^{-i\alpha}\sin\beta \\[2ex] \dfrac{-i}{\sqrt{2}} e^{i\gamma}\sin\beta & \dfrac{i}{\sqrt{2}} e^{-i\gamma}\sin\beta & \cos\beta \end{bmatrix}
$$

It is the time dependence contained in the first transformation matrix which is governed by the order fluctuations, that is, fluctuations in $\mathbf{N}(\mathbf{r}, t)$. As deviations in the orientation of $\mathbf{N}$ are small, only the terms to the first order in $\delta\theta$ are retained. The second transformation matrix describes the reorientation of the molecule. If we take the

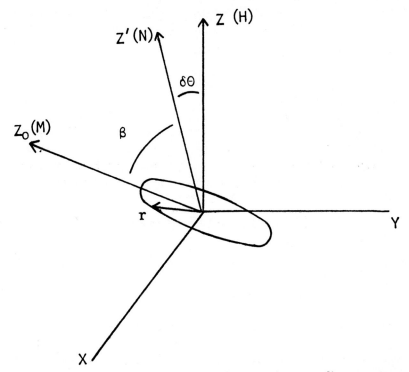

Figure 1. The internuclear vector **r** and the various coordinate systems: the laboratory frame with the z-axis in the direction of the applied magnetic field, **H**; the primed frame with the z'-axis in the direction of the instantaneous nematic director, **N**; and molecular frame with the z_0-axis parallel to the long axis of the molecule.

molecule to be cylindrically symmetric or rod shaped it is free to rotate about its long axis while its long axis is partially ordered about **N**. The direction cosines l_0, m_0 and n_0 describe **r** in the molecular frame and are taken to be fixed as a rigid molecule is assumed.

Using Eq. (4) the correlation functions in Eq. (2) take on the form

$$\langle F_1(0)F_1^*(t)\rangle = \tfrac{1}{16}\langle(e^{i\phi(0)}\,\delta\theta(0)\,e^{-i\phi(t)}\,\delta\theta(t))$$
$$\cdot\times(1-3\cos^2\beta(0))(1-3\cos^2\beta(t))\rangle F_0^2 \qquad (5)$$

$$+\text{SIMILAR TERMS}$$

The terms not shown in Eq. (5) all contain terms periodic in γ and α. By assuming the fluctuations of the director to be uncoupled from the molecular reorientations and by noting the large disparity in time scales between the two motions Eq. (5) becomes[5]

$$\langle F_1(0) F_1^*(t) \rangle = \tfrac{1}{16} \langle e^{i\phi(0)} \delta\theta(0) \, e^{-i\phi(t)} \delta\theta(t) \rangle$$
$$\cdot \times \langle 1 - 3\cos^2\beta(0) \rangle^2 F_0^2 \qquad (6)$$

where $F_0 = 1 - 3n_0^2$.

The terms periodic in γ and α which were not written down in Eq. (5) all average to zero. Since all of the terms in $\langle F_2(0) F_2^*(t) \rangle$ are periodic in γ and α this correlation function does not contribute. The terms $\delta\theta \, e^{i\phi}$ are the fluctuations δN studied by the Orsay Liquid Crystal Group. The second term on the right in Eq. (6) is the square of the degree of order, S, and Eq. (6) can thus be written

$$\langle F_1(0) F_1^*(t) \rangle = \tfrac{1}{4} \langle \delta N(0) \, \delta N(t) \rangle S^2 (1 - 3\cos^2\theta_0)^2 \qquad (7)$$

where θ_0 is the fixed angle between the internuclear vector and the long axis of the molecule. From Eq. (2) it follows that

$$J_1(\omega) = \tfrac{1}{4} S^2 (1 - 3\cos^2\theta_0)^2 \int_{-\infty}^{\infty} \langle \delta N(0) \, \delta N(t) \rangle e^{i\omega t} \, dt \qquad (8)$$

The long range order fluctuations involve modes in which the frequency[1] associated with a wave vector q is $\omega(q) = i(Kq^2 + \Delta\chi H^2)/\eta$ where K is the deformation constant of the nematic liquid crystal; η, an average of the Leslie coefficients; $\Delta\chi$, the anisotropic part of the diamagnetic susceptibility and H the strength of the external magnetic field in which the liquid crystal sample resides. The thermal amplitude[1] of the modes is $kT/(Kq^2 + \Delta\chi H^2)V$ where V is the volume and $Kq^2 + \Delta\chi H^2$ is the energy density of mode q.

The correlation function $\langle \delta N(0) \, \delta N(t) \rangle$ based on these modes was first worked out by Pincus[10] then by Blinc[7] who included the magnetic field terms. The effect of the magnetic field on T_1 is discussed in the next section.

Magnetic Field Effects on Spin-Lattice Relaxation

The effects of an external magnetic field on order fluctuations have been discussed by deGennes and the Orsay Liquid Crystal Group.[1] The results of their theory have been applied by Blinc et al.[7] to calculate the correlation function $\langle \delta N(0) \, \delta N(t) \rangle$ in Eq. (8). Using their results Eq. (8) becomes

$$J_1(\omega) = \frac{1}{8\pi}(1 - 3\cos^2\theta_0)^2 \frac{S^2}{K^{3/2}} \frac{kT\eta^{1/2}}{[1 + (R/\omega)^2]^{1/4}} \frac{\sin\left[\frac{1}{2}\tan^{-1}(\omega/R)\right]}{\sin\left[\tan^{-1}(\omega/R)\right]} \frac{1}{\omega^{1/2}}$$

$$(9)$$

where $R = \Delta\chi H^2/\eta$.

If we take $\Delta\chi \approx 10^{-5}$, $\eta \sim 10^{-2}$ poise and $H \sim 10^4\,G$ as typical values for these parameters then we obtain $R \sim 10^5\,\text{sec}^{-1}$. It is seen from Eq. (9) that for values of $\omega \approx R = 10^5\,\text{sec}^{-1}$, one would expect to observe magnetic field effects. Experimentally, this can be accomplished in two ways: by use of $T_{1\rho}$ measurements[11] or by making T_1 measurements on nuclear spins which have low values of γ. The use of $T_{1\rho}$ measurements have the advantage that one can hold ω in Eq. (9) constant by making all of the measurements at the same magnitude of the rotating magnetic field H_1 while the external magnetic field H is varied.

We have made $T_{1\rho}$ measurements on protons in p-methoxy-benzylidene-p'-n-butylanaline (MBBA) over a variety of magnetic field strengths for constant values of $H_1 = 13 \pm 2G$. It is seen from Eq. (9) that if ω or γH_1 is sufficiently small one might expect the condition $R \gg \omega$ to be met. In this case it follows from Eq. (9) that for constant ω

$$J_1(\omega)^{-1} \propto H.$$

$$(10)$$

If on the other hand $R \ll \omega$, that is no external field effects, $J(\omega)$ is of course independent of H.

The results of $T_{1\rho}$ measurements are shown in Fig. 2. The measurements were made on a Brüker B-KR-332s pulsed system with the sample maintained at the temperature $T_{\text{red}} = 96$. The result shows no field effects within the error of the experiment although there is a trend in the direction predicted by Eq. (9) if these effects were becoming significant at the values of H_1 used. It would therefore seem appropriate to neglect the effect of the applied magnetic field on spin-lattice relaxation measurements.

Temperature and Frequency Dependence of T_1

Using Eqs. (1) and (8) we write T_1 for protons as

$$T_1^{-1} = \tfrac{9}{32}\gamma^4\hbar^2 r^{-6}(1 - 3\cos^2\theta_0)^2 S^2 \int_{-\infty}^{\infty} \langle \delta N(0)\,\delta N(t)\rangle e^{i\omega t}\,dt \quad (11)$$

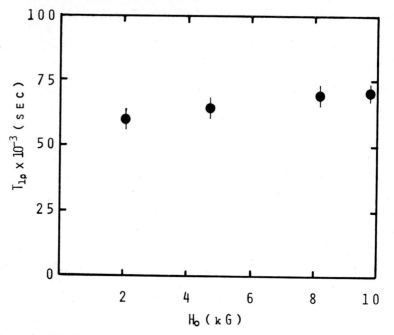

Figure 2. Spin-lattice relaxation in the rotating frame for proton spins in MBBA at $T_{red} = 96$ where the spin-locking field strength H_1 was kept at a constant value of $13\,G$ while the applied magnetic field H was varied.

Since magnetic field effects can be neglected we follow Pincus[10] in calculating $\langle \delta N(0)\, \delta N(t) \rangle$. Including the diffusion constant, D, the expression for $T_1'^{-1}$ now becomes

$$T_1'^{-1} = \frac{9}{16\sqrt{2\pi}} \frac{\gamma^4 \hbar^2}{r^6} (1 - 3\cos^2 \theta_0)^2 \frac{S^2}{K} \frac{kT}{(K/\eta + D)^{1/2}} \frac{1}{\omega^{1/2}} \qquad (12)$$

Equation (12) can be easily adapted to spin 1 nuclei which relax via the quadrupole interaction. The quadrupole Hamiltonian for a spin of 1 is formally equivalent to the dipole–dipole interaction Hamiltonian for two interacting nuclei of spin $\frac{1}{2}$ provided $(\gamma\hbar)^2/r^3$ is replaced by $e^2qQ/2$ where q is the electric field gradient, Q the quadrupole moment of the nucleus and e the electronic charge. If θ' is now taken to be the angle between the direction of the principal axis of the field gradient and the molecular axis, T_1^{-1} becomes

$$T_1^{-1} = \frac{9}{64\sqrt{2\pi}} \frac{e^4 q^2 Q^2}{\hbar^2} (1 - 3\cos^2 \theta')^2 \frac{S^2}{K} \frac{kT}{(K/\eta + D)^{1/2}} \frac{1}{\omega^{1/2}} \qquad (13)$$

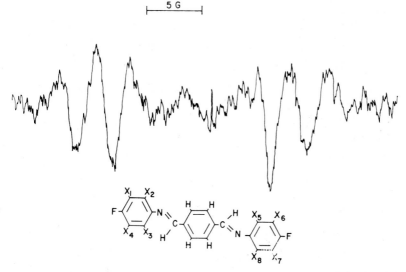

Figure 3. The molecule and deuteron spectra for terephthalbis-(4-animo-fluorobenzene), TAFB, in the nematic liquid crystalline phase at $T = 163\,°C$. The deuterated positions are the x positions in the diagram.

We compare these relationships with measured values of T_1 for protons in terephthalbis-(4-amino-fluorobenzene), TAFB and deuterons in TAFB-d_8. The molecular structure of TAFB-d_8 is shown in Fig. 3 along with its corresponding quadrupole spectra. Figure 4 shows T_1 for protons in TAFB at temperatures extending through the nematic range and into the isotropic liquid at frequencies 8 MHz, 20 MHz and 50 MHz. The values of T_1 for the deuterons in TAFB-d_8 are shown in Fig. 5. These plots are made versus $T_{\mathrm{red}} = 100\,T/T_k$ where T is the absolute temperature and T_k the absolute temperature of the clearing point.

With exception of special cases[13] the temperature dependence for the protons in TAFB is typical of that seen in compounds such as p-azoxyanisole. That is, the variation throughout the nematic range is not large; less than a factor of two. The same appears to be true for deuterons. In order to make a fit of Eqs. (12) and (13) to the data it would be necessary to know the details of the temperature dependence of the Leslie coefficients as well as the diffusion constant. Unfortunately, such information is not available although a rough approximation can be made. Since $K \propto S^2$, Eqs. (12) and

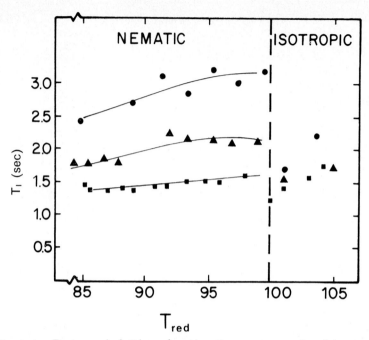

Figure 4. Proton spin-lattice relaxation times versus reduced temperature in TAFB at 8 MHz (squares), 20 MHz (triangles) and 50 MHz (circles).

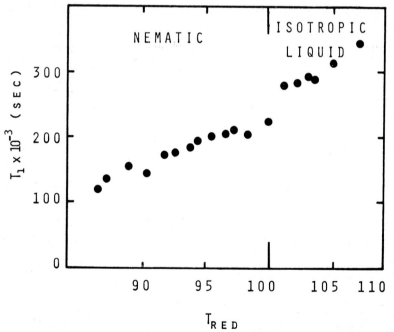

Figure 5. Quadrupole spin-lattice relaxation times for deuterons in TAFB-d_8 taken at a frequency of 8 MHz.

(13) predict $T_1 \propto D^{1/2}/T$ for modes whose lifetimes are diffusion limited and $T_1 \propto S/\eta T$ for those which are not. Since neither of the last two expressions are expected to be strongly temperature dependent the data would not appear to contradict the theory.

The measured frequency dependence of T_1 for three different compounds is shown in Fig. 6. Within experimental error the data appear to follow the relation $T_1 = A + B\omega^{1/2}$. On the basis of Fig. 6 one would not expect a large variation of $T_{1\rho}$ for varying values of H_1 where H_1 is kept greater than the dipolar line width. This is in fact what is seen in Fig. 7 for MBBA. The implications of this measurement are discussed in a latter section. Similar data have been observed for PAA.[14] The finite value of the intercept A

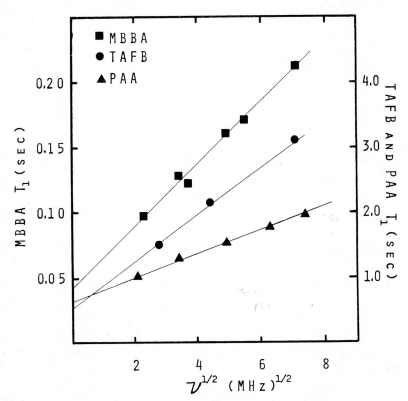

Figure 6. Frequency dependence of the proton spin-lattice relaxation times for: p-methoxybenzylidene-p'-butylaniline, MBBA, at $T_{\mathrm{red}} = 96$; tere-phthalbis-(4-animo-fluobenzene), TAFB, at $T_{\mathrm{red}} = 96$; and p-azoxyanisole, PAA at $T_{\mathrm{red}} = 99$.

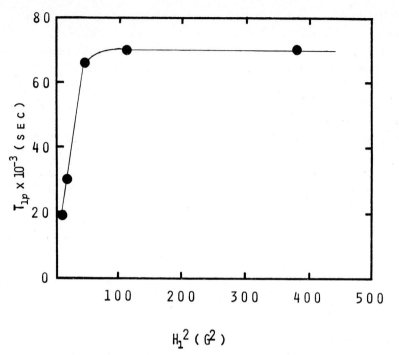

Figure 7. Spin-lattice relaxation in the rotating frame for M protons in MBBA at $T_{red} = 96$ in which the spin-locked field strength, H_1, was varied.

is disturbing since it is not predicted by the theory described in this paper. There is a tendency at first to attribute the intercept to other additive frequency independent relaxation mechanisms; however, this would give $T_1^{-1} = A + B\omega^{-1/2}$ which is not what is observed.

As a check on the mechanism used in arriving at Eqs. (11) and (12) we have calculated and measured the ratio of $(T_1)_{Proton}/(T_1)_{Quad}$ in TAFB-d_8. Reasoning that the quadrupole relaxation would be less likely to be affected by neighboring molecules it would stand a greater chance of agreeing with theory. Using Eqs. (12) and (13) we get

$$\frac{(T_1)_{dipole}}{(T_1)_{quad}} = \frac{(e^2qQ/2\hbar)^2\,(1 - 3\cos^2\theta')^2}{(\gamma^2\hbar/r^3)^2\,(1 - 3\cos^2\theta_0)^2} = \frac{(\Delta H)_Q^2}{(\Delta H)_D^2} \qquad (14)$$

Using 19 G for quadrupole splitting from Fig. 3 and 3.6 G for the dipole splitting[15] at the same $T_{red} = 87$, we obtain a ratio of

$[(T_1)_P/(T_1)_Q]_{\text{calc}} = 30$.   This is to be compared with the measured
value of 10 taken from Figs. 4 and 5 at $T_{\text{red}} = 87$.   This would tend
to indicate that the protons are being relaxed at least in part by
intermolecular interactions.   It should be mentioned here that the
value of T_1 for protons in TAFB and in TAFB-d_8 at 8 MHz was the
same within experimental error.

Another test of the mechanism was to dissolve into MBBA a
solute which had a considerably smaller degree of order than the
liquid crystal solvent.   Since $T_1 \propto S^{-2}$ one would expect a larger
value for T_1 for the solute.   It is possible to measure T_1 for the protons
of the solute apart from the liquid crystal protons provided the
disparity in their respective values of T_2 is large enough.   Such is the
case for tetramethylsilane (TMS) dissolved in MBBA.   The value
of T_2 for TMS in MBBA is 0.3 sec while it is $\sim 10^{-4}$ sec for the protons
in MBBA.   One can then observe a spin-echo from the TMS alone
from which T_1 can be measured.   The measured values of T_1 are

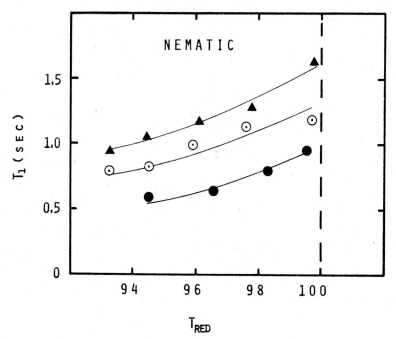

Figure 8. Temperature and frequency dependency of T_1 for protons in
TMS dissolved in MBBA. 50.2 MHz (triangles), 24.2 MHz (open circles), and
12.0 MHz (Closed Circles).

shown on Fig. 8. Although they are larger than that of MBBA (Fig. 6) at the same frequency, nothing quantitative can be derived since one is not sure of the magnitude of cross-relaxation processes. It is interesting that frequency dependence is still observed. Since the degree of order of TMS[16] is so small one would not expect to see a frequency dependence at all although as mentioned earlier the TMS spins might be cross-relaxing with the MBBA spins and thereby displaying their T_1 character.

The diffusion rate of the TMS molecules in the liquid crystalline matrix has been measured. These measurements are described in an adjoining article.

Preparation of Deuterated TAFB

Terephthal-*bis*(4-fluoroaniline)-2, 3, 5, 6, 2′, 3′, 5′, 6′-d_8 was synthesized from terephthalaldehyde and 4-fluoroaniline-2, 3, 5, 6-d_4 by refluxing an ethanol solution. Recrystallization from ethanol ($3X$) gave the pure anil (67%) mp, 151–151.5° (crystal-nematic), clearing temperature, 235–236° (nematic-isotropic). Mass analysis (with an AEI MS-12 mass spectrometer operated at 70 eV, 100 μA ionizing current, 8 kV accelerating potential, 1500 resolving power) gave the parent ion (m/e 328) as the most intense peak in the spectrum with the M-1 (m/e 327) ion at 66.4% relative intensity. Non-deuterated terephthal-*bis*(4-fluoroaniline) has an M-1 (m/e 319) ion at 83.5% relative intensity. Low voltage (nominal instrument reading: 8 eV, 20 μA ionizing current) spectra of either deuterated or non-deuterated anil show only the parent ion and no M-1 ion. These results indicate there was no significant contamination with anil only partly deuterated on the terminal aromatic rings.

The 4-fluoroaniline-2, 3, 5, 6-d_4 used for synthesis† of the anil was itself prepared (overall yield: 14.9%) from benzene-d_6 (99.5% minimum isotopic purity) by the sequence: mononitration, reduction to aniline-d_5, conversion to fluorobenzene-d_5 (Schiemann reaction), nitration and reduction. The 4-nitrofluorobenzene-2, 3, 5, 6-d_4 was separated from isomers by vacuum fractional distillation. The two reduction steps were accomplished by treatment of a refluxing

† Details for preparation of deuterated TAFB may be obtained by corresponding to one of the authors D.L.F.

alcoholic solution with hydrazine and palladium. Mass analysis of the aniline derivatives showed ratios of the parent and M-1 ions comparable to those for non-deuterated derivatives confirming that no hydrogen exchange occurred during reduction.

Discussion

As described earlier, one would expect the theoretical frequency dependence to be more in accord with $T_{1\rho}$ than T_1 measurements particularly in the case of proton spins. This follows from the argument that T_1 measurements may be sensitive to those fluctuation modes near their cut-off wavelength whereas $T_{1\rho}$ measurements are not. From Eq. (12) one would expect an $H_1^{1/2}$ dependence for $T_{1\rho}$. On the contrary, we find from Fig. 7 that there is little variation of $T_{1\rho}$ with H_1 for values of H_1 greater than the line width. This seems to be consistent with the T_1 measurements as there is also seen to be little variation of T_1 in the region near the intercept in Fig. 6 from 0.1 to 0.5 MHz which is the region of $T_{1\rho}$ measurements. No short wavelength limiting effects therefore appear to be present. These results in addition to the results of the $(T_1)_D/(T_1)_Q$ ratio indicate that intermolecular dipole–dipole interactions are important in proton spin-lattice relaxation. Further, quadrupole spin-lattice relaxation on deuterons, N^{14}, etc. would appear to be a better process for studies of fluctuation phenomena in liquid crystals. Some of these studies have already been made.[17]

Acknowledgements

We are indebted to Mr. Ying Yen Hsu for a significant portion of the synthetic work and to Mr. Howard J. Eyman for the mass analyses. One of us J.W.D. would like to acknowledge Dr. D. S. Moroi for his helpful remarks on the T_1 calculation. For mass spectra determination we are indebted to the National Science Foundation for the AEI MS 12 mass spectrometer purchased in part with funds provided by NSF Departmental Instrument Grant GP–8539.

REFERENCES

1. The Orsay Liquid Crystal Group, *J. Chem. Phys.* **51**, 816 (1969).
2. Brown, G. H., Doane, J. W. and Neff, V. D., *Critical Reviews in Solid State Sciences*, Vol. 1 (The Chemical Rubber Co., Cleveland, Ohio).
3. deGennes, P. G., *Mol. Cryst. and Liq. Cryst.* **7**, 325 (1969).
4. deGennes, P. G., *Compt. Rend.* **266**, 15 (1968).
5. Doane, J. W. and Johnson, D. L., *Chem. Phys. Letters* **6**, 291 (1970).
6. Doane, J. W. and Visintainer, J. J., *Phys. Rev. Letters* **23**, 1421 (1969).
7. Blinc, R., Hogenboom, D. L., O'Reilly, D. E. and Peterson, E. M., *Phys. Rev. Letters* **23**, 969 (1969).
8. Weger, M. and Cabane, P., *J. Phys. (Paris) Colloq.* **7100**, 72 (1969).
9. Dong, Ronald Y. and Schwerdtfeger, C. F., *Solid State Commun.* **8**, 707 (1970).
10. Pincus, P., *Solid State Commun.* **7**, 415 (1969).
11. Abragam, A., *The Principles of Nuclear Magnetism* (Oxford Univ. Press, London, 1961), pp. 291 and 560.
12. The Euler angles used here follow the convention of H. Goldstein, *Classical Mechanics* (Addison-Wesley Publishing Company, Inc. Cambridge, Mass., 1950), pp. 107–109.
13. Dong, Ronald Y., Marusic, M. and Schwerdtfeger, C. F., *Solid State Commun.* **8**, 1577 (1970).
14. Dong, Ronald Y., Forbes, W. F. and Pintar, M. M. (to appear in *Solid State Commun.*).
15. Bravo, N., Doane, J. W., Arora, S. L. and Fergason, J. L., *J. Chem. Phys.* **50**, 1398 (1969).
16. Snyder, L. C. and Meiboom, S., *J. Chem. Phys.* **44**, 4057 (1966).
17. Cabane, B. and Clark, W. G., *Phys. Rev. Letters* **25**, 91 (1970).

Thermal Fluctuations and Proton Spin-Lattice Relaxation in Nematic Liquid Crystals†

ASSIS F. MARTINS

Laboratoire de Résonance Magnétique
Centre d'Etudes Nucléaires de Grenoble
Cedex 85, 38-Grenoble-Gare, France

Received October 15, 1970; *in revised form January* 8, 1971

Abstract—Measurements of the spin-lattice relaxation time T_1 in both nematic and isotropic phases of normal (PAA) and methyl-deuterated (PAA-CD$_3$) p-azoxyanisole are reported and discussed. For both materials, T_1 varies linearly with temperature in the isotropic phase, just above the transition. In order to explain this behaviour two processes are discussed: diffusion and thermal fluctuations in the local order parameter. It is shown crudely that diffusion, in this region, is to be expected as a " correlated " process. Recent measurements of D are criticized within this context, but no definite conclusion can be drawn. A simple theoretical approach of the fluctuations in the order parameter is proposed which accounts for the observed behaviour of $T_1(T)$. In the nematic phase of PAA-CD$_3$, T_1 does not depend on temperature. The frequency dependence is the same as for PAA. Our results show the relative importance of short range phenomena and allow us to question the meaningfulness of earlier discussions of experimental data on the unique basis of Pincus's formula.

1. Introduction

Recent developments on the continuum theory of liquid crystals have led to important studies of the thermal fluctuations in the orientational order of the molecules. It has been recognized that these fluctuations are very large for long wavelengths and therefore give rise to some important phenomena. Light scattering, for instance, is controlled by these fluctuations. We also expect that they contribute to the nuclear spin-lattice relaxation through the modulation of the dipole-dipole interaction of the spins located on one molecule. This is most strongly suggested by the fact that the

† Presented at the Third International Liquid Crystal Conference in Berlin, August 24–28, 1970. This research has been supported by the " Instituto de Alta Cultura," Lisbon, Portugal.

calculated[1] spectrum of the fluctuations possesses a branch in the radio frequency region.

This contribution to the nuclear spin relaxation has been derived theoretically by Pincus[2] from the results of Ref. 1. Assuming that orientational and diffusive motions of the liquid crystal molecules are uncoupled, he starts with the following correlation function:

$$G(t) = (2\pi)^{-3} \int d\mathbf{q} \left(\frac{k_B T}{K q^2}\right) e^{-(K/\eta)q^2 t} e^{-D q^2 t} \qquad (1)$$

considering only the dipole-dipole interaction of a proton pair located on one molecule. His final result may be written:

$$T_1 \propto \frac{K}{TS} \left[\omega \left(D + \frac{K}{\eta}\right)\right]^{1/2}. \qquad (2)$$

In these formulae K is some average of the Frank elastic constants,[3] S is the degree of order, η is some average of the viscosity coefficients appearing in the hydrodynamic theory of Leslie,[4] D is the diffusion constant and q is a fluctuation mode wavevector.

Expression (2) or an extension of it,[5] has been contrasted to some experimental data but conclusions of different authors do not agree very well.[5-8] The frequency dependence of the spin-lattice relaxation time T_1 given by (2) is found to be in good agreement with experiments, except at very low frequencies, where this formula cannot be valid because it gives infinitely high relaxation rates. On the contrary, the temperature dependence of T_1 predicted by the expression above does not at all follow the experimental data.[7-9]

We felt that discussion of the mentioned experimental results on the basis of expression (2) should not allow definitive conclusions on the validity of the theory. As already stated, the model used by Pincus considers only two spins located on the axis of the elongated molecule and it is the relaxation of this pair, arising from the modulation of the dipole-dipole interaction through thermal fluctuations of the director $\mathbf{n}(\mathbf{r})$, which is calculated. If we look at the p-azoxyanisole molecule it appears clearly that benzene ring protons satisfy rather well this model (cross interactions are here relatively weak) but protons of the methyl groups are in a very different situation. Furthermore, it is expected that the contribution of these protons to the overall (measured) relaxation time is rather important.

In order to test this argument and discuss more closely the validity of the theory, measurements of the proton spin-lattice relaxation time were performed with methyl-deuterated p-azoxyanisole (PAA-CD_3). The experimental results are presented here together with some new data on normal PAA. Both nematic and isotropic phases are considered.

2. Experimental

The measurements were made with a Brüker B-KR 321 s variable-frequency pulsed NMR spectrometer. The data were obtained by employing the 180°–90° pulse sequence method in the usual manner. For the measurements and stabilization of temperature a Brüker B-ST 100/700 apparatus has been used.

All samples of PAA used were highly purified by zone refining, degassed by repeated freezing and melting under vacuum and then sealed in evacuated ($p \lesssim 10^{-4}$ mm Hg) glass containers. The PAA-CD_3 was synthetized in our laboratory and purified by a double recrystallization from ethanol. Evacuated samples were then prepared as for PAA.

PAA-CD_3, which is PAA with the CH_3 groups replaced by CD_3, was prepared according to a known[10] two steps procedure used for synthetizing p-azoxyanisole. It consists essentially in the reduction of the corresponding nitroderivative. In the first step, deuterated nitroanisole was prepared according to the following scheme:

$$CD_3ONa + Cl(C_6H_4)NO_2 \rightarrow CD_3O(C_6H_4)NO_2 + NaCl$$

The CD_3ONa has been obtained from the reaction of pure sodium with CD_3OD. In the second step of the preparation, reduction of $CD_3O(C_6H_4)NO_2$ by sodium methylate was accomplished.

3. Results and Discussion: Nematic Phase

Our measurements of the nuclear spin-lattice relaxation time T_1 in the nematic phase of PAA agree rather well with those of Doane et al.,[7,9] already published, therefore they will not be reproduced here.

Figure 1 shows a part of our experimental data on T_1 in both nematic and isotropic phases of PAA-CD_3. This material has nearly the same macroscopic properties as PAA, namely, the same temperature range for the nematic phase. In the nematic phase of

PAA-CD$_3$ the T_1 values are lower than those found for PAA in the same conditions. The frequency dependence of T_1 is the same as before but there is no dependence on temperature (Fig. 1) within the experimental error.

These results show, first, the correctness of our feeling on the relative importance of the methyl protons' contribution to the relaxation. As a consequence, we can say that earlier discussions of experimental values of T_1 as a function of temperature on the basis of Pincus's formula are not meaningful. Second, the disagreement between predictions of (2) and experience remains, although it is not so striking as before.† But even in the present case, one might not have the right to compare directly theory and experimental results. Before doing that we must be sure that the spectral density $J(\omega)$ contains no contribution, at the nuclear Larmor frequency, coming from short or medium range phenomena. Rotation of methyl groups in PAA around their symmetry axes is one of these phenomena and we have seen how much it influences the character of the curve $T_1(T)$.

A better way to test Pincus's result (2) would be to carry out T_1 measurements at lower frequencies. But in choosing the frequency range of the experiments we have to remember that expression (2) predicts infinitely high relaxation rates when ω vanishes and this cannot be valid.

For many short range phenomena, the spectral density is constant up to frequencies of the order of the inverse of the characteristic time of the motion. This implies that at low enough frequencies these short range phenomena will contribute to the relaxation rate $T_1^{-1}(\omega)$ with a constant term. In fact, reported measurements on several

---

† After this work was presented, it came to the author's attention a paper by Doane *et al.*, *Chem. Phys. Lett.* **6**, 291 (1970), which slightly modifies Pincus's expression (2): in place of S one must put S^2. This modification seems to give qualitative agreement with the data in fig. 1. A rigorous comparison between theory and experimental results cannot be made until the functions $D(T)$, $K(T)$ and $\eta(T)$ be known exactly. Note that $K(T)$ is some average of the Frank coefficients $K_{ii}(i = 1,2,3)$ and $\eta(T)$ is an orientational average of the Leslie viscosity coefficients. Another paper by T. C. Lubensky, *Phys. Rev.* **A2**, 2497 (1970), gives by a somewhat different technique, $1/T_1 \sim \omega_D^2\, t_c + 1/T_1'$ where $\omega_D^2\, t_c$ is the corrected Pincus's result and $1/T_1'$ represents fluctuations in the magnitude of S and short distance variations in the direction of preferred order.

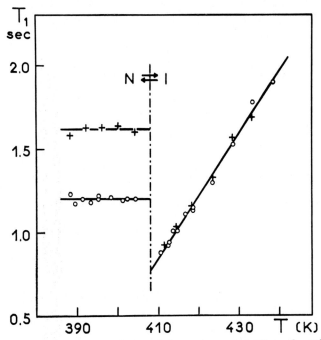

Figure 1. Temperature dependence of the proton spin-lattice relaxation time in PAA-CD$_3$; data for two frequencies: ◯, 24 MHz; +, 56 MHz. The straight line $T_1(T)$ referring to the isotropic phase (I) fits the data for 24 MHz; the other points are simply superimposed.

nematic liquid crystals show that $T_1^{-1} \sim A + B(\omega)$. But we cannot assign a definite meaning to the constant A until a correction to the Pincus's formula is introduced in order to allow realistic predictions for vanishing frequencies. Our work is at present oriented towards the solution of these problems. In particular, we should like to know whether diffusion is the dominant process contributing to the values of T_1 found for PAA-CD$_3$. This is strongly suggested when the results in Fig. 1 are contrasted with recent measurements of D published by Blinc et al.,[11] at least if the measured diffusion coefficients really refer to the translational motion of the molecules. The same type of measurements performed with PAA-CD$_3$ would allow one to stress or discard this interpretation.

4. Results and Discussion: Isotropic Phase

Let us consider first the case of PAA-CD$_3$. As shown in Fig. 1, in the region just above the nematic-isotropic transition T_1 depends on temperature according to the following expression:

$$T_1 \sim T_1^* + \alpha \Theta \tag{3}$$

where T_1^* and α are constants and Θ is some temperature. Our experiments prove that for PAA-CD$_3$ T_1^* and α do not depend on the frequency (within the 10–60 MHz range studied).

Two kinds of phenomena can in principle be expected to contribute to relaxation in the isotropic phase, just above the transition. One is self-diffusion and the other is the fluctuation in some parameter characterizing the strong local order of the fluid in this region of temperature.

Very few measurements of the self-diffusion coefficient D have been published[5,11] and it has been argued that D behaves as in normal liquids, i.e.

$$D = D_0 \exp \left(- \Delta E / kT \right) \tag{4}$$

This is to be expected far enough above the transition but is very questionable if the region just above T_c is considered. In this region, which has a 20–30 degrees temperature range, many experimental results suggest the existence of a very strong short range molecular order. This means that inside a region of linear dimensions ξ motions of different molecules are strongly correlated (ξ is the correlation length). In a rather crude approximation, we can expect that under the influence of a driving force F the molecules move together with a mean velocity v so that the mobility $\mu = D/kT = v/F$ is given by $\mu \sim 1/\eta\xi$ (Stokes). It follows that $D\eta \sim \xi^{-1}$ and we expect diffusion to be a " correlated " process.

In this case expression (4) is not applicable just above the nematic-isotropic transition. A close examination of the published[5,11] experimental values of D shows that extrapolation into this region of the high temperature behavior may be inadequate. Unfortunately, the number of published experimental points up to 30 degrees above T_c is very few and their dispersion too great so that no definite conclusion can be drawn on this point.

If expression (4) was valid and nuclear relaxation was essentially due to diffusion, then our empirical formula (3) would be in fault. On the other hand, we have not yet a model for " correlated " diffusion detailed enough to allow a comparison between theory and our experimental results. For this reason we turn now to the analysis of the second process mentioned above which is also expected to contribute to relaxation.

Fluctuations in the local order referred to above are believed to be the fundamental cause of many special phenomena which appear just above the transition temperature T_c. We shall consider that the interaction responsible for spin-lattice relaxation is modulated by these fluctuations. The relevant correlation function is boldly assumed to be of the form:

$$G(t) = (2\pi)^{-3} \int d\mathbf{q} G(q, 0) \exp(-t/\tau) \tag{5}$$

where $G(q, 0)$, is the mean square fluctuation of the q-mode and the integral is extended over a region of dimension ξ^{-1} (ξ is the correlation length). $G(q, 0)$ is calculated from the free energy density in the usual manner.[12] As stated by De Gennes[13] the free energy density $g(\mathbf{r})$, in the isotropic phase, near T_c, may be written as a power series expansion in some appropriate order parameter $Q(\mathbf{r})$

$$g(\mathbf{r}) = g_0 + aQ(\mathbf{r})^2 + bQ(\mathbf{r})^3 + \cdots$$
$$+ c[\nabla Q(\mathbf{r})]^2 \tag{6}$$

where g_0 is independent of Q. We are disregarding a term imposed by the external field always present in our NMR experiments.

In the following discussion we neglect all terms of order higher than two, in the expression (6), although the term of order Q^3 has in this case a precise meaning: it states the fact that nematic-isotropic transition is first order. Further, we suppose that the contribution to fluctuations of the two remaining terms (i.e. those other than g_0) are comparable in magnitude. This enables us to follow the Landau treatment of the second order phase transitions. Then, starting from Eq. (6), taking the Fourier components and using the equipartition theorem, the thermal amplitude of the fluctuations in the order parameter is readily seen to be

$$G(q, 0) = \frac{k_B T}{2(a + cq^2)}$$

$$= \frac{k_B T}{2c} \cdot \frac{1}{q^2 + \xi^{-2}} \quad (q \ll \xi^{-1}). \tag{7}$$

By substitution of (7) in (5) and integration one obtains readily the explicit form of the correlation function.

Now, as $1/T_1 \propto J(\omega)$, in order to get T_1 we have to calculate the component $J(\omega)$ at the nuclear Larmor frequency of the Fourier transform of the correlation function (5). We obtain:

$$J(\omega) \simeq \frac{1}{6\pi^2} \frac{k_B T}{c} \tau \xi^{-1} \tag{8}$$

if $q^2\xi^2 \ll 1$ and $\omega < 1/\tau$ as expected in the present case.

From a simple (assumed) transport equation[13,14] one obtains $\tau = 1/\Gamma a$ where Γ is a transport coefficient (dimensionally it is the inverse of a viscosity). Equation (7) shows that $\xi^2 = c/a$ and within the framework of the Landau theory we expect[15]

$$a \sim \Theta^r$$
$$c \sim \Theta^{r-2v} \tag{9}$$

with $\Theta = T - T^*$. This temperature T^* must be slightly below the first order transition temperature T_c.[13,16] From (8) and (9) we find

$$T_1 \propto \frac{1}{T} \left(\frac{1}{\tau}\right) \Theta^{r-3v} \tag{10}$$

This result is to be contrasted with experimental data. First we note that this theory does not give the constant term T_1^* appearing in the empirical relation (3). Disregarding this, we may put $1/T \simeq 1/T_c$ and $1/\tau \sim \Theta^{4/3}$ according to recent light scattering measurements of Litster et al.[17] for MBBA (p-methoxybenzylidene-p-n-butylaniline) whose structure is rather similar to that of PAA. Then, if (10) is to agree with results in Fig. 1, one must write

$$\gamma - 3v + 4/3 \simeq 1$$

A possible solution of this equation is given by $v = \frac{1}{2}$ and $\gamma \simeq 1.17$, in rather good agreement with the expected values.

These results do not exclude the possibility of some contribution of the self-diffusion to the relaxation. Further work is needed before the complete solution of this problem is to be given.

Let us finally return to the case of normal PAA. Figures 2 and 3 show the results of our measurements in the isotropic phase of this material.

In this case the temperature dependence of T_1 (Fig. 2) is still given

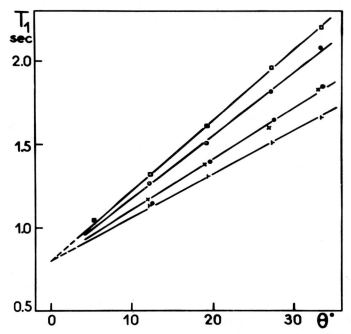

Figure 2. Temperature dependence of the proton spin-lattice relaxation time in the isotropic phase of PAA. Very pure samples: $\bigcirc$, 12 MHz; $\square$, 36 MHz. Thermal degraded sample (after several tens of hours of usage): $\bullet$, 12 MHz; $\times$, 48 MHz; $\vdash$, 60 MHz. The value $T_c - T^*$ has not been measured in these experiments.

by expression (3) but the coefficient α is now frequency dependent. Thus T_1 depends on the frequency in the peculiar manner shown by Fig. 3 and varies linearly with temperature $\Theta = T - T^*$, all lines diverging from the point (T^*, T_1^*). The observed frequency dependence of T_1 must be attributed to the motion of methyl protons. However, the form of the curves $T_1(\omega)$ is not yet fully understood.

Thermal degradation, even in highly purified materials, is generally observed when liquid crystals are used for a long time especially in the isotropic phase. We have shown (Fig. 2) that this degradation only affects the coefficient $\alpha(\omega)$ by a factor independent of frequency. This factor essentially gives the thermal history of the sample.

5. Concluding Remarks

Considerable progress has been achieved in this two year period

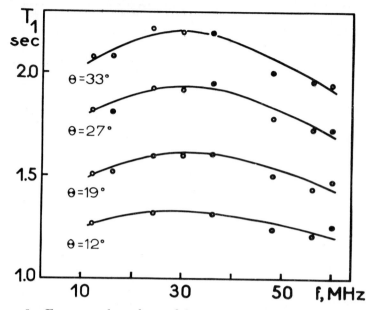

Figure 3.   Frequency dependence of the proton spin-lattice relaxation time in the isotropic phase of PAA.

of research in understanding the mechanisms of the nuclear magnetic relaxation in liquid crystals.   However, the essential problems are still to be resolved.   The theoretical approaches of De Gennes and Pincus are simple approximations and we dont know yet the exact experimental conditions for their validity.   The relative importance of long range fluctuations and short range phenomena is not fully established within the frequency range of the usual NMR experiments. A more recent problem concerns the nature of the self-diffusion process.   A diffusion coefficient D independent of temperature (process with no activation energy) has been measured for the nematic phases of PAA and anisalazin,[11] but the precise meaning of this is not clear.

Acknowledgements

The author is indebted to Mrs. M. C. Schouler and Miss P. Baladda for preparing PAA-CD$_3$ and to Mr. A. Rousseau for some experimental assistance.

REFERENCES

1. Orsay Liquid Crystal Group, *J. Chem. Phys.* **51**, 816 (1969).
2. Pincus, P., *Solid State Comm.* **7**, 415 (1969).
3. Frank, F. C., *Disc. Faraday Soc.* **25**, 19 (1958).
4. Leslie, F. M., *Quart. J. Mech. App. Math.* **19**, 357 (1966).
5. Blinc, R., Hogenboom, D. L., O'Reilly, D. E. and Peterson, E. M., *Phys. Rev. Letters* **23**, 969 (1969).
6. Weger, M., Cabane, B., *J. Physique* **30**, C4–72 (1969).
7. Doane, J. W. and Visintainer, J. J., *Phys. Rev. Letters* **23**, 1421 (1969).
8. Dong, R. Y. and Schwerdtfeger, C. F., *Solid State Comm.* **8**, 707 (1970).
9. We have measured T_1 (T) at $f = 12$ MHz in the nematic phase of PAA, with a highly purified and degassed sample, and obtained the same curve as in Ref. 7. Our values are about 5% higher.
10. Grignard, V., Dupont, G. and Locquin, R., *Traité de Chimie Organique*, t. XV, p. 431, Masson et Cie Ed., Paris 1948.
11. Blinc, R. and Dimic, V., *Phys. Letters* **31A**, 531 (1970).
12. See for instance: Landau, L. D. and Lifshitz, E. M., *Statistical Physics*, ch. XII. Pergamon Press, London, 1959.
13. De Gennes, P. G., *Phys. Letters* **30A**, 454 (1969).
14. Landau, L. D. and Khalatnikov, I. M., *Dok. Akad. Nauk SSSR* **96**, 469 (1954).
15. Kuramoto, Y., *Progr. Theor. Phys.*, **41**, 604 (1969).
16. Cabane, B. and Clark, W. G., *Phys. Rev. Letters* **25**, 91 (1970).
17. Litster, J. D. and Stinson, T. W., *J. Appl. Phys.* **41**, 996 (1970).

NMR Spectra of 1,2-Difluorobenzene and 1,1-Difluoroethene in Nematic Solvents. Anisotropy of Indirect Fluorine Couplings and Molecular Geometry†

J. GERRITSEN and C. MacLEAN

Scheikundig Laboratorium der Vrije Universiteit, de Lairessestraat 174, Amsterdam, The Netherlands

Received October 6, 1970

Abstract—The interpretation of the NMR spectra of 1,2-difluorobenzene, partially oriented in nematic solvents, leads to a very small anisotropy in the indirect coupling between the fluorine nuclei. A geometrical model of this molecule is given.

In 1,1-difluoroethene, a strong anistropy in J_{FF} is found. Taking $\langle 1/r_{HH}^3 \rangle / \langle 1/r_{FF}^3 \rangle = 0.6691$, the tensor elements obtained are

$$
\begin{aligned}
J_{xx} &= -720 \pm 39 \, \text{Hz} \\
J_{yy} &= +339 \pm 39 \\
J_{zz} &= +478 \pm 26
\end{aligned}
$$

if the x-axis is chosen along the C=C bond and the z-axis perpendicular to the molecular plane.

1. Introduction

The NMR spectra of partially orientated molecules can be described in terms of the Hamiltonian[1]:

$$
\begin{aligned}
\mathscr{H} = & -\frac{1}{2\pi} \sum_i \gamma_i (1 - \sigma_i) H_0 I_{zi} \\
& + \sum_{i>j} (D_{ij}^{dd} + D_{ij}^{\text{ind}}) \{ I_{zi} I_{zj} - \tfrac{1}{4}(I_{+i} I_{-j} + I_{-i} I_{+j}) \} \\
& + \sum_{i>j} J_{ij} \{ I_{zi} I_{zj} + \tfrac{1}{2}(I_{+i} I_{-j} + I_{-i} I_{+j}) \}
\end{aligned}
$$

The experimentally determined anisotropic coupling D_{ij}^{exp} is composed of two parts. One contribution, D_{ij}^{ind}, arises from the anisotropic

---

† Presented at the Third International Liquid Crystal Conference in Berlin, August 24–28, 1970.

part of the indirect coupling J and the other contribution, D_{ij}^{dd}, is the averaged dipole–dipole interaction. These two contributions can not be separated experimentally:

$$D_{ij}^{\text{exp}} = D_{ij}^{dd} + D_{ij}^{\text{ind}}$$

There is evidence that D_{ij}^{ind} for proton–proton couplings is zero.[2] The aim of this study is to investigate to what extent indirect interactions between fluorine nuclei are anisotropic. If $D_{ij}^{\text{ind}} = 0$ then

$$D_{ij}^{\text{exp}} = D_{ij}^{dd}$$

The dipole–dipole couplings and the molecular geometry are related by

$$D_{ij}^{dd} = K_{ij} \left\langle \frac{3 \cos^2 \theta_{ij} - 1}{r_{ij}^3} \right\rangle$$

where K_{ij} is a constant, θ_{ij} the angle between the magnetic field direction and the axis connecting the nuclei i and j, separated by a distance r_{ij}; the average is taken over all motions. A generally accepted assumption in liquid crystal NMR work is, that there is no correlation between the orientation of a rigid molecule and the distances within it, so that these can be separated. This means that

$$D_{ij}^{dd} = K_{ij} \overline{(3 \cos^2 \theta_{ij} - 1)} \cdot \left\langle \frac{1}{r_{ij}^3} \right\rangle$$

2. Anisotropy of J_{FF}

In order to decide whether D_{FF}^{ind} is zero or non-zero, use can be made of the fact that in some molecules an axis connecting fluorine nuclei is parallel to an axis connecting protons. In the case of 1,1-difluoroethene, for example, the ratio

$$\frac{D_{FF}^{dd}}{D_{HH}^{dd}} = \frac{K_{FF}}{K_{HH}} \cdot \frac{\langle 1/r_{FF}^3 \rangle}{\langle 1/r_{HH}^3 \rangle}$$

is a constant. The ratio of the corresponding experimental couplings is given by

$$\frac{D_{FF}^{\text{exp}}}{D_{HH}^{\text{exp}}} = \frac{D_{FF}^{dd} + D_{FF}^{\text{ind}}}{D_{HH}^{dd}} = \frac{K_{FF}}{K_{HH}} \cdot \frac{\langle 1/r_{FF}^3 \rangle}{\langle 1/r_{HH}^3 \rangle} + \frac{D_{FF}^{\text{ind}}}{D_{HH}^{dd}}$$

If this ratio varies in experiments with essentially different orientations, one can conclude that $D_{FF}^{\text{ind}} \neq 0$. The change of this ratio is most significant in the region where D_{HH}^{dd} is comparatively small. The criterion for the existence of anisotropy in indirect couplings given here can be used for all ratios of direct couplings, arising from pairs of nuclei whose interconnecting axes are parallel.

Once the existence of D_{FF}^{ind} has been established, it is of interest to evaluate its value from the experimental data. In 1,2-difluorobenzene, nine anisotropic couplings are measured. The four proton–proton couplings are purely dipolar. If we now assume that the same holds true for the four anisotropic proton–fluorine couplings, the eight proton–proton and proton–fluorine couplings can be used to calculate the four geometrical unknowns and the two parameters that describe the orientation of this molecule. From the geometrical and orientational parameters calculated in this way, D_{FF}^{dd} can be deduced. D_{FF}^{ind} can then be obtained, using the relation $D_{FF}^{ind} = D_{FF}^{exp} - D_{FF}^{dd, \ calc}$.

In 1,1-difluoroethene, the geometry can not be obtained from the three proton–proton and proton–fluorine couplings, because the number of unknowns (two geometrical and two orientational parameters) exceeds the number of dipolar couplings. In this case, the microwave geometry was used, without any vibrational corrections.

3. Results

The experimental data for 1,2-difluorobenzene are collected in Table 1. The orientational parameters are given in the notation of Snyder.[1] From the figures in Table 1 one can conclude that D_{FF}^{ind} is very small in this molecule. Although the orientation varied significantly, the ratio of $D_{FF}^{exp}/D_{45}^{exp}$ is nearly constant. Furthermore, the values of D_{FF}^{ind}, calculated along the lines mentioned above, are also small. In combination with microwave data[3,4], a molecular geometry was computed (Table 2). Details of these experiments will be reported elsewhere.[5]

Comparison of the experiments of orientated 1,1-difluorethene by Buckingham et al.[6] and by Spiesecke and Saupe[7] already suggests the existence of an anisotropy in J_{FF}. In Table 3 our data of 1,1-difluoroethene are given. Indeed the change in $D_{FF}^{exp}/D_{HH}^{exp}$ with varying orientation is appreciable. In each experiment, D_{FF}^{ind} can be calculated using data from the microwave geometry.[8]

TABLE 1   Final Results for 1,2-difluorobenzene

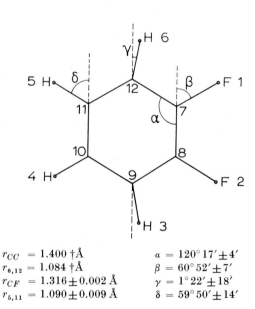

exp.	$C_{x^2-y^2}/C_{3z^2-r^2}$	$D_{FF}^{\exp}/D_{45}^{\exp}$	$D_{FF}^{\mathrm{ind}} = D_{FF}^{\exp} - D_{FF}^{dd,\ \mathrm{calc}}$
1	0.382	0.713	0.9 ± 2.4 Hz
2	0.341	0.705	2.9 ± 3.0
3	0.333	0.707	2.4 ± 2.6
4	0.550	0.702	0.5 ± 0.5

TABLE 2   A possible geometry of 1,2-difluorobenzene, consistent both with Microwave- and NMR data.   All $C–C$ distances are taken equal and no corrections for vibrations have been made

$r_{CC} = 1.400 \dagger$Å $\alpha = 120°\,17' \pm 4'$
$r_{6,12} = 1.084 \dagger$Å $\beta = 60°\,52' \pm 7'$
$r_{CF} = 1.316 \pm 0.002$ Å $\gamma = 1°\,22' \pm 18'$
$r_{5,11} = 1.090 \pm 0.009$ Å $\delta = 59°\,50' \pm 14'$

† assumed values

TABLE 3   Final Results for 1,1-difluoroethene

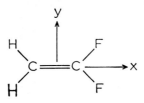

exp.	$C_{x^2-y^2}/C_{3z^2-r^2}$	$D_{FF}^{\exp}/D_{HH}^{\exp}$	$D_{FF}^{\mathrm{ind}}/C_{3z^2-r^2}$
1	-0.440	0.756	311
2	-0.489	0.875	343
3	-0.613	-0.129	365
4	-0.715	0.382	405
5	-0.895	0.493	438
6	-0.392	0.687	244
$D_{HH}^{dd}=0$	-0.577		

The relation between D_{FF}^{ind} and the tensor components of J_{FF} is given by[1]

$$\frac{D_{FF}^{\mathrm{ind}}}{C_{3z^2-r^2}} = \frac{2}{3\sqrt{5}}\left\{J_{zz}-\tfrac{1}{2}(J_{xx}+J_{yy})\right\}_{FF} + \frac{C_{x^2-y^2}}{C_{3z^2-r^2}}\,\frac{1}{\sqrt{15}}\left\{J_{xx}-J_{yy}\right\}_{FF}$$

In Fig. 1, $D_{FF}^{\mathrm{ind}}/C_{3z^2-r^2}$ is plotted against $C_{x^2-y^2}/C_{3z^2-r^2}$. Using the relation

$$J_{FF} = \tfrac{1}{3}(J_{xx}+J_{yy}+J_{zz}) = +32.5\,\mathrm{Hz},$$

the separate components of the J tensor can be calculated:

$$J_{xx} = -720 \pm 39\ \mathrm{Hz}$$
$$J_{yy} = +339 \pm 39$$
$$J_{zz} = +478 \pm 26$$

taking $\langle 1/r_{HH}^3\rangle/\langle 1/r_{FF}^3\rangle = 0.6691$. The margins of error given, are probable errors based on the accuracy of the fit.

4. Discussion

The reported values of the tensor components of J_{FF} in 1,1-difluoroethene are highly dependent on the choice of $\langle 1/r_{HH}^3\rangle/\langle 1/r_{FF}^3\rangle$.

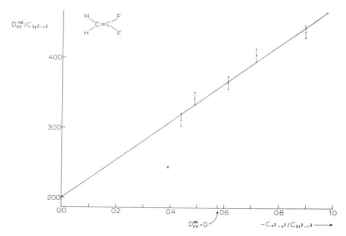

Figure 1. Least squares adaptation of experimental parameters in 1,1-difluoroethene.

However, for all reasonable ratios, the components are large compared to the isotropic value of J_{FF}.

The experiments 1–5 (Table 3) were performed in ethoxy-benzylidene-butyl-aniline, where experiment 6 was done in a mixture of azo compounds. Experiment 6 is indicated as a cross in Fig. 1. These experiments show that the tensor components of J_{FF} are different in these two nematic solvents, which indicates that these tensor components are solvent dependent, a result which is physically reasonable.

Recent calculations of the anisotropy in indirect couplings[9-12] are in disagreement with the experimental values, but these calculations are highly approximate in nature and are far from decisive up to now.

REFERENCES

1. Snyder, L. C., *J. Chem. Phys.* **43**, 4041 (1965).
2. Diehl, P. and Khetrapal, C. L., in " NMR Basic Principles and Progress " I, Springer Verlag, Berlin (1970).
3. Hatta, A., Hirose, C. and Kozima, K., *Bull. Chem. Soc. Japan* **41**, 1088 (1968).
4. Nygaard, L., Hansen, E. R., Hansen, R. L., Rastrup-Andersen, J. and Sørensen, G. O., *Spectrochim. Acta* **23A**, 2813 (1967).
5. Gerritsen, J. and MacLean, C., *Spectrochim. Acta.*

6. Buckingham, A. D., Burnell, E. E. and De Lange, C. A., *Mol. Phys.* **16**, 299 (1969).
7. Spiesecke, H. and Saupe, A., *Mol. Cryst.* **6**, 287 (1970).
8. Laurie, V. W. and Pence, D. T., *J. Chem. Phys.* **38**, 2693 (1963).
9. Barfield, M., *Chem. Phys. Lett.* **4**, 518 (1970).
10. Nakatsuji, H., Kato, H., Morishima, I. and Yonezawa, T., *Chem. Phys. Lett.* **4**, 607 (1970).
11. Buckingham, A. D. and Love, I., *J. Magn. Res.* **2**, 338 (1970).
12. Nakatsuji, H., Hirao, K., Kato, H. and Yonezawa, T., *Chem. Phys. Lett.* **6**, 541 (1970).

Self-diffusion in Liquid Crystals†

R. BLINC, V. DIMIC, J. PIRŠ, M. VILFAN and I. ZUPANČIČ

University of Ljubljana
Institute "J. Stefan"
Ljubljana, Yugoslavia

Received November, 16, 1970; in revised form December 28, 1970

Abstract—The temperature dependence of the diffusion coefficients in PAA, anisalazine, 4,4'-diheptyloxy-azoxybenzene, anhidrous Na-palmitate and Na-palmitate-water mixtures has been studied by quasi-elastic scattering of cold neutrons and by the variable gradient proton spin echo method.

Introduction

The most basic property of liquid crystals is that they flow while sustaining an ordered structure. Very little however is known on the nature of this process on a molecular basis, and only recently the first attempts have been made to measure diffusion coefficients in nematic systems.[1,2]

To throw some additional light on this problem we decided to measure the temperature dependence of the diffusion coefficients in some thermotropic and lyotropic liquid crystals. Systems exhibiting nematic as well as smectic ordering were included in our study.

The methods used were quasi-elastic incoherent cold neutron scattering and variable field gradient proton spin echo measurements. It should be stressed that whereas in the spin echo method the true translational self-diffusion coefficient is measured, quasi-elastic cold neutron scattering is sensitive to both translational and rotational motions of the molecules.[3] Whereas the measuring period in NMR diffusion measurements is typically $10^{-3} - 10^{-2}$ sec, neutron scattering detects diffusive motions which occur in a time of about 10^{-11} sec.

The cross section for quasi-elastic cold neutron scattering may be approximated by a Lorentzian line with a half-width that depends on the true self-diffusion coefficient describing the translational motion

† Presented at the Third International Liquid Crystal Conference in Berlin, August 24–28, 1970.

of the molecular center of gravity, and on another coefficient describing the proton motion relative to the center of gravity. This relative motion can be rotation or rotational diffusion, which may occur in small steps or in large jumps. It is expected that in systems of low viscosity the translational term is dominant whereas in high viscosity systems the width of the quasi-elastic peak will be determined by rotational diffusion. Following Larsson,[4] the asymptotic quasi-elastic line width is in the limit $K^2 \to \infty$ given by

$$(\Delta\omega)_{K^2 \to \infty} = 2\left(\frac{1}{\tau_0} + \frac{2}{3} D_p K^2\right) \tag{1}$$

whereas it is in the limit $K^2 \to 0$ given by:

$$(\Delta\omega)_{K^2 \to 0} = 2 \cdot \text{``} D \text{''} \cdot K^2. \tag{2}$$

Here $\hbar K$ is the momentum transfer in the scattering process, τ_0 is the time the molecule spends in a quasi-stable position before jumping to a new state or site, D_p is the coefficient describing the protonic rotational diffusion on the surface of a sphere around the molecular center of gravity, and

$$\text{``} D \text{''} = D + D_{\text{rel}} + D_{\text{mix}} \tag{3}$$

is an apparent diffusion coefficient which is a sum of the true self-diffusion coefficient D, a fictitious coefficient $D_{\text{rel}} \geqslant D_p$ describing the motion of the average proton relative to its molecular center of gravity and a small mixture term, D_{mix}, between the relative motion and the center of gravity motion.

The NMR spin echo method[5] for the determination of the diffusion coefficient, on the other hand, is based on the observation of an extra damping of the transverse nuclear magnetization due to a change in the Larmor frequency as a result of translational diffusion of the molecule across the inhomogeneous applied magnetic field. Rotational diffusion does not result in a significant change in the proton Larmor frequency during the time of the experiment and is therefore not observable.

The spatial dependence of the applied magnetic field across the sample can be described as

$$H_z = H_0 + (\mathbf{G} \cdot \mathbf{r}) \tag{4}$$

where $\mathbf{G}$ can be assumed to be a constant. The equation of motion[6] of the transverse magnetization $m = M_x + iM_y$ precessing in the $x - y$ plane after a 90° pulse is

$$\frac{\delta m}{\delta t} = i\omega_0 m - \frac{m}{T_2} - i\gamma(\mathbf{G} \cdot \mathbf{r})m + \nabla \cdot D \cdot \nabla m \qquad (5)$$

where $\omega_0 = \gamma H_0$ is the unperturbed Larmor frequency, T_2 is the spin-spin relaxation time, and D is the self-diffusion constant tensor. The solution of this equation is particularly simple for a time independent field gradient $\mathbf{G}$. After a refocusing 180° pulse applied at a time τ after the 90° pulse, we obtain:

$$m(t) = m_0 \exp\left[i\omega_0 t + i\gamma(\mathbf{G} \cdot \mathbf{r})(t - 2\tau) - \left(\frac{\gamma^2 \mathbf{G} \cdot D \cdot \mathbf{G}t^3}{12} + \frac{t}{T_2}\right)\right] \qquad (6)$$

Expression (6) predicts the formation of a spin echo at a time $t = 2\tau$ the amplitude of which depends on the applied field gradient and the self-diffusion constant D. By measuring the amplitude of the echo as a function of the applied field gradient or by varying t at fixed G we thus obtain D.

All molecular displacements between the 90° and 180° pulse contribute to the attenuation of the echo in the above method. In order to limit the diffusion time as well as to be able to use larger field gradients, it is often useful[6] to apply the gradient in the form of two very short pulses of width δ the first of which is applied after the 90° and the second after the 180° pulse. We thus have a procedure to detect motion in the interval Δ between the two pulses. The additional attenuation of the echo due to molecular diffusion in this interval Δ is easily obtained from Eq. (5) and is given by

$$m(\Delta) = m_0 \exp\left[-\gamma^2 \delta^2 \mathbf{G} \cdot D \cdot \mathbf{G}\Delta\right]. \qquad (7)$$

Equation (7) reduces in the case of isotropic diffusion to the well-known expression:

$$m(\Delta) = m_0 \exp\left[-\gamma^2 \delta^2 G^2 D \Delta\right]. \qquad (8)$$

Experimental Procedure

The quasi-elastic broadening of the Be-filtered neutron beam has been measured with the time of flight spectrometer on line with a CDC 1700 computer at the Triga Mark II reactor in Ljubljana at the angles $\delta = 24°, 51°, 76°$ and $110°$. The corresponding momentum transfer in the scattering process is $K = 4\pi/\lambda_0 \sin \delta/2$ where $\lambda_0 = 3.96\,\text{Å}$. A liquid methane cold neutron source in the tangential channel has been used. The samples were placed into a cylindrical container. The thickness of the samples was such that the transmission was about 90%. The temperature was measured with three copper-constantan thermocouples to $\pm 1\,°\text{C}$. No attempt was made to orient the samples so that only the average of the diffusion constant tensor was obtained in neutron scattering.

The NMR diffusion measurements were performed on a home built pulsed spectrometer operating at 37 MHz. A constant as well as a pulsed field gradient was used. Unless otherwise stated the component of the D tensor parallel to the magnetic field, $D_\parallel$, was measured.

Results

(1) P-azoxyanisole (PAA): A typical dependence of the broadening of the quasi-elastic neutron peak on the square of the momentum transfer for nematic PAA is shown on Fig. 1a. The results shown on this figure were obtained after the inelastic background—centered at 12 cm^{-1} and probably representing —CH_3 rotation—was subtracted. It can be clearly seen that no horizontal saturation value is approached. The slope of the tangent to the curve at high momentum transfers gives the rotational contribution, $4/3\,D_p$, and the intersection of the tangent with the $\Delta\omega$ axis gives $2/\tau_0$. The slope of the line width curves near the origin ($K^2 \to 0$) on the other hand gives the apparent diffusion coefficient 2 "D". At 120 °C we thus obtain $\tau_0 = 2.5 \times 10^{-12}$ sec, $D_p = 1.6 \times 10^{-6}$ cm^2/sec and "D" = $(0.75 \pm 0.5) \times 10^{-5}$ cm^2/sec. The pure rotational contribution thus seems to represent only a small part of "D".

The temperature dependence of the quasi-elastic broadening is quite puzzling.

In the solid phase from room temperature up to 112 °C no quasi-elastic broadening could be observed demonstrating that "D" is lower than 10^{-6} cm^2/sec.

In the nematic phase, on the other hand, there is a very distinct broadening. Contrary to expectations, however, the momentum transfer dependence of the broadening was found to be identical at

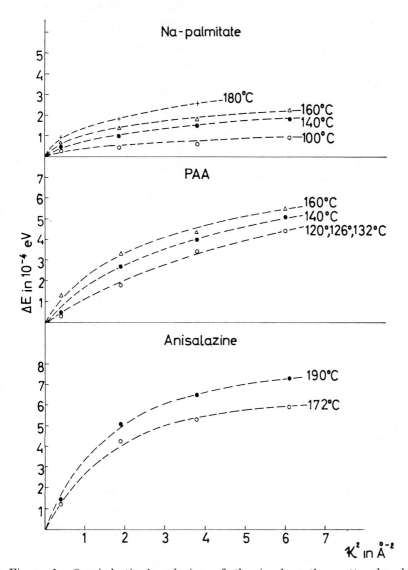

Figure 1. Quasi-elastic broadening of the incoherently scattered cold neutron line in (a) Na-palmitate, (b) PAA and (c) anisalazine as a function of the square of the momentum transfer.

120 °C, 126 °C and 132 °C.   The apparent diffusion coefficient "D" thus does not seem to depend on temperature in nematic PAA (Fig. 2).

In the isotropic liquid phase the diffusion coefficient "D" exponentially increases with increasing temperature.   Both the value and the activation energy $E = 8$ kcal/mol are rather close to the ones obtained by the proton spin echo method.[1]   This means that in liquid PAA, "D" is determined by the translational contribution. The value of $D_{\parallel}$ measured by the proton spin echo method in the liquid-like region right below the nematic-liquid transition is somewhat higher than "D" obtained from the neutron scattering data. This might be due to the anisotropy of the diffusion constant tensor. Preliminary measurements in nematic PAA have namely shown that $D_{\parallel} > D_{\perp}$.

It should be mentioned that the value of the translational self-diffusion coefficient D obtained from the Einstein equation

$$D = \frac{kT}{6\pi r \eta} \tag{9}$$

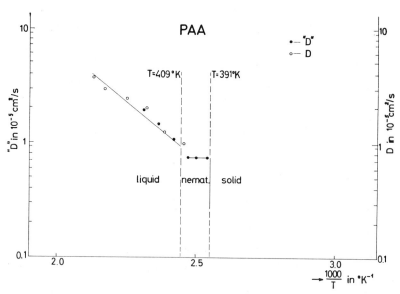

Figure 2.   Temperature dependence of the diffusion coefficients in PAA. "D" is the apparent diffusion coefficient obtained from the neutron scattering data as $K \rightarrow 0$, and D is the self-diffusion coefficient determined by NMR.

is by a factor of ten smaller than "D" or D as determined by neutron scattering respectively NMR measurements. As PAA is far from being a spherical molecule for which Eq. (9) is valid, this discrepancy is not too serious.

One way to explain the temperature independence of "D" in the nematic phase would be to assign "D" as being due to rotation of the PAA molecules around their principal symmetry axes. Such motion is known to occur in nematic PAA. Within this model it is however hard to understand the relatively good agreement between the NMR and neutron scattering data.

Alternatively one could explain the temperature independence of "D" by the fact that the components of the D tensor have opposite temperature dependences as is this indeed the case for the viscosity coefficients.[7]

A definite explanation of the above results and in particular of the puzzling temperature independence of "D" in the nematic phase has to be postponed until the temperature behavior of all the elements of the diffusion constant tensor is known. Work along these lines is in progress.

(2) Anisalazine: The neutron scattering results for this compound which exhibits a nematic phase between 168 °C and 182 °C are rather similar to the ones obtained for PAA. The value of "D" does not depend on temperature in the nematic phase and equals to "D" $=$ 1.3×10^{-5} cm²/sec. The value of D_p at 172 °C is 2.4×10^{-6} cm²/sec. In the liquid region a normal thermally activated diffusion rate is observed (Fig. 3). The NMR results seem to agree with the neutron data in the isotropic liquid just above the nematic region.

(3) 4,4'-Diheptyloxy-azoxybenzene (PAH): This compound which is a higher homologue of PAA, exhibits a smectic mesophase between 65° and 89 °C and a nematic one between 89 °C and 118 °C. The neutron scattering results are again very puzzling: "D" is temperature independent *throughout* the smectic and the nematic phase (Fig. 4). Its value is "D" $= (0.5 \pm 0.05) \times 10^{-5}$ cm²/sec. D_p, on the other hand, equals 3×10^{-6} cm²/sec in the smectic phase and significantly changes on going to the nematic region. In the liquid phase above 118 °C we again find a normal, thermally activated temperature dependence of "D". The self-diffusion coefficients D, determined by NMR, agree rather well with the neutron data.

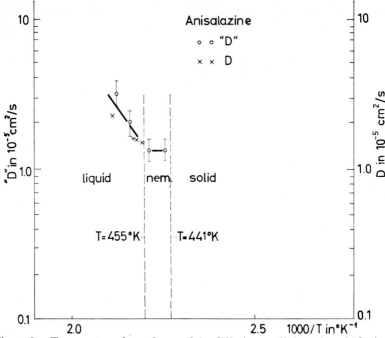

Figure 3.   Temperature dependence of the diffusion coefficients in anisalazine.

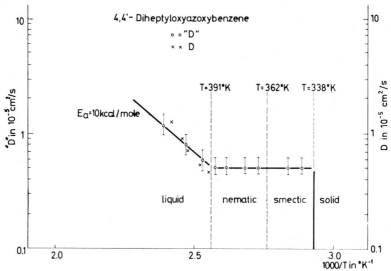

Figure 4.   Temperature dependence of the diffusion coefficients in 4,4'-diheptyloxy-azoxybenzene (PAH).

To throw some additional light on these surprising results we measured the Zeeman and the dipolar (Fig. 5) proton spin-lattice relaxation times as a function of temperature. The Zeeman relaxation time measured at $\omega_0/2\pi = 37$ MHz is rather long in the solid phase and drops abruptly on going to the smectic phase, where it continues to increase with increasing temperature throughout the smectic and nematic phase until leveling off just before the nematic-liquid transition. On going to the liquid phase, there is again a discontinuous drop in T_1, followed by an exponential increase with increasing temperature in the liquid phase.

The dipolar proton spin-lattice relaxation time T_{1D}, on the other hand, shows a different behavior. It decreases with increasing temperature in the solid and discontinuously increases on going to the smectic mesophase, where it exponentially increases with increasing temperature. This means that the characteristic time τ for diffusion—which, however can be of rotational or translational origin—is longer than 10^{-4} sec in the solid and shorter than that in the smectic mesophase, where it behaves like $\tau = \tau_0 \exp{(E/kT)}$. In the nematic mesophase, on the other hand, T_{1D} is practically temperature independent, and by a factor of 4 shorter than T_1. Whether T_{1D} is in the nematic phase dominated by order fluctuations or by diffusion is still an open question. Here as well as in PAA, measurements of the anisotropy of the diffusion constant tensor might help to solve this problem.

(4) Anhidrous Na-palmitate (NaP): To see whether the surprising temperature independence of "D" is limited to homologues of PAA or whether it is a more general characteristic of liquid crystals we decided to investigate anhidrous NaP which is known to undergo five different smectic liquid crystal transitions[8] before melting.

In contrast to the previous cases "D" was found to be exponentially dependent on temperature (Fig. 6), and varied between 10^{-6} cm²/sec in the "subcurd" and 10^{-5} cm²/sec in the "superwaxy" phase. Because of the too large broadening of the quasielastic peak, "D" could not be measured at higher temperatures. An estimate of D_p and of the mean square displacements obtained from the Debye-Waller factor shows that the translational contribution to "D" is very small.

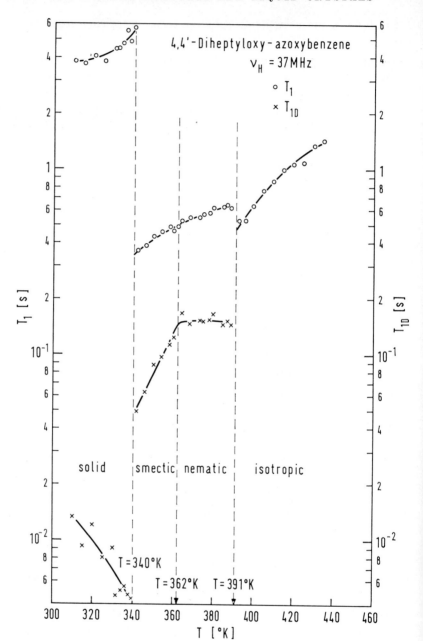

Figure 5.   Temperature dependences of the Zeeman and dipolar proton spin-lattice relaxation times in PAH.

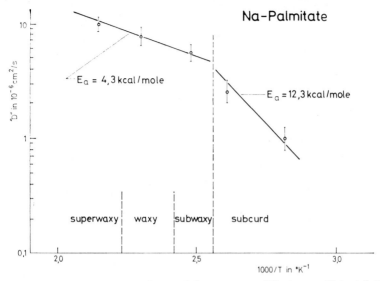

Figure 6.   Temperature dependence of the apparent diffusion coefficient " D " in anhidrous Na-palmitate (NaP).

This conclusion is confirmed by a direct measurement of the translational self-diffusion coefficient D by the proton spin echo method. The NMR method could be used only above 525 °K where the proton line becomes sufficiently narrow to allow the observation of spin echoes.   The self-diffusion coefficients D (Fig. 7) are of the order of 6×10^{-6} cm²/sec in the subneat and neat (smectic B) mesomorphic phase, whereas an extrapolation of the neutron scattering results yields " D " $= 2 \times 10^{-5}$ cm²/sec in this temperature region.   The translational contribution to " D " in NaP is thus small indeed.

The most surprising result is however the fact that the translational self-diffusion coefficients D in contrast to " D " do not seem to depend on temperature in the mesomorphic phase.   In the isotropic liquid phase, on the other hand, a normal, thermally activated temperature dependence of D is found.   The self-diffusion behavior of smectic NaP is thus analogous to the one found in PAA.

(5) Na-palmitate-water mixtures (NaP-H₂O): Lyotropic liquid crystals which are formed by the addition of water to various amphiphilic materials, seem to play an important role in many biological systems including cell membranes.   The liquid crystalline phases are limited by an upper temperature at which the transition to the

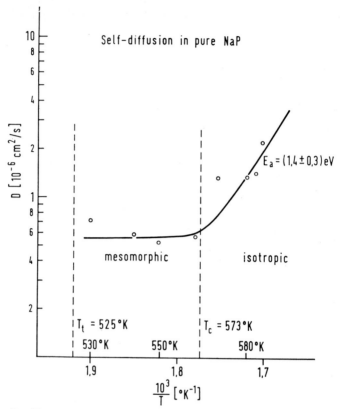

Figure 7.   Temperature dependence of the self-diffusion coefficient D in NaP as determined by NMR.

isotropic liquid occurs and a lower one at which ejection of water takes place and an amorphous solid or gel is formed.   The *neat* phase (Fig. 8) is lamellar and smectic: the hydrocarbon chains are arranged in parallel equidistant double layers which alternate with intervening layers of water.   In the hexagonal *middle* phase, on the other hand, the hydrocarbon molecules form a two dimensional lattice of parallel cylinders with intervening water channels (Fig. 8).   It was the purpose of our study to investigate the diffusion properties of the H_2O molecules in these channels.

Deuteron resonance measurements[9] have shown that the motion of the D_2O molecules in such systems is not completely isotropic and that there is on the time average a small amount of preferential ordering of the D_2O molecules. The temperature dependence of the quadrupole splitting of the D_2O NMR spectrum for a 30% NaP-70% D_2O mixture is shown in Fig. 9. The spectra are of the " powder " type as expected for randomly oriented regions of spin 1 nuclei with a zero asymmetry parameter. The splitting first increases with

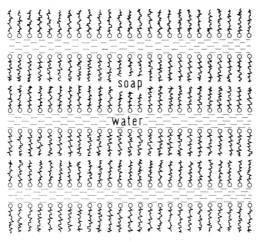

lamellar mesophase

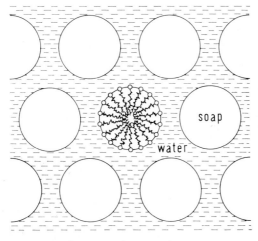

hexagonal mesophase

Figure 8.   Structures of the " neat " lamellar and the " middle " hexagonal mesophases of NaP-H_2O systems.

increasing T, stays nearly constant and then disappears on going to the isotropic liquid. It should be mentioned that a similar behavior was observed in the lamellar as well as in the hexagonal phase. In view of the fact that the maximum splitting increases with decreasing D_2O content it is tempting to explain the observed D_2O splitting as a result of " fast " exchange between " free " D_2O molecules within the channel and " bound " D_2O molecules at the polar ends of the hydrocarbon chains. This model also explains the fact that a single deuteron line is observed except very close to the temperature of the transition to the isotropic liquid. The deuteron spins thus see a time averaged electric field gradient

$$\bar{q} = q_{\text{bound}}\, p + q_{\text{free } D_2O}\, (1-p) \tag{10}$$

where p is the fraction of the time the D_2O molecule spends in a " bound " state and q_{bound} and q_{free} are the maximum components of the electric field gradient tensor in the " bound " respectively the " free " state. In case of an axially symmetric field gradient ($\eta = 0$) q is related to the quadrupole splitting of the deuteron NMR line by $\Delta v = \frac{3}{4}e^2qQ/h$, where Q is the quadrupole moment of the deuteron. As the electric field gradient tensor of a free D_2O molecule in water

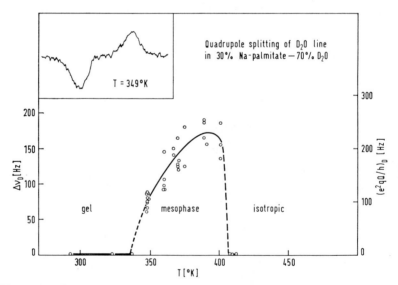

Figure 9. Temperature dependence of the quadrupole splitting of the deuteron D_2O NMR spectrum in a 70% D_2O–30% NaP system.

is averaged out by molecular motion, one may assume that $q_{\overrightarrow{\text{free } D_2O}} \to 0$, and that

$$\bar{q} = q_{\text{bound}}\, p. \tag{11}$$

If this model is correct one can immediately obtain the temperature dependence of the self-diffusion coefficients of the H_2O molecules as:

$$D_{\parallel} = D_{\text{NaP}} \cdot p + D_{H_2O} \cdot (1-p) \tag{12}$$

where D_{NaP} is the self-diffusion coefficient of those H_2O molecules which are rigidly bound to the NaP groups and D_{H_2O} is the self-diffusion coefficient of the free H_2O molecules. As $D_{\text{NaP}} \ll D_{H_2O}$, in the liquid crystalline state, we have

$$D_{\parallel} \approx D_{H_2O}(1-p), \quad T < T_{l.c. \to i.l.} \tag{13}$$

The experimental results are shown in Fig. 10 for both the hexagonal and the lamellar phase of the NaP-H_2O system. In both cases the diffusion coefficients exponentially increase with increasing temperature before *dropping* on going to the isotropic liquid.

The self-diffusion coefficients in the water channels are quite large and are at $350\,°K$ in the 30% NaP-70% H_2O system only by a factor of 3 lower than the ones measured in pure H_2O at the same temperature and with the same spacing (40–100 msec) between the $90°$ and the $180°$ pulses. The values of $D_{\parallel}$ increase with increasing H_2O content.

It should be also mentioned that in the isotropic liquid state the self-diffusion coefficients for a 30% NaP-70% H_2O and a 30% NaP-70% D_2O mixtures are identical and are of the order of 3.10^{-6} cm²/sec. This means that in the isotropic liquid in contrast to Eq. (13).

$$D \approx D_{\text{NaP}}, \quad T > T_{l.c. \to i.l.} \tag{14}$$

i.e., $p \approx 1$, what can be understood only if a significant change in p accompanies the liquid crystal → isotropic fluid transition.

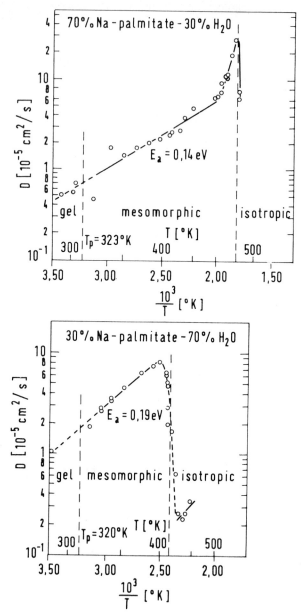

Figure 10.   Temperature dependences of the self-diffusion coefficients D of the H_2O molecules in both lamellar and hexagonal NaP-H_2O systems.

REFERENCES

1. Blinc, R., Hogenboom, D. L., O' Reilly, D. E. and Peterson, E. M., *Phys. Rev. Letters* **23**, 969 (1969).
2. Blinc, R. and Dimic, V., *Phys. Letters* **31A**, 10 (1970). Janik, J. A., Janik, J. M., Otnes, K. and Riste, T., paper presented at the III. Liquid Crystal Conference, Berlin, (1970).
3. Singwi, K. S. and Sjolander, A., *Phys. Rev.* **119**, 863 (1960).
4. Larsson, K. E., *Phys. Rev.* **67**, 171 (1968).
5. Abragam, A., *The Principles of Nuclear Magnetism*, (Oxford University Press, 1961).
6. Stejskal, E. O., *J. Chem. Phys.* **43**, 3597 (1965).
7. Miesowizc, M., *Nature* **136**, 261 (1935); **158**, 27 (1946).
8. Powel, B. D. and Puddington, I. E., *Can. J. Chem.* **31**, 828 (1953). Nordsieck, H., Rosevear, F. B. and Ferguson. R. H., *J. Chem. Phys.* **16**, 175 (1948).
9. Lawson, K. D. and Flaut, T. J., *J. Phys. Chem.* **72**, 2066 (1968). Charvolin, J. and Rigny, P., *J. de Phys.* **30**, C4—76 (1969).

Liquid Crystal Ordering in the Magnetic and Electric Fields Studied in 4,4'-di-n-heptyloxyazoxybenzene by EPR†

M. ŠENTJURC and M. SCHARA

Institute "J. Stefan",
Ljubljana,
Yugoslavia

Received September 29, 1970; in revised form November 11, 1970

Abstract—The 4,4'-di-n-heptyloxyazoxybenzene (PAH) liquid crystal order-ing in the presence of the magnetic and dc electric fields was studied in the smectic and nematic mesophase. In the smectic phase the molecules are aligned with the long molecular axes perpendicular to the dc electric field direction, as contrasted to the parallel orientation with the dc electric field direction in the nematic phase. Effects of anisotropy in the plane perpendi-cular to the long molecular axes are observed.

1. Introduction

Electron paramagnetic resonance can be used to study the ordering of a liquid crystal mesophase, but first a paramagnetic impurity has to be introduced to make the measurement possible. The axially symmetric vanadylacetylacetonate (VAA) complex was found to be a convenient paramagnetic centre since a satisfactory alignment with the solvent molecules is obtained.[1] The nematic phase of p-azoxyanisole (PAA) was studied by electron paramagnetic resonance in the presence of a dc electric field.[2] From the angular dependence in the magnetic field it was concluded that the molecular distribution about their long molecular axes is not axially symmetric. In order to extend the same technique to another liquid crystal, where the nematic and smectic mesophase measurements are possible the 4,4'-di-n-heptyloxyazoxybenzene (PAH) was used.

† Presented at the Third International Liquid Crystal Conference in Berlin, August 24–28, 1970.

2. Results and Discussion

PAH, a higher homologue of PAA, undergoes three liquid crystal transitions (solid-smectic $T = 65°$, smectic-nematic $T = 90°$ and nematic-isotropic $T = 118\,°C$). The smectic mesophase, where the nematic order in magnetic field was partially maintained, was studied by Francis and Luckhurst.[3] An angular dependence of the hyperfine splitting due to the dissolved vanadylacetylacetonate (VAA) paramagnetic complex was followed and a decrease of the long range orientational order was observed.

When a dc electric field was applied on the PAH in the nematic phase the molecules do orient with the long molecular axes along the electric field direction and the results of the angular dependence resembles those of PAA (Fig. 1). The hyperfine splitting between

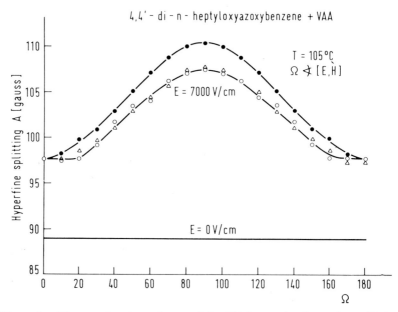

Figure 1. The angular dependence of the VAA complex hyperfine splitting in the PAH nematic phase matrix with respect to the relative orientation of the dc electric and magnetic fields directions. (○○○ represent the experimental values, ●●● the calculated values for an axial distribution of $A_\parallel$ direction about the electric field, △△△ the calculated values for unaxial distribution of $A_\parallel$).

the lines corresponding to the nuclear spin projections m and $-m$ is given by the equation:

$$\frac{\Delta E_{m,-m}}{2m} = a + \tfrac{1}{3}(A_{\parallel} - A_{\perp})\,(3\cos^2 U - 1)$$

where a, $A_{\parallel}$ and $A_{\perp}$ are the isotropic, and the general components of the hyperfine tensor. U is the angle between the magnetic field direction and the $A_{\parallel}$ hyperfine component, which can be expressed:

$$\cos^2 U = \sin^2 \Omega\,\overline{\sin^2 \alpha \sin^2 \phi} + \cos^2 \Omega\,\overline{\cos^2 \alpha}$$

$$+\, 2 \sin \Omega \cos \Omega\,\overline{\sin \alpha \cos \alpha \sin \phi}$$

for an asymmetric distribution of the $A_{\parallel}$ axis orientation about the electric field. Ω is an angle between the electric and magnetic field, α and ϕ are spherical coordinates of the $A_{\parallel}$ direction. Assuming that the optical axis and the electric field coincide, the experimental values for the averages are:

$$\overline{\cos^2 \alpha} = 0.261 \quad \overline{\sin^2 \alpha \sin^2 \phi} = 0.347 \quad \overline{\sin \alpha \cos \alpha \sin \phi} = -0.005$$

A qualitative explanation of the above coefficients could be given assuming that the distributions of the normals to the molecular plane of the paramagnetic complex in α and ϕ about the optical axis are not correlated, and that $\sin^2 \phi \leqslant 0.5$. The value of $\sin^2 \phi$ is limited according to the collective ordering of the liquid crystal molecules with their planes preferentially oriented in the magnetic field direction.[2] Since the calculated curve is well aligned with the experimental one it can be concluded that the molecular order does not change with the relative orientation of both fields.

From the values of the PAA coefficients[2]:

$$\overline{\cos^2 \alpha} = 0.186 \quad \overline{\sin^2 \alpha \sin^2 \phi} = 0.478 \quad \overline{\sin \alpha \cos \alpha \sin \phi} = -0.055$$

we can suggest that during the angular dependence measurements, when H and E are not parallel, the magnetic field partially increases the order along the long molecular axes. This is not the case for PAH, which is explainable since the molecules are heavier and longer according to the end group attached. Therefore, the effect of the inplane orientation is directly observable and the curves are well aligned as compared to the discrepancies in the PAA case.

The angular dependence measurement on Fig. 1 could also be explained with the deviation of the optical axis from the electric field direction reflected in a decreased ordering parameter according to the fast molecular diffusional motion.   But it is necessary to assume that the optical axis direction is changing with the relative orientation of the electric and magnetic fields.   In this case the saturation effects on Fig. 4 are hard to explain.   Therefore, we have chosen the inplane ordering of molecules, being in agreement with the nonaxially symmetric molecular shape.

When the electric field is switched on at 105 °C the 50 % decrease in the ordering parameter from $S = -0.223$ to $S = -0.108$ is obtained which is contrasted by only a 1 % decrease from -0.24 to -0.22 for PAA. S is the ordering parameter defined for the $A_\parallel$ direction of the VAA paramagnetic solute.[1,4]

When the crystal is cooled down from the nematic phase to the smectic one, (Fig. 2) the molecules retain the preferential direction

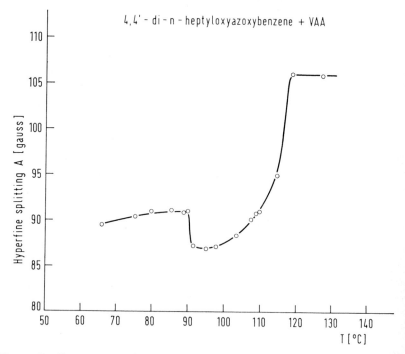

Figure 2.   Temperature dependence of the VAA hyperfine splitting in the PAH.

along the magnetic field, with a lowering of order from $S = -0.245$ to $S = -0.191$ just below the transition point which slowly increases to $S = -0.212$, near the smectic-solid transition temperature, being thus in a close agreement to the results of Francis and Luckhurst.[3] Therefore the angular dependence measurements in the magnetic field are possible (Fig. 3). Just as in the nematic phase we can try

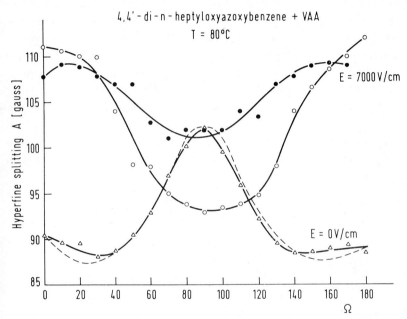

Figure 3. The angular dependence of the VAA hyperfine splitting in the PAH smectic mesophase. (○○○ and ●●● represent the angular dependences with respect to the relative orientation of dc electric and magnetic fields and △△△ represent the angular dependence with respect to the preferential long axis molecular direction retained from the nematic phase relative to the magnetic field direction. The dotted line is calculated for the unaxial distribution at $A_\parallel$).

to define the long range orientational ordering and the averages, defining the nonaxial distribution as follows:

$$\overline{\cos^2 \alpha} = 0.201 \quad \overline{\sin^2 \alpha \sin^2 \phi} = 0.229 \quad \overline{\sin \alpha \cos \alpha \sin \phi} = -0.057$$

Here a larger disturbance of molecular ordering or the preferential orientation of both anisotropy defining directions takes place. This disturbance is reversible since the angular dependence is symmetric about the 90° value (Fig. 3). The deeps at 35° could be explained as the start of the inplane anisotropy influence.

When the dc electric field is applied to the smectic phase along the magnetic field, the direction of the long molecular axes are turned by 90° and a complete change of the collective molecular orientation is evident. In the electric field a preferential direction for the long molecular axes is not defined except for being in the plane perpendicular to the electric field and therefore the measured angular dependence is not reproducible. These are in fact the two extreme experimental values presented on (Fig. 3). It is therefore hard to estimate the ordering parameters for the smectic phase in an electric field.

It is interesting that the electric field effect is saturated in both mesophases at the same dc value, $E = 4500$ V/cm, when H and E are perpendicular (Figs. 4, 5). This value is nearly twice as high as measured for PAA. As expected the preferential direction in the smectic phase is only slightly disturbed when the electric field is removed.

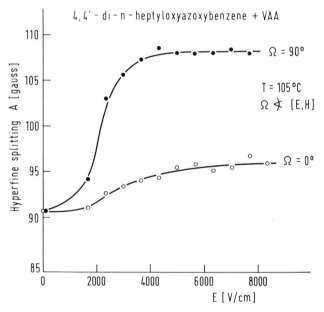

Figure 4. The hyperfine splitting of VAA complex dissolved in the PAH nematic mesophase as a function of the dc electric field strength ○○○ for E and H parallel and ●●● for E and H perpendicular.

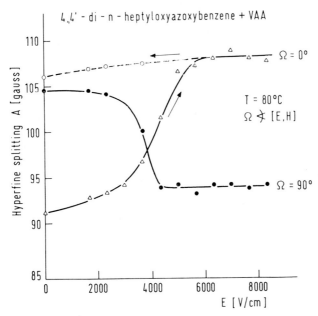

Figure 5. The hyperfine splitting of VAA complex dissolved in the PAH smectic mesophase as a function of the dc electric field strength ●●● for E and H perpendicular, and △△△ for E and H parallel.

3. Conclusion

The results presented have only a relative value since the VAA complex does only partly follow the solvent mesophase order.[1] But it can be suggested that the liquid crystal molecules should not be treated as axially symmetric about their long molecular axes. Therefore, two preferential directions can set in with respect to the collectively ordered molecules in the two mesophases of PAH.

REFERENCES

1. Chen, D. H., James, P. G. and Luckhurst, G. R., *Mol. Cryst. and Liq. Cryst.*, **8**, 71 (1969).
2. Schara, M. and Šentjurc, M., *Solid State Communications*, **8**, 593 (1970).
3. Francis, P. D. and Luckhurst, G. R., *Chem. Phys. Letters* **3**, 213 (1969).
4. Saupe, A., *Z. Naturf.* **19a**, 161 (1964).

EPR Study of the Temperature Dependence of Molecular Rotation in Nematic Liquid Crystals†

C. F. SCHWERDTFEGER, M. MARUŠIČ and A. MACKAY

Department of Physics
University of British Columbia
Vancouver, Canada

and

R. Y. DONG

Department of Statistics
University of Waterloo
Waterloo, Canada

Received October 12, 1970; *in revised form December* 11, 1970

Abstract—The EPR spectrum of vanadyl acetylacetonate dissolved in viscous nematic liquid crystals has been studied as a function of temperature. A plot of the effective order parameter versus temperature shows a definite discontinuity in slope as the molecular rotation passes from weakly to strongly hindered motion. It is shown that viscosity effects do not completely account for this discontinuity in slope. These results are supported by nuclear spin lattice relaxation measurements on the pure liquid crystals which indicate a change in the dominant relaxation mechanism at the same temperature. In slightly less viscous nematics an approximate correction for the viscosity brings the experimental data into fair agreement with a universal curve calculated by Luckhurst.

Introduction

EPR experiments in liquid crystals are made by dissolving a small amount (nominally $\sim 10^{-3}$ M) of paramagnetic material in the liquid crystal and observing the change in the measured value for the hyperfine coupling in going from the isotropic liquid to the nematic phase. Such measurements have been made in nematic liquid crystals as a function of temperature,[1,2] concentration of a second solute[3] and electric field.[4,5] Although several paramagnetic materials have been studied, the most commonly used probe is vanadyl acetylacetonate (VACA). The advantages of VACA are its

† Presented at the Third International Liquid Crystal Conference in Berlin, August 24–28, 1970.

391

large anisotropic hyperfine tensor, high temperature stability and solubility in many liquid crystals. In this paper we would like to concentrate on the degree of order of VACA in liquid crystals obtained from the measured effective hyperfine coupling and its use in studying the properties of liquid crystals.

Experimental Procedure

The EPR spectra were obtained at 9.1 KMHz using a conventional straight detection system and 100 K Hz field modulation. Field positions were measured to ± 0.1 G with a proton magnetometer. The microwave sample cavity was placed in a glass sleeve with a heater coil wrapped around the sleeve and this combination was placed in a glass dewar situated between the magnet pole pieces. The modulation coils were mounted on the stainless steel TE_{102} cavity. The cavity was copper plated to increase the Q value (loaded $Q \sim 4000$). The power dissipated by the 3–10 G modulation employed raised the temperature noticeably and the system required about one half hour to come to equilibrium after the temperature was changed. The temperature measuring thermistor was placed in the sample liquid just outside of the cavity. The thermistors were magnetic but in this arrangement did not affect the large line width spectrum (~ 25 G). The temperature could be held constant to within $\pm 0.1\,^{\circ}$C and the difference across the sample was less than $0.5\,^{\circ}$C. Measurements below room temperature were made with a Varian cavity and an air flow system. Under these conditions the temperature difference across the sample was $\sim 1\,^{\circ}$C. The NMR spin lattice relaxation measurements were obtained with a pulse technique which has been previously described.[6]

The liquid crystals were used as obtained without further purification since the nematic-isotropic transition temperatures were in good agreement with the literature values. The mole fraction of vanadyl acetylacetonate in solution was about 10^{-3}. The liquid crystals studied and their measured transition temperatures with and without VACA are given in Table 1. The temperature measurements were made on a Perkin-Elmer DSC-1B direct scanning calorimeter. The viscosity measurements were made with a Fenske capillary tube 300–J781 in a temperature controlled oil bath. Since we are mainly

TABLE 1

Liquid Crystal	Tc (Lit)	Temperature °C Tc (Meas.)	Tc (10⁻³M VACA)
I 4-methoxy benzylidene-4-amino-α-methyl cinnamic acid-n-propyl ester	89	83	78
II 4-methoxy benzylidene-n-butyl anilene (MBBA)	47	47	44
III 4-methoxy-axobenzene-4-oxy-capronate	106	106	102

interested in relative viscosities we quote in this paper only the kinematic viscosity (η/ρ) in centistokes. The viscosity in centipoise (η) is not very different numerically since the densities of the liquid crystals discussed are close to one.

Results and Discussion

Vanadyl acetylacetonate is a planar molecule whose symmetry is slightly non-axial ($\sim 5\%$). It situates in the liquid crystal with its symmetry axis at right angles to the optic axis. Detailed descriptions of the EPR spectrum expected for VACA in liquid crystals under the extreme conditions of complete motional averaging[1,3,7] and essentially frozen molecules[4,8] have been given. A motionally averaged spectrum consists of eight hyperfine lines whose separation is determined in the isotropic phase by the average hyperfine coupling,

$$a = \tfrac{1}{3}A_{\parallel} + \tfrac{2}{3}A_{\perp}. \tag{1}$$

Here we have taken[4] $A_{\parallel} = -503.4$ MHz and $A_{\perp} = -189.5$ MHz.

In the nematic phase the measured effective coupling constant a is smaller than in the isotropic phase because of the increased order and a degree of order of the system can be defined as[1]

$$S \equiv \tfrac{1}{2}\langle 3\cos^2\theta - 1 \rangle = \tfrac{1}{2}\frac{(\langle a \rangle - a)}{\tfrac{1}{3}(a - A_{\perp})} \tag{2}$$

When the molecules become very hindered in their motion owing to a large viscosity they can be considered as frozen during the time of a Larmor precession and a " glassy " type spectrum results. In this case the derivative of the absorption spectrum[4] consists of eight slightly asymmetric absorption-like lines whose separation is determined by $A_\perp$ and eight smaller peaks whose separation is determined by $A_\parallel$. To obtain the order parameter in such a spectrum one must use the relative intensities of the " perpendicular " and " parallel " lines.[4,8]

Most nematic liquid crystals with transition temperatures below 200 °C have viscosities which place them somewhere between these two extremes. We, therefore, have made an estimate of the effect of viscosity on the observed spectra in liquid crystals.

Consider an isotropic liquid as the viscosity is increased, e.g., by cooling, one first observes a normal isotropic spectrum. As the viscosity increases to the point where the molecules become so hindered in their motion that they do not tumble fast compared to the Larmor period ($\sim 10^{-10}$ sec) their spectrum starts to be incompletely averaged. The lines start to broaden and the separation between lines decreases. This continues until the molecules move so slow that they are essentially fixed during a Larmor period. A " glassy " or fixed spectrum then results. That this is indeed the case is demonstrated in Fig. 1 which shows a plot of the measured hyperfine splitting obtained from the total width of the spectrum as a function of the kinematic viscosity for VACA dissolved in

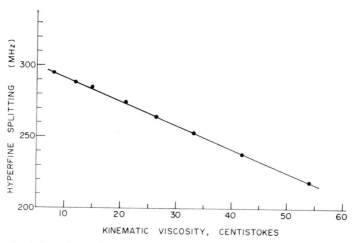

Figure 1. Hyperfine splitting versus kinematic viscosity for 10^{-3}M vanadyl acetylacetonate described in " Octoil " vacuum pump oil.

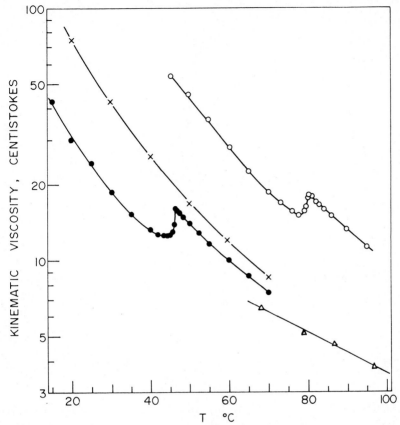

Figure 2.   Kinematic viscosity versus temperature for Octoil, ×, and liquid crystals: I, ○; II, ●; III, △ (see Table 1).

" Octoil ",† a vacuum pump oil.   This oil was chosen because its viscosity covers the range of the viscosities of the liquid crystals used in this investigation in a similar temperature range.   A comparison of these kinematic viscosities is given in Fig. 2.   One should note that the measured hyperfine splitting for the VACA in oil already deviates from the isotropic value at a viscosity of ∼5 centistokes, therefore, one would expect a similar effect to occur in liquid crystals at comparable viscosities.   Figure 3 shows this effect in liquid crystal III (See Table 1).   The order parameter has been

† dioctylphthalate.

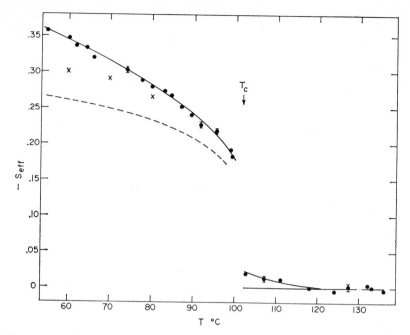

Figure 3.   Plot of the effective order parameter versus temperature for
Vanadyl acetylacetonate ($\sim 10^3 M$) dissolved in liquid crystal III.   The
dashed curve is the theoretical curve calculated by Luckhurst (Ref. 2).   The
points denoted by × are corrections for viscosity as described in the text.

calculated using Eq. (2) but because viscosity also enters we have
relabelled it S-effective.   We attribute the deviation in the isotropic
phase from 120–102 °C to the viscosity.   Luckhurst has calculated
the theoretical shape of the degree of order versus temperature[2]
and compared it to measurements in eight different liquid crystals.
We reproduce his theoretical curve as the dashed line in Fig. 3.   We
have normalized to our data at $\sim T_c$.   Our results closely resemble
the curves obtained by Luckhurst.   In all cases the experimental
slope is greater than the theoretical slope.   Luckhurst has proposed
that a modification of the potential function might produce a better
fit.   We suggest that a large part, if not all, of the deviation from
the theoretical curve can be explained by the effect of viscosity.
Qualitatively the effect would be larger at lower temperatures and
would give a larger apparent order than that actually present.   As
a first approximation we have considered that the true order and

viscosity effects are additive, $S_{eff} = S_{true} + S_{vis}$.   In order to calculate S_{vis} one must use the true average viscosity of the liquid
crystal and not the kinematic viscosity.   A comparison of viscosity
data in other nematic liquid crystals[9] indicates that the average
viscosity will approximately continue on slightly lower than the
isotropic curve.   We have taken it to be parallel to the oil viscosity
for our calculation.   Normalizing to the liquid crystal data at 99 °C
we obtain the points marked × in Fig. 3.   These points would be
fairly close to a curve parallel to the dashed curve in the figure and
show that the viscosity indeed has a large effect on the order parameter determined from the measured hyperfine splitting and could
account for the discrepancy in slopes.   In order to make a more
quantitative conclusion we require the true order parameter of the
liquid crystal with the VACA dissolved in it.   Optical studies to
determine this are in progress in our laboratory.

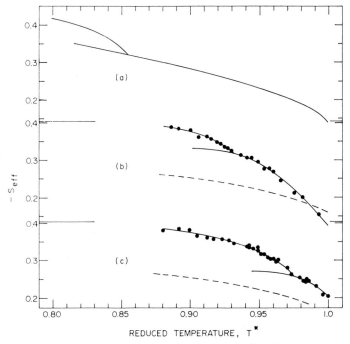

Figure 4.   Effective order parameter versus reduced temperature $T^* = T/T_K$, for vanadyl acetylacetonate dissolved in the liquid crystals: (a) bis (4′-n-octyloxybenzal)-2-chloro-1,4-phenylenediamine (Ref. 1),   (b) II, and (c) I.

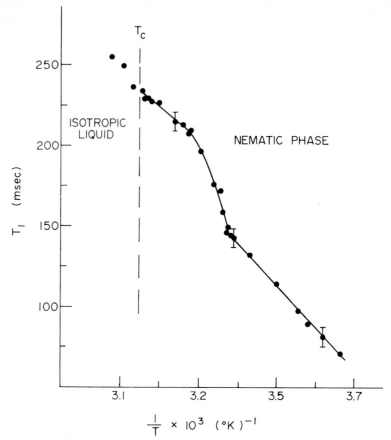

Figure 5.   Proton relaxation time T_1 versus reciprocal of the temperature at 18.2 MHz for the liquid crystal II.

As seen in Fig. 2, liquid crystals I and II are very viscous when compared with III. In Fig. 4 is plotted the effective order parameter versus reduced temperature for three viscous liquid crystals. Curve (a) is from recent work by Fryburg and Gelerinter[1] for the liquid crystal bis   (4'-n-octyloxybenzal-2-chloro-1,4-phenylenediamine). Curves (b) and (c) are liquid crystals II and I of Table 1. The discontinuity in the slope of curve (a) has been ascribed to viscosity effects. Recent NMR spin relaxation (T_1 and $T_{1\rho}$) measurements on liquid crystal I,[10] however, show that there is a change in the dominant mechanism of relaxation at the temperature of the slope discontinuity ($\sim 69\,°C$). We have performed T_1 measurements on the liquid crystal II and found a similar change in the relaxation at

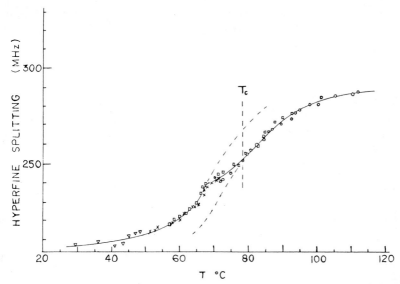

Figure 6.   Hyperfine splitting in MHz versus temperature for several samples of vanadyl acetylacetonate ($\sim 10^{-3}$M) dissolved in liquid crystal I.   The dashed curves which represent viscosity effects are discussed in the text.

the temperature of the slope discontinuity ($\sim$25 °C). This is shown in Fig. 5. This implies that the liquid crystal is undergoing some physical change. In order to further elucidate this point we have plotted the hyperfine splitting of VACA dissolved in liquid crystal I as a function of temperature in Fig. 6. The dashed curves represent a normalized fit to the viscous oil data. One sees that at T_c the experimental points depart from the normal viscous curve. This is due to a combination of an abrupt decrease in viscosity and an increase in order of the system. As one lowers the temperature further there is a discontinuous change in the slope of the curve. Since both the viscosity and order are smoothly varying functions, it would seem that some other effect must cause the change. This is supported by the NMR T_1 measurements. One possible explanation could be the proposal of Freiser[11] of a uniaxial to biaxial phase transition.   Since Haas[12] has recently demonstrated electro-optically that certain liquid crystals including MBBA are biaxial, such a transition is not out of question.

Obviously further experiments which are more sensitive to direction in the liquid crystal than the current NMR and EPR measurements are required before the existence of such a transition can be proven. We feel that the best method of observing this transition would be optically.

In conclusion, we have shown that viscosity effects must be taken into account in interpreting EPR experiments in liquid crystals. We have, in addition, observed a change in the properties of the viscous liquid crystals in their nematic change in both our NMR and EPR results. We suggest that this change may be a uniaxial to biaxial transition.

REFERENCES

1. Fryburg, G. C. and Gelerinter, E., *J. Chem. Phys.* **52**, 3378 (1970).
2. Chen, D. H., James, P. G. and Luckhurst, G. R., *Mol. Cryst.* **8**, 789 (1969).
3. Chen, D. H. and Luckhurst, G. R., *Trans. Faraday Soc.* **65**, 656 (1969).
4. Schwerdtfeger, C. F. and Diehl, P., *Mol. Phys.* **17**, 417 (1969).
5. Chen, D. H. and Luckhurst, G. R., *Mol. Phys.* **16**, 91 (1969).
6. Dong, R. Y. and Schwerdtfeger, C. F., *Solid State Comm.* **8**, 707 (1970).
7. Glarum, S. H. and Marshall, J. H., *J. Chem. Phys.* **46**, 55 (1967).
8. James, P. G. and Luckhurst, G. R., *Mol. Phys.* **19**, 489 (1970).
9. Porter, R. S. and Johnson, J. F., " Rheology " IV, F. Eirich, Editor, John Wiley, New York (1968), p. 317.
10. Dong, R. Y., Marusic, M. and Schwerdtfeger, C. F., *Solid State Comm.* **8**, 1577 (1970).
11. Freiser, M. J., *Phys. Rev. Letters* **24**, 1041 (1970).
12. Haas, W., Adams, J. and Flannery, J. B., *Mol. Cryst.* (paper 7–11, Third Inter. Liquid Crystal conference) and private communication.

Ion Binding in Liquid Crystals Studied by NMR.
I. The Cetyltrimethylammonium Bromide/Hexanol/Water System†

GÖRAN LINDBLOM and BJÖRN LINDMAN

Division of Physical Chemistry 2
The Lund Institute of Technology
Chemical Center, P.O.B. 740
S–220 07 Lund 7, Sweden

Received October 15, 1970; *in revised form December* 7, 1970

Abstract—The nuclear magnetic relaxation of ^{81}Br in the liquid crystalline phases in the ternary system cetyltrimethylammonium bromide (CTAB)/hexanol/water was investigated. The dependence of the nuclear magnetic resonance line width on the composition of the samples is discussed. In the lamellar mesophase the ^{81}Br NMR line width decreases when either the hexanol or the water concentration is increased. This is interpreted as a release of counter-ions from the charged surfaces by hexanol, and as a reinforced hydration of the bromide ions, respectively. Below a molar ratio of about one between hexanol and CTAB the binding of the bromide ions is strongly dependent on this ratio. A comparison is made between the line width in the mesomorphous phases with lamellar and hexagonal structure and the line width in the proximate isotropic solution phases. It appears that the binding of the ions is stronger in the hexanol-deficient part of the lamellar mesophase than in the isotropic water-rich solution phase. In the hexanol-rich part of the lamellar mesophase with high water content the line widths are the same as in the isotropic hexanol-rich solution phase with high water concentration. The binding of the ions in the hexagonal mesophase is similar to that in concentrated aqueous solutions of CTAB.

Introduction

In the last few years there has been a number of applications of nuclear magnetic relaxation techniques to the study of ion binding in systems containing association colloids. The studies by this method have dealt with counter-ion binding in systems containing

† Presented at the Third International Liquid Crystal Conference in Berlin August 24–28, 1970.

micelles of the normal type [1-3] or of the reversed type. [4-6] It seems clear at present that this technique offers a convenient way of obtaining rather detailed information on the interaction between ions and other species in a solution. The purpose of the present work is to determine the degree to which this method is capable of providing enlightenment about the binding of ions in amphiphilic mesomorphous phases. Ekwall *et al.* [7] carried out a thorough investigation of the phase equilibria in the three-component system cetyltrimethyl-ammonium bromide (CTAB)-hexanol-water at 25 °C. Their study demonstrates that two liquid crystalline phases exist in the ternary system, one with a lamellar structure (denoted D) and one with two-dimensional hexagonal structure (denoted *E*). (Fig. 1). The present paper is concerned with ^{81}Br NMR studies of these mesophases.

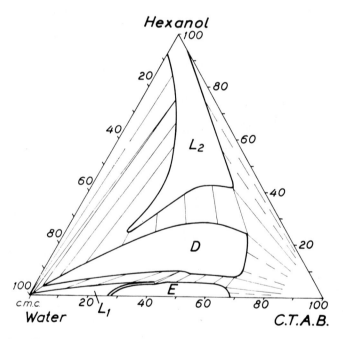

Figure 1. Ternary phase diagram for the system cetyltrimethylammonium bromide/*n*-hexanol/water at 25 °C according to Ekwall *et al.* [7] Compositions are given in per cent by weight. *D* and *E* denote regions with lamellar and hexagonal mesomorphous phases, respectively, L_1 and L_2 are regions with isotropic solution phases.

Experimental

NMR MEASUREMENTS

The ^{79}Br and ^{81}Br NMR measurements were performed with a Varian V–4200 NMR spectrometer equipped with a 12 inch V–3603 magnet and a Varian Mark II Fieldial as described previously.[6] The sample temperature was $29 \pm 2\,°C$. In the determinations of the frequency dependence, the sample temperature was kept constant (at about 34 °C) by means of a Varian V–4540 temperature controller. This instrument was also used in the investigations of the temperature dependence. The actual temperature in the sample was measured with a thermocouple before and after the recording of each series of spectra at a given temperature, and is accurate within $\pm 0.5\,°C$.

The reported line widths are the arithmetical means of 2–4 spectra, and the individual measurements are usually within 5% of the average.

MATERIALS

CTAB and n-hexanol were obtained from the British Drug Houses Ltd. Poole, England. CTAB was recrystallized twice from ethanol and hexanol was distilled once. The preparation of the samples was as described by Ekwall and co-workers.[7]

Results and Discussion

Atomic nuclei with spin quantum numbers (I) greater than $1/2$ generally have electric quadrupole moments. The predominant nuclear magnetic relaxation mechanism in fluid systems is in this case usually the interaction between the nuclear electric quadrupole and fluctuating electric field gradients at the nucleus. Abragam and Pound[8,9] have given an expression for the longitudinal relaxation rate ($1/T_1$) due to the quadrupole interactions for a nucleus of spin I:

$$\frac{1}{T_1} = \frac{3}{40}\frac{2I+3}{I^2(2I-1)}\left(\frac{e^2qQ}{\hbar}\right)^2 \tau_c \tag{1}$$

Here eQ is the nuclear electric quadrupole moment, eq is the principal component of the electric field gradient tensor, $\hbar = h/2\pi$ where h is Planck's constant and τ_c is the correlation time of the field gradient components. The asymmetry parameter, η, has been neglected in Eq. (1). Eq. (1) is valid for the case in which the motion is rapid enough to give $\omega_0 \tau_c \ll 1$, where ω_0 is the nuclear Larmor frequency. In this case the transverse relaxation time T_2 equals T_1, the longitudinal relaxation time. The inverse value of T_2 is proportional to the resonance line width, ΔB, which implies that the following equation is valid when $T_1 = T_2$:

$$\Delta B = Kq^2\tau_c \tag{2}$$

In Eq. (2) K is a constant for a given nucleus. Thus line width measurements yield the product of q^2 and τ_c. These quantities are of great interest since they are determined by the bonding properties of the ions and by the microdynamic properties of the system studied. Unfortunately a separation of q^2 and τ_c is difficult, but a comparison of data for different systems is nevertheless informative.

If all of the ions under consideration are bound in the same way in the solution, i.e. only one site exists, Eq. (2) gives the line width. When the ions are exchanging between several sites with different bonding properties and the residence times in the different sites are much smaller than the relaxation times, the line width is given by[10]:

$$\Delta B_{obs} = \sum_i p_i \Delta B_i \tag{3}$$

ΔB_{obs} is the observed line width and ΔB_i is the line width for the ions in site i. The mole fraction of the total number of ^{81}Br nuclei situated in site i is denoted by p_i.

The applicability of Eqs. (2) and (3) to the interpretation of our findings will now be examined. It should be noted that we have failed to observe any splittings of the ^{81}Br resonance signals. (Of course this does not necessarily exclude the presence of a splitting, it may be due to insufficient intensity of the outer peaks. By improved experimentation we are currently studying this problem in more detail.) If quadrupole splitting is actually absent we may then interpret our results in terms of relaxation. Even if a first-order quadrupole splitting is present the line width of the central peak will, for nuclei having half integer spin quantum numbers, be determined by relaxation if the splitting is great enough to make overlap between the central peak and the outer peaks insignificant. Measurements (at 33.5 °C) showed no frequency dependence of the line width for a sample with the composition 62.3% CTAB, 17.7% hexanol and 20.0%

water and it was concluded that this was a case of extreme narrowing, i.e. $T_1 = T_2$, and thus Eq. (2) is applicable. That Eq. (3) (i.e. a case of fast exchange) is valid in the present situation can be concluded from measurements of the ratio between ΔB (^{79}Br) and ΔB (^{81}Br) which is 1.55 for a sample with the above composition. This value is in good agreement with the value calculated from the expression

$$\frac{\Delta B(^{79}\mathrm{Br})}{\Delta B(^{81}\mathrm{Br})} = \frac{Q^2(^{79}\mathrm{Br})}{Q^2(^{81}\mathrm{Br})} \cdot \frac{\gamma(^{81}\mathrm{Br})}{\gamma(^{79}\mathrm{Br})} = 1.545$$

where γ is the magnetogyric ratio. Thus we may assume that Eq. (3) is applicable (cf. Ref. (3)), and the marked line narrowing with increasing temperature (Fig. 2) provides further support for the

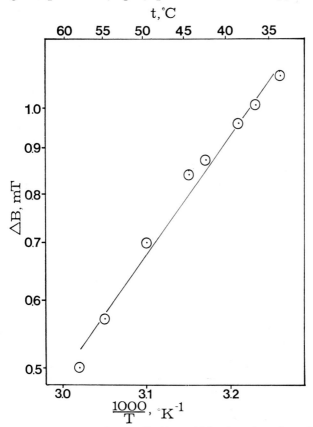

Figure 2. The logarithm of the ^{81}Br line width plotted against the inverse absolute temperature for a sample with the composition 20.0% water, 17.7% hexanol and 62.3% CTAB. Temperature range 33.5°–57.7 °C.

validity of Eq. (3).   The observed ratio $\Delta B(^{79}\mathrm{Br})/\Delta B(^{81}\mathrm{Br})$ further-more supports our assumption that the observed NMR signal is not affected by first-order quadrupole splittings.   The contribution from second-order quadrupole interactions is small since the line widths are independent of the magnetic field strength.   (For $^{35}\mathrm{Cl}$ second-order quadrupole splittings have been observed in a similar system).[11]

The results presented in Fig. 3 are concerned with the variation of the line width with the water content at a constant ratio of 2.3 w/w between CTAB and hexanol.   (All concentrations are given in per

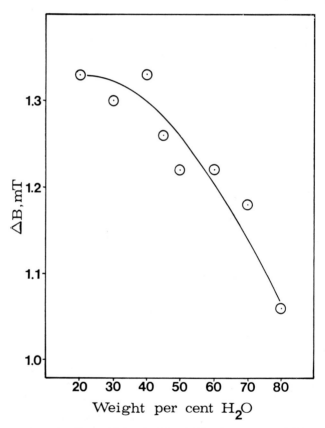

Figure 3.   The $^{81}\mathrm{Br}$ line width, ΔB (in millitesla), as a function of water concentration (in per cent by weight) in the lamellar phase (D) in the ternary system CTAB–hexanol–water.   The ratio between the content of CTAB and hexanol was kept at a constant value, 2.3 w/w.   Temperature 29 °C.

cent by weight.) It is obvious from the figure that the line width increases with decreasing water concentration, the changes being most marked at high water content.

This observation is also valid when the water content is varied at constant hexanol concentration (Fig. 4). The line width changes from 1.2 to 0.8 mT (T = tesla, $1T = 10^4$ gauss) for a variation in the water content from 20 to 50 per cent by weight. In Fig. 5 the line width is given as a function of the CTAB concentration at a constant

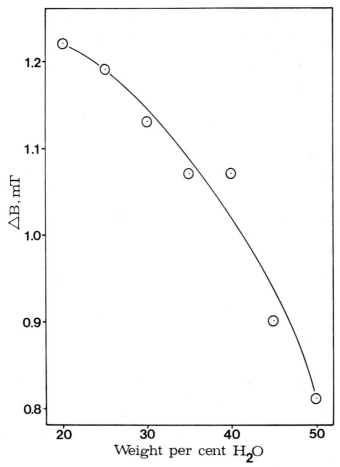

Figure 4. The observed line width, ΔB (in millitesla), for ^{81}Br as a function of the water concentration at constant hexanol concentration, 17.7%, in the lamellar phase (D) in the CTAB–hexanol–water system. Temperature 29 °C.

ratio of 2.3 w/w between water and hexanol. It is clear that the line width increases immensely with increasing CTAB content in the entire concentration range investigated.

An increasing NMR line width can normally be assumed to indicate an enhanced binding of the ion under consideration (see *e.g.* Refs. (1), (6), (12) and (13)). Thus it may be inferred from Fig. 3 that decreasing the water concentration leads to a firmer binding of the bromide ions. It is known from X-ray diffraction measurements[7] that the thickness of the water layer between the amphiphilic

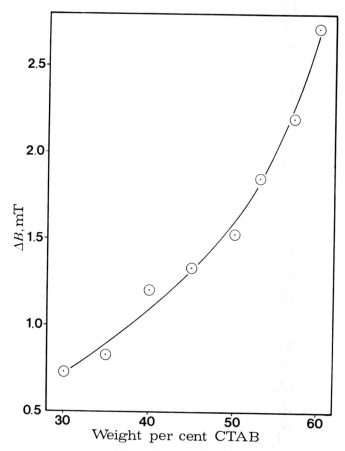

Figure 5. The ⁸¹Br line width, ΔB (in millitesla), as a function of the CTAB concentration at a constant ratio of 2.3 w/w between water and hexanol in the lamellar phase (D) in the ternary system CTAB–hexanol–water. Temperature 29 °C.

layers decreases with decreasing water content. Hence it seems probable that an increasing part of the bromide ions may be adsorbed at the amphiphilic surface when the water content decreases. The changes in line width on variation of the water content is however moderate (Figs. 3 and 4) and consequently the water concentration alone can not account for the very large line widths observed in the CTAB-rich part of the mesophase (Fig. 5).

In almost the entire mesomorphic phase D the line width decreases with increasing hexanol concentration if the ratio between surfactant and water is constant. Thus at a constant ratio of 0.7 w/w between CTAB and water the line width decreases from 1.3 to 0.9 mT for changes in hexanol concentration between 15 and 20%. When the ratio in question is 2.3 w/w the line width decreases from 2.7 to 1.3 mT if the hexanol content varies between 12 and 24%. On the other hand, on addition of hexanol to lamellar mesophase with a high hexanol concentration, the line width does not change appreciably.

It may be postulated that an increasing hexanol content and/or an increasing water content results in a decreasing binding of the bromide ions in the lamellar mesophase. Predominantly, the line width is determined by the molar ratio between hexanol and CTAB (Fig. 6). Thus it may be seen from Fig. 6 that when this molar ratio is less than about unity the line width increases strongly with decreasing hexanol concentration. It is also clear that when the number of hexanol molecules per CTAB molecule is larger than one, the variation in line width is considerably less. (It is interesting to note that an alteration in the mechanism of water uptake in this mesophase occurs at roughly the same molar ratio between hexanol and CTAB.)[7]

In the hexagonal phase (E) the ^{81}Br line width is practically independent of sample composition (Table 1) and only a slight increase in line width on increasing the CTAB concentration can be observed. These observations indicate that the counter-ion binding is very similar in different parts of this phase. In spite of considerable variations in the macroscopic viscosity over the region E the microdynamic properties, as sensed by the bromide ions, are practically constant. Our observations of a constant counter-ion binding correlate with the observed large areas per hydrophilic

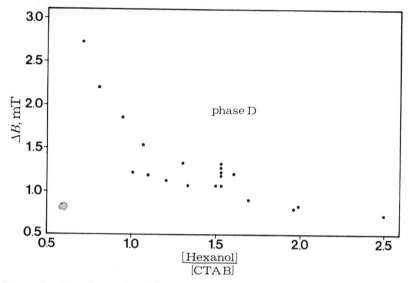

Figure 6.　The observed ^{81}Br line width, ΔB (in millitesla), as a function of the molar ratio hexanol to CTAB in the lamellar phase (D) in the CTAB–hexanol–water system at various water concentrations.　Temperature 29 °C.

group at the amphiphile/water interface.[7]　The ^{81}Br line width is independent of the hexanol concentration in the E phase (Table 1). This also holds true for the distance between the amphiphilic cylinders.[7]

The lamellar mesophase D can be in equilibrium with both the isotropic phases L_1 (water-rich) and L_2 (hexanol-rich) and the hexagonal mesophase E can be in equilibrium with the L_1 phase.

TABLE 1　^{81}Br nuclear magnetic resonance line widths in the mesomorphic hexagonal phase E in the cetyltrimethylammonium bromide/hexanol/water system.　Concentrations in per cent by weight.　Temperature 29 °C.

CTAB (%)	H$_2$O (%)	Hexanol (%)	ΔB (mT)
30.0	70.0	0.0	0.73
40.0	60.0	0.0	0.74
50.0	50.0	0.0	0.75
60.0	40.0	0.0	0.76
65.0	35.0	0.0	0.80
38.5	59.0	2.5	0.73
48.5	49.0	2.5	0.78
58.5	39.0	2.5	0.81

Thus it is of interest to compare the bromide ion binding in the different phases. Firstly it may be noted that the line width at the highest water content in the D phase is larger than that of the broadest signal observed in the L_1 phase (about 0.8 mT, Ref. (14)). Hence, in spite of a high water content, the counter-ions are more firmly bound than anywhere in the L_1 phase. In the upper left hand region of the D phase with a high content of hexanol the line width has a value comparable with that determined in the water-rich part of the L_2 phase[6] which consists of so-called reversed micelles.[15] This implies that the binding of the counter-ions is not very much altered on going from this part of the mesophase to the water-rich part of the isotropic solution phase L_2. A similar result is found for the other mesophase denoted E: the binding in the right hand part of the L_1 phase[14] is of the same strength as in the water-rich part of the mesophase (Table 1). It should be noted that although the line widths in the mesophases are usually large, they are of the same order of magnitude as in the micellar solutions. This indicates that the microdynamic properties of the mesophases, in the vicinity or the bromide ions, are not very different from those of the isotropic micellar solutions.

After this qualitative discussion we will now try to rationalize our findings in terms of electric field gradients and correlation times. Unfortunately a separation of these factors is not directly possible and can only be achieved when more extensive relaxation data are available. It is known that in the L_1 solutions the field gradients are important.[16] Since the line widths are of comparable magnitude in the mesophases it seems reasonable to assume that the field gradients are important for determining the line widths also in the present case. The field gradients may either be due to binding of the counter-ions at the amphiphilic surface, or by location of the ions in a stabilized water lattice (cf. Refs. (3) and (17)).

A simple model assuming only two sites for the bromide ions, (i.e. either they are extensively solvated by water, or they are associated with the cations) seems to be useful for the discussion. The factors now determining the line width were previously stated in connection with Eq. (3). Even at as high a water content as 80% the line width in the D phase is 1.06 mT (Fig. 3), while in an aqueous solution of an alkali bromide the width of the ^{81}Br nuclear magnetic resonance signal is 0.02–0.03 mT even at relatively high concentrations.[18,19]

This line width corresponds to a bromide ion which is nearly symmetrically surrounded by water molecules. Thus it may be presumed that the bromide ions in the present case experience field gradients, which are orders of magnitude larger than in a normal aqueous solution. This strongly implies that a large part of the bromide ions are adsorbed at the amphiphilic surface even at high water contents. On solubilization of hexanol in the liquid crystal it seems reasonable to assume that the hexanol molecules orient themselves with their hydrophobic part within the hydrocarbon layer and their hydrophilic OH-groups towards the water. Measurements of ^{81}Br relaxation rates in the upper part of the lamellar mesophase (rich in hexanol) give lower relaxation rates than samples deficient in hexanol at the lower boundary in the same phase. This may be interpreted as a displacement of the equilibrium between bound counter-ions and solvated ions for the benefit of the bromide ions in the water layer. A similar course is shown in the right hand part of the L_1 phase containing hexanol.[14] Such a mechanism is also indicated from conductivity studies of soap solutions when an organic amphiphile is added.[20-22] At least two mechanisms may explain the release of counter-ions as the hexanol content is increased: Firstly the hydration of the lamellar surfaces will depend on the molar ratio of hexanol to CTAB in the lamellae; this will in turn affect the hydration of the counter-ions. Secondly the charge density on the lamellar surfaces will vary with the molar ratio of non-ionic to ionic amphiphile.[7]

Thus far we have discussed our data in terms of electric field gradients with the only justification that the quadrupole relaxation in the corresponding micellar solutions seems to be determined by the field gradients.[16] The contribution to the line widths from changes in the correlation times may not be deduced at the present stage of our investigation. It may, nevertheless be assumed that an increase in line width in most cases is paralleled by an increase in correlation time. Thus the change in the binding of the counter-ions will at the same time cause a change in electric field gradients and reduce the mobility of the bromide ions. At least at high water contents the motion of the bromide ions seems to depend on the motion of the water molecules and consequently one possible way of obtaining a deeper understanding of the line broadening mechanisms would be to study the water nuclear magnetic relaxation.

The value of the apparent energy of activation for the relaxation process obtained from a least-squares treatment for a sample with the composition 62.3% CTAB, 20.0% water and 17.7% hexanol (Fig. 2) is very high (26.7 ± 0.8 kJ/mole) compared with the value of 8–11 kJ/mole[23,24] normally found in aqueous solutions of alkali bromides. Several workers (see Refs. (3), (4), (17), (24) and (25)) have discussed the activation energies of the relaxation process for ions in solution. It may be concluded that the high value of the energy compared to for example an aqueous alkali bromide solution indicates that the bromide ions are much more firmly bound in the present case. (Of course in liquid crystalline systems one also has to consider the possibility of structural changes when the temperature is altered.)

Acknowledgements

Professor Per Ekwall is heartily thanked for his kind interest in this work and for valuable proposals and comments. We are grateful to Dr. Krister Fontell, Professor Sture Forsén, Dr. Åke Johansson, Dr. Leo Mandell and Mr. Håkan Wennerström for discussions in connection with this work. The technical assistance of Mr. Hans Lilja and Miss Annika Lagerberg is gratefully acknowledged. Dr. Robert Carter kindly revised the English of this text.

REFERENCES

1. Eriksson, J. C., Johansson, Å. and Andersson, L.-O., *Acta Chem. Scand.* **20**, 2301 (1966).
2. Danielsson, I., Lindman, B. and Ödberg, L., *Suom. Kemistilehti B*, **43**, 209 (1970).
3. Lindman, B., Wennerström, H. and Forsén, S., *J. Phys. Chem.*, **74**, 754 (1970).
4. Lindman, B. and Ekwall, P., *Kolloid-Z. Z.-Polym.*, **234**, 1115 (1969).
5. Lindman, B. and Ekwall, P., *Mol. Cryst.* **5**, 79 (1968).
6. Lindblom, G., Lindman, B. and Mandell, L., *J. Colloid Interface Sci.*, **34**, 262 (1970).
7. Ekwall, P., Mandell, L. and Fontell, K., *J. Colloid Interface Sci.* **29**, 639 (1969).
8. Abragam, A. and Pound, R. V., *Phys. Rev.* **92**, 943 (1953).
9. Abragam, A., " The Principles of Nuclear Magnetism ", Clarendon Press, Oxford 1961.
10. Emsley, J. W., Feeney, J. and Sutcliffe, L. H., " High Resolution Nuclear Magnetic Resonance Spectroscopy ", Vol. I, Pergamon Press, London 1965, p. 485.

11. Lindblom, G., Wennerström, H. and Lindman, B., *Chem. Phys. Letters* **8**, 489 (1971).
12. Lindqvist, I. and Lindman, B., *Acta Chem. Scand.* **24**, 1097 (1970).
13. Stengle, T. R., and Baldeschwieler, J. D., *J. Amer. Chem. Soc.* **89**, 3045 (1967).
14. Lindblom, G., Lindman, B. and Mandell, L. To be published.
15. Ekwall, P., Mandell, L. and Solyom, P. To be published.
16. Lindblom, G. and Lindman, B. To be published.
17. Lindman, B., Forsén, S. and Forslind, E., *J. Phys. Chem.* **72**, 2805 (1968).
18. Hertz, H. G., *Z. Elektrochem. Ber. Bunsenges. Phys. Chem.* **65**, 20 (1961).
19. Hertz, H. G., Stalidis, G. and Versmold, H., *J. Chim. Phys.* Numéro special, Oct. 1969, p. 177.
20. Passinen, K. and Ekwall, P., *Acta. Chem. Scand.* **9**, 1438, 1450 (1955).
21. Ekwall, P., Sten, A. and Norman, A., *Acta Chem. Scand.* **10**, 681 (1956).
22. Lawrence, A. S. C., Boffey, B., Bingham, A. and Talbot, K. Proceedings 4th Internat. Congress on Surface Active Substances, Brussels, 1964, Vol. II, Section B., p. 673.
23. Hertz, H. G., " Progress in NMR Spectroscopy ", Vol. III, Pergamon Press, Oxford 1967, p. 159.
24. O'Reilly, D. E., Schacher, G. E. and Schug, K., *J. Chem. Phys.* **39**, 1756 (1963).
25. Endom, L., Hertz, H. G., Thül, B. and Zeidler, M.D., *Ber. Bunsenges. Phys. Chem.* **71**, 1008 (1967).

Proton and Deuteron Magnetic Resonance Studies of Lamellar Lyotropic Mesophases†

ÅKE JOHANSSON and TORBJÖRN DRAKENBERG

Division of Physical Chemistry 2
The Lund Institute of Technology
P.O.B. 740, S–220 07 Lund 7, Sweden

Received October 2, 1970; in revised form December 22, 1970

Abstract—Lyotropic liquid crystals of the lamellar type have been studied by means of deuteron and proton magnetic resonance. The deuteron resonance from D_2O molecules exhibit quadrupole splitting in the region of ~ 0 to 11 kHz. The origin of this splitting and its dependence on system composition and temperature has been investigated in both two- and three-component systems, containing different amphiphiles, such as n-octylamine, the corresponding hydrochloride and hydrobromide, nonylphenol polyethylene glycol ethers, n-octanoic acid and n-decanol. It has been shown that the quadrupole splitting can give information concerning the rate of deuteron exchange between water and amphiphilic molecules. Effects of solubilization of hydrocarbons on the quadrupole splitting have also been investigated. High resolution proton resonance signals have also been observed and the width and shape of these signals are discussed.

Some of the mesophases investigated can be aligned by means of a magnetic field of *ca.* 14 kilogauss. The alignment is displayed in both deuteron and proton resonance spectra.

1. Introduction

The application of NMR spectroscopy for the study of liquid crystals has been the subject of some recent review articles.[1–3] Relatively few of these papers have referred to lyotropic mesomorphic phases,[2,3] while the majority has concerned different types of thermotropic liquid crystals.[1] Since lyotropic mesophases have been shown to play an important role in biological systems,[4] we believe that a deeper understanding of their properties and structures could also illuminate some important biological problems, for example the

† Presented at the Third International Liquid Crystal Conference in Berlin, August 24–28, 1970.

function of membranes. This work is mainly concerned with mesomorphic phases of the lamellar type with alternating layers of
amphiphilic molecules and water. A large number of X-ray studies
of such phases[5] indicates that in the amphiphilic layers the molecules
are oriented parallel to each other with their long axis in a direction
essentially perpendicular to the layer. With regard to the water
layers, however, little is known about the structural changes originating from the interaction with the polar groups of the amphiphilic
molecules. The main purpose of this investigation was to obtain
further insight into the amphiphile-water interaction by means of
proton and deuteron resonance measurements on various mesomorphic phases.

2. Experimental

2.1. SAMPLE PREPARATION

Mesomorphic phases were prepared from mixtures of the following
amphiphilic substances with deuterium oxide:

n-octylamine (OA), OAHCl, OAHBr, cetyltrimethylammonium
bromide (CTAB), nonylphenol decaethylene glycol ether (NF-10),
nonylphenol hexaethylene glycol ether (NF-6), n-octanoic acid and
n-decanol.

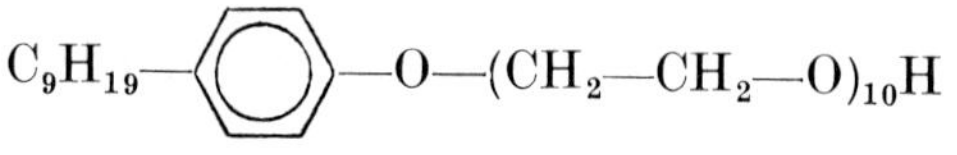

$$C_9H_{19}-\!\!\bigcirc\!\!-O-(CH_2-CH_2-O)_{10}H \qquad NF\text{-}10$$

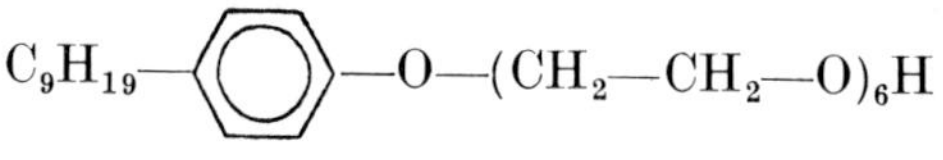

$$C_9H_{19}-\!\!\bigcirc\!\!-O-(CH_2-CH_2-O)_6H \qquad NF\text{-}6$$

In some cases hexadecane and p-xylene were solubilized in the phases.
Purified samples of NF-10 and NF-6 were supplied by the Institute
for Surface Chemistry in Stockholm. The numbers of polyethylene
oxide units given in the above formulae are actually mean values of a
distribution. The remaining chemicals were purchased from the
British Drug Houses Ltd, Poole, England and from Fluka AG,
Buchs, Switzerland, at the maximum purity available (always
$\geqslant 99\%$). The D_2O used in the deuterated samples was obtained
from Norsk Hydro, Norway and the enrichment amounted to 99.8%.

The samples were prepared by weight in glass ampoules or 5 mm

NMR tubes, which were immediately sealed off. The mixing was generally done by shaking at an elevated temperature, in most cases above the melting point of the mesomorphic phase. In some cases ultrasonic vibrations were applied to the samples in order to ensure homogeneity. The randomly oriented mesomorphic phases were prepared by decreasing the temperature of the corresponding isotropic solutions in the absence of the magnetic field, while the magnetically aligned phases were prepared by slowly decreasing the temperature of isotropic samples in the magnetic field ($\sim$14 kilogauss).

The phase diagrams of the binary and ternary systems studied in this investigation are given in the following references: OA—H_2O,[6] OAHCl—H_2O,[7] OA—OAHCl—H_2O,[8] OA—n-octanoic acid—H_2O,[8] OA—p-xylene—H_2O,[6] OAHCl—n-decanol—H_2O,[7] NF-10†—p-xylene—H_2O,[9] NF-10—n-hexadecane—H_2O,[9] NF-6†—p-xylene —H_2O,[9] CTAB—n-hexanol—H_2O.[10] The range of stability of the lamellar phase in the system OA—OAHBr—D_2O was estimated from the phase diagram of the system OA—OAHCl—H_2O.

2.2. NMR MEASUREMENTS

Wide-line NMR measurements were performed using a Varian V-4200 spectrometer equipped with a 12 inch V-3603 magnet. The magnetic field was regulated by a Varian Mark II Fieldial and the sample temperature was controlled by means of a Varian V-4540 Temperature Controller. At each temperature setting the actual temperature was measured using a copper-constantan thermocouple. The temperature was found to be accurate within $\pm$ 0.3 °C. Unless otherwise specified, all measurements were made at 20 °C. In order to facilitate a very slow temperature decrease ($\sim$0.1 °C/10 min), necessary for the preparation of oriented phases, a 10-turn 25Ω potentiometer was connected in series with the temperature setting resistor of the V-4540, and the external potentiometer was continuously varied by means of a motor with a low-geared transmission.

The frequency used in the wide-line measurements on deuterium was 9.1785 MHz. The variable frequency oscillator of the wide-line spectrometer was stabilized within $\pm$ 1 Hz by means of a crystal

† The substances denoted by NF-6 and NF-10 in this paper are called EMU-02 and EMU-09, respectively, in Ref. (9).

oscillator. The power of the radio frequency field was always chosen so that no measurable saturation effect occurred. The magnetic field inhomogeneity, as measured on a D_2O sample, amounted to 20–30 milligauss. Most spectra were recorded using a 20 or 40 Hz modulation of the magnetic field and a small modulation amplitude compared with the linewidths. In spectra in which quadrupole coupling is observed, the linewidth can not be easily extracted from the spectrum, and in those cases the modulation amplitude was instead chosen so that no measurable change in line-shape resulted from a 50% increase in modulation amplitude.

The experimental parameter in the deuteron resonance spectra which is of primary interest is the frequency separation, $\Delta\nu$, between the absorption maxima in the powder patterns. The value of $\Delta\nu$ is approximately equal to the separation, $\Delta\nu'$, between the maximum and minimum in the derivative spectrum. However, when the line broadening superimposed on the powder pattern is not negligible compared with the quadrupole splitting, a correct evaluation of $\Delta\nu$ must take the complete lineshape of the powder pattern into consideration. This could be done by fitting a theoretical spectrum with a superimposed line broadening to the experimental spectrum. Instead of using this rather tedious procedure we have calculated a series of powder patterns assuming different linewidths, and in this way it has been possible to estimate the error resulting from the assumption that $\Delta\nu = \Delta\nu'$. The corrected value of $\Delta\nu$ can be approximately evaluated from the following expression

$$\Delta\nu = \Delta\nu' - (0.36 \pm 0.05)\,\delta \qquad (1)$$

where δ is the width at half maximum of the large peaks in the derivative spectrum. This expression is valid up to $\delta/\Delta\nu' \approx 0.5$. All experimental values have been corrected according to this procedure. The estimated error in the values of $\Delta\nu$ amounts to less than $\pm 5\%$.

High resolution experiments were performed using a Varian A-60A spectrometer equipped with a Varian V-6040 Temperature Controller. The r.f. field and sweep rate were always chosen to avoid distortion of the signals due to either fast sweep or saturation. The device for slow temperature decrease was also used for the high resolution experiments.

3. Deuterium Magnetic Resonance in Randomly Oriented Systems

3.1. THEORY

In the ^{2}H NMR spectra of the randomly oriented phases there were observed characteristic " powder " patterns arising from coupling of the deuterium quadrupole moment and the electric field gradients (EFG: s) at the nuclear position. Such patterns were first observed in other anisotropic mesomorphic phases by Lawson and Flautt[11,12] and later by Black, Lawson and Flautt,[13] Ellis, Lawrence, McDonald and Peel[14] and Charvolin and Rigny,[15] and they were, except in Ref. (14) explained as resulting from a partial orientation of the water molecules within randomly oriented aggregates in the sample. However, as pointed out by Ellis et al.,[14] when the amphiphilic molecules contain exchangeable protons, such as amines, carboxylic acids and alcohols, the quadrupole splitting may arise not only from partially oriented D_2O molecules, but also from deuterons covalently bound to partially oriented amphiphilic molecules. In the OA—D_2O system this mechanism of orientation of deuterium EFG:s has been found to be important. Different types of orientation mechanisms will be discussed in sec. 3.3.

It is of interest to note that rapid exchange of protons between partially oriented H_2O molecules will average out the dipole-dipole coupling while exchange of deuterons in partially oriented D_2O will not eliminate the quadrupole splitting (cf. Ref. (16)).

The interaction between a nuclear spin ($I = 1$) and an axially symmetrical EFG gives rise to a splitting of the resonance line into a doublet, with the frequency separation $\Delta\nu$ given by[17]

$$\Delta\nu = \left| \frac{3e^2qQ}{2h} \cdot \left\langle \frac{3}{2}\cos^2\theta - \frac{1}{2} \right\rangle \right| \qquad (2)$$

where q is the axial EFG, Q is the quadrupole moment of the nucleus ($I = 1$), θ is the angle between the applied magnetic field and the axis of the EFG, and the brackets denote time average.

In a polycrystalline sample all directions of the EFG relative to the magnetic field are equally probable and time independent. In such a case the ($3\cos^2\theta - 1$) dependence of the quadrupole splitting gives rise to a powder pattern, in which the frequency separation between the two absorption maxima equals $3e^2qQ/4h$.[17]

In the case of a liquid crystal, however, the fact that θ is time dependent must be considered. A very useful formalism for the description of molecular orientation in liquid crystals has been developed by Saupe[18] and further treated by Buckingham and McLauchlan.[19] In the latter paper the authors have considered the case of partially oriented water molecules undergoing rapid re-orientation. For a molecule with C_{2v} symmetry three elements of the orientation matrix are sufficient to describe the mean orientation, namely S_{11}, S_{22} and S_{33} in the nomenclature used in Ref. (19). However, all three are not necessary since only two are independent $(S_{11} + S_{22} + S_{33} = 0)$. The three molecule-fixed coordinate axes, 1, 2 and 3, have been chosen as depicted in Fig. 1. If the EFG is axially symmetric and its principal tensor component is directed along the O—D bond, the quadrupole splitting can be written as[19]

$$\Delta \nu = \left| \frac{3}{2h} \cdot e^2 qQ \left[S_{11} \left(\frac{3}{2} \cos^2 \beta - \frac{1}{2} \right) + \frac{1}{2} (S_{22} - S_{33}) \sin^2 \beta \right] \right.$$
$$\left. \cdot \left\langle \frac{3}{2} \cos^2 \Omega - \frac{1}{2} \right\rangle \right| \quad (3)$$

where β is half the D—O—D angle of water ($= 51° 16'$), and Ω is the angle between the direction of the magnetic field and the constraint giving rise to the orientation.

Figure 1.   Choice of axes in the coordinate system fixed to the D_2O molecule.

Since a lamellar phase represents a uni-axial structure, the constraint set up by this structure is parallel to the direction perpendicular to the planes. In the phases investigated the experiments clearly show that once the lamellar phase has formed, the direction of the constraint is *unaffected* by the magnetic field, *i.e.* a powder pattern will not change to a measurable degree when the sample has been kept in the magnetic field for several days. (Still, most phases flow when the sample is tilted.)

In a randomly oriented phase a powder pattern is observed, with the frequency separation between the two absorption maxima being given by

$$\Delta v = \left| \frac{3e^2qQ}{4h} \cdot S \right| \qquad (4)$$

where S is identical with the factor

$$\left[S_{11} \left(\frac{3}{2} \cos^2 \beta - \frac{1}{2} \right) + \frac{1}{2} (S_{22} - S_{33}) \sin^2 \beta \right]$$

characterizing the partial orientation of the water molecules with respect to the direction perpendicular to the water layers. Accurate experimental values of the quadrupole coupling constant, e^2qQ/h (in the following denoted by E_Q) and the asymmetry parameter, η, in D_2O are only known for the solid and gaseous states. The value of E_Q amounts to 215 kHz [20] (mean value) and 305 kHz [21,22] in the solid and gaseous states, respectively; the corresponding η values are 0.100 [20] and 0.115, [21] respectively. It is reasonable to assume that, in the liquid state, both E_Q and η are intermediate between the values in solid and gaseous D_2O and closer to the values in the solid state.

The asymmetry of the EFG has not been considered in Eqs. (2)– (4). In fact, no theoretical treatment of the motional averaging of an asymmetric EFG has been reported in the literature. However, the observed spectra show a lineshape characteristic of a symmetric EFG, *i.e.* the separation between the outer shoulders of the absorption line is within experimental error exactly twice the separation between the maxima. It therefore appears that the average EFG is nearly symmetric and consequently Eq. (4) is applicable although the definition of S is only approximate. Changes in the observable quantity, Δv, can not be unambiguously related to a change in S unless the value of E_Q is constant. The value of E_Q may be influenced by variations in the degree of hydrogen bonding. The difference in the value of E_Q between solid and gaseous D_2O is not more than *ca.* 50%, and we therefore assume that the relatively small variations in the degree of hydrogen bonding present in the systems investigated do not markedly influence the value of E_Q.† However, since the value of E_Q is not known, we will in the following use the parameter $E_Q \cdot S$ for characterizing the partial orientation of D_2O.

† This assumption is supported by deuteron relaxation investigations. [22a]

For deuterons bound to the amphiphilic groups the S parameter is defined as $\langle 3 \cos^2 \theta - 1 \rangle$ (cf. Eqs. (2)–(4)) but in this case it is difficult to give an explicit expression for S in terms of orientation matrix elements. The parameter $E_Q \cdot S$ will also be used in this case to characterize the partial orientation.

The effect of chemical exchange on NMR lineshape in the presence of quadrupole coupling has not yet been given any detailed theoretical treatment. However, on the basis of the general principles of NMR it is possible to make some qualitative statements. Let us assume that deuterons are exchanging between chemically distinguishable sites, 1, 2, 3..., which in the absence of exchange exhibit the quadrupole splittings $\Delta\nu_i$, $i = 1, 2, 3, \ldots$. If the lifetimes of the deuterons in the individual sites are much longer than the inverse of the differences in quadrupole splittings, i.e. $1/|(\Delta\nu_i - \Delta\nu_j)|$, separate resonance signals will be observed from the deuterons in the various sites. If, on the other hand, the lifetimes are much shorter than $1/|(\Delta\nu_i - \Delta\nu_j)|$, only an average resonance signal will be observed, for which the quadrupole splitting is given by

$$\Delta\nu = \sum_i x_i \Delta\nu_i \tag{5}$$

where x_i is the fraction of deuterons situated in site i. (Cf. also Ref. (14)). For the intermediate case, i.e. when the lifetimes and the values of $1/|(\Delta\nu_i - \Delta\nu_j)|$ are of the same order of magnitude, a more complicated lineshape may be expected.

3.2. RESULTS

In Fig. 2 the value of $E_Q \cdot S$ for D_2O is plotted vs. the mole fraction of D_2O in various types of lamellar mesomorphic phases at 20 °C. With the assumption that E_Q in D_2O equals 215 kHz, the S values of the partially oriented water molecules range between ca. 0.02 and ~ 0 in the phases investigated. From Fig. 2 it is apparent that an increasing mole fraction of D_2O, i.e. an increase in the thickness of the water layer, causes a reduction of $E_Q \cdot S$. This may indicate that a specific interaction occurs between the water molecules and the amphiphile. (The unusually large values of $E_Q \cdot S$ observed in the OA—D_2O system originate from a rapid exchange of water and amino deuterons, as will be discussed later.)

The temperature dependence of $E_Q \cdot S$ is illustrated in Fig. 3 for

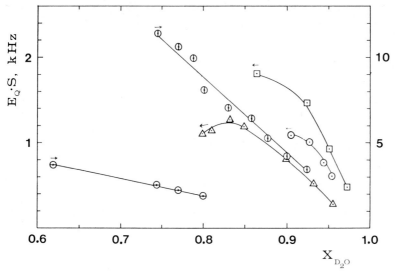

Figure 2. $E_Q \cdot S$ as a function of mole fraction of D_2O in different lamellar mesophases. Arrows indicate the proper ordinate scale.

Left ordinate scale:

   ⊡ NF-6
   ○ NF-10
   △ NF-10—p-xylene (mole ratio 1 : 2.5)

Right ordinate scale:

   ⬦ OA
   ⊖ OAHCl

the different systems up to the melting point of the mesomorphic phases. The value of $E_Q \cdot S$ is usually lower at higher temperatures, probably due to a diminished degree of orientation of the D_2O and/or amphiphile molecules. (The increase in $E_Q \cdot S$ observed in the OAHCl—D_2O system is also accompanied by an increased line broadening and will be discussed later.) The relative decrease of the $E_Q \cdot S$ value at temperatures approaching the melting point varies considerably from system to system. Ellis et al.[14] found in a lamellar phase of 1-mono-octanoin—D_2O that the value of $E_Q \cdot S$ showed no significant change in the temperature interval 15–40 °C.

The influence of the composition of the amphiphilic layer on the value of $E_Q \cdot S$ has been investigated in four ternary systems prepared by adding n-octanoic acid, OAHCl or OAHBr to the binary system OA—D_2O and by adding n-decanol to OAHCl—D_2O. In lameller

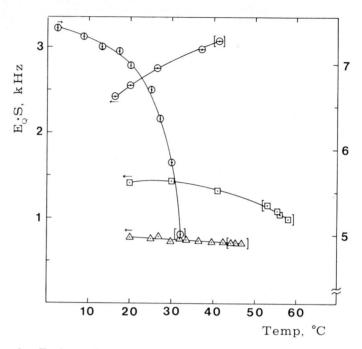

Figure 3. $E_Q \cdot S$ as a function of temperature. The parentheses indicate the presence of various amounts of isotropic phase and the arrows indicate the proper ordinate scale.

Left ordinate scale:

    ◠ OAHCl—D$_2$O (mole ratio 1 : 2.90)
    △ NF-10—D$_2$O (mole ratio 1 : 17)
    ⊡ NF-6—D$_2$O (mole ratio 1 : 12)

Right ordinate scale:

    ⊕ OA—D$_2$O (mole ratio 1 : 4.88)

phases with the mole fraction of D$_2$O constant at 0.770 the compositions of the amphiphilic layer was varied within the limits of stability of the various lamellar phases. In Fig. 4 $E_Q \cdot S$ is plotted vs. the molar ratio of acidic amphiphile to total amphiphile. The figure shows that an increase in the proportion of ionic amphiphile will generally lead to a reduction of $E_Q \cdot S$. Furthermore, there seems to be a counter-ion effect on the value of $E_Q \cdot S$, which may be seen from a comparison of OAHCl and OAHBr. In the system OAHCl—D$_2$O two different quadrupole splittings are observed. These have been assigned to ammonium and water deuterons which,

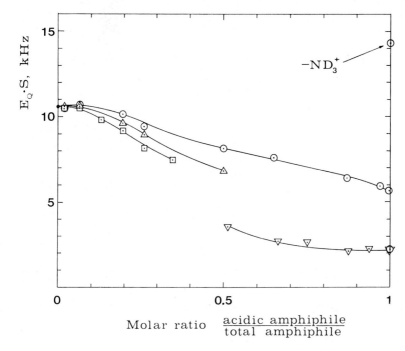

Figure 4. $E_Q \cdot S$ *vs.* the molar ratio of acidic amphiphile/total amphiphile at a constant mole fraction of D_2O equal to 0.770.

   ○ OA—OAHCl
   △ OA—OAHBr
   ⊡ OA—*n*-octanoic acid
   ▽ *n*-decanol—OAHCl.

The point marked by ○, for which $E_Q \cdot S$ equals 5.7 kHz, corresponds to an abscissa value of 0.997.

due to slow deuteron exchange, give rise to separate resonance signals. In Figs. 2 and 3 the values of $E_Q \cdot S$ refer to the water deuterons.

In order to investigate the extent to which the S parameter is sensitive to solubilization, *p*-xylene was added to lamellar phases of NF-6—D_2O and NF-10—D_2O. To the latter system *n*-hexadecane was added in a separate experiment. The effect of the addition of non-amphiphilic compounds is shown in Fig. 5. On the addition of *n*-hexadecane to the NF-10—D_2O system $E_Q \cdot S$ is found to be approximately constant. Large amounts of *p*-xylene can be added

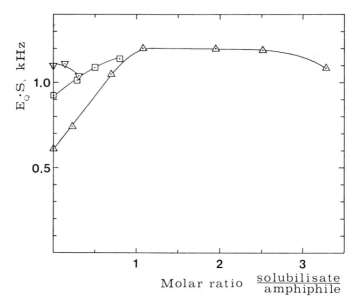

Figure 5. The influence of solubilization on the value of $E_Q \cdot S$ at constant molar ratio, x_{aw}, of amphiphile/water.

△ p-xylene in NF-10—D$_2$O, x_{aw} = 1 : 21
▽ n-hexadecane in NF-10—D$_2$O, x_{aw} = 1 : 10
⊡ p-xylene in NF-6—D$_2$O, x_{aw} = 1 : 20.

to the NF-6—D$_2$O and NF-10—D$_2$O systems, leading to a considerable increase in $E_Q \cdot S$. In the NF-10—D$_2$O system more than three p-xylene molecules can be solubilized per amphiphile molecule, but the value of $E_Q \cdot S$ only increases up to a concentration of *ca.* one p-xylene per amphiphile molecule.

3.3. DISCUSSION

(a) *General Considerations*

The quadrupole splittings observed in the deuteron magnetic resonance spectra of the mesomorphic systems investigated originate from an anisotropic orientation of the EFG : s felt by deuterons. This can arise either from partial orientation of D$_2$O molecules or from covalent binding of deuterons to the amphiphilic molecules in the lamellae. A partial orientation of water molecules may arise from their interaction with the hydrophilic groups of the amphiphile and it is possible to conceive of at least three different mechanisms of molecular interaction, which to some extent may give rise to a transfer of the partial orientation of the amphiphilic molecules to the water molecules: (i) hydrogen bonding, (ii) ion-dipole and/or dipole-dipole interaction, (iii) dispersion forces.

A change in the quadrupole splitting can arise both from a change in the amphiphile-water interaction and from an altered degree of partial orientation of the amphiphilic molecules. According to the commonly accepted picture of the organization of lamellar mesophases[5] the orientation of the amphiphilic molecules must be highly anisotropic, and thus the relative change in their degree of orientation is expected to be small. We therefore assume that the variations in S observed on changing the composition of the hydrophilic part of the system are to a large extent caused by a change in the water-amphiphile interaction, but it is not possible, from the experimental results in the present investigation, to separate the two effects.

A mechanism of interaction between water and amphiphile molecules likely to be of little importance is that due to anisotropic dispersion forces (iii) which would require a penetration of water molecules into the hydrocarbon region of the lamellae. It is true that in the case of polyethylene oxide surfactants penetration of water molecules to the ether oxygen groups will most probably occur, but then the interaction is likely to be dominated by the mechanisms involving hydrogen bonding (i) and/or dipole interaction (ii). Recent investigations of micellar systems[23] have led to the hypothesis that water molecules may penetrate to the hydrocarbon region of the micelles. If such a mechanism significantly contributed to the preferential orientation of water molecules in anisotropic mesophases, a measurable quadrupole splitting would also be observed in the absence of hydrogen bonding, as for example in the hexagonal phase of CTAB—D_2O. Preliminary investigations indicate, however, that $E_Q \cdot S$ in this system is very small. (See also Sect. 3(e).) The ion-dipole interaction can only contribute to the water orientation in the presence of ionic surfactants.

The result of the amphiphile-water interaction can be thought of as an orientation of the water molecules close to the hydrophilic groups, the remaining water molecules being less affected. This mechanism can only be consistent with the experimental results if rapid exchange is assumed between oriented and isotropic water, since in all systems investigated a simple powder pattern without any central peak is observed using deuterium magnetic resonance. (Cf. also Ref. (12)). The term " rapid exchange " used in the foregoing discussion means that the rate of exchange is much larger than the deuteron quadrupole interaction (of the order of 10^4 sec^{-1}). At rapid exchange of D_2O molecules between two sites, 1 and 2, corresponding to different quadrupole splittings, $\Delta\nu_1$ and $\Delta\nu_2$, the observed splitting, $\Delta\nu$, would be given by

$$\Delta\nu = x_1\Delta\nu_1 + x_2\Delta\nu_2 \tag{6}$$

where x_1 and x_2 are the fractions of D_2O molecules in the two sites (cf. Eq. (5)). Let us consider the model proposed by Lawson and Flautt[12] in which the two sites correspond to surfactant-associated water and self-associated water. If the self-associated water is considered to be essentially isotropic the corresponding term in Eq. (6) would vanish. If we assume that the number of water molecules bound to the hydrophilic groups is small compared with the number of isotropic water molecules and is directly proportional to the number of amphiphile molecules, Eq. (6) would lead to the following expression for the quadrupole splitting.

$$\Delta\nu = \text{const.} \ (1 - x_{D_2O})\Delta\nu_b \tag{7}$$

In this equation x_{D_2O} denotes the mole fraction of D_2O in the system and $\Delta\nu_b$ is the quadrupole splitting for the bound D_2O molecules. Therefore, under the further assumption that $\Delta\nu_b$ is independent of the composition of the system, the quadrupole splitting due to partial orientation of the water molecules would, at high water content, decrease approximately linearly at increasing mole fraction of D_2O.

(b) Effects of Deuteron Exchange between Water and Amphiphile

In most mesophases studied in this investigation the amphiphilic molecules contain exchangeable protons, such as amine, hydroxyl and carboxyl protons, and we have therefore also to consider the possible effects of deuteron exchange on the observed quadrupole splittings. The previously discussed two-site model has then to be modified to also include the chemically distinguishable deuteron sites on the amphiphilic molecules. However, since in all systems investigated the water deuterons only give rise to one average resonance signal, the discussion may be simplified by assuming only one water deuteron site corresponding to the average quadrupole splitting of the water deuterons. In the case of slow deuteron exchange between water and amphiphilic molecules, separate resonance signals may be observed for the different types of deuterons, which is found to be the case in the OAHCl—D_2O system (Fig. 4). If, on the other hand, the deuterons are rapidly exchanging between water and amphiphilic molecules, an average quadrupole splitting will be observed (cf. Eq. (5)), which is given by

$$\langle \Delta v \rangle = x_w \Delta v_w + \sum_i x_{ai} \Delta v_{ai} \tag{8}$$

where x_w is the mole fraction of water deuterons and x_{ai} is the mole fraction corresponding to the ith site of exchangeable amphiphilic deuterons. Δv_w and Δv_{ai} are the respective quadrupole splittings in the absence of exchange.

The fact that an average *proton* chemical shift is observed for water, amino and carboxyl protons in the mesomorphic phases investigated indicates that the rate of proton exchange is in these cases rapid enough to average out the chemical shift differences between the various types of protons. An important question for the interpretation of the quadrupole splitting data is whether this rate of exchange is sufficiently rapid to also average out the differences in quadrupole splitting. In the OAHCl—D_2O system separate powder patterns are observed at 20 °C for amino and water deuterons while only a very small addition of OA will change the spectrum into a single powder pattern, in which the splitting is consistent with Eq. 8. (See Fig. 4). These observations are in accordance with the known pH dependence of the amino proton exchange rate.[24] We therefore conclude that in the OA—OAHCl—D_2O system, the observed quadrupole splitting is a mean value of the splitting in the amino and water deuterons except at low pH. In the OAHCl—D_2O system an upper limit can be established for the rate of amino deuteron exchange at 20 °C. This is given by the difference in quadrupole splitting at slow exchange, $\sim 10^4$ sec^{-1}.

In the system OA—n-octanoic acid—D_2O the degree of protonation of the carboxylic groups is expected to be extremely small, and consequently the binding of deuterons to these groups will not measurably influence the value of $E_Q \cdot S$.

In the case of hydroxyl groups proton magnetic resonance measurements have shown that in the NF-6—H_2O system (mole ratio 1 : 1, corresponding to an isotropic phase[9]), the temperature has to be increased to ca. 70 °C before hydroxyl and water proton resonance lines coalesce. Therefore, at that temperature the rate of exchange is of the same order of magnitude as the chemical shift difference between water and hydroxyl protons (ca. 10 Hz). Consequently, the exchange rate at 20 °C will certainly be much too slow to average out the quadrupole coupling for hydroxyl and water deuterons, which is of the order of kHz. However, attempts to observe separate hydroxyl and water deuteron quadrupole splittings in the lamellar phase have failed, most probably due to the small mole fractions of hydroxyl deuterons. The effect of hydroxyl deuteron exchange on $E_Q \cdot S$ will be thoroughly discussed elsewhere.[25] Ellis et al.[14] have explained the quadrupole splitting observed in the lamellar phase of 1-mono-octanoin—D_2O as originating only from rapid exchange between hydroxyl and water deuterons. In view of the results of the present investigation we would suggest that the quadrupole splitting in this system can alternatively be explained as an effect of partial orientation of water molecules. (Cf. also Ref. (25).)

Our experimental results concerning the effects of deuteron exchange on the measured quadrupole splittings may be summarized in the following way. In the OA—D_2O system the average splitting between water and amine deuterons is observed even upon the addition of acidic amphiphile. Only at low pH are separate resonance signals obtained. For the amphiphiles containing hydroxyl groups the deuteron exchange has been found to be slow in the systems investigated. However, in this case, the separate hydroxyl deuteron resonance has not been observed, probably due to its low intensity.

(c) *Temperature Dependence of* $E_Q \cdot S$

The value of $E_Q \cdot S$ seems in most cases to decrease at higher temperature, probably due to a decrease in the degree of partial orientation of water molecules. The increase in $E_Q \cdot S$ (Fig. 3) and the increased line broadening at higher temperature observed in a lamellar phase of OAHCl—D_2O may tentatively be interpreted as due to chemical exchange phenomena.

No theoretical expressions are available for the complete description of the coalescence of two powder patterns arising from quadrupole interaction, with increasing rate of exchange. We assume, however, that the theoretical principles developed by Gutowsky, McCall and Slichter[26] for exchange effects on NMR lineshapes in the presence of chemical shifts and spin-spin couplings may also be valid in the case of quadrupole coupling, at least as long as the direction of the constraint is the same in the chemically distinguishable positions. In the lamellar phase of OAHCl—D_2O this direction is parallel to the optical axis for both N—D and O—D bonds. With increasing temperature the rate of exchange between ammonium and water deuterons is expected to increase and this may, according to the theory mentioned above,[26] result in an increase in the line broadening superimposed upon the theoretical powder patterns and also in an approach of the two powder patterns towards the powder pattern corresponding to rapid exchange. The latter effect may account for the increased splitting of the narrow powder pattern with increasing temperature (Fig. 3). This interpretation is supported by the preliminary observation that no increase in $E_Q \cdot S$ with increasing temperature is observed on rapid deuteron exchange produced by the addition of a small amount of OA to the system OAHCl—D_2O. Since the resonance corresponding to the ammonium deuterons is difficult to detect, its change with temperature has not yet been studied.

A similar increase in $E_Q \cdot S$ at increasing temperature has recently been reported in systems containing hydroxylic deuterons[25] and it has also been explained in terms of exchange phenomena.

(d) *Validity of Two-Site Model for Water Orientation*

The hypothetical mechanism for the partial orientation of the water molecules which was discussed above and which led to Eq. 7 may now be compared with the experimental results in Fig. 2. It should be pointed out that a linear decrease in $E_Q \cdot S$ with increasing mole fraction of D_2O similar to that proposed by Eq. (7) may also be inferred in the case of rapid exchange between amphiphile and water deuterons (*cf.* Ref. (14)), but a different slope is expected. Fig. 2 shows that, in the systems investgated, the hypothetical and oversimplified model can account for the approximately linear decrease in $E_Q \cdot S$ with increasing mole fraction of D_2O observed at high water content, but it is not in all cases capable of describing the detailed variation in $E_Q \cdot S$ at lower water content.   Ellis *et al.*[14] have found a linear decrease in the quadrupole splitting in accordance with Eq. (7) in a lamellar phase of 1-mono-octanoin—D_2O.   In mesophases containing ionic amphiphiles marked deviations from such a linear dependence have been observed.[25]

(e) *Interpretation of the S Parameter*

The definition of S as given in Eq. (4), though not exactly valid for an asymmetric EFG, may be used for a qualitative discussion of the dependence of S on the preferential orientation of D_2O molecules. As stated previously, two of the orientation matrix elements are mutually independent.   Choosing for example S_{11} and S_{22} the S parameter may be written:

$$S = S_{11} \cos^2 \beta + S_{22} \sin^2 \beta = 0.375\, S_{11} + 0.625\, S_{22} \qquad (9)$$

(assuming that $\beta = 52° 16'$).   According to Eq. (9) S equals zero either if $S_{11} = S_{22} = 0$, *i.e.* in an isotropic system, or if $S_{11} = -1.67\, S_{22}$.   Variations in the S parameter may similarly be due either to changes in *degree* of orientation or changes in the *direction* of preferred orientation.   The latter can be demonstrated using the models in Fig. 6.   The S values were calculated according to Ref. (19), but they are not directly comparable with the experimental, firstly because exchange between bound and unbound water molecules must be considered and secondly since the motion of amphiphilic molecules will also influence the degree of orientation of the water molecules.   The calculated S values should therefore be reduced by a factor which is assumed to be approximately equal in the three cases. Case *a* corresponds to hydrogen bonding between a deuteron in the D_2O molecule and a lone-pair orbital on the hydrophilic group, case *b* to hydrogen bonding between a lone-pair orbital on D_2O and protons on the hydrophilic groups, and case *c* corresponds to ion-dipole interaction.   As can be seen from Fig. 6 cases *a* and *b* correspond to approximately the same absolute magnitude of S, while case *c* gives a very small value of S.   Therefore, according to this simple model, when preferential orientation of water is produced by ion-dipole interaction a relatively small value of S may be expected.   This may contribute to the decrease in $E_Q \cdot S$ generally observed with an

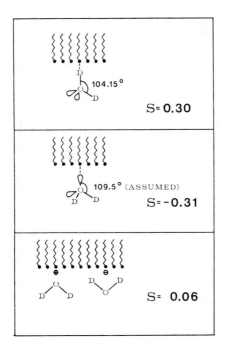

Figure 6. Theoretical values of the orientation parameter, S, for three different modes of orientation of the D_2O molecules.

increase in the proportion of ionic amphiphile in the lamellae (*cf.* Fig. 4). Furthermore, in the middle phase of CTAB—D_2O in which water molecules can not be hydrogen bonded to the hydrophilic groups, and consequently in which ion-dipole interaction may be the most important mechanism of orientation, a very small value of $E_Q \cdot S$ is observed (< 0.04 kHz).

We assume that an interpretation of variations in S in terms of the degree of orientation rather than the mode of orientation may be adequate only as long as the water bonding properties of the amphiphile are approximately constant. This is expected to be valid in most binary systems of amphiphile—water, but not in general in ternary systems.

(f) *Effects of Solubilization on $E_Q \cdot S$*

The solubilization of *p*-xylene in lamellar phases of NF-6—D_2O and NF-10—D_2O is found to markedly increase the value of $E_Q \cdot S$

(Fig. 5). In the latter system, in which up to three p-xylene molecules per NF-10 molecule can be solubilized, the value of $E_Q \cdot S$ only increases up to 1 molecule of solubilisate per amphiphilic molecule. This may suggest that the p-xylene molecules are located close to the hydrophilic groups at low concentrations, thereby increasing the degree of orientation of these groups. This could occur for example by means of a specific interaction between the aromatic rings in the p-xylene and NF-10 molecules. At higher concentrations of p-xylene the solubilization can be expected to result in an incorporation of p-xylene molecules in the aliphatic region of the lamellae, which would not primarily influence the degree of order of the hydrophilic groups. The solubilization of n-hexadecane in the system NF-10— D_2O does not markedly influence the value of $E_Q \cdot S$. These results from solubilization in lamellar mesophases may be compared with proton NMR investigations on solubilization in micellar systems[27] which indicate that aromatic hydrocarbons are in some cases located close to the polar groups of the amphiphile.

4. High Resolution PMR in Randomly Oriented Phases

The broadening mechanism of NMR absorption lines in liquid crystals was discussed by Weber[28] and later reviewed by Lawson and Flautt[2] for the case of amphiphilic systems. The dominating line broadening mechanism is considered to be the intramolecular magnetic dipole-dipole coupling,[28,2] which will not be averaged to zero in a system with anisotropic molecular motion. In a recent report on relaxation time measurements in amphiphilic mesomorphic phases Hansen and Lawson[29] suggested that molecular diffusion through magnetic inhomogeneities may also contribute to the line-width. This has also been proposed by Penkett, Flook and Chapman[30] and by Kaufman, Steim and Gibbs.[31]

In the lamellar phase of NF-10—H_2O only two high resolution PMR signals are observed, one from the water protons (halfwidth *ca.* 10 Hz) and one from the polyethylene oxide chain protons (halfwidth *ca.* 30 Hz). The signals from the aromatic and aliphatic protons are strongly broadened as is the normal situation in such phases,[2] and are not observable. Preliminary measurements have shown that the linewidth of the polyethylene oxide protons is approximately independent of the magnitude of the magnetic field and we therefore conclude that the dipole-dipole coupling is the main broadening mechanism in this case. The relatively narrow linewidth indicates a rather high mobility of the polyethylene oxide chains which may result from a solvation effect of the water molecules. Another factor which may reduce the linewidth of the protons in these chains compared with ordinary aliphatic chains is the reduced intramolecular dipole-dipole coupling due to the ether oxygen bridges. The width of the water proton resonance signal in the NF-10—H_2O system increases somewhat with increasing magnetic field, but not in direct proportion to the magnetic field. From studies of the corresponding macroscopically oriented system (*cf.* Section 5) we conclude that the broadening of the water proton resonance line in this system may in part be due to dipole-dipole coupling in the partially oriented water molecules.

In the lamellar phases of OA—H_2O, OAHCl—H_2O, OA—OAHCl —H_2O and OA—n-octanoic acid—H_2O only the average resonance signal of water and amine protons is observable using high resolution techniques. In these systems a fine structure is observed in the resonance signal. This effect has been discussed in a previous paper,[32] where theoretical lineshapes were deduced under the assumption that the water protons experience different magnetic fields in the directions parallel and perpendicular to the lamellae. The agreement between experimental and calculated spectra is very good. The water proton resonance linewidths in these systems are considerably smaller than in the NF-10—H_2O system if the effect of susceptibility anisotropy is eliminated as described in Ref. (32). This may be due to a reduction of the dipole-dipole coupling by means of a higher water proton exchange rate in the amine–water system. The proton exchange in water is known to be both acid- and base-catalyzed.[33]

We intend to make a more detailed investigation of the proton resonance line broadening in these systems.

5. Magnetically Aligned Systems

The phases discussed in the preceding section can best be characterized as liquid crystalline "powders". Lawson and Flautt[11] and

Black *et al.*[13] demonstrated that lyotropic mesophases can be macroscopically oriented in magnetic fields, and they showed that such phases offered advantages compared with nematic phases as solvents in NMR studies of oriented molecules. As mentioned above the lamellar phases examined in this investigation do not spontaneously orient in the presence of a magnetic field of about 14 kilogauss. However, if the phases are heated above the melting point and then very slowly cooled (~ 0.1 °C/10 min.) in the magnetic field, some of the phases orient and maintain their orientation for at least 24 hours, even if the oriented sample is turned 90° from its original direction in the magnetic field. This persistent orientation is somewhat paradoxical since the macroscopic viscosity of the phases is not very high; they easily flow when the sample is tilted. The effect of magnetic orientation has been thoroughly studied in the NF-10—water system. The macroscopic orientation is displayed in both deuterium and proton resonance spectra.

In Fig. 7 high resolution proton magnetic resonance spectra recorded at various angles between the original orientation direction and the magnetic field are shown. At an angle of *ca.* 55° there is a minimum in the linewidth for the amphiphile protons, especially those of the polyethylene oxide chain. The most probable explanation for the observed angular variations in the linewidths is an incomplete averaging of the dipole-dipole coupling through molecular rotation. This process would necessarily result in a line broadening proportional to $(3 \cos^2 \Omega - 1)$, where Ω is the angle between the axis of rotation (roughly coinciding with the optical axis of the lamellar system) and the magnetic field direction.[34] This broadening vanishes at $\Omega \approx 55°$, leading to the linewidth minimum. A similar angular dependence of the proton resonance linewidth has previously been observed in an oriented lamellar mesophase.[35] The fact that the observed minimum in line broadening occurs when the oriented sample is turned an angle of $\sim 55°$ from its original position in the magnetic field indicates that the molecular long axis is preferentially aligned parallel to the direction of the magnetic field during the slow cooling procedure. The residual linewidth at the observed minimum may have several explanations. A complete averaging through molecular rotation would imply perfect alignment, which can certainly not be expected. Another contribution to the linewidth can also

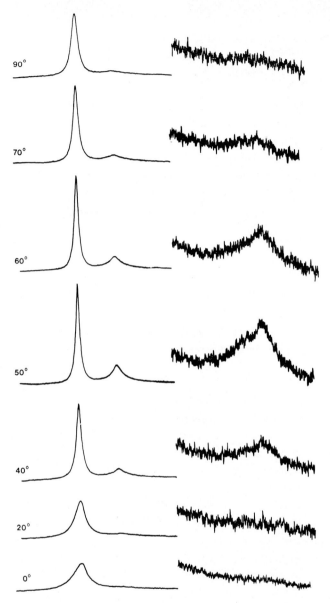

Figure 7. High resolution PMR spectra of an oriented lamellar mesophase of NF-10—H$_2$O, molar ratio 1 : 13, at different angles of rotation of the sample from its direction during the formation of the mesophase. From left to right the peaks correspond to the water protons, the polyethylene oxide chain protons and the aliphatic protons. For recording the right peak a tenfold amplification was used. Temperature: $45 \pm 1\,°$C.

arise from magnetic inhomogeneities, as recently suggested by several authors. [29-31]

It may be seen from Fig. 7 that the linewidth of the water proton resonance is also angular dependent. This is interpreted as a residual dipole interaction arising from the anisotropic rotation of the water molecules. Proton exchange is assumed not to be sufficiently rapid to completely average out the dipole interaction. Buckingham and McLauchlan[19] have given the following expression for the dipole coupling, Δ^{HH}, in partially oriented water molecules

$$\Delta^{HH} = \frac{3}{2} \left| \left(\frac{3}{2} \cos^2 \Omega - \frac{1}{2} \right) L^{HH} \cdot S_{22} \right| \tag{10}$$

where

$L^{HH} = \hbar (\gamma^H)^2 / \pi (r^{HH})^3$

γ^H is the magnetogyric ratio for H,

r^{HH} is the interproton distance in water,

Ω is the angle between the constraint direction and the magnetic field, and

S_{22} has the same meaning as in Eq. (3).

Therefore, if the direction of the constraint coincides with the optical axis of the lamellae the linewidth of the water protons would also show the same type of angular dependence as that of the amphiphile protons. (See Fig. 7.)

The macroscopic orientation of the lamellar phase is also reflected in the quadrupole coupling observed in D_2O. This was for the first time observed by Lawson and Flautt.[11] Equation 3 shows that even the quadrupole coupling should be proportional to $(3 \cos^2 \Omega - 1)$, and this is in fact observed (Fig. 8). This angular dependence of the quadrupole coupling supports the conclusions from the proton resonance measurements, namely that the lamellar phase is aligned in the magnetic field with its optical axis parallel to the magnetic field direction. Therefore, sample spinning during the formation of the mesophase in the magnetic field will lead to a randomly oriented phase. The preferred direction of molecular orientation is consequently different from that in the lyotropic mesophase studied by Black et al.[13]

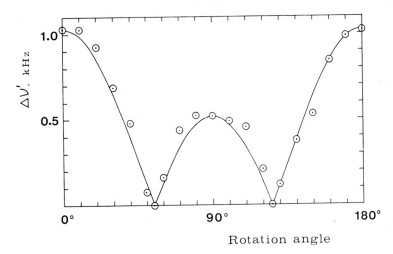

Figure 8. Frequency separation in the quadrupole doublet from oriented lamellar mesophase of NF-10—D_2O, mole ratio 1 : 17, as a function of the angle of sample rotation from the direction at the formation of the mesophase. (Temperature: $27 \pm 1\,°C$.)

Acknowledgements

The authors are most grateful to Prof. Sture Forsén for his encouragement and many fruitful discussions, as well as valuable suggestions during this work. Dr. Stig Friberg is heartily acknowledged for initiating this investigation and providing some essential chemicals. The authors are also thankful to Dr. Robert E. Carter for valuable linguistic criticism.

REFERENCES

1. See for example Saupe, A., *Angew. Chem.* **7**, 97 (1968); Meiboom, S. and Snyder, L. C., *Science* **162**, 1337 (1968); Luckhurst, G. R., " Liquid Crystalline Systems ", G. W. Gray and P. A. Winsor, Ed. (to be published).
2. Flautt, T. J. and Lawson, K. D., Advances in Chemistry Series No. 63, " Ordered Fluids and Liquid Crystals ", American Chemical Society, Washington, D.C. 1967, Chapter 3.
3. Johansson, Å. and Lindman, B., " Liquid Crystalline Systems ", G. W. Gray and P. A. Winsor, Ed. (to be published).
4. See for example Luzzati, V., " Biological Membranes, Physical Fact and Function ", D. Chapman, Ed., Academic Press, London 1968, p. 71.
5. See for example Luzzati, V., Mustacchi, H., Skoulios, A. and Husson, F., *Acta Cryst.* **13**, 660 (1960).

6. Friberg, S. and Mandell, L., *J. Pharm. Sci.* **59**, 1001 (1970).
7. Ekwall, P., Mandell, L. and Fontell, K., *Mol. Cryst. and Liq. Cryst.* **8**, 157 (1969).
8. Friberg, S. (private communication).
9. Friberg, S. Mandell, L. and Fontell, K., *Acta Chem. Scand.* **23**, 1055 (1969).
10. Ekwall, P., Mandell, L. and Fontell, K., *J. Colloid Interface Sci.* **29**, 693 (1969).
11. Lawson, K. D. and Flautt, T. J., *J. Am. Chem. Soc.* **89**, 5489 (1967).
12. Lawson, K. D. and Flautt, T. J., *J. Phys. Chem.* **72**, 2066 (1968).
13. Black, P. J., Lawson, K. D. and Flautt, T. J., *Mol. Cryst. and Liq. Cryst.* **7**, 201 (1969).
14. Ellis, B., Lawrence, A. S. C., McDonald, M. P. and Peel, W. E., " Liquid Crystals and Ordered Fluids ", J. F. Johnson and R. S. Porter, Ed., Plenum Press, New York 1970, p. 277.
15. Charvolin, J. and Rigny, P., *J. Phys.* **30**, Suppl. Colloque C4, C4–76 (1969).
16. Woessner, D. E. and Snowden, Jr., B. S., *J. Chem. Phys.* **50**, 1516 (1969).
17. Cohen, M. H. and Reif, F., " Solid State Physics " Vol. V, F. Seitz and D. Turnbull, Ed., Academic Press Inc., New York 1962, p. 321.
18. Saupe, A., *Z. Naturforsch.* **19a**, 161 (1964).
19. Buckingham, A. D. and McLauchlan, K. A., " Progress in NMR Spectroscopy ", Vol. II, J. W. Emsley, J. Feeney and L. H. Sutcliffe, Ed., Pergamon Press, Oxford 1967, p. 63.
20. Waldstein, P., Rabideau, S. W. and Jackson, J. A., *J. Chem. Phys.* **41**, 3407 (1964).
21. Poesner, D. W., *Aust. J. Phys.* **13**, 168 (1960).
22. Treacy, E. B. and Beers, Y., *J. Chem. Phys.* **36**, 1473 (1962).
22a. Deverell, C., " Progress in NMR Spectroscopy ", Vol. IV, J. W. Emsley, J. Feeney and L. H. Sutcliffe, Ed., Pergamon Press, Oxford 1969, p. 268.
23. Muller, N. and Birkhahn, R. H., *J. Phys. Chem.* **71**, 957 (1967) and **72**, 583 (1968).
24. Grunwald, E., Löwenstein, A. and Meiboom, S., *J. Chem. Phys.* **27**, 630 (1957).
25. Persson, N.-O. and Johansson, Å., *Acta Chem. Scand.* (in press).
26. Gutowsky, H. S., McCall, D. V. and Slichter, C. P., *J. Chem. Phys.* **21**, 279 (1953).
27. Eriksson, J. C. and Gillberg, G., *Acta Chem. Scand.* **20**, 2019 (1966).
28. Weber, K.-H., *Ann. Physik* (7), **3**, 1 (1959).
29. Hansen, J. R. and Lawson, K. D., *Nature* **225**, 542 (1970).
30. Penkett, S. A., Flook, A. G. and Chapman, D., *Chem. Phys. Lipids* **2**, 273 (1968).
31. Kaufman, S., Steim, J. M. and Gibbs, J. H., *Nature* **225**, 743 (1970).
32. Drakenberg, T., Johansson, Å. and Forsén, S., *J. Phys. Chem.* **74**, 4528 (1970).
33. Meiboom, S., *J. Chem. Phys.* **34**, 375 (1961).
34. Powles, J. G. and Gutowsky, H. S., *J. Chem. Phys.* **21**, 1704 (1953).
35. de Vries, J. J. and Berendsen, H. J. C., *Nature* **221**, 1139 (1969).

NMR Study of Molecular Motions in the Mesophases of Potassium Laurate—D₂O System†

J. CHARVOLIN‡ and P. RIGNY

Département de Physico-Chimie
Centre d'Etudes Nucléaires de Saclay
91–Gif-sur-Yvette, France

Received October 23, 1970; *in revised form January* 25, 1971

Abstract—In the presence of water amphiphilic molecules display a large number of phases. As shown by X-ray studies the structures of these phases are characterized by a large scale periodic organization of aqueous and paraffinic media. Moreover, in the mesophases, these same X-ray diagrams show that this long range order coexists with a short range disorder in the paraffinic chains moiety.

Previous studies of the NMR line shape of paraffinic protons had suggested this disorder to be dynamical. We present and discuss here pulsed NMR measurements, performed on the paraffinic protons of potassium laurate—D₂O samples, in the lamellar mesophase, in order to gain a better knowledge of the details of the motions involved.

The complex shape of the free precession decay can approximately be analysed into " solid-like " (gaussian) and " liquid-like " (exponential) components. This suggests that the motion is not uniform along the paraffinic chain: protons close to the polar head are less mobile than those at the end of the chain. The first experience residual dipolar interactions (measured by the second moments of the gaussian signals) while these are averaged out for the second which exhibits a transverse relaxation time T_2 (measured by the time constant of the exponential signal). Despite the complexity of the free precession decay the measured value of relaxation time T_1 is the same for all the protons and is frequency independent.

Second moments and relaxation data indicate that the surfactant molecules undergo rapid deformations ($\tau_R \simeq 10^{-9}$ sec.) about the C—C bonds which (modulating intramolecular interactions) are responsible for T_1 and that a slow molecular diffusion ($\tau_S \simeq 10^{-6}$ sec.) over macroscopic distances is responsible for T_2, averaging out intermolecular interactions.

---

† Presented at the Third International Liquid Crystal Conference in Berlin, August 24–28, 1970.

‡ Permanent address: Laboratoire de Physique des Solides, Faculté des Sciences, 91 Orsay, France.

1. Introduction

From soaps to more sophisticated biological phospholipids, amphiphilic molecules form, in the presence of water, liquid crystalline phases. The short and intermediate length fatty acids and their salts give the clearest examples of such lyotropic liquid crystals. These molecules contain a hydrocarbon chain and a terminal polar group. The property of amphiphily describes their behaviour in a solvent, commonly water. The polar head is hydrophilic and the hydrocarbon chain hydrophobic. In a solvent the polar heads associate and thus define a surface which separates the aqueous medium from the paraffinic one. The geometrical shape of this surface depends on the water content and the temperature. In fact these lyotropic systems are also thermotropic; it is the action of both solvent and temperature which gives rise to the original and complex polymorphism of these systems, ranging from the solid crystalline state to the isotropic liquid via the liquid crystalline mesophases.

The phase diagrams of soap-water and lipid-water systems have long been studied using crystallographic methods. Great progress towards the understanding of these mesophases is being made with X-ray scattering techniques. These liquid crystalline phases are characterized by:[1]

1. Large scale organization, the distribution of aqueous and hydrocarbon media is periodic in one, two, or three dimensions;
2. Small scale disorder within both media, particularly the paraffinic one.

The second point, affecting short range interactions, can be studied using NMR techniques which allow one to investigate local static and dynamic structures. This has been illustrated by previous studies on the behaviour of water in similar structures: some water molecules are strongly bounded to the barrier surface defined by the polar heads while others are free from the surface. A molecular exchange takes place between the two sets.[3,4] In the paraffinic moiety the disorder was shown to be dynamical and it was suggested that the motion of a CH_2 group in a chain should depend very much on its distance from the polar head.[2,3] Recent EPR experiments on spin labelled lipids lead to similar conclusions.[5]

In order to obtain more quantitative information concerning the motions of the paraffinic chains we have undertaken pulsed NMR experiments on CH_2 protons of the potassium laurate—D_2O system in its lamellar mesophase. After introducing the effects of molecular motions on NMR signals, we shall present preliminary relaxation data suggesting the existence of two types of motions : slow molecular diffusion and progressive deformations of the paraffinic chains.

2. Study of Molecular Motions by Pulsed NMR

In pulsed NMR[6a], one puts a spin system out of its state of thermal equilibrium in the external magnetic field H_0. A RF pulse tilts the nuclear magnetization out of the H_0 direction. After this excitation, the spin system recovers equilibrium in two simultaneous ways :

1. In a plane normal to H_0, the transverse component decays to zero in a time T_2, giving the so-called free precession signal ;
2. Along H_0, the longitudinal component recovers its equilibrium value in a time T_1.

These two relaxation processes must be distinguished since in the first case the process does not require energy exchange (the transverse spin components simply get out of phase), while in the second case the spin system must exchange with the lattice an energy of the order of the coupling energy of the spins with the magnetic field H_0.

In non-metallic systems these two types of relaxation are generally induced by the spin–spin dipolar interactions and their modulation by lattice motions.

A. Effects of Motions on NMR Signals

In a rigid solid each nuclear spin, fixed on a lattice site, experiences the local magnetic field due to the dipolar magnetic moments of neighbouring spins. The distribution of the local fields gives the NMR absorption line a gaussian shape characterized by a second moment m_2. In pulsed experiments the transverse components of the spins are forced out of phase with this static distribution in a time

$$T_2^{RL} \simeq m_2^{-1/2} \quad (RL \text{ for rigid lattice, } m_2 \text{ in sec}^{-2}).$$

The free precession signal decays according to

$$S_{(t)} = S_{(0)} \exp\left(-\frac{m_2}{2}t^2\right)$$

which is the Fourier transform of the gaussian line.[6a]

When a molecular motion, faster than $m_2^{1/2}$ sets in, the dipolar couplings between nuclear spins are averaged out and the absorption line width is due to second order effects of the modulated interaction. Experimentally, the absorption line gets narrower than the rigid lattice one and its shape tends to be Lorentzian. The free precession signal then decays as

$$S_{(t)} = S_{(0)} \exp\left(-\frac{t}{T'_2}\right)$$

which is the Fourier transform of a lorentzian line of width T_2^{-1}.

It was shown,[7] in this motionally narrowed case, that the efficiencies of the relaxation mechanisms depend upon the Fourier spectrum of the frequencies of motion. Very useful approximations of the formula derived in Ref. 7 couple the relaxation rates to the motional correlation time

$$(T_1)^{-1} \simeq 2h^2\tau(1 + \omega_0^2 \tau^2)^{-1} \tag{1}$$

$$(T_2)^{-1} \simeq 2h^2\tau \tag{2}$$

where h^2 is the square of the modulated interaction and ω_0 is the nuclear Larmor frequency.

NMR is a powerful tool for the study of molecular motions. It can detect a molecular movement as soon as its frequency is of the order of the rigid lattice line width (a few 10^4 hertz). From the degree of line narrowing, one can identify the type of motion involved. From the effect on T_1, one can deduce its frequency, if in the range of a few 10^7 hertz. Even very slow motions, down to a few hertz, can be detected now since the development of measurements of T_1 in the rotating frame.[8]

B. Dynamically Heterogeneous Systems

As was shown in the preceding paragraph NMR properties of materials are strongly influenced by the motions of nuclei: this gives rise to complex signals whenever several motions coexist in a system or when the rates of the motions are distributed over a range of values. The system is then heterogeneous with respect to its dynamical structure.

Previous NMR studies[2,3] suggested that such a situation prevails in the case of the paraffinic chains of lipid-water systems in the liquid crystalline state. The degree of motion of a CH_2 group should depend very much on its distance from the polar head, the end of the chain being expected to move rather freely while the beginning should be more rigid. Under these conditions, the absorption line will contain both narrow and broad components. The latter are generally difficult to extract from the absorption spectrum and to analyse. In order to surmount this difficulty we have made free precession experiments where broad components of the absorption line are Fourier transformed into fast decaying components; their observation is limited only by the recovery time of the pulsed apparatus.

The signal of the protons of a definite CH_2 group will have the form[6b]:

$$S_{(t)} = S_{(0)} \exp\left(-\frac{m_2}{2} t^2 - \frac{t}{T_2} \right)$$

where the second moment m_2 corresponds to residual dipolar interactions while the transverse relaxation time T_2 is due, on the contrary, to the modulated part of this interaction. T_2 and m_2 are, of course, complicated functions of the distance of the CH_2 group from the polar head and of the details of the motions.

3. Experimental

A. SAMPLES

Our experiments were made with the potassium laurate—D_2O system[9] ($CH_3(CH_2)_{10}CO_2K$—D_2O hereafter called $C_{12}K$—D_2O). The anhydrous soap was prepared in the Laboratoire de Génétique Moléculaire (C.N.R.S.): the fatty acid is neutralized by potash in ethanolic solution and slowly crystallized, the product is washed in ethanol then dried. The heavy water is isotopically pure at 99.78%. The different concentrations were prepared by weighing of the required quantities of $C_{12}K$ and D_2O. Homogeneized by heating to 80 °C the solutions were also centrifuged back and forth through a constriction of the sample tube to increase homogeneity and to eliminate air bubbles. The concentrations, going from 14% to 30% D_2O (in weight) were chosen to give samples in the lamellar mesophase between 40 and 90 °C. In this phase the soap molecules are organized in parallel and equidistant bimolecular layers (smectic mesophase). The soap lamellae, full of disordered paraffinic chains, are limited by the polar heads which keep the aqueous medium apart from the hydrocarbon one.

B. Apparatus

The second moments, m_2, and the transverse relaxation time, T_2, were obtained from direct analysis of the free precession decay observed after a " $\pi/2$ pulse " which tilts the magnetization from the direction of the external magnetic field H_0 to a plane normal to it. The longitudinal relaxation time, T_1, was obtained by the conventional " recovery " method[6a] using two " $\pi/2$ pulses " separated by variable time intervals. The pulsed spectrometer is of the single coil type, the dead time is 15 μs at 10 MHz and 8 μs at 30 MHz. Experiments were performed at different temperatures, from 40 to 90 °C, by means of a thermally controlled flow of gaseous nitrogen around the sample tube.

4. Results and Interpretation

A. Free Precession Decays

The critical analysis of the free precession decays is given in Ref. 10, in this paragraph we sum up the essential results. Figure 1 shows the semi-logarithmic plot of a typical free precession signal obtained from the CH_2 protons of a $C_{12}K$—D_2O sample in the lamellar mesophase. The complex shape of the signal can be interpreted in terms of the previously mentioned heterogeneity of the motions of the paraffinic chains. It can be decomposed into three parts: two linear in t^2, one linear in t. Following the discussion of §2–B we analyse it as the superposition of two " solid-like " ($T_2 \gg m_2^{-1/2}$) and one " liquid-like " components. This analysis does not necessarily imply discontinuities in the behaviour of the CH_2 groups along the chain but considering three regions must be a good approximation.

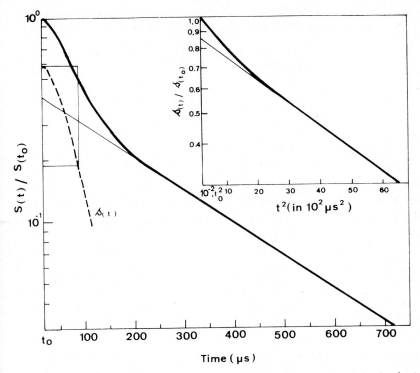

Figure 1. Logarithmic plot of the free precession decay, $S_{(t)}$, obtained at 30 MHz after a $\pi/2$ pulse, from a $C_{12}K$—28% D_2O sample in the lamellar phase at 90 °C. t_0 is the sum of the pulse width plus the recovery time of the apparatus. $s_{(t)}$ enlarged in the inset as a function of t^2, is the difference between the total decay and its exponential part.

It seems reasonable to assume that protons close to the polar head are less mobile than others and that they give the " solid-like " signal of largest second moment. Only a rough maximum value of 6 gauss² (determined at 90 °C for a 14% D_2O sample) can be given for this second moment for, in this fast decay region, part of the signal is lost in the apparatus recovery time. Then the second moment decreases, first to a water content and temperature independent value of 0.57 ± 0.09 gauss² in the second " solid-like " region, finally to zero in the " liquid-like " one. This last region very likely concerns protons of the chain end, its decay is characterized by a transverse relaxation time $T_2 = 270 \pm 20$ μsec. Extracted from Fig. 1, the percentages of protons in each part of the

TABLE 1   Relative fractions (in %) of Protons of the Paraffinic Chains in " Solid-like " and " Liquid-like " Regions as a Function of the Water Content. The $C_{12}K—D_2O$ samples are all in the lamellar mesophase at 90 °C.

Water content: $\dfrac{D_2O \text{ weight}}{\text{total weight}}$		0.14	0.22	0.25	0.28	0.30
" Solid-like " spins	$m_2 = 6$ gauss^2	31	15	9	6	0
	$m_2 = 0.57$ gauss^2	44	50	50	51	54
" Liquid-like " spins	$m_2 = 0$ and $T_2 = 270$ μsec	25	35	41	43	46

chain are indicated in Tables 1 and 2 for several temperatures and D_2O concentrations. It can be seen that the " liquid-like " component is not due to the very mobile methyl protons, for they represent no more than 13% of the total protons number; nor is it due to residual H_2O in D_2O. An increase of mobility can be expected when temperature or water content increase, this is the general trend one observes in Tables 1 and 2 where the mobile part of the chain becomes more important with temperature and concentration.

TABLE 2   Relative Fraction (in %) of Protons of the Paraffinic Chains in " Solid-like " and " Liquid-like " Regions as a Function of Temperature for a $C_{12}K—28\%$ D_2O Sample in the Lamellar Mesophase.

Temperature (°C)		44	55	73	90
" Solid-like " spins	$m_2 = 6$ gauss^2	8	7	7	6
	$m_2 = 0.57$ gauss^2	66	64	58	51
" Liquid-like " spins	$m_2 = 0$ and $T_2 = 270$ μsec	26	29	35	43

The shape of the free precession signals have been interpreted here as coming from partially averaged dipolar interactions. The order of magnitude of the first second moment, $m_2 \simeq 6$ gauss^2, compares well with the values obtained for alkanes rotating around their longitudinal axis.[11] The absence of frequency second moment variations indicates that the anisotropic moment responsible for the partial averaging of the dipolar interactions is fast compared to the second moment reduction.[6b] Similar shapes can also result from molecular diffusion in an inhomogeneous magnetic field; however a test consisting of a study of the spin system responses to suitable excitations has been proposed[10] and enables one to choose between the two alternatives. No effect of field inhomogeneity is apparent with our samples.

Other authors, investigating similar systems, have reported frequency dependent line widths[12] or free induction decays[13] while we have not been able to see such a dependence from 7 to 30 MHz. We believe these discrepancies to be due to differences in samples preparations; the mean size of the monocrystalline domains being perhaps an important factor governing the reorientation ability, in the magnetic field, of each diamagnetically anisotropic domain.

B. Relaxation Times

The transverse relaxation time T_2 of the " liquid-like " protons is 270 ± 20 μsec; it increases slightly with temperature with an activation energy of the order of 0.5 kcal/mole. The T_2 of " solid-like " protons ought to be obtained by other methods (e.g. $T_{1\rho}$ measurements). Only one longitudinal relaxation time T_1 is observed within our limit of error. Its value at 90 °C is 0.68 ± 0.04 sec. It increases with temperature having an activation energy of 5.5 kcal/mole as shown in Fig. 2. The measurements were made from 7 to 30 MHz but no frequency dependence was observed. This last result immediately shows that a motion rapid compared to the inverse Larmor frequency is responsible for T_1 (equation 1). Its characteristic correlation time is $\tau_R < 10^{-8}$ sec. But for such a fast motion, the associated T_2 would be equal to T_1,[7] T_2 being smaller than T_1 a slower motion is responsible for T_2. Under these conditions accurate values of the characteristic times of the motions and of the strength of the interactions they modulate cannot be given without further experiments.

C. Proposed Model

The rapid motion, responsible for the longitudinal relaxation, probably consists of internal isomeric rotations about the C—C bonds of the paraffinic chain. The measured T_1 activation energy is consistent with the heights of the barriers hindering internal

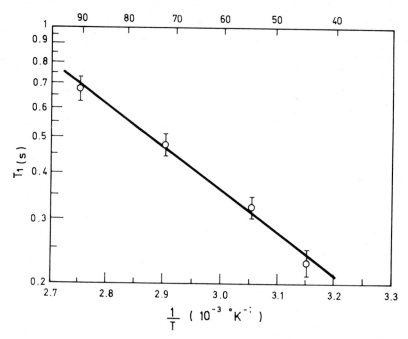

Figure 2.   Longitudinal relaxation time T_1 plotted as a function of the inverse absolute temperature.   The measurements were made with a $C_{12}K$—28% D_2O sample in the lamellar phase, at a frequency of 30 MHz.   The activation energy is 5.5 kcal/mole.

rotations in alkanes[14] and assuming these rotations to be described by an harmonic potential the characteristic time τ_R of this rapid motion can be estimated with[15]

$$\tau_R^{-1} \simeq \frac{kT}{\hbar} \exp\left(-\frac{\Delta E}{kT}\right)$$

giving a rough value of $\tau_R \simeq 10^{-9}$ sec.

Such a motion is also met in long chain polymers where it seems to be a predominant T_1 relaxation mechanism.[16]   However in our case the single T_1 behaviour would be inconsistent with the " three parts in the chain " model considered in paragraph 4–A unless we introduce spin diffusion.[17]   This point will be discussed later.   A general deformation results from all these segmental fast motions.

In the lamella, the laurate molecule is in such an anisotropic medium that this general motion can be schematized as having its amplitude and isotropy increasing from the polar head to the methyl end; this can explain the progressive averaging of the spin–spin dipolar interactions and so the decrease of the second moment from 6 gauss^2 close to the polar head to zero at the end of the chain. Such a statement has to be developed considering the rotameric jump probability according to the position of the C—C bond in the chain, as will be stressed in the next paragraph.

The slower motion, responsible for the transverse relaxation, could be a two dimensional diffusion of the laurate molecule in the plane of the lamellae modulating the intermolecular dipolar interaction. Taking an average intermolecular interaction of 2 gauss^2 one can deduce, from the experimental T'_2 and equation 2, a characteristic time τ_S for this slow diffusion of roughly 10^{-6} sec. The existence of such a diffusion has not been directly proved in the lamellar phase but a similar motion can be seen, in an obvious way, in the cubic isotropic mesophase of the same system $C_{12}K—D_2O$.[10] It is very likely that diffusion also occurs in lamellar mesophase but its effects on the NMR properties differ from those in the cubic mesophase owing to the anisotropy of the structure.

D. DISCUSSION

In setting forth the model of the motions existing in the system under study a few points were stated although we need more experimental results to support them. We are going to reconsider them from a more critical point of view.

First, spin diffusion was invoked to explain the uniqueness of T_1 even though three types of spins can be considered in the chain. Spin diffusion acts as follows: if part of an heterogeneous spin system is strongly coupled to the lattice, while the rest is weakly coupled, the first part may act as an energy sink for the whole system, spin–spin interactions in the rest of the system can conduct energy to the fast relaxing part at a rate τ_D^{-1} of the order of the dipolar spin–spin coupling (expressed in sec^{-1}). Such a mechanism makes the spin lattice relaxation time T_1 uniform over the whole system and the relaxation rate can be limited either by the diffusion rate or by the relaxation rate of the energy sink. At the temperatures of our experiments (from 40 to 90 °C) the reorientation of the methyl groups is very rapid[17] and the rate flow, $T_1^{-1} \simeq 10^{-1}$ sec^{-1}, of their Zeeman energy to the lattice is too small compared to the measured relaxation rate $T_1^{-1} \simeq 1$ sec^{-1}, so that they cannot act as an energy sink. The diffusion rate in the " solid-like " part of the chain being very fast $\tau_D^{-1} \simeq 10^4$ sec^{-1} the longitudinal relaxation rate is certainly limited by the capacity of an energy sink which is to be found in the fast rotameric jumps taking place in the whole " liquid-like " part of the chain. In this condition the measured relaxation rate must be equal to the relaxation rate of one proton in the " liquid-like " part weighted by the ratio of the number of " liquid-like " protons to the total number of protons. This effects the correlation time τ_R by a factor of about 2 (see Table 1).

In presenting the model it was also stated that from the fast isomeric rotations a general swinging of the methyl end of a chain results, the polar head being fixed on the water-soap interface. An important problem is the relation between the local correlation time and the one for this general swinging motion. The general idea about a theoretical model is that an isomeric rotation, giving the methyl end too wide a displacement, would have to be less probable than those distorting the chain progressively. This supposes that the motions in a chain have to be treated from a collective point of view ; the probability of occurrence of one rotameric jump depending upon the conformation of the chain. In this model the general deformation of the chain would be characterized by a longer correlation time than the one of the fast local isomeric rotations. Such a slower motion, modulating intermolecular interactions, could be taken as responsible for the transverse relaxation instead of the molecular diffusion. However, the activation energy of T_2 is very much smaller than that of the isomeric rotations giving rise to the swinging motion. This seems to indicate that this last motion is not effective for the transverse relaxation which seems to be due to the molecular diffusion.

5. Conclusion

The molecular motions existing in the lamellar mesophase of the potassium laurate-D_2O system have been investigated by means of pulsed NMR; our interest was focussed on the dynamical disorder of the paraffinic chains. Relaxation data obtained on this system show evidence of two types of motions which can be schematized in the following way:

—isomeric fast rotations about the C—C bonds deform the paraffinic chain; their effects increasing from the polar head to the methyl end. They progressively average to zero the intra-molecular spin–spin interactions. Their characteristic time is of the order of 10^{-9} sec;

—a slower motion, which is a two-dimensional diffusion of the laurate molecule in the plane of its lamellae, has a correlation time of the order of 10^{-6} sec.

The order of magnitude of these times are somewhat out of the ranges of motion rates accurately attainable by the simple NMR methods we have used. Moreover, the discussion has shown that this model was a very crude one and that several points need further developments:

—the isomeric rotations relax the Zeeman energy, but the uni-formization of T_1 by spin diffusion and the localization on the chain of the energy sink have to be emphasized;

—a statistical description of the general folding of the chain, resulting from these isomeric rotations will be very useful in casting light on the progressive averaging of the dipolar inter-molecular interactions as well as on the modulation of inter-molecular ones by this motion;

—molecular diffusion modulates also the latter and its role in the transverse relaxation has to be more precisely defined.

Answers to these questions need, in particular, an extension of NMR experiments towards the investigation of slower molecular motions.

REFERENCES

1. Luzzati, V., *Third International Liquid Crystal Conference*, Berlin, August 24–28, 1970.
2. Lawson, K. D. and Flautt, T. J., *Mol. Cryst.* **1**, 241 (1966).
3. Lawson, K. D. and Flautt, T. J., *J. Phys. Chem.* **72**, 2066 (1968).
4. Charvolin, J. and Rigny, P., *J. Phys.* **30C4**, 76 (1969).

5. Hubbell, W. L. and McConnell, H. M., *Proc. Nat. Acad. Sc. U.S.* **64**, 20 (1969).
6. Abragam, A., *The Principles of Nuclear Magnetism* (a) Chap. III (b) Chap. X, Oxford University Press, London, 1961.
7. Bloembergen, N., Purcell, E. M. and Pound, R. V., *Phys. Rev.* **73**, 679 (1948).
8. Douglass, D. C. and Jones, G. P., *J. Chem. Phys.* **45**, 956 (1966).
9. Husson, F., Mustacchi, H. and Luzzati, V., *Acta Cryst.* **13**, 668 (1960).
10. Charvolin, J. and Rigny, P., *J. Magn. Res.* **4**, 40 (1971).
11. Andrew, E. R., *J. Chem. Phys.* **18**, 607 (1950).
12. Penkett, S. A., Flook, A. G. and Chapman, D., *Chem. Phys. Lipids* **2**, 273 (1968).
13. Hansen, J. R. and Lawson, K. D., *Nature* **225**, 542 (1970).
14. Borisova, N. P. and Volkenstein, V. M., *Zh. Strukt. Khim.* **2**, 469 (1961).
15. Eyring in *Theory of Rate Processes* McGraw Hill, New York, 1941.
16. Liu, K. J. and Ullman, R., *J. Chem. Phys.* **48**, 1158 (1968).
17. Anderson, J. E. and Slichter, W. P., *J. Phys. Chem.* **69**, 3099 (1965).

4 X-Ray and Structure

X-Ray Photographic Studies of Liquid Crystals†
II. Apparent Molecular Length and Thickness in Three Phases of Ethyl-p-ethoxybenzal-p-aminobenzoate‡

ADRIAAN DE VRIES

Liquid Crystal Institute
Kent State University
Kent, Ohio 44240, U.S.A.

Received July 29, 1970

Abstract—A general theory is developed for the relation between the molecular length and the position of a diffraction maximum found at diffraction angles of the order of 4°, for nematic and isotropic phases containing elongated molecules. Using this theory and a previously developed one for the relation between the intermolecular distance and the position of the major diffraction maximum at larger diffraction angles, molecular parameters are determined for three phases of ethyl-p-ethoxybenzal-p-aminobenzoate. These parameters are: the thickness of the smectic layers (19.941 Å), the length of the molecules in the isotropic phase (21.4 Å), and the intermolecular distances in the smectic (4.894 Å), nematic (4.932–4.950 Å), and isotropic phases (4.950–5.182 Å), all as a function of temperature. From these data, densities and volume expansion coefficients are calculated which agree very well with literature data on similar compounds.

There appears to be no room for rotation of the molecules around their long axes, not even in the isotropic phase. In the isotropic liquid the experimentally determined molecular length is very close to the calculated length of the stretched molecule (21.6 Å), but the thickness of the smectic layers is significantly less than this. The angle between the long molecular axes and the smectic planes (in the smectic A phase) is found to be very close to 90°. The nematic phase' appears to be a classical nematic phase: there is no significant ordering of the molecules apart from the near parallelism of the long axes of neighboring molecules.

The transition temperatures found are: C—L = 93.4 °C; N—L = 87.6 °C; S—N = 80.4 °C.

† Research supported by contract F44620–69–C–0021 monitored by the Air Force Office of Scientific Research.

‡ Paper presented at the Third International Liquid Crystal Conference Berlin, West Germany, August 1970.

457

1. Introduction

The work reported is part of an ongoing program for the quantitative determination of molecular parameters in liquid crystalline phases. This program was undertaken because we feel that the determination of these molecular parameters (the apparent molecular length and thickness) for a number of compounds will enable us to draw valuable conclusions with regard to the molecular packing in liquid crystals and in the related isotropic liquid phases. The results obtained so far are encouraging; in the first paper in this series[1] we showed that there are at least two different types of nematic phases (the classical nematic phase and the cybotactic nematic phase), and we were able to present a model for the molecular arrangement in the cybotactic nematic phase. In this paper some conclusions will be drawn with regard to the molecular packing in the smectic A phase[2] and in the classical nematic phase. As more compounds will be investigated, we expect to be able to draw further conclusions and to confirm the earlier ones.

Since little work has been done so far in this area, we had to develop some new theories and formulas for the interpretation of the X-ray diffraction effects encountered in the study of liquid crystals. In the previous publication[1] we showed that there was a diffraction ring (called the " inner ring ") related to the length of the molecules, and a diffraction ring (called the " outer ring ") caused by the interaction of neighboring, parallel molecules. A theory was developed for the nner diffraction ring of cybotactic nematic phases, and a general theory was worked out for the diffuse outer diffraction ring of smectic, nematic, and isotropic phases. We also gave the formula which should be used in calculating the intermolecular distance from the diameter of the outer ring. This paper presents a general theory for the relation between the position of the inner diffraction ring and the length of the molecules in classical nematic and isotropic liquid phases containing elongated molecules; we also will report numerical data on a specific compound.

This compound, ethyl-p-ethoxybenzal-p-aminobenzoate (EEB for short), $C_2H_5O \cdot C_6H_4 \cdot CH{=}N \cdot C_6H_4 \cdot COOC_2H_5$, was selected for several reasons. It had a smectic A and a nematic phase, a combination that we wished to study (we reported earlier[1] on nematic phases related to smectic C phases). The molecule is short; this means that the inner diffraction ring occurs at larger diffraction angles and thus can be measured more accurately. The molecule is relatively rigid; this facilitates the interpretation of the results. The transition temperatures are fairly low; this reduces the chance for decomposition of the material during the measurements.

The data reported in this paper are the thickness of the smectic layers, the length of the molecules in the isotropic phase, and the intermolecular distances in the smectic, nematic and isotropic phases, all as a function of temperature. From these data we calculated volume expansion coefficients and densities for the various phases, and we compared these calculated values with data from the literature. The agreement appears to be very good.

Since there was some disagreement between the transition temperatures obtained from various sources, we also made careful measurements of these temperatures.

2. Experimental Procedures

X-ray diffraction patterns from samples in glass capillaries (0.5 and 1.0 mm diameter) were recorded on flat pieces of film with the camera described earlier,[1] using Ni-filtered Cu radiation. The same setup was also used for the determination of the transition temperatures. Relative values for these temperatures were obtained from the thermometer in the thermostat which circulated oil through the copper block which held the capillaries. Subsequently, this thermometer was calibrated using capillaries with melting point standards†; the calibration points were reproducible to within 0.1 °C from their mean values.

To determine the diameters of the diffraction rings we used the following procedures. For the reflections from the smectic layers (which are *sharp* reflections) we measured the diameter of the second order diffraction ring (the highest order clearly visible on the photographs) with a ruler, directly on the film. The diameters for all the other, more diffuse, maxima were determined by scanning the films on a densitometer (a Siemens recording photometer), recording the

---

† These standard substances were obtained from the Mettler Instrument Corporation.

density patterns on charts and measuring these charts with the same ruler used for the measurements of the smectic inner rings. For these measurements the position of a maximum was defined as the point of intersection of the two straight lines drawn through the practically straight upper portions of the slopes on either side of the maximum.

To calibrate the diameters thus obtained, we also measured the diameter of the 111 reflection of aluminum (lattice spacing 2.3284 Å), using capillaries filled with aluminum powder.

For the calculation of the intermolecular distance D (in this paper we shall always take this to mean the average distance between the long axes of neighboring parallel molecules) from the diameter of the outer diffraction ring (the main diffuse diffraction maximum in photographs from smectic, nematic and isotropic phases), we shall always use here the formula[1] $2D \sin \theta = 1.117\lambda$, where θ is one half of the angle between the incident X-ray beam and the diffracted beam (calculated from the diameter of the diffraction ring and the sample-to-film distance) and λ is the wavelength of the radiation (1.5418 Å for our measurements).

3. Results

In the discussion of the X-ray data in this section, special attention has been given to the alignment condition of the samples. This has been done because the alignment has considerable influence on the accuracy of the measurement and upon what measurements can be made, and because it is possible that the packing of the molecules might be slightly different in well-aligned regions as compared to regions with random orientation, e.g., in a well-aligned region the intermolecular distance might be shorter. We have found no convincing evidence for this in our results, but nevertheless it seemed advisable to record the state of alignment of the samples.

The results obtained from the X-ray measurements have all been presented in the form of graphs, and where appropriate the best straight line through the data points has been calculated with the method of least-squares. There is, of course, no real reason why the relationships presented in the graphs would have to be given by straight lines, but our data gave no indications that other curves should be used.

THE TRANSITION TEMPERATURES

Transition temperatures for the crystal-isotropic liquid point (C—L), the nematic–isotropic liquid point (N—L), and the smectic–nematic point (S—N) have been reported in the literature[2] and also had been determined in our Institute by various methods (see Table 1, columns 1–5). Since these data did not agree too well, and

TABLE 1   Transition Temperatures in °C

	1	2	3	4	5	6	7
C—L	92.1	94.2	93.8	92.5	92.0	93.0	93.4
N—L	82.4	85.3	84.1	86.6	87.2	87.2	87.6
S—N	77.7	77.4	76.5	79.0	80.1	80.0	80.4

The origins of the various sets of data are: (1) Demus and Sackmann[2]; (2), (3) microscopic observations on two different batches; (4) DTA (differential thermal analysis) from the same material as used for (2); (5) DTA results from zone-refined material; (6) X-ray-oven data from the same material as used for (2) and (4); (7) X-ray-oven data from the same material as used for (5).

also since a question was raised concerning the existence of a second smectic phase at lower temperatures,[3] we decided to determine these transition temperatures as accurately as possible using the heating system from the X-ray camera and observing the sample through a low-powered microscope. This method had the advantage of allowing one to keep the sample for extended periods of time at any given temperature (constant to less than 0.1 °C); thus, the speed of the transition, which is sometimes slow, is of no influence. The reproducibility of the measurements was very good; the transition temperatures were always within 0.1° from their mean values.

The values thus obtained (Table 1, columns 6 and 7) differ considerably (up to 5 °C) from the literature data (column 1) and from the microscope data (columns 2 and 3). The differences with the DTA data (columns 4 and 5) are of the order of 1°. Zone refinement of the material resulted in raising all transition temperatures by 0.4° (columns 6 and 7). We also found that the N—L and C—L temperatures of the zone-refined material went down fairly rapidly toward those of the not zone-refined material if the material was kept at temperatures above the C—L point, and also that the C—L temperature of a sample of the not zone-refined material decreased by about 0.25° in the course of time.

The values in column 7 of Table 1 appear to us to be the most reliable ones; they are the ones used in the following schematic phase diagram of EEB:

$$
\text{(ca. 70°)} \quad
\begin{array}{ccc}
\text{Solid} & \xleftarrow{\quad 93.4° \quad} & \text{Isotropic liquid} \\
\uparrow & & \uparrow \; 87.6° \\
\text{Smectic} & \xleftarrow{\quad 80.4° \quad} & \text{Nematic}
\end{array}
$$

As far as the possible existence of a second smectic phase at lower temperature is concerned, our photographs did not show any change in the diffraction pattern down to 70 °C, and our measurements (Figs. 1 and 2) do not indicate any significant change in the molecular parameters down to 72 °C. So if there is a second smectic phase, it is very unlikely that it exists above 72 °C.

THE SMECTIC PHASE

In the discussion of the X-ray diffraction photographs of the smectic phase we shall distinguish between the *inner* diffraction maxima, which are caused by the smectic layer arrangement (we usually observed the first and the second order of this reflection against the smectic planes), and the *outer* diffraction maxima, which are caused by the interaction between neighboring parallel molecules.[1] There are other, less pronounced, diffraction effects visible on the photographs, but they will not be discussed in the present paper.

In this section, and in the following ones, we shall first discuss the outer diffraction maxima and next the inner diffraction maxima. All photographs of the smectic phase of samples in 0.5 mm capillaries indicated a strong alignment of the long molecular axes approximately parallel to the direction of the capillary axis (the one photograph made using a 1.0 mm capillary showed much less alignment). The planes of the smectic layers appeared to be perpendicular to the direction of the long molecular axes, and thus approximately perpendicular to the walls of the capillary. This behavior is in agreement with microscopic studies, in which pseudoisotropic textures were not or seldom observed for this compound.[2]

Because of this strong alignment the two maxima in the outer diffraction ring were very strong and extended only over a limited area on the photograph. Measurements of the diameter of the outer diffraction ring were, therefore, accurate in the direction of these maxima (which are situated diametrically opposite each other when the molecular axes are perpendicular to the incident beam) or in directions close to the direction of the maxima, but measurements in other directions could not be made. From each photograph two or more measurements were made, and from the average for each photograph we calculated the corresponding intermolecular distance D. These distances are plotted in Fig. 1. They comprise the results from

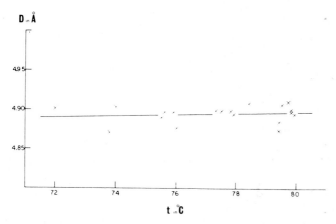

Figure. 1.   The intermolecular distance in the smectic phase as a function of temperature.

seven series of photographs, obtained from four different capillaries using three slightly different sample-to-film distances (caused by small changes in the setup). The agreement between the measurements is seen to be quite good. A least-squares analysis of the data indicated that the best straight line through the set of data points (the line drawn in Fig. 1) had a slight positive slope of 0.0009 Å/degree, with a standard deviation σ of 0.001 Å/degree. The standard deviation σ for the individual data points was 0.01 Å.

For the measurement of the diameter of the inner ring the same set of photographs was used, plus one photograph taken at only 0.2 °C below the S—N point (the outer maxima were not measured on this photograph because the exposure time had been so much shorter than usual that the outer maxima were not well enough developed). The strong alignment of the molecules again limited the directions in which the diameter of the inner ring could be measured, and sometimes we could make only one measurement per film.

The sharpness of the inner ring maxima indicated that they were caused by regular arrangements of large numbers of smectic layers parallel to each other. For the calculation of the corresponding lattice distance d (the " thickness " of one smectic layer) we used, therefore, the regular Bragg equation $2d \sin \theta = n\lambda$, where n is the order of the reflection ($n = 2$ for our measurements). Values of d for each photograph are plotted in Fig. 2; the agreement between

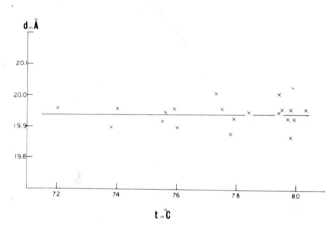

Figure 2. The layer thickness in the smectic phase as a function of temperature.

the measurements again is very good. The least-squares line has a slight positive slope (0.0007 Å/degree), not significantly different from zero ($\sigma = 0.004$). For the individual data points we found $\sigma = 0.04$ Å (which corresponds to an error in the measurement of the ring diameter of 0.04 mm).

THE NEMATIC PHASE

On the photographs of the nematic phase we measured the outer diffraction ring (associated with the intermolecular distance), and an inner diffraction ring (to be discussed in more detail further on in this paper) which was found in about the same position as the first order inner ring of the smectic phase.

The degree of alignment of the molecules varied, but was always much lower than in the smectic phase. Nematic phases at temperatures close to the N—L point, obtained by cooling the liquid phase, were always without visible alignment; if cooled down further to 0.2 or 0.3 °C above the S—N point, they nearly always showed moderate alignment. Nematic phases obtained by heating the smectic phase always showed moderate to weak alignment just above the S—N point, and gradually lost their alignment when the temperature was raised further. Remarkably, most alignment was shown by the nematic phase obtained from the smectic sample (mentioned above) which showed the least alignment (this was with a 1.0 mm capillary, the only one of this size used). But even here the ratio between the intensities of the maxima and the minima in the outer ring was only about 2.[†] The direction of preferred orientation made an angle of about 55° with the capillary axis in this case; the angles found in the other cases varied roughly from 50° to 90° (Demus and Sackmann[2] report that samples between flat glass plates were mostly pseudoisotropic).

All films were measured in four directions making angles of 0°, 45°, 90°, and 135°, respectively, with the direction of the maxima. There were no clear indications that the diameter of the outer ring was a function of the scanning direction, although the data from the photographs from the 1.0 mm capillary suggested that the diameter in the direction of the minima might be slightly smaller (about 0.5%) than in the direction of the maxima. The intermolecular distances D calculated from the average diameter for each photograph are

---

[†] In all these cases no magnetic field was applied. In a case in which we applied a magnetic field, at an angle of about 60° to the axis of a capillary of 0.5 mm diameter, there was a fairly strong alignment of the molecules parallel to the field. When the magnet was removed, the alignment remained fairly strong ($I_{max}/I_{min} = 6$), but the direction of preferred orientation changed to an angle of about 80° with the capillary axis. The smectic phase obtained by cooling the nematic phase under the influence of the magnetic field showed again the alignment of the molecules parallel to the capillary, which appears to be typical for the smectic phase of EEB.

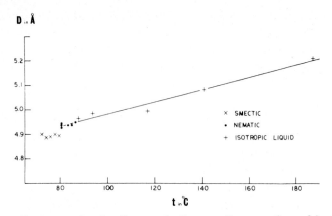

Figure 3.   The intermolecular distance in the smectic, nematic, and isotropic phase as a function of temperature.   For the smectic phase the data have been averaged in groups to reduce the number of points.

plotted in Fig. 3.   The least-squares line through these values had a slope of 0.0017 Å/degree ($\sigma = 0.0010$), but this line is not shown on the graph, as will be discussed further in the section on the isotropic liquid phase.   For the individual data points we found $\sigma = 0.01$ Å.

For the inner diffraction ring the difference in intensity between the maxima and the minima was usually much greater than for the outer ring.   The most reliable measurements were those obtained from scans through the centers of the maxima, from photographs on which these maxima were well developed; only these data are reported on in this paper.   The spacings, calculated from these measurements with the formula $2d \sin \theta = \lambda$, are presented in Fig. 4. The fact that we used d values calculated with the Bragg equation does not mean that we assume any kind of space lattice in this nematic phase.   This equation was employed here only to be able to make some comparisons between the data obtained from the smectic, nematic, and isotropic phases (see under " Discussion ").

THE ISOTROPIC LIQUID PHASE

Here there are no problems due to alignment of the molecules in the sample, and the inner and outer rings were measured in several directions.

The outer rings were somewhat less intense than those from the

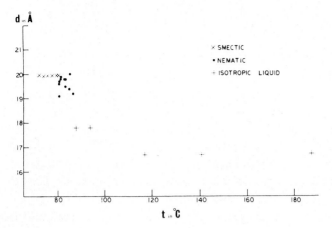

Figure 4.   The lattice spacing calculated from the diameter of the inner ring as a function of temperature.   For the smectic phase the data have been averaged in groups to reduce the number of points.

nematic phase, but they could still be measured well; the inter-molecular distances calculated from these measurements are presented in Fig. 3.   The slope of the least-squares line through these points was 0.0025 Å/degree ($\sigma = 0.0003$); for the individual data points σ was 0.02 Å.   Comparing this slope with that found for the nematic phase we see that they are equal well within the limits of error.   In addition, it was found that the least-squares line for the isotropic phase, if extrapolated into the nematic phase, passed very close to the center of gravity of the nematic data points, again well within the limits of error (the corresponding D values were: for the nematic data 4.940 Å with $\sigma = 0.003$, for the extrapolated line 4.944 Å with $\sigma = 0.016$).   We decided, therefore, to calculate the least-squares line for the combined data from the nematic and isotropic phases, and to plot this line in Fig. 3.   The slope of this line was 0.00250 Å/degree, $\sigma = 0.00013$.

The measurements of the diameter of the inner ring were rather inaccurate because this ring is not very pronounced in the isotropic phase.   The d values obtained from these measurements (using Bragg's equation) are plotted in Fig. 4.   No attempt has been made to draw a curve through these points, because the relatively large errors allow several different interpretations.

4. Discussion

THE INNER DIFFRACTION RING FROM THE NEMATIC AND
ISOTROPIC PHASES

A diffuse inner diffraction ring, at a diffraction angle of the order
of 4°, has been observed by us for all nematic and cholesteric phases
that we have studied so far, and also for the liquid phase of all liquid
crystalline materials we have studied so far.[6] Literature data on
this kind of diffraction effect are extremely scarce. Usually this ring
apparently is intercepted by the beam stop or masked by the high
background around the beam stop.

It should be emphasized here that one should distinguish between
at least two different types of diffuse inner diffraction rings. First,
there are the fairly weak rings as found in the nematic and isotropic
phases of EEB, in all liquid and cholesteric phases we investigated,
and in most of the nematic phases. Second, there are the quite intense rings found in the nematic phases of certain specific compounds[1,4]; these rings have been interpreted by us[1] as indicating
that a large number of molecules is organized in groups (called cybotactic groups) which have a much higher degree of order than the
normal nematic phase (called the classical nematic phase). Starting
from this theory, it would be possible to explain the much weaker
inner rings as indicative of remnants of cybotactic groups. Although
this interpretation may be correct for certain phases, we would like
to propose here a much more general explanation for these weak
inner rings, which does not require the organization of molecules in
any kind of groups and which we feel is a much more probable explanation for most cases.†

Let us direct our attention to a single molecule of EEB in the
nematic or the isotropic phase, and in particular to its electron
density distribution projected onto the long axis of the molecule.
In a first approximation this electron density may be considered

---

† This explanation is not meant for, nor is it applicable to, the cybotactic
nematic phases[1,5]; it is intended only for the classical nematic phase (in
which the only order is the approximate parallelism of each molecule with
respect to its neighbors), for the isotropic phase, and for the cholesteric
phase.

constant† except at the ends of the molecule, where it becomes much lower because at the ends we have only hydrogen atoms and possibly also some open space before we get to the next molecule. An electron density distribution like this, with an extended, more or less flat maximum in the middle and a minimum at each end, will give the same diffraction pattern as an electron density distribution with an extended minimum in the middle and a maximum at each end, or, in other words, as a diatomic molecule. The length of this " diatomic molecule " is equal to the distance between the electron density minima at the ends of the real molecule, and this distance may be taken as the " length " of the real molecule (this length will include half of the total free space, if any, at the two ends of the molecule).

The diffraction pattern from the hypothetical diatomic molecule will only show distinguishable maxima when its length is more or less constant. One will be able to observe it, therefore, only for fairly rigid molecules. Also, the length of the molecule should be significantly different from its width; otherwise, the diffraction pattern associated with the " diatomic molecule " will merge with the rest of the diffraction pattern (in terms of the two diffraction rings discussed in this paper: the inner and outer ring will come together). But if both conditions are fulfilled, the diffraction pattern associated with the " diatomic molecule " should be observable, and diatomic molecules of the proper length (of the order of 30 Å) would indeed give their main diffraction maximum in the region where we have observed the inner ring. We propose, therefore, that this diffraction effect is responsible for many of the weak inner diffraction rings we have observed (e.g., those in the nematic and liquid phases of EEB), and that similar diffraction effects[7,8] should occur for all non-crystalline materials containing molecules with sufficiently anisotropic shape and for which the long dimension is fairly constant.‡

† It there are sufficiently well defined maxima and/or minima in the electron density distribution within the molecule, this may give rise to additional diffraction maxima. These are not discussed here.

‡ Other authors[9] have substituted heavy atoms at the ends of elongated molecules to be able to measure the length of the molecule. From the above discussion it follows that another way of using heavy atoms would be to substitute them in the center of the molecule; they will then enhance the already present diffraction effect from the electron density minima at the ends of the molecule.

Assuming, as we shall do in this paper, that the above theory is correct, the next question is what the relationship is between the length of the molecule and the position of the maxima of the inner diffraction ring. The answer to this question is that the relationship depends greatly upon the degree and the direction of alignment of the molecules in the sample. If the orientation of the molecules is completely random, the relationship between the molecular length l and the diffraction angle 2θ is given by the Keesom formula[1,10]: $2l \sin \theta = 1.229\lambda$. If all the molecules are strictly parallel to each other and perpendicular to the direction of the incident beam, the relationship is $l \sin 2\theta = \lambda$. If all the molecules are strictly parallel to the direction of the incident beam, the relationship is $l(1 - \cos 2\theta) = \lambda$. It will be clear that one can calculate the length of the molecule from the position of the maxima of the inner diffraction ring only if the degree and the direction of alignment are known.

This variation in the relationship between l and θ is apparently what caused the large spread in our θ measurements from the inner ring in the nematic phase (Fig. 4), for this spread is much larger than expected from the error in measurements. Consequently, we have not been able to calculate any molecular length values for the nematic phase. This result is not entirely negative, however. The large spread in θ values shows that in the nematic phase of EEB the position of the maxima of the inner ring indeed depends upon the alignment, and this in turn indicates[5] that the nematic phase of EEB is not a cybotactic nematic phase but a classical nematic phase. Thus, the impossibility of determining l serves as an indication of the type of the nematic phase.

In the isotropic liquid we may assume a random arrangement of the molecules and use $2l \sin \theta = 1.229\lambda$. The values of l calculated this way are plotted in Fig. 5. As pointed out in the section on " The Isotropic Liquid Phase ", several different curves could be drawn through these points. In Fig. 5 we have drawn a straight, horizontal line† at an average l value (in the calculation of this value more weight was given to the more accurate measurements at lower

† Based on a comparison of the temperature dependence of measured densities with that of intermolecular distances obtained from X-ray photographs, Falgueirettes[11] concludes that the molecular length in p-azoxyanisole stays essentially constant in the liquid phase, and also when going into the nematic phase.

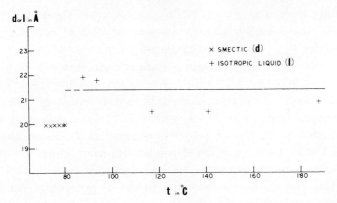

Figure 5.   The layer thickness in the smectic phase and the molecular length in the isotropic phase, as a function of temperature.   For the smectic phase the data have been averaged in groups to reduce the number of points.

temperature); the line was extended into the nematic phase as a broken line, to indicate that most probably the molecular length in the nematic phase is equal to that in the liquid phase.† This line falls at 21.4 Å, which is in very good agreement with the calculated molecular length of 21.6 Å which was obtained as follows. Assuming a planar molecule, a zig-zag arrangement for the end groups, and taking the directions of the end groups as close as possible to the direction of the line through the centers of the two benzene rings, and using the bond lengths and angles given in Table 2, the positions of the atoms were plotted on a piece of graph paper.   The distance between the two hydrogen atoms at the ends of the molecule was measured and to this was added twice the van der Waals radius of hydrogen (1.17 Å).   The distance so obtained (21.6 Å) was checked

TABLE 2   Bond Lengths and Angles Used in Model

C—C	1.52 Å	C-⁼-C	(benzene ring)	1.40 Å
C—O	1.42 Å	C—O	(in =C—O—)	1.39 Å
C—H	1.08 Å	C—C	(in =C—ϕ)	1.45 Å
C=N	1.32 Å	C—N	(in =N—ϕ)	1.42 Å
C=O	1.23 Å			

All bond angles from a C or N atom carrying a double bond were taken to be 120°; all other angles between single bonds 112°.

† See footnote on previous page.

by building molecular models (CPK models, from the Ealing Corporation); these models gave a distance of 21.3 Å, assuming the same van der Waals radius for hydrogen†.

As mentioned above, no nematic data are given in Fig. 5, but it may be noted here that all d values (Fig. 4) were smaller than 21.4 Å, or, in other words, that all measured 2θ values were larger than the one calculated from $2d \sin \theta = \lambda$, with $d = 21.4$ Å. Assuming that in the nematic phase $l = 21.4$ Å, the measured 2θ values are thus in agreement with the theory developed above, from which it follows that the observed 2θ value can never be smaller than the one obtained from the relation $l \sin 2\theta = \lambda$ (which is practically equal to $2l \sin \theta = \lambda$ for l values of 20 Å or more).

Summarizing this section on the inner ring data we would like to point out that use of the Bragg equation for these data would have left us with a number of strange results (Fig. 4): Most d values for the nematic phase are smaller than those for the smectic phase, and the d values for the isotropic phase are again smaller than those for the nematic phase; this is the opposite of the expansion one would normally expect upon heating. Also, the data for the nematic phase show a spread much greater than expected from the experimental errors. The theory for the inner diffraction ring, developed in this section, gives a satisfactory solution for these problems: The factor 1.229 leads to a good agreement between measured and calculated molecular length (also for other compounds[12]) and to a good relation between the smectic and the isotropic data (Fig. 5); the varying relationship between l and θ explains the spread in the nematic data.

THE THICKNESS OF THE SMECTIC LAYERS

The average value for the thickness of the smectic layers, over the temperature range investigated, is 19.941 Å, 1.46 Å (7%) less than the molecular length measured in the isotropic phase. Sackmann et al.[13] point out that they find this apparently too short layer thickness for all smectic A phases investigated by them, and we can confirm this on the basis of our own investigations on this and other compounds. Sackmann et al. suggest a non-stretched arrangement

† Demus and Sackmann[2] report a length of 22.5 Å obtained from a Stuart-Briegleb model; we do not understand the large difference between their measurements and ours.

of the hydrocarbon chains as the cause for this effect. But in view of that facts that in crystalline solids the hydrocarbon chains are usually stretched and that our measurements on the isotropic phase indicate that the molecule is stretched in that phase too, this explanation does not seem to be very likely to us. Also, we found in another compound with much longer hydrocarbon chains that, although these chains were apparently unstretched at higher temperatures in the isotropic phase, they appeared to become more and more stretched as the temperature was lowered, approaching the fully stretched configuration at the S—L point.[12] It would seem unlikely that the chains would become unstretched again upon further cooling (i.e., in the smectic phase). Another explanation of the short distance between the layers would be that the molecules make a certain angle with the normal to the smectic planes; for EEB this angle would have to be about 21°. Sackmann et al. point out, however, that this would disagree with the microscopic observation that the aligned smectic A phase is optically uniaxial. Also, this skewed configuration would be in contradiction with our X-ray photographs of the aligned smectic phase of EEB, which show clearly that the direction of the long molecular axes (obtained from the position of the maxima in the outer ring[1]) is within a few degrees from the direction of the normal to the smectic planes (obtained from the position of the maxima in the inner ring). As a possible solution we should like to suggest here that the ends of the molecules of each layer penetrate the adjacent layers to a limited depth, in this case about 1.5 Å. Further investigations will be necessary, however, to obtain more conclusive evidence on this point. For instance, viscosity studies might be of interest, for the deeper the penetration, the higher the viscosity would be expected to be.

INTERMOLECULAR DISTANCES

The average intermolecular distance for the smectic phase is 4.894 Å (Table 3). It is of interest to compare this value with some dimensions from a model of the molecule. The thickness of a benzene ring is twice the van der Waals radius for carbon, 3.6 Å, and the width of a benzene ring (drawn with one carbon atom at the top and one at the bottom) is 6.7 Å, so the average of the two is 5.15 Å, 0.25 Å larger than the average intermolecular distance. This means

TABLE 3   Intermolecular Distances

Phase	Temperature	Distance†
Smectic	71.5 °C	4.890 Å
	80.4	4.898
Nematic	80.4	4.932
	87.0	4.950
Isotropic	180.0	5.182

† From the least-squares lines in Figs. 1 and 3.

that the packing of the molecules within the layers, although irregular (as indicated by the diffuse character of the outer ring). must be quite tight.   A more or less free rotation of the molecules around their long axes is highly unlikely (this conclusion is in agreement with the position taken by Gray[14]).   A herringbone packing, similar to that proposed by Gulrich and Brown,[15] would seem to be a much more probable model.

In the nematic phase the packing is not much looser (Table 3) and rotation of the molecules must still be regarded as very unlikely (again in agreement with Gray[14]).   The interpretation of the small change in the measured intermolecular distance at the S—N point is not yet clear.   This change in D may be a direct consequence of the change in phase, or, in view of the possibility of a variation of the intermolecular distance with the degree of alignment (see introductory paragraphs of Sec. 3), it may be caused by the large change in the degree of alignment at the S—N point.

At the N—L point there does not seem to be any change in the intermolecular distance, which suggests that the arrangement of the molecules with respect to each other is quite similar in the two phases† (this similarity is also indicated by the fact that the amount of heat associated with the N—L transition is very small; see Fig. 6): in the isotropic phase, too, the molecules are approximately parallel to their nearest neighbors, and, especially at temperatures close to the N—L point, there is little space for rotation of the molecules around their long axes.

It is tempting to suggest, on the basis of our observations, the following picture of the change in the molecular arrangement when

† The same conclusion was reached by Falgueirettes[11] with regard to the isotropic and nematic phases of p-azoxyanisole.

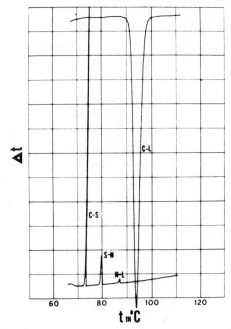

Figure 6.   Differential thermal analysis plot from a sample of zone-refined EEB.

going from the smectic, via the nematic, to the isotropic phase of EEB.   In all three phases (at least for temperatures not too far above the N—L point) the arrangement of the molecular planes of neighboring molecules is essentially the same (e.g., a herringbone-type packing), and the main change upon going from one phase to another takes place in the longitudinal arrangement of the molecules: in the smectic phase the relationship between the positions of neighboring molecules is fixed and regular, in the nematic phase this relationship is quite irregular but still more or less fixed,† and in the isotropic phase the molecules are free to move in the direction of the long axis.

VOLUME EXPANSION COEFFICIENTS AND DENSITIES

Assuming an idealized arrangement of the molecules, each molecule occupying (in the direction of its long axis) a space of length l

† This kind of arrangement for the nematic state was suggested to us by Dr. D. P. Shoemaker and by Dr. R. K. Mishra.

(or d, in the smectic phase) and surrounded (in the plane perpendicular to its long axis) by six other molecules at a distance D, it is possible to calculate the volume expansion coefficient and the density. A comparison of these calculated values with experimentally determined ones constitutes a further test of the correctness of the theory and the formulas used in this paper to obtain D, l, and d.

With a molecular arrangement as described in the above paragraph, the volume per molecule is $v = lD^2 \cos 30°$ (replace l by d for the smectic phase). From the values of d, l, and D at different temperatures we have calculated the volume expansion coefficient as $\beta = (v_2/v_1 - 1)/(t_2 - t_1)$. These values of β are presented in Table 4 together with values obtained from the literature. The value for β

TABLE 4   Volume Expansion Coefficients in 10^{-5} (°C)$^{-1}$

Compound		Isotropic	Nematic	Smectic	Solid
Ethyl-p-ethoxybenzal-p-aminobenzoate	(EEB)	83	—	40	—
p-Methoxybenzylidene-p'-cyanoaniline[15]	(MBC)	92	97	—	—
p-Azoxyanisole[16]	(PAA)	75	72	—	—
Phenol[17]		109	—	—	—
Paraffin,[17] 0–16 °C		—	—	—	32
Caoutchouc[17]		—	—	—	23

in the isotropic phase of EEB compares very well with those of the isotropic and nematic phases of the two other liquid crystalline materials (MBC and PAA), and all these are comparable to the value for phenol (though the latter is somewhat larger). The value of β for the smectic phase of EEB is much smaller, and tends more towards that of solid materials like paraffin, but the accuracy of this β value is much less than of β for the isotropic liquid, so no conclusions can be drawn at this point.

From the molecular weight (297.35) and the volume per molecule we calculated also the densities at various temperatures. These are given in Table 5, again compared with literature data on other compounds. We see that the density of the isotropic phase of EEB compares very well with those of the isotropic and nematic phases

TABLE 5   Densities in gr/cm³

Compound†	Isotropic	Nematic	Smectic	Solid
EEB	1.09 (87.6°)‡	1.09 (80.4°)§	1.196 (71.4°)	—
	1.01 (180°)	—	1.192 (80.4°)	—
MBC[15,18]	1.076 (120°)	1.093 (107°)	—	1.22
PAA[16,19]	1.138 (142°)	1.182 (100°)	—	1.38
EAP[18]	—	—	—	1.21

† EAP is *p*-ethoxybenzol-*p*-azophenyl propionate; for the other abbreviations, see Table 4.

‡ The values in parentheses are the temperatures in °C at which the densities were determined.

§ Assuming the same molecular length as in the isotropic phase (21.4 Å).

of MBC.†   The densities of the solid phases of MBC and EAP (both compounds that give liquid crystalline phases on melting) are very similar to each other, and the density of the smectic phase‡ of EEB is very close to the densities of these solid phases; this is in agreement with what one would expect, since the packing of the molecules in a smectic phase is most probably very similar to that in the solid phase.

5. Summary

We have presented in this paper accurately measured molecular parameters for the smectic, nematic, and isotropic phases of EEB. On the basis of these data and other observations we have drawn some general conclusions with regard to the packing of the molecules in these phases.   There appears to be no room for a more or less

† The densities of all phases of PAA (especially the solid and the nematic phases) appear to be higher than the corresponding densities for the other compounds listed in Table 5.   It is of interest to note here that the nematic phase of PAA appears to contain cybotactic groups of molecules (higher homologues of PAA show strong evidence of the presence of cybotactic groups, as may be seen from a comparison of references 1 and 4).   We suggest that the high density of the nematic phase of PAA is related to the existence of cybotactic groups, since these groups have a more regular arrangement of the molecules as compared with a classical nematic phase, and thus probably will give rise to a higher density.

‡ This density is calculated assuming that the molecules stand perpendicular to the smectic planes (arguments in support of this have been given in the section on " The Thickness of the Smectic Layers ").

free rotation of the molecules around their long axes, not even in the isotropic liquid. In the isotropic liquid the experimentally determined molecular length (21.4 Å) is very close to the calculated length of the stretched molecule (21.6 Å), but the thickness of the smectic layers (19.941 Å) is significantly less than this. The angle between the long molecular axes and the smectic planes is found to be very close to 90°, in agreement with the contention of Sackmann *et al.* that in the smectic *A* phase the molecules stand perpendicular to the planes. The nematic phase appears to be a classical nematic phase, *i.e.*, there is no significant ordering of the molecules apart from the near parallelism of the long axes of neighboring molecules.

Several of these conclusions depend upon the correctness of the formulas we used in the calculation of the molecular parameters, and of the theories behind the formulas. To test these formulas we calculated densities and volume expansion coefficients on the basis of the X-ray data, and we have shown that these calculated densities and expansion coefficients agree remarkably well with experimentally determined values for other liquid crystalline compounds. This agreement may be considered as supporting evidence indicating that the theories and assumptions used in the calculations are correct. It seems appropriate to summarize here these theories and assumptions.

(1) The intermolecular distance D between elongated molecules in the smectic, nematic, and istropic phases is obtained from the diffraction angle of the outer diffraction ring with the formula $2D \sin \theta = 1.117\lambda$.

(2) The effective length l of an elongated molecule in the istropic phase (and in the randomly oriented classical nematic phase) is obtained from the diffraction angle of the inner diffraction ring with the formula $2l \sin \theta = 1.229\lambda$.

(3) For the calculation of the densities of the smectic, nematic, and isotropic phases of EEB one can assume an idealized arrangement of the molecules, in which each molecule is occupying a space of length l (or d, in the smectic phase) and is surrounded by six molecules at a distance D.

Acknowledgements

The author gratefully acknowledges the help of several members of the staff of the Liquid Crystal Institute: Dr. P. R. Patel and Mr. A. Mehta, who prepared the compound and performed microscopic and DTA studies; Dr. J. T. S. Andrews, who zone-refined the material; Mr. P. Standley, who assisted in collecting the data; and Mr. Y. S. Lee, who made the DTA graph reproduced in Fig. 6. He also thanks Mr. W. Y. Lee for permission to use his density data prior to publication.

REFERENCES

1. De Vries, A., *Mol. Cryst. and Liq. Cryst.*, **10**, 219 (1970).
2. Demus, D. and Sackmann, H., *Z. physik. Chem.* (Leipzig), **222**, 127 (1963).
3. Uhrich, D. L. and Detjen, R. E., private communication.
4. Chistyakov, I. G. and Chaikowsky, W. M., *Mol. Cryst. and Liq. Cryst.*, **7**, 269 (1969).
5. De Vries, A., *Mol. Cryst. and Liq. Cryst.*, **10**, 31 (1970).
6. De Vries, A., *Acta Cryst.*, **A25**, S135 (1969).
7. Stewart, G. W. and Morrow, G. M., *Phys. Rev.*, **30**, 232 (1927).
8. Morrow, R. M., *Phys. Rev.*, **31**, 10 (1928).
9. Brady, G. W., Wasserman, E., and Wellendorf, J., *J. Chem. Phys.*, **47**, 855 (1967).
10. Warren, B. E., *Phys. Rev.*, **44**, 969 (1933).
11. Falgueirettes, J., *Bull. Soc. franç. Minér. Crist.*, **82**, 171 (1959).
12. De Vries, A., Annual Report to the U.S. Army under contract DA–44–009–AMC–1074(T) (1969), and unpublished work.
13. Sackmann, H., Diele, S., and Brand, P., paper given at the Eighth Int. Congr. Cryst., Stony Brook (1969).
14. Gray, G. W., *Molecular Structure and the Properties of Liquid Crystals*, p. 258, London, Academic Press (1962).
15. Gulrich, L. W. and Brown, G. H., *Mol. Cryst.*, **3**, 493 (1968).
16. Maier, W. and Saupe, A., *Z. Naturf.*, **15a**, 287 (1960).
17. *Handbook of Chemistry and Physics*, Cleveland, Chemical Rubber Co. (1958).
18. Lee, W. Y., private communication.
19. Carlisle, C. H. and Smith, C. H., *Acta Cryst.*, **A25**, S47 (1969).

X-ray Diffraction and Polymorphism of Smectic Liquid Crystals I. A-, B- and C-modifications†

S. DIELE, P. BRAND and H. SACKMANN

Martin-Luther-Universitat
402 Halle-Saale Sektion Chemie
German Democratic Republic

Received November 27, 1970; *in revised form May* 12, 1971

Abstract—X-ray diffraction patterns of 14 substances have been studied in non-oriented samples in the smectic modification s_A, s_C, and s_B. In all three modifications a sharp reflexion was found at small angles. At large angles a diffuse reflexion was found in the modifications s_A and s_C, and a sharp reflexion in the modification s_B. In all cases the calculated layer separation d is smaller than the molecular length L in the most stretched molecular structure. The X-ray patterns obtained from oriented samples of two substances are described and compared with the results obtained by other investigators. Further the results of the investigation of the equatorial intensity distribution are described.

1. Introduction

Investigations into miscibility relations between liquid crystalline modifications of several substances allow us to distinguish so far, in addition to the nematic (n) and cholesteric (ch) modifications, five types of smectic modifications, which are designated as modifications A, B, C, D, E (s_A through s_E).[1,2] The variants of polymorphism obtained are summarized in Table 1. In the third column the modifications are named, which originate from the isotropic phase at the clearing point with decrease of the temperature. These proceed then at temperatures T_1, T_2, T_3 to further modifications. More recently systematic caloric[3] and optical[4] investigations have been done on this subject.

X-ray studies on smectic modifications were performed by K. Herrmann[5] and recently by Chistyakov *et al.*[6] on a few substances. The newest results on this subject are reported by de Vries[7]

† Presented by title at the Third International Liquid Crystal Conference, August 24–28, 1970 in Berlin.

481

TABLE 1   System of Polymorphism

		T_1	T_2	T_3	Number of investigated cases
(a)	is	n			more than 1000
	is	chol.			more than 50
(b$_1$)	is	s_A			more than 50
(b$_2$)	is	s_C			about 30
(c$_1$)	is	n	s_A		about 30
	is	chol.	s_A		7
(c$_2$)	is	n	s_B		2
(c$_3$)	is	n	s_C		about 30
(d$_1$)	is	s_A	s_B		about 20
(d$_2$)	is	s_A	s_C		about 25
(d$_3$)	is	s_A	s_E		4
(d$_4$)	is	s_C	s_B		4
(d$_5$)	is	s_D	s_C		1
(e$_1$)	is	n	s_A	s_B	about 10
(e$_2$)	is	n	s_A	s_C	2
(e$_3$)	is	n	s_C	s_B	1
(e$_4$)	is	s_A	s_C	s_B	6
(e$_5$)	is	s_A	s_D	s_C	1
(f)	is	n	s_A	s_C s_B	4

and Levelut and Lambert.[8] The important question is whether a structural basis corresponds to the classification given. It is natural to begin with comparative studies of non-oriented samples on a large scale and then to move to a detailed investigation of oriented samples.

2. Experimental

The method of Guinier was used for the investigations on non-oriented samples. A sample-holder, which may be heated, controls the temperature to better than 0.5 °C in the temperature-range from 20 to 200 °C. The sample is melted down in a boring of an aluminum cylinder and is irradiated axially. The pictures of the oriented samples were taken by the flat-film method and a totally reflecting glass capillary was used as the collimator.[9,10] The sample was placed in a heated glass capillary tube and irradiated vertically to the cylinder axis. The distribution of the intensity and the line profile were recorded with a goniometer.

3. Results and Possible Interpretation

3.1. INVESTIGATIONS OF NON-ORIENTED SAMPLES

The substances studied are listed in Table 2. The variant of polymorphism is named in column 3 (in parenthesis the classification in Table 1). References for details, for example on transition-behaviour or transition-temperatures, are found in column 8.

The X-ray diffraction patterns of the non-oriented samples of the A-, B- and C-modifications show the picture described earlier[5] for single smectic modifications. Two interferences exist (apart from the reflexions of higher order), an inner ring at Bragg angles from 1–2° and an outer ring at Bragg angles from 10–11°. Other interferences are not found even with longer exposure-times. The interpretation is known in principle: Layers of molecules exist which are formed by a more or less parallel orientation of the long axes of the molecules. The outer-ring existing at wide angles corresponds with the lateral distances of the molecular axes, the ring at small angles corresponds with the layer separation.

In the A-modification the inner ring is sharp and the outer ring diffuse (Fig. 1). Therefore, the lateral distances of the molecules may possess a largely statistical distribution. The phases of the C-modifications have more or less the same X-ray pattern. Six substances (Table 2) exhibit an A-modification at higher temperatures in addition to the C-modification. In these cases a direct comparison is possible of the diffraction patterns of the two phases. The position of the inner ring does not change in transition from the C- into the A-modification. We have recorded the line profiles of the outer ring with a counter-tube goniometer. The line profiles of the outer ring are generally somewhat more diffuse and flat in the A-modification.

In all substances studied in the B-modification the inner ring as well as the outer ring is found with sharp profile as compared with the A- and C-modifications (Fig. 1).

These results substantially verify results from nine substances with smectic polymorphism as given by K. Herrmann. Accordingly

TABLE 2 Substances Investigated by X-ray Diffraction in This Report; d is the thickness of the smectic layers (calculated after Braggs Law); l is the length of the molecules obtained from Stuart–Briegleb models; $\varDelta = L - d$; d_w is the inter-molecular distance in the smectic layers (calculated after Bragg's Law)

No.	Substance	Polymorphism		d(Å)	L(Å)	$\varDelta$(Å)	d_w(Å)	Lit. reference
1.	n-amyl-4(4-n-octyloxybenzylideneamino)—cinnamate	s_A, s_B	(d_1)	31.6	35.5	3.9	4.1	(13)
2.	n-amyl-4(4-n-nonyloxybenzylideneamino)—cinnamate	s_A, s_C, s_B	(e_4)	32.9	37.0	4.1	4.2	(11)
3.	n-amyl-4(4-n-decyloxybenzylideneamino)—cinnamate	s_A, s_C, s_B	(e_4)	33.2	38.5	5.3	4.1	(11)
4.	n-amyl-4(4-n-dodecyloxybenzylideneamino)—cinnamate	s_A, s_C, s_B	(e_4)	36.6	41.5	4.9	4.3	(11)
5.	iso-amyl-4(4-n-octyloxybenzylideneamino)—cinnamate	s_A, s_C, s_B	(e_4)	30.6	34.0	3.4	4.3	(11)
6.	di-n-hexyl-4,4'-azoxy-cinnamate	s_A, s_C	(d_2)	30.5	37.5	7.2		(12)
7.	4,4'-di-n-undecyloxyazoxybenzene	s_C	(b_2)	31.5	46.0	14.5		(12)
8.	4-n-hexyloxy-3-nitro-diphenyl-4'-carboxylic acid	n, s_A, s_C	(e_2)	35.4	22.0	8.6		(2)
9.	di-allyl-4,4'-azoxy-α-methylcinnamate	s_A	(b_1)	25.2	28.5	3.3		(12)
10.	ethyl-4(4-methylbenzylideneamino)—cinnamate	s_A, s_B	(d_1)	20.1	22.0	1.9	4.1	(3) (12)
11.	ethyl-4(4-ethoxybenzylideneamino)—cinnamate	n, s_A, s_B	(e_1)	21.4	24.0	2.6	4.1	(3) (12)
12.	ethyl-4(4-methoxybenzylideneamino)—cinnamate	n, s_A, s_B	(e_1)	21.0	23.0	2.0		(3) (12)
13.	4-(4-n-nonyloxybenzylideneamino)—azobenzene	n, s_A, s_B	(e_1)	29.4	31.5	2.1	4.1	(15)
14.	4,4'-di-n-heptyloxyazoxybenzene	n, s_C	(c_3)					(12) (16) (17)

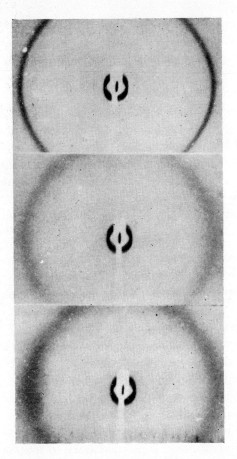

Figure 1.   Diffraction patterns of modifications s_B, s_C and s_A of substance No. 4 (from top to bottom).

these modifications should be either from types s_A and s_C or types s_B. This is also the case for the substances included in our investigations of the miscibility.[11,14,15]

The transitions $s_B \to s_A$ and $s_B \to s_C$ were found to take place in an interval from 1 to 2 °C in general agreement with microscopic observations and in contradiction to the former investigations by K. Herrmann.[5]

The investigations of the three modifications s_A, s_B and s_C allow us to discern some further details.   In column 4 of Table 2 the layer-separation d is written down as calculated from the inner ring according to Bragg's Law. In column 5 the length L of the molecules is recorded, as estimated by means of " Stuart–Kalotten " in the most stretched arrangement of the hydrocarbon chains. In column 6 the difference $\Delta = L - d$ can be seen. Here the error in the measurement of the inner ring and the error in the estimate of L must be taken into account. We reckon with a total error margin of 2 Å. In all cases $d < L$ has been found. It is a notable feature that the greater ($\Delta > 3.5$ Å) differences are found only in substances with long aliphatic hydrocarbon chains on both sides of the largely inflexible middle part. In the case of substance No. 8 a formation of double molecules is assumed.

Two explanations could be offered for the difference Δ, possibly in combination :

1. The inclination of the considerably stretched molecules to the layer causes the difference Δ. In extreme cases inclinations up to $30°$ occur. A special arrangement of the molecules is then necessary to guarantee the optical uniaxial character found in the A- and B-modifications in numbers 1, 4, 12.

2. The difference Δ is caused by the existence of other orientations of the hydrocarbon chains, which are possible because of the partial rotation around the C—C bonds. This could explain the great differences in molecules with long hydrocarbon chains. Also, the small increase of the values in the mean lateral distances within the homologous series is thus made intelligible. For this hypothesis it is not necessary to assume an inclination of the molecular axes. Therefore, difficulties do not exist in interpretation of the double-refraction. (i.e. the explanation of the double-refraction in Tl-salts from fatty acids, in which the buckling of the hydrocarbon-chains is also used, see Ref. (21).)

For the discussion of d-values of the substances recorded in Table 2 it is not important in which modification the inner ring is measured. The dependence on the temperature of the inner ring is very small. To what extent this could be detected, is shown in Tables 3 and 4 (these tables can serve as an example for all investigations).

In column 7, d_w is given as calculated from the wide sharp ring of the B-modification using Bragg's Law. Within the homologous

TABLE 3 Position of Inner and Outer Diffraction Ring for Substance No. 4 as a Function of the Temperature (ϑ: Bragg angle)

No.	$T(°C)$	Type	Inner ring $\vartheta°$	$d(Å)$	Outer ring $\vartheta°$	$d(Å)$
1	77	B	1.18	37.4	10.4	4.3
2	84	B	1.18	37.4	10.4	4.3
3	89.2	B	1.19	37.1	10.3	4.3
4	93	B	1.20	36.8	10.3	4.3
5	96	C	1.23	36.0		
7	107.2	A	1.21	36.5		
8	113	A	1.21	36.5		

TABLE 4 Position of Inner and Outer Diffraction Ring for Substance No. 11 as a Function of the Temperature (ϑ: Bragg angle)

No.	$T(°C)$	Type	Inner ring $\vartheta°$	$d(Å)$	Outer ring $\vartheta°$	$d(Å)$
1	79.5	B	2.04	21.6	10.9	4.1
2	84	B	2.05	21.5	10.9	4.1
3	90	B	2.05	21.5	10.9	4.1
4	99	B	2.05	21.5	10.9	4.1
5	114	B	2.05	21.5	10.9	4.1
7	115	B	2.06	21.4	10.7	4.1
8	115	B	2.05	21.5	10.7	4.1
9	116.8	A	2.06	21.4		
10	124	A	2.07	21.3		
11	131.5	A	2.07	21.3		
12	139.5	A	2.07	21.3		
13	137.5	A	2.04	21.6		
15	147	A	2.08	21.2		

series (substances No. 1 to 4, Table 2) a small increase (apart from No. 3) in the lateral distances of the molecules calculated from the wide sharp ring of the B-modification is observed with increasing chain length.

3.2. INVESTIGATIONS ON ORIENTED SAMPLES

Samples of substance No. 5 (Table 2) were oriented in a magnetic field. This substance exhibits all 3 modifications in the sequence s_A, s_C, s_B with decreasing temperature. Oriented samples in the various smectic modifications can be obtained by cooling of the sample, in the magnetic field, from the isotropic phase to the desired temperature. Also, oriented samples of the C- and A-modification with the same X-ray patterns are obtained, if the oriented sample of the B-modification was heated outside the magnetic field.

In Fig. 2 the X-ray pattern of the three modifications are shown. The outer ring is crescent shaped. The broadening takes place at the transition from the B into the C- and A-modifications analogous to the transition in non-oriented samples. The inner ring degenerates to a reflexion lying on the meridian of the pattern (also seen in the second and third order).

The reflexions are more spot-like in the B-modification and become crescent shaped in transition to C- and A-modifications. From this an alignment of the layers is derived vertically to the cylindrical axis of the sample. The rigid alignment of the layer in the B-modifications is progressively removed in the C- and A-modifications. The position of the inner reflexion vertical to the position of the outer reflexion is an expression of the fact that the molecules stand vertical to the layer in the C- and A-modification.

A similar pattern was recorded first in the C-modification of substance No. 14, Table 2 (Fig. 3). The lunar interference maxima of the inner reflexion and of the outer lie again on the meridian or on the equator of the pattern. The repetition of the experiment with samples of smaller diameters (0.9 mm instead of 1.5 mm) yielded the X-ray pattern in Fig. 4. The inner ring is weak. On it two doublet-like interference spots are positioned on the equator line. Several maxima on the outer interference are visible on the original film. The connecting line between the strongest maxima forms an angle of about 45° with the equator.

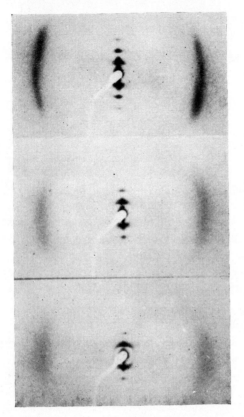

Figure 2. Diffraction patterns of oriented samples of substance No. 5; the modifications s_B, s_C and s_A (from top to bottom).

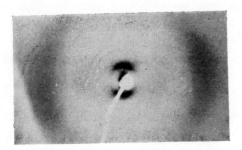

Figure 3. Diffraction patterns of substance No. 14; the modification s_C.

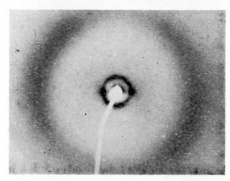

Figure 4.   Diffraction patterns of substance No. 14; the modification s_C.

The latter seems to confirm the result given by de Vries[16] in a schematic diagram of the interferences of the same substance in the C-modification.

On the other hand Chistyakov and Chaikowsky[17] found a degeneration of the inner ring to four spots. Thus at present three types of X-ray diagrams of oriented samples of the same substance in the C-modification exist.

It therefore seems advisable not to discuss further the respective structure suggestions[16,17] but to attempt to make accurate analysis of the influence of the experimental conditions.

3.3. INVESTIGATION OF THE DISTRIBUTION OF EQUATORIAL INTENSITY

The calculation of cylindrical distribution functions of the distribution of equatorial intensity of oriented samples offers the possibility of obtaining information on the lateral arrangement of the molecular axes.

This method was used with success by Falgueirettes[18] and Delord[19] for the nematic phase and by Chistyakov and his collaborators[17] for the nematic and smectic phases.

It is possible to go two ways[20] which lead basically to the same results:

1. By normalization of the irradiated intensity on one atom you may calculate the distribution of the atoms projected on an area arranged vertical to the molecular axes.
2. By normalization of the irradiated intensity on one molecule you may calculate the distribution of the molecular axes in the layer.

In starting our investigations we have used the first procedure. The specimens had the form of a flat sheet and were oriented as described in Section b. The correction for absorption was negligible. The diffracted intensity was recorded by a goniometer using a proportional counter. The experimental set-up permits recording of the intensity up to a Bragg angle of 30°. The cylindrical distribution functions were calculated in the way described in reference 20.

The distribution functions calculated for substance No. 4, Table 2, in the modifications s_A, s_C and s_B are plotted in Fig. 5. The functions exhibit two maxima ($r_1 = 4.6\,\text{Å}$; $r_2 = 9.0\,\text{Å}$), the positions of which scarcely change in transition to another modification.

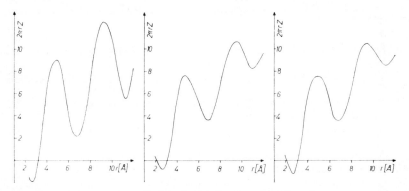

Figure 5. The atomic cylindrical distribution function for s_B, s_C and s_A (from left to right) of substance No. 4.

First, it should be noted that the remarkable difference in the intensity distributions in the distribution functions of the modification s_B on the one hand and on the other, the modifications s_C and s_A are very much reduced. Thus, it seems that only a drop in the statistical fluctuation-width of the lateral molecular distances is connected with the transition from s_A into s_C and s_B. The absence of the other maxima in the distribution function shows that no defined relations of the neighboring molecules exist in the modification s_B. Other statements are made by Levelut and Lambert.[8] They point out the existence of a hexagonal layer lattice in the B-modification of two substances which they studied.

The cause for the small number of the maxima in the distribution function by comparison with the calculations of other authors[20] can be seen in the symmetrical structure of the molecule and in the practical circular cross-section of the substance studied.

REFERENCES

1. Sackmann, H. and Demus, D., *Fortschritte d. chem. Forsch. Berlin*, Heidelberg, New York, **12**, 349 (1969).
2. Demus, D., Kunicke, G., Neelsen, J. and Sackmann, H., *Z. Naturforsch.* **23a**, 84 (1968).
3. Arnold, H., Demus, D., Koch, O., Nelles, A. and Sackmann, H., *Z. Phys. Chem.* **185**, 240 (1969).
4a. Pelzl, G., Dissertation Halle(S) 1969.
4b. Pelzl, G. and Sackmann, H., *Trans. Faraday Soc.*, in preparation.
5. Herrmann, K., *Z. Kristallogr.* **92**, 49 (1935).
6. Chistyakov, I. B., Schabischev, L. S., Jarenov, R. J. and Gusakova, L. A., *Mol. Cryst. and Liq. Cryst.* **7**, 279 (1969).
7. de Vries, A., *Mol. Cryst. and Liq. Cryst.* **11**, 361 (1970).
8. Levelut, A. and Lambert, M., *C.R. Acad. Sci. Paris*, in print (preprint obtained from the authors).
9. Unangst, D. and Zimmermann, B., *Z. Experim. Tech. Phys.* **12**, 320 (1964).
10. Damaschun, G. and Weh, C., *Feingerätemeßtechnik* **17**, 274 (1968).
11. Demus, D., Sackmann, H., Kunicke, G., Pelzl, G. and Salffner, R., *Z. Naturforsch* **23a**, 76 (1968).
12. Arnold, H., Demus, D. and Sackmann, H., *Z. Phys. Chem.* **222**, 15 (1963).
13. Salffner, R., Diplomarbeit Halle, 1967.
14. Arnold, H. and Sackmann, H., *Z. Elektrochem.* **63**, 1171 (1959).
15. Demus, D. and Sackmann, H., *Z. Phys. Chem.* **238**, 215 (1968).
16. de Vries, A., *Acta Crystallogr.* **A25**, S135 (1969).
17. Chistyakov, I. G. and Chaikowsky, W. M., *Mol. Cryst. and Liq. Cryst.* **7**, 269 (1969).
18. Falgueirettes, J., *Bull. Soc. Fr. Mineral Crystallogr.* **82**, 171 (1959).
19. Delord, P., *J. Phys. (Paris)* **30**, C 4–14 (1969).
20. Wainstein, B. K. and Chistyakov, I. G., *Dokl. Akad. Nauk SSSR* **153**, 327 (1963).
21. Pelzl, G. and Sackmann, H., *Mol. Cryst. and Liq. Cryst.*, in print.

Investigation of a
Smectic Tetramorphous Substance†

D. DEMUS, S. DIELE, M. KLAPPERSTÜCK, V. LINK and H. ZASCHKE

Sektion Chemie,
Martin-Luther-Universität Halle,
402 Halle, German Democratic Republic

Received October 27, 1970; *in revised form March* 8, 1971

Abstract—2-(4-*n*-pentylphenyl)-5-(4-*n*-pentyloxyphenyl)-pyrimidine has been prepared. By microscopic investigation, differential scanning calorimetry, dilatometric measurements and X-ray investigation, four different smectic modifications have been stated. The microscopic textures and the relations of miscibility suggest that two of these modifications can be assigned to the group smectic A and C. The other two smectic modifications cannot be assigned to any of the five known groups of smectic modifications. Their characteristics require the establishment of two new groups of smectic modifications with the arbitrary symbol smectic F resp. G.

1. Introduction

In recent years Sackmann and coworkers[1,2] have worked systematically on the problem of polymorphism in the smectic state of thermotropic liquid crystals. Investigating their microscopic textures, relations of miscibility and X-ray diffraction patterns, they have found five groups of smectic modifications, which they called A, B, C, D, E. It is to be assumed that there are more than these five groups. In order to find new groups of smectic modifications the best chance is to investigate substances which exhibit polymorphism in the smectic state.

2. Preparation of the Substance

We have synthesized a substance with four smectic modifications in the following way:

† Presented by title at the Third International Liquid Crystal Conference in Berlin, August 24–28, 1970.

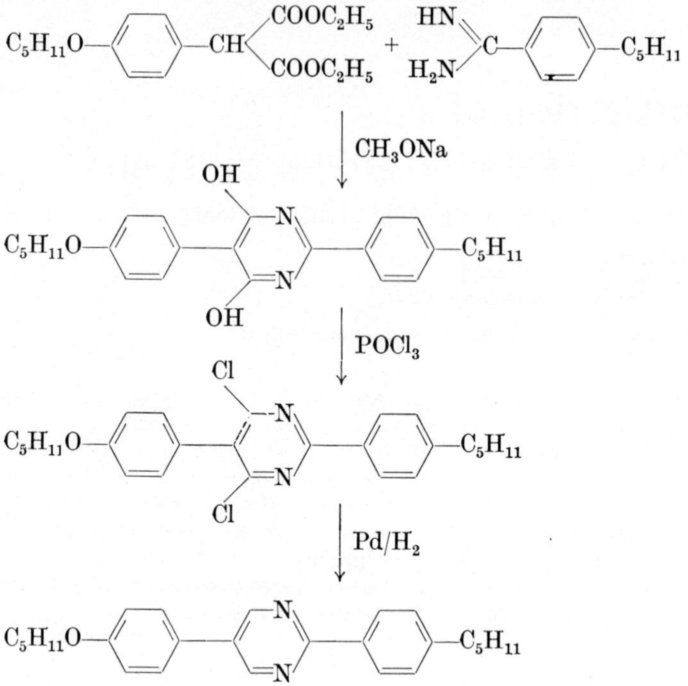

2-(4-n-Pentylphenyl)-5-(4-n-pentyloxyphenyl)-pyrimidine

A detailed description of the preparation is given in reference 3.

3. Scheme of Transitions and Microscopic Textures

This pyrimidine derivative shows the following transitions:

crystalline $\xleftarrow{\ 79\ }$ smectic IV $\xleftarrow{\ 102,7\ }$ smectic III $\xleftarrow{\ 113,8\ }$ smectic II $\xleftarrow{\ 144\ }$ smectic I $\xleftarrow{\ 210\ }$ isotropic liquid

All transitions can be observed under the microscope (polarized light, magnification 120 ×). Starting from the crystalline state one obtains by the first heating unspecific textures, namely paramorphoses. In this case it is difficult to see all transitions.

With decreasing temperature one obtains specific textures and the transition phenomena are more visible.

The textures have been observed for two preparations: preparation 1 has been made with not especially treated glasses, preparation 2 has been made with especially cleaned glasses.

The typical texture of smectic I is a focal conic texture, especially a fan-shaped texture, as known from the observation of the smectic A-modifications.[1,2] This texture has been photographed for preparation 1 (Fig. 1). The characteristics of this texture were first described by Friedel[8] and are given in some review articles.[9,10,11] Preparation 2 shows in the same temperature interval a pseudo-isotropic texture.[2]

By cooling of preparation 1 the transition to the modification smectic II takes place. Smectic II usually shows a broken fan-shaped texture (Fig. 2). The focal domains of the texture given in Fig. 1 are preserved in the outer contours, but the inner details are altered. A great number of discontinuities appears. Smectic II also occurs in a smectic schlieren texture, which has been photographed for preparation 2 (Fig. 3). The broken fan-shaped texture as well as the smectic schlieren texture are typical of smectic C-modifications.[1,2]

By further cooling, the transition to smectic II takes place and the picture of Fig. 2 alters to Fig. 4, which has been photographed for preparation 1. This texture has some similarities with the fan-shaped texture, but there are many stripes in the focal domains.

Figure 1. Focal conic (fan-shaped) texture of smectic I.

Figure 2. Broken fan-shaped texture of smectic II.

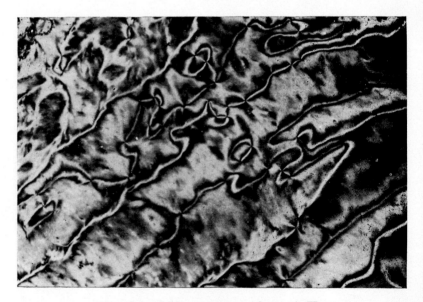

Figure 3. Schlieren texture of smectic II.

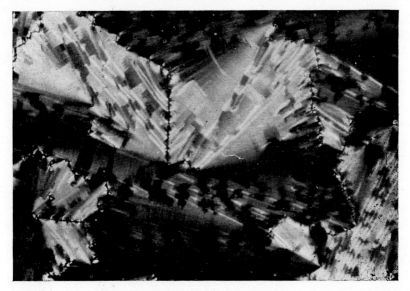

Figure 4. Striped fan-shaped texture of smectic III.

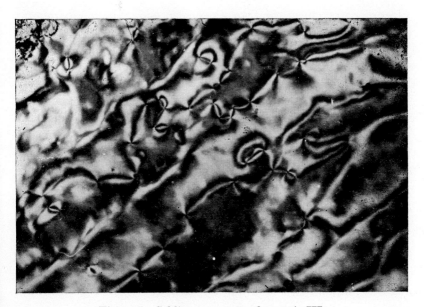

Figure 5. Schlieren texture of smectic III.

In preparation 2 smectic III also occurs in a schlieren texture (Fig. 5) which is very similar to the smectic C-modification.

After the transition to smectic IV the texture of Fig. 4 alters to the texture of Fig. 6, which has been obtained for preparation 1. This texture consists of optically homogeneous domains. Only some contours of the fan-shaped texture are preserved. Under the same circumstances preparation 2 shows a mosaic texture (Fig. 7), which is similar to the mosaic texture of the smectic B-modifications. [1,2]

On the second heating to higher temperatures preparation 1 shows the textures of Figs. 6, 4, 2 and 1 and preparation 2 shows the textures of Figs. 7, 5, 3 with only very little differences. These textures are typical of the four smectic modifications and can be used together with other properties for the identification of the type of the smectic modification.

All four smectic modifications are viscous and can be deformed by slight pressure on the cover glass of the microscopic preparation.

4. Calorimetric Investigation

In order to confirm the transitions seen under the microscope we have investigated the substance by thermal analysis with a Perkin–Elmer differential scanning calorimeter DSC 1B. The curve given in Fig. 8 was obtained. All transitions are indicated by a peak in the curve.

By evaluation of the curve we have calculated the enthalpies and entropies of transition (see Fig. 8). The peak of the transition smectic C/smectic A was too small to allow the quantitative evaluation of the enthalpy of transition. Only the order of magnitude has been estimated.

5. Density Measurements

By a capillary method we have investigated the thermal expansion of the compound up to the smectic A modification. Because of experimental difficulties we were not able to measure the density of the crystalline and isotropic liquid state. The densities range between 1.1 and 1.05 and there are anomalies in the neighbourhood

Figure 6.   Texture of smectic IV.

Figure 7.   Mosaic texture of smectic IV.

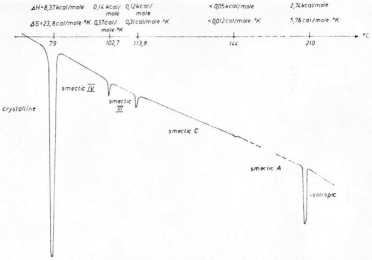

Figure 8.   Results of calorimetric investigation.

of the transition temperatures (Fig. 9).   These anomalies can be better seen from the curve showing the temperature dependence of the thermal expansion coefficient (Fig. 10).

The curve of the density is nearly linear in the region of smectic I, smectic II, smectic III; in the case of smectic IV the curve is concave to the temperature axis.   The density changes of the transitions are relatively small:

0.26% smectic IV/smectic III, 0.52% smectic III/smectic II, 0.20% smectic II/smectic I.

All transitions exhibit pre- and post-transition effects (Fig. 10).

6. X-ray Diffraction Measurements

For a better characterization of the smectic modifications we have made some preliminary X-ray diffraction measurements.   (Guinier-method).

The smectic I modification shows one sharp inner ring (with its second order) and one diffuse outer ring (Fig. 11a).   This behaviour is the same as in the case of the smectic A modifications: the inner ring indicates the distance of the layers (here $d = 26.8$ Å, calculated molecule length from Stuart–Kalotten ca. 30 Å), the

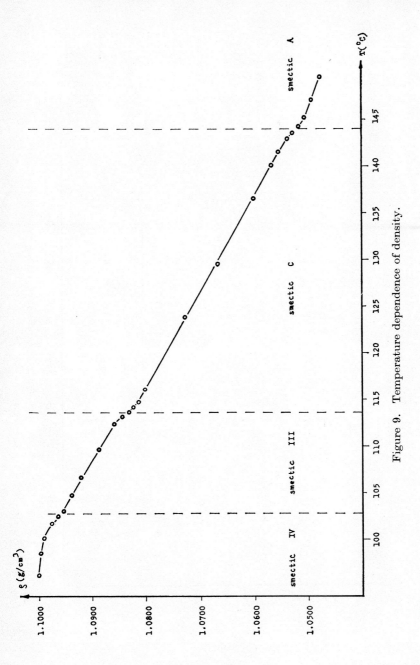

Figure 9.   Temperature dependence of density.

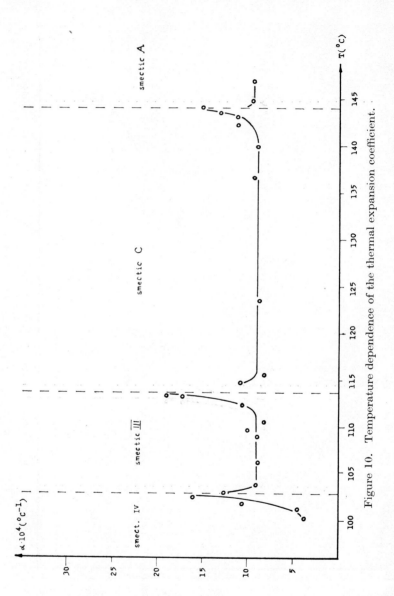

Figure 10.   Temperature dependence of the thermal expansion coefficient.

diffuse outer ring is a measure of the distance of the molecules within a layer (*ca.* 4.5 Å). Together with the observation of the microscopic texture it is to be assumed that smectic I is a smectic A modification.

The X-ray diffraction pattern of smectic II (Fig. 11b) shows only slight differences from smectic I: the inner ring is a little larger ($d = 23.4$ Å), the outer ring is somewhat sharper. The microscopic texture of smectic II suggests a smectic C-modification; with this the X-ray diffraction pattern is compatible.

The X-ray diffraction pattern of smectic III is very similar to that of smectic II, only the inner ring is a little larger, ($d = 23.0$ Å) the outer ring is somewhat sharper (Fig. 11c). The smectic IV modification shows a very altered picture (Fig. 11d): there is a sharp and textured inner ring (with its second order ($d = 22.1$ Å)); and several outer rings. This points to a layer structure with a specific not random arrangement of the molecules within the layers.

7. Investigation of the Relations of Miscibility

The results of the texture observation and the X-ray diffraction measurement show that smectic I is a smectic A modification and smectic II a smectic C modification. According to the rule of selected miscibility of Sackmann and coworkers[1,2] regions of an uninterrupted series of mixed liquid crystals are possible between

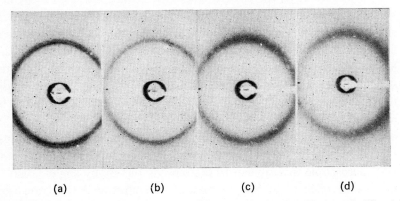

(a)   (b)   (c)   (d)

Figure 11.   X-ray diffraction patterns.   (a) smectic I; (b) smectic II; (c) smectic III; (d) smectic IV.

modifications having the same symbol. In order to confirm the designation of the smectic modifications I and II as A and C we have investigated the diagram of state of the substance with 2,5-*di*-(4-*n*-heptylphenyl)-pyrazine,[4,5] a compound which has 2 smectic modifications A and C respectively. Figure 12 shows that there are indeed regions of uninterrupted modifications, while the regions of smectic III and smectic IV are separated by heterogenous regions from the other smectic phases. With some other substances we have tried to find a series of uninterrupted mixed liquid crystals between smectic III or IV and smectic B, but in all cases without success.

8. Discussion

The substance investigated shows four smectic modifications. All transitions are reproducible with increasing and decreasing temperature. We have confirmed the transitions by microscopic observation, thermal analysis and density measurements.

By X-ray diffraction measurements, the texture observation and the relations of miscibility, smectic I was found to belong to the group smectic A, and smectic II to the group smectic C. For this reason there is only a very small transition enthalpy between the two modifications according to the other investigated cases of a transition smectic A/C.[6,7]

The structures of the smectic phases I, II and III seem to be not very different. In all three cases the X-ray diffraction pattern shows a sharp inner ring and a diffuse outer ring, which suggests a layer structure with random distribution of the molecules within the layers. The modification smectic III shows differences in the texture as well as in the X-ray diffraction pattern from the smectic modifications marked B, D and E.[1,2] By this reason it is necessary to assign this modification to a new group marked F.

Smectic IV shows an X-ray diffraction pattern with several rings, but it seems to be not really crystalline: it shows a viscous behaviour, the microscopic texture can be altered completely by slight pressure on the cover-glass of the microscopic preparation; the transition smectic III–smectic IV cannot be noticeably supercooled; from this modification starts a noticeable region of mixed crystals in the

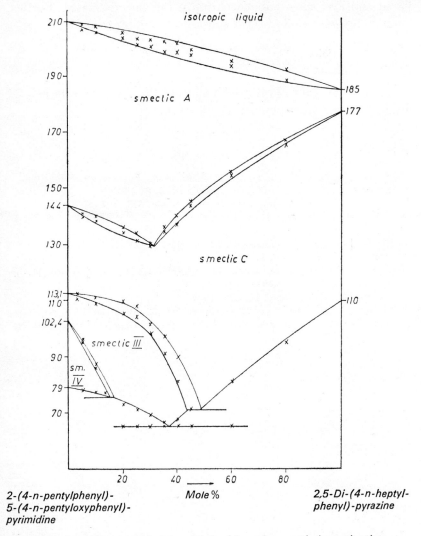

Figure 12.   Diagram of state, obtained by microscopic investigation.

binary system (see Fig. 12).   By means of this preliminary investigation we cannot exactly describe the structure of this modification, but the X-ray diagram points to a new group of smectic modifications marked G.

Some homologues of the investigated substance have been prepared and also show polymorphism in the smectic state.   Further detailed investigation of these substances is in preparation.

Acknowledgements

We are indebted to Prof. Sackmann and Prof. Schubert for helpful discussions and their interest in this work.

REFERENCES

1. Sackmann, H. and Demus, D., *Fortschr. chem. Forschg.* **12**, 349 (1969).
2. Sackmann, H. and Demus, D., *Mol. Cryst.* **2**, 81 (1966).
3. Schubert, H. and Zaschke, H., *J. prakt. Chem.* **312**, 494 (1970).
4. Schubert, H., Hacker, R. and Kindermann, K., *J. prakt. Chem.* 4, **37**, 12 (1968).
5. Weißenborn, H., *Diplomarbeit Halle*, 1967.
6. Arnold, H., *Mol. Cryst.* **2**, 43 (1966).
7. Arnold, H., Demus, D., Koch, H. J., Nelles, A. and Sackmann, H., *Z. phys. Chem.* Leipzig, **240**, 185 (1969).
8. Friedel, G., *Ann. Phys.*, **18**, 273 (1922).
9. Brown, G. H. and Shaw, W. G., *Chem. Rev.* **57**, 1049 (1957).
10. Gray, G. W., *Mol. Structure and the Properties of Liquid Crystals*, London–New York, Academic Press, 1962.
11. Chistyakov, I. G., *Liquid Crystals* (in Russian), Moscow 1966.

Liquid-Crystalline Structures of Binary Systems α-ω Soap/Water†

BERNARD R. GALLOT

Centre de Biophysique Moléculaire
45-Orleans-02
France

Received October 12, 1970

Abstract—We have studied by X-ray diffraction method the structure of binary systems α-ω alkali soap/water. We have shown that these systems exhibit only one liquid crystalline phase of smectic type. We have studied the influence on the structural parameters of the following factors: concentration, temperature, nature of the metal, length of the paraffinic chain, electric state of the polar groups.

Introduction

For several years we have studied, by X-ray diffraction, the structures occurring in anhydrous mono and di alkali soaps as a function of temperature. We have shown that the number of structures possible for disoaps is by far smaller than for monosoaps; if three types of structural elements (lamellae, discs and ribbons) have been identified for monosoaps,[1-6] only one type (lamellae) has been found with disoaps.[7]

Do dialkalisoap-water systems exhibit a similar simplification in their behaviour? In order to answer this question, we have undertaken, by X-ray diffraction, the study of water solutions of potassium and rubidium α-ω soaps with 16 and 22 carbon atoms (α-ω diacids with 16 and 22 carbon atoms being the only diacids commercially available).

We shall indicate these disoaps by: 1–16 K, 1–22 K, 1–16 Rb and 1–22 Rb; the chemical formula corresponding to the 1–22 K soap, for instance, being:

$$KOOC—(CH_2)_{20}—COOK$$

† Presented at the Third International Liquid Crystal Conference in Berlin August 24–28, 1970.

507

Experimental

Disoaps were prepared by exact neutralization of diacid in methanolic solution by potassium or rubidium methanolate, followed by precipitation and washing with anhydrous ether.

Samples of binary systems were prepared by direct weighing of soap and water. After homogenizing by prolonged heating and cooling to room temperature the mixtures were put into solvent-tight cells in order to examine them with X-rays. The concentration c (grams of soap per gram of solution) of each solution was determined by drying the sample after the X-ray diffraction experiment.

X-ray diffraction measurements were performed in a Guinier type focusing camera, operating in vacuum and equipped with both a bent-quartz monochromator and a device for recording the diagrams of samples heated at high temperatures (kept constant to $\pm 1\,°C$).

Results

(A) DESCRIPTION OF THE STRUCTURES

All X-ray diffraction patterns from the liquid crystalline phases can be indexed as follows:

—in the small angle region: a series of three (00l) reflections, typical of a layered structure.

—in the wide angle region: a diffuse halo at 4.5 Å showing that the paraffinic c chains take up a disordered conformation, more similar to that of a liquid paraffin than to that of a crystal.

Therefore, the structure is lamellar and consists of a set of plane, parallel, equidistant sheets; each sheet results from the superposition of two layers: one formed by the hydrophobic paraffinic chains, the other by water; polar groups form an interface between water and hydrocarbon chains in liquid state.

The inter-sheet spacing d is given by X-ray experiments.

The paraffinic layer thickness d_1, the water layer thickness d_2 and the specific surface of the polar groups S are calculated by formulae based on simple geometry:

$$d_1 = \frac{d}{1 + \rho_1/\rho_2 \; 1 - c/c}$$

$$d_2 = d - d_1$$

$$S = \frac{M}{A \rho_1 d_1}$$

where c is the concentration in soap of molecular weight M

ρ_1 the density of soap[8]

ρ_2 the density of water.

(B) Domain of Stability of the Lamellar Structure

The detailed determination of the domains of stability of the liquid-crystalline phases we met with was not the aim of our work. However, we did take care to locate their approximate boundaries, with the sole purpose of being sure to have only one phase in the samples we examined.

Examination of the diffraction diagrams showing supplementary lines in their central part and sharp lines situated in the region of large Bragg angles allowed us to detect phase separation between coagel and lamellar liquid crystalline structure.

Phase separation between lamellar liquid crystalline structure and micellar solution was generally revealed only after calculating the structural parameters, the curves representing them as functions of the composition showing singular points.

(C) Influence of the Concentration

We have plotted the variation of the structural parameters (Tables 1 and 2) of the lamellar structure *versus* soap concentration, in Fig. 1 for the system 1–22 K/water at 121 °C, in Fig. 2 for the system 1–16 K/water at 104 °C, in Fig. 3 for the system 1–16 Rb/water at 86 °C and in Fig. 4 for the system 1–22 Rb/water at 86 °C.

When the soap concentration of the four systems increases:

—the inter-sheet spacing d decreases,

—the soap layer thickness d_1 increases,

—the water layer thickness d_2 decreases,

—the specific surface S decreases.

TABLE 1   Variation of Structural Parameters *Versus* Soap Concentration

Soap	C	d(Å)	d_1(Å)	d_2(Å)	S(Å²)	N
1–22 K ($T = 104\,°C$) $\rho_1 = 1,14$	$0,50_4$	$32,5_4$	$14,9_6$	$17,5_8$	$43,5_0$	$4,3_5$
	$0,52_0$	$32,3_2$	$15,3_8$	$16,9_4$	$42,3_2$	$4,6_3$
	$0,53_9$	$32,2_2$	$15,9_6$	$16,2_6$	$40,7_8$	$5,0_1$
	$0,56_6$	$31,9_6$	$16,6_8$	$15,2_8$	$39,0_2$	$5,5_7$
	$0,59_0$	$31,9_2$	$17,4_5$	$14,4_7$	$37,3_2$	$6,1_5$
	$0,59_8$	$31,6_7$	$17,5_8$	$14,0_9$	$37,0_1$	$6,3_7$
1–22 K ($T = 121\,°C$) $\rho_1 = 1,12$	$0,50_4$	$32,1_5$	$14,8_2$	$17,3_3$	$44,7_0$	$4,2_9$
	$0,56_6$	$31,1_5$	$16,3_0$	$14,8_5$	$40,6_5$	$5,5_0$
	$0,59_0$	$30,9_1$	$16,9_3$	$13,9_8$	$39,1_3$	$6,0_7$
	$0,64_5$	$30,7_2$	$18,5_8$	$12,1_4$	$35,6_7$	$7,6_7$
	$0,65_8$	$30,5_8$	$18,9_1$	$11,6_7$	$35,0_5$	$8,1_2$
	$0,63_7$	$30,4_4$	$19,3_0$	$11,1_4$	$34,3_3$	$8,6_8$
1–16 K ($T = 104\,°C$) $\rho_1 = 1,24$	$0,53_8$	$24,1_6$	$11,4_0$	$12,7_6$	$42,4_4$	$6,1_4$
	$0,55_5$	$23,8_9$	$11,6_9$	$12,2_0$	$41,4_0$	$6,5_7$
	$0,57_0$	$23,8_1$	$12,0_1$	$11,8_0$	$40,3_0$	$6,9_9$
	$0,57_9$	$23,7_0$	$12,1_7$	$11,5_3$	$39,7_6$	$7,2_5$
	$0,62_6$	$23,3_9$	$13,1_5$	$10,2_4$	$36,8_0$	$8,8_2$
	$0,64_6$	$23,2_3$	$13,5_6$	$9,6_7$	$35,6_9$	$9,6_8$
	$0,68_5$	$23,1_5$	$14,4_8$	$8,6_7$	$33,4_3$	$11,4_6$

TABLE 2   Variation of Structural Parameters *Versus* Soap Concentration

Soap	C	d(Å)	d_1(Å)	d_2(Å)	S(Å²)	N
1–22 Rb ($T = 86\,°C$) $\rho_1 = 1,23$	$0,46_0$	$33,9_9$	$13,6_5$	$20,3_4$	$48,8_0$	$3,3_5$
	$0,48_6$	$33,3_7$	$14,2_3$	$19,1_4$	$46,8_0$	$3,7_1$
	$0,51_4$	$32,7_9$	$14,8_9$	$17,9_0$	$44,7_3$	$4,1_5$
	$0,54_6$	$31,9_5$	$15,5_2$	$16,4_3$	$42,9_0$	$4,7_1$
	$0,59_0$	$31,1_0$	$16,5_2$	$14,5_8$	$40,3_2$	$5,6_5$
	$0,61_4$	$30,5_5$	$16,9_7$	$13,5_8$	$39,2_4$	$6,2_3$
	$0,64_2$	$30,2_4$	$17,7_1$	$12,5_3$	$37,6_0$	$7,0_5$
1–16 Rb ($T = 86\,°C$) $\rho_1 = 1,37$	$0,55_4$	$24,2_4$	$11,3_3$	$12,9_1$	$43,7_5$	$5,8_8$
	$0,60_0$	$23,8_7$	$12,2_8$	$11,5_9$	$40,3_7$	$7,1_0$
	$0,62_5$	$23,7_0$	$12,8_3$	$10,8_7$	$38,6_6$	$7,8_9$
	$0,64_3$	$23,5_8$	$13,2_2$	$10,3_6$	$37,5_2$	$8,5_4$
	$0,66_0$	$23,4_0$	$13,5_3$	$9,8_7$	$36,6_5$	$9,1_9$
	$0,69_5$	$23,0_9$	$14,2_4$	$8,8_5$	$34,8_1$	$10,7_8$
	$0,73_9$	$23,2_0$	$15,4_6$	$7,7_4$	$32,0_7$	$13,3_8$

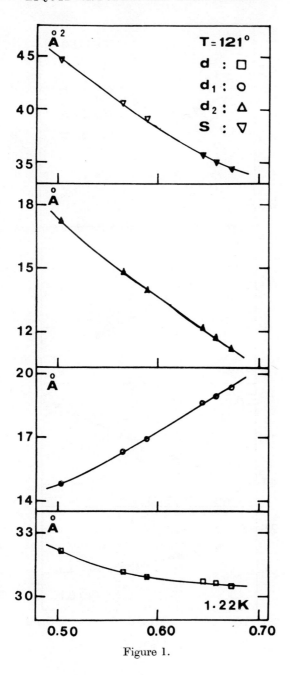

Figure 1.

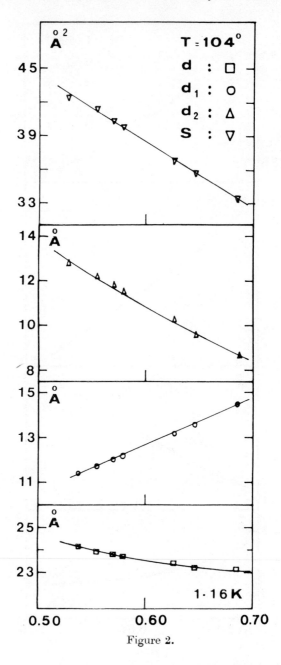

Figure 2.

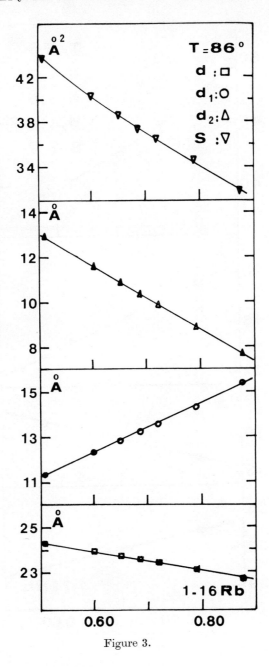

Figure 3.

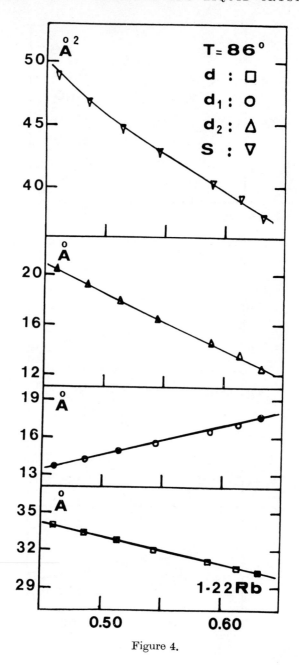

Figure 4.

(D) Influence of the Temperature

In Fig. 5, we have plotted, at constant soap concentration (57%) the variation of the inter-sheet spacing of the three following soaps: 1–22 Rb, 1–22 K and 1–16 K, versus temperature.

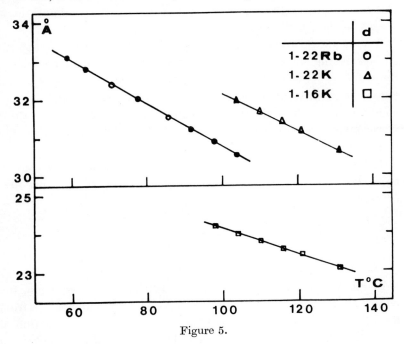

Figure 5.

For the three soaps the inter-sheet spacing d decreases when the temperature increases like in the case of the neat phase of anhydrous soaps.

The values of the linear contraction coefficient $\alpha = 1/d\ \Delta d/\Delta T$ are collected in Table 3.

TABLE 3   Values of the Linear
Contraction Coefficient

Soap	$10^4\ \alpha$
1–22 Rb	17,4
1–22 K	15,4
1–16 K	13,7

(E) Discussion

How can we explain the variation of the structural parameters with concentration, temperature, nature of the polar group, length of the paraffinic chain? What is the respective influence of the electrical state of the aqueous regions and of the configurational energy of the paraffinic chains?

Among the structural parameters we have described, the specific surface is the most interesting to solve this problem, because it immediately reflects the antagonism between polar groups and paraffinic chains. For an identical state of hydration, one can compare soaps of different molecular weight and impute all S variation to the exclusive influence of the configurational energy of the paraffinic chains.

Therefore, to discuss our results, we shall consider the variation of S versus N (number of gram molecular weight of soap per litre of water):

$$N = \frac{2000\rho_2}{M} \cdot \frac{c}{1-c}$$

(1) Case of monosoaps

In Fig. 6,[9] we have plotted, in a logarithmic representation, the variation of S versus N, at 86 °C, for eight potassium monosoaps from 8 to 22 carbon atoms. All the points representing the variation of S versus N fall on the same curve. Therefore S is independent of the length of the paraffinic chain and this conclusion is true for all temperatures as it is shown by Fig. 7.[9]

For monosoaps the variation of S with N is of the type:

$$S = S_0 N^{-p}$$

and it seems that the role of the " electrical state " [9] of the aqueous regions is by far more important than the role of the configurational energy of the paraffinic chains.

(2) Case of disoaps

Now let us see what happens with disoaps.

We have plotted the variation of S versus N: in Fig. 8 for dipotassium soaps with 22 and 16 carbon atoms and for potassium

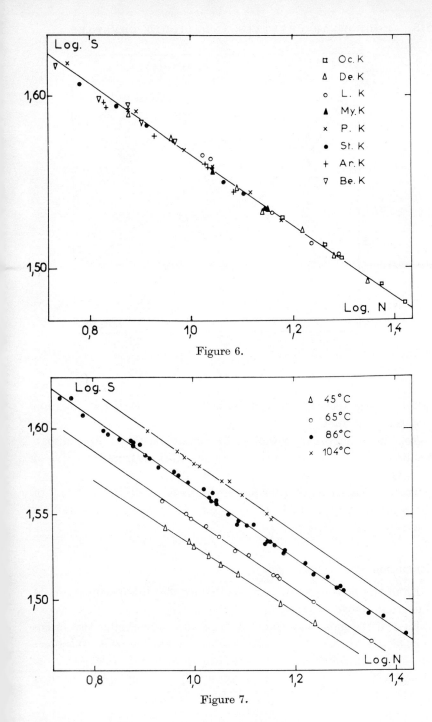

Figure 6.

Figure 7.

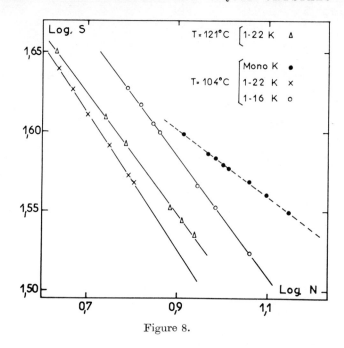

Figure 8.

monosoaps at the same temperature (104 °C) and in Fig. 9 for rubidium disoaps with 22 and 16 carbon atoms and for rubidium monosoaps at 86 °C.

For rubidium soaps as well as for potassium soaps, each disoap has its own curve and the two curves are different from the curve of monosoaps.

Therefore it seems that for disoaps both the " electrical state " of the aqueous regions and the configurational energy of paraffinic chains play a large part.

Conclusion

From the present study, we can deduce two fundamental results concerning binary water-soap systems.

First, if the monosoap-water systems generally exhibit two meso-morphic structures[9,10]: a cylindrical and a lamellar ones, and some-times three mesomorphic structures (the third being cubic); the α-ω disoap-water systems always exhibit only one mesophase with a lamellar structure.

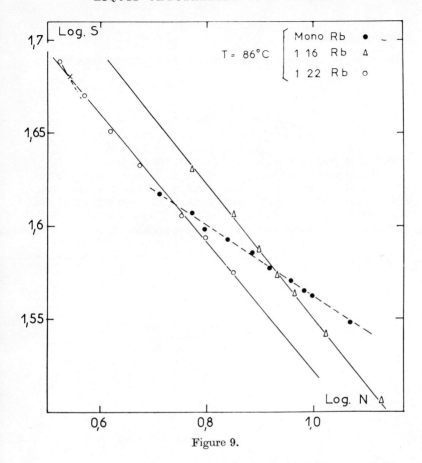

Figure 9.

We may point out a second fundamental difference between water-monosoap and water-disoap systems. In water-monosoap systems, the role of the " electrical state " of the aqueous regions seems by far more important than the role of the configurational energy of the paraffinic chains; while, in water-disoap systems, both the " electrical state " of the aqueous regions and the configurational energy of the paraffinic chains play a large part.

The different behaviour of the two kinds of soaps seems to be the result of the presence of a polar group at each end of the molecule of disoap: this presence reducing the number of configurations allowed to be taken by the paraffinic chain.

Acknowledgements

Discussions with Dr. A. Skoulios are gratefully acknowledged.

REFERENCES

1. Skoulios, A. and Luzzati, V., *Acta. Cryst.* **14**, 278 (1961).
2. Gallot, B. and Skoulios, A., *Acta. Cryst.* **15**, 826 (1962).
3. Gallot, B. and Skoulios, A., *Mol. Cryst.* **1**, 263 (1966).
4. Gallot, B. and Skoulios, A., *Kolloid-Z.u.Z. Polymere* **209**, 164 (1966).
5. Gallot, B. and Skoulios, A., *Kolloid-Z.u.Z. Polymere* **210**, 143 (1966).
6. Gallot, B. and Skoulios, A., *Kolloid-Z.u.Z. Polymere* **213**, 143 (1966).
7. Gallot, B. and Skoulios, A., *Kolloid-Z.u.Z. Polymere* **222**, 51 (1968).
8. Gallot, B., Thèse, Université de Strasbourg (1965).
9. Gallot, B. and Skoulios, A., *Kolloid-Z.u.Z. Polymere* **208**, 37 (1966).
10. Husson, F., Mustacchi, H., and Luzzati, V., *Acta. Cryst.* **13**, 668 (1960).

Study of Liquid-Crystalline Structures of Polystyrene-Polybutadiene Block Copolymers by Small Angle X-ray Scattering and Electron Microscopy†

ANDRÉ DOUY and BERNARD R. GALLOT

C.B.M.
45–Orleans 02
France

Received October 12, 1970; in revised form February 1, 1971

Abstract—We have studied by small angle X-ray scattering and electron microscopy the liquid crystalline structures exhibited by polystyrene-polybutadiene block copolymers. For that purpose we have developed an original method of electron microscopy. The types of structure (lamellar and hexagonal) and the values of the structural parameters found by X-ray diffraction and by electron microscopy are in good agreement. Induced by this good agreement we have applied our method of electron microscopy to the study of solutions of copolymers at all concentrations and we may picture a way of formation for liquid-crystalline structures exhibited by block copolymers.

1. Introduction

Using well-focused and strictly monochromatic X-rays, we have already shown,[1,2] by small angle X-ray scattering that AB polystyrene-polybutadiene (PS-PB) block copolymers exhibit, in solution in preferential solvents of polystyrene, liquid-crystalline structures for solvent concentration smaller than 45%.

We have also shown, by X-ray diffraction[3] that, when the composition of the copolymer changes, the liquid-crystalline structure of the copolymer also changes. We have found that:

—if the copolymer contains less than 35% of polybutadiene the structure is hexagonal,

—if the copolymer contains between 35 and 60% of polybutadiene the structure is lamellar,

† Presented at the Third International Liquid Crystal Conference in Berlin, August 24–28, 1970.

—if the copolymer contains more than 60% of polybutadiene the structure is hexagonal.

We know that[1] the hexagonal structure consists of a set of indefinitely long cylinders arranged in a regular hexagonal two-dimensional array. But different questions arise about this stucture. Which block is in the cylinders, the soluble block or the insoluble one? Is the same block in the cylinders for copolymers containing less than 35% of polybutadiene and for copolymers containing more than 60% of polybutadiene?

X-ray diffraction cannot surely solve the problem. It only says: the structure is hexagonal and the distance D between the axes of two neighboring cylinders is x Å. So it is necessary to hypothesize on the position of the blocks for calculating the diameter of the cylinders. But, if we study the cylinders by electron microscopy, we surely solve the problem. Therefore we have undertaken the study of concentrated solution of polystyrene-polybutadiene block copolymers by using both small angle X-ray scattering and electron microscopy.

2. Preparation and Characterization of Block Copolymers

Polystyrene-polybutadiene (PS-PB) block copolymers were prepared by anionic polymerization under high vacuum.[1]

Molecular weight (Table 1) determinations were performed by light scattering, osmometry and Gel Permeation Chromatography.

TABLE 1   Molecular Weights and Compositions of the Copolymers

Cop.	M_w PS	% PB	$M_{w\,Cop.}$
SB. 32	49.000	30.5	70.500
SB. 33	49.000	39.8	81.400
SB. 34	49.000	50.2	98.400
SB. 36	49.000	71.7	173.000
SB. 1	71.000	39	117.000

3. Preparation of Solid Samples

As electron microscopy requires solid samples thinner than 1000 Å, we have used as preferential solvents of polystyrene different monomers easily polymerizable by UV light (styrene, methylmetha-crylate, vinyl acetate···) and applied the following method to prepare our samples.[4]

At first, by small angle X-ray scattering, we resolve the structure of the mesomorphic gels prepared with the monomer as a preferential solvent. Then we make a total polymerization of the monomer by UV light. At last, by small angle X-ray scattering, we verify that the periodic structure has not been destroyed by polymerization and we measure its new parameters.

In Fig. 1 we give an example of the variation of the structural parameters during polymerization. We have plotted the structural parameters of the lamellar structure before polymerization of the methylmethacrylate (black points) and after polymerization of the methylmethacrylate (white points) for the copolymer SB. 33.

We see that during polymerization:

—the inter-sheet spacing d decreases
—the thickness d_A of the polystyrene soluble layer decreases
—the thickness d_B of the polybutadiene insoluble layer remains constant.

After studying the solid sample by X-ray diffraction, we cut it with an ultramicrotome (Ultratome III L.K.B.). We stain the diene block by fixation of osmium tetroxide on the double bonds of poly-butadiene by allowing the sections to stand in the vapour of osmium tetroxide dissolved in an aqueous solution of sodium cacodylate for about 3 hours). Then we study the ultrathin section with an electron microscope (Hitachi HU. IICS).

Some questions may arise about our sample preparative method. Is there any polymerization of the monomer induced by X-rays during the exposure of the mesomorphic gels? Is there any fixation of osmium tetroxide on some unpolymerized monomer or on poly-styrene and polymethecrylate? We have verified that in our experi-mental conditions X-rays do not polymerize the styrene or the MMA and that there is no unpolymerized monomer remaining in our solid samples. We have also verified that there is no fixation of Osmium tetroxide on polystyrene and polymethylmethacrylate homopolymers with our staining procedure.

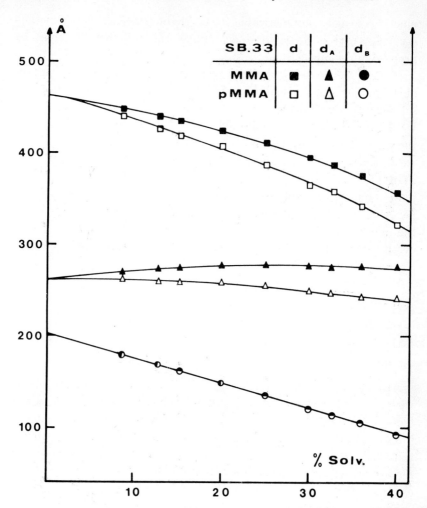

Figure 1.   Variation of structural parameters during polymerization.   Structural parameters of lamellar structure (a) before polymerization of methyl-methacrylate (black points);   (b) after polymerization of methylmethacrylate (white points) for the copolymer SB. 33.

4. Study of Liquid-Crystalline Structures

In Figs. 2 to 7 we give examples of electron micrographs provided by ultrathin sections of solid samples prepared from solutions of copolymers in methyl methacrylate (MMA).

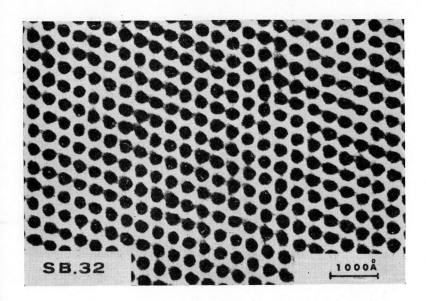

Figure 2.   Electron micrograph of the copolymer SB. 32.

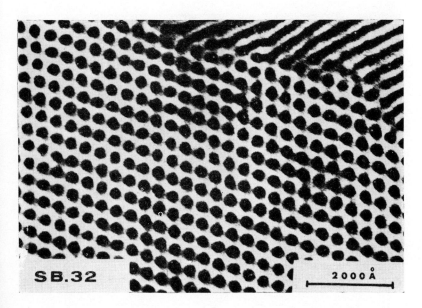

Figure 3.   Electron micrograph of the copolymer SB. 32.

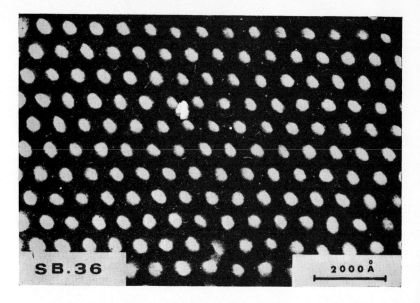

Figure 4.   Electron micrograph of the copolymer SB. 36.

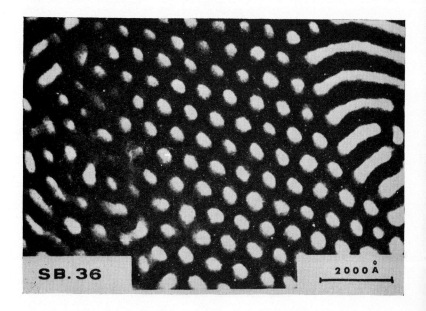

Figure 5.   Electron micrograph of the copolymer SB. 36.

Figure 6.   Electron micrograph of the copolymer SB. 33.

Figure 7.   Electron micrograph of the copolymer SB. 34.

As we have coloured the samples by fixation of osmium tetroxide on the double bonds of polybutadiene, polystyrene appears in white and polybutadiene in black in all electron micrographs.

A. CASE OF THE HEXAGONAL STRUCTURE

Figures 2 and 3 are electron micrographs of sections of the co-polymer SB. 32 having a composition of 30,5% polybutadiene.

In the Fig. 2 we see black spots on a white background. The spots have the shape of circles which are distinct and isolated; they are arranged on an hexagonal array. The circles are cross-sectional views of cylinders (the plane of cutting is practically perpendicular to the axis of the long cylinders).

In the right upper corner of Fig. 3, we see some stripes, alternatively black and white; these stripes are sections of cylinders cut by a plane parallel to their axis. Therefore the structure cannot be cubic, but necessarily consists of a set of indefinitely long cylinders arranged in a regular hexagonal two-dimensional array.

In Figs. 2 and 3 the circles are black and we are sure that the cylinders are filled with polybutadiene.

Figures 4 and 5 show electron micrographs of sections of the copolymer SB. 36 having a composition of 71,7% polybutadiene.

In Fig. 4 we see a section of the long cylinders by a plane nearly perpendicular to the direction of their axes and we observe white circles arranged on an hexagonal array.

In the main part of Fig. 5 we observe white spots which have nearly the shape of ellipses (the plane of cutting makes a small angle with the plane perpendicular to the direction of the axis of the cylinders). In the right part of the Fig. 5, we observe some cylinders cut by a plane parallel to the direction of their axes. Therefore, like in the case of the copolymer SB. 32, the structure is hexagonal. But, for the copolymer SB. 36, the circles being white the cylinders are filled by the polystyrene in solution in the solvent.

From the four preceding micrographs we can conclude that if the copolymer contains less than 35% of polybutadiene the cylinders are filled with polybutadiene, but if the copolymer contains more than 60% polybutadiene the cylinders are filled with polystyrene.

B. Case of the Lamellar Structure

In Figs. 6 and 7 we give examples of electron micrographs provided by sections of the lamellar structure which covers the field of compositions in polybutadiene between 35 and 60%.

The sections have been made in a direction perpendicular to the plane of the sheets of the lamellar structure and we observe a striated structure. In this striated structure, the black stripes contain the polybutadiene and the white stripes contain the polystyrene and the polymerized solvent.

If we compare the micrograph of the copolymer SB. 33 containing 39,8% of polybutadiene (Fig. 6) with the micrograph of the copolymer SB. 34 containing 50,2% of polybutadiene (Fig. 7) we see that when the composition in polybutadiene of the copolymer increases the broadness of the black stripes of polybutadiene increases as it has been demonstrated elsewhere. [3,4]

These micrographs reveal an ordered structure which extends over several microns. The order which is seen in Figs. 6 and 7 and in similar other pictures, extend appreciably further than can be recorded on a single negative; in fact it covers the full area of a hole of the grid without any essential interruption of this order within it.

C. Comparison of the Structural Parameters Found by X-ray and Electron Microscopy

We have shown how one can distinguish the different structures by electron microscopy. Now we have to compare the values of the structural parameters found by X-ray diffraction (X.R.) and by electron microscopy (E.M.).

We have collected (as an example) in Tables 2 and 3 the values of the structural parameters of solid samples prepared from solutions of copolymers in 30 ± 1% of MMA.

For the hexagonal structure, the structural parameters have been measured on electron micrographs resulting from sections by a plane perpendicular to the axis of the cylinders and in which the circles are well isolated (see Fig. 2 for instance).

For the lamellar structure, the structural parameters have been measured on electron micrographs resulting from sections by a plane perpendicular to the plane of the sheets. If we cut the lamellar

TABLE 2   Comparison of the Values of the Structural Parameters Found by X-rays (X.R.) and Electron Microscopy (E.M.) for the Two Types of Hexagonal Structure

| | S.B. 32 | | SB. 36 | |
	X.R.	E.M.	X.R.	E.M.
D(Å)	380	360	663	710
2R(Å)	205	180	460	400

TABLE 3   Comparison of the Values of the Structural Parameters Found by X-rays (X.R.) and Electron Microscopy (E.M.) for the Lamellar Structure

| | S.B. 33 | | S.B. 34 | |
	X.R.	E.M.	X.R.	E.M.
d(Å)	365	375	424	440
d_A(Å)	247	240	253	240
d_B(Å)	118	135	171	200

structure by planes making different angles with the plane of the sheets, the thickness found for the sheets is a minimum when the plane of cutting is perpendicular to the plane of the sheets.

In order to facilitate the understanding of Tables 2 and 3 we recall that:

(1) for the hexagonal structure:
   —D is the distance between the axis of two neighboring cylinders
   —$2R$ is the diameter of the cylinders
(2) for the lamellar structure:
   —d is the inter-sheet spacing
   —d_A is the thickness of the polystyrene soluble layer
   —d_B is the thickness of the polybutadiene insoluble layer.

Examination of Tables 2 and 3 shows that the agreement between the values of the structural parameters found by X-ray diffraction (X.R.) and by electron microscopy (E.M.) is very good:

   —about 6% for D and d
   —about 15% for $2R, d_A$ and d_B.

A similar agreement is found for solid samples prepared from copolymer solutions of different concentrations in styrene or MMA.

5. Study of Dilute Solutions

Induced by this good agreement, we have applied our method of study by electron microscopy to the field of higher concentrations in solvent, i.e. concentrations between 45 and 99% of solvent. In this field of concentrations there is no regular periodicity, so X-ray diffraction is very difficult to be applied and gives very poor results.

We shall take the example of the copolymer SB. 1 containing 39% of polybutadiene and giving a lamellar structure for solvent concentrations smaller than 45%. All the samples used for electron microscopic studies have been prepared by polymerization of solutions of the copolymer in styrene monometer. We have chosen styrene as solvent in order to prevent any effect of incompatibility between polymeric chains during the polymerization of the monomer.

For solvent concentrations smaller than 45% the structure is lamellar, and one can see in Fig. 8 the black stripes of polybutadiene and the white stripes of polystyrene, for a composition of 32% of solvent.

When the solvent concentration increases and exceeds 45%, the regularity of the lamellar structure decreases. The lamellae of polybutadiene edge away from one another and do not remain plane and parallel. The disorder increases with solvent concentration; it is higher for 70% (Fig. 10) than for 49% (Fig. 9).

For a solvent concentration of about 75% the lamellar structure crashes and gives raise to cylinders more or less rectilinear (Fig. 11). When the solvent concentration increases the cylinders edge away from one another and break into shorter cylinders (Figs. 12 and 13).

At last, for a concentration of 1% of copolymer (99% of solvent), the average length of the cylinders of polybutadiene is about 5 times their diameter (Fig. 14).

6. Conclusion

From this paper we can draw two important conclusions. First, we bring the material proof of the existence of liquid-crystalline

Figure 8.   Electron micrograph of the copolymer SB. 1 plus 32% polystyrene.

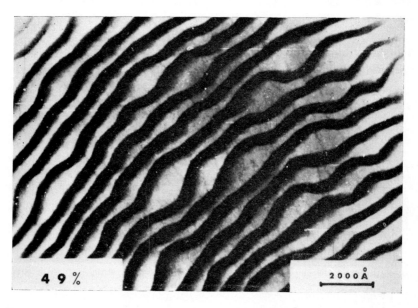

Figure 9.   Electron micrograph of the copolymer SB. 1 plus 49% polystyrene.

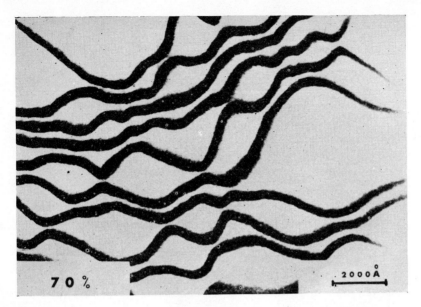

Figure 10.   Electron micrograph of the copolymer SB. 1 plus 70% polystyrene.

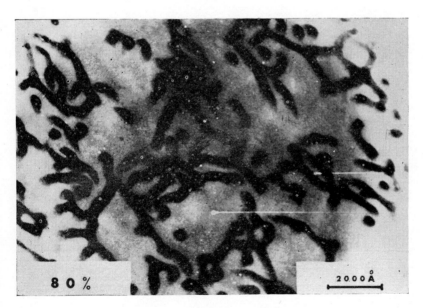

Figure 11.   Electron micrograph of the copolymer SB. 1 plus 80% polystyrene.

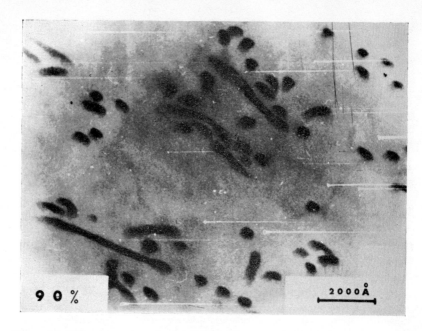

Figure 12.   Electron micrograph of the copolymer SB. 1 plus 90% polystyrene.

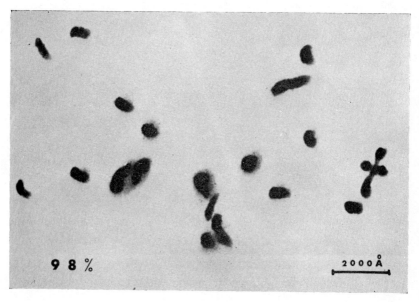

Figure 13.   Electron micrograph of the copolymer SB. 1 plus 98% polystyrene.

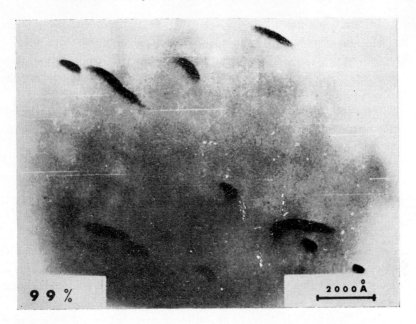

Figure 14.   Electron micrograph of the copolymer SB. 1 plus 99% polystyrene.

structures for concentrated solutions of block copolymers. Secondly we show the mechanism of formation of liquid-crystalline structures.

Different authors have already studied concentrated solutions of block copolymers by X-ray diffraction[5,6,7] and proposed three models of structure (lamellar, hexagonal and cubic). They have also shown that the nature of the blocks, the composition of the copolymer, the nature and the concentration of the solvent are the principal factors governing the type of structure and the values of the structural parameters adopted by the copolymers.[1] In this paper we give electronmicrographs of liquid-crystalline structures exhibited by block copolymers and therefore we demonstrate directly the reality of their existence. We also show, by our technique of electron microscopy, the existence of two types of hexagonal structures one with cylinders filled with the insoluble block and corresponding to copolymers containing less than 35% of the insoluble block, the other with cylinders filled with the soluble block in solution in the solvent and corresponding to copolymers containing more than about

60% of the insoluble block. Lastly, we prove the accuracy of our former conclusions[1] inferred from the study of block copolymers by small angle X-ray scattering since the types of structure and the values of the structural parameters found by X-rays and electron microscopy are in good agreement (Tables 2 and 3).

The second important conclusion concerns the formation of liquid crystalline structures. Our study of copolymer solutions of all concentrations show that, starting from very dilute solutions where mono and pluri molecular micellae have been postulated,[8] we pass through aggregates of different sizes and shapes (at first cylindrical aggregates: Figs. 14 to 11; then lamellar aggregates: Figs. 10 and 9;) and we reach a lamellar liquid-crystalline structure for copolymers containing between 35 and 60% of the insoluble block (Fig. 8). A nearly similar process is found for copolymers containing less than 35% or more than 60% of the insoluble block, but it does not involve lamellar aggregates and leads to an hexagonal liquid crystalline structure (Figs. 2 and 4).

Such a formation of liquid-crystalline structures would be of some interest to explain the disagreement between the conclusions about the structure of " dry copolymers " drawn by different authors[9] from electron microscopic studies of films prepared by evaporation from dilute solutions of copolymers. Depending on the speed of evaporation they fix any structure corresponding to concentrations between 1 and 100% of polymer. On the contrary, with our solid sample preparative method (by polymerization of a monomer used as a solvent of the copolymer) we have the advantage of studying systems in equilibrium[5] and of any concentration between 1 and 100% of copolymer. Furthermore, we are able to perform (for solvent concentration smaller than 45%) our studies by X-rays and electron microscopy on the same samples.

Is it necessary to claim that our solid samples form a new class of rigid polimeric materials presenting a large interest in an industrial point of view. These materials are two or three component systems depending on the fact that the monomer used as a polymerizable solvent is or is not the monomer of one block, and their properties can be changed at will by changing the nature and the amount of the monomer.

Acknowledgements

Professor J. Bardolle, from the University of Orleans, is greatly acknowledged for allowing us to use his electron microscope.

We also acknowledge the Referee for inducing us to give more details on our solid sample preparative method.

REFERENCES

1. Douy, A., Mayer, R., Rossi, J. and Gallot, B., *Mol. Cryst. and Liq. Cryst.* **7**, 103 (1969).
2. Douy, A. and Gallot, B., *C.R. Acad. Sci. Paris* **268**, 1218 (1969).
3. Douy, A. and Gallot, B., *Makromol. Chemie*, in press.
4. Douy, A. and Gallot, B., *IUPAC International Symposium on Macromolecules*, Leiden, 1970 (Preprint 1-22, p. 99).
5. Douy, A. Gervais, M. and Gallot, B., *C.R. Acad. Sci. Paris* **270**, 1646 (1970).
6. Gallot, B., Mayer, R. and Sadron, C., *C.R. Acad. Sci. Paris* **263**, 42 (1966).
7. Skoulios, A. and Finaz, G., *J. Chim. Phys.* 473 (1962).
8. Gallot, Y., These, Strasbourg (1964).
9. Hendus, H., *Kolloid Z.* **216**, 110 (1967).
   Bradford, E. B., *J. Polymer Sci.* A. **1–6**, 1661 (1968).
   Inoue, T., *J. Polymer Sci.* A. **2–7**, 1283 (1969).
   Lewis, *Nature* **223**, 494 (1969).
   Matsuo, M., *Polymer* **10**, 79 (1969).

Phase Diagram of Systems: Block Copolymer-Preferential Solvent of One Block†

MONIQUE GERVAIS, ANDRÉ DOUY and BERNARD GALLOT

Centre de Biophysique Moléculaire
45–Orleans–02
France

Received October 15, 1970; *in revised form November* 23, 1970

Abstract—We have studied by small angle X-ray scattering and differential scanning calorimeter different systems block copolymer/preferential solvent of one block.

For copolymers owning two amorphous blocks such as polystyrene-polybutadiene, in solution in toluene, we have only one liquid-crystalline structure which disappears at about 180 °C; this structure is lamellar if the copolymer contains between 35 and 60% of polybutadiene.

For copolymers owning an amorphous and a crystallizable block such as polystyrene-polyethyleneoxide, we have found two liquid-crystalline structures L.C. and L.L., which are both lamellar but differ by the state of the polyethyleneoxide chains. Below about 50 °C we have found the structure L.C. with crystallized polyethyleneoxide chains; between 50 and about 170 °C, we have found the structure L.L. with liquid polyethyleneoxide chains. The field of the structure L.C. is smaller with nitromethane which is a preferential solvent of polyethyleneoxide than with diethylphtalate which is a preferential solvent of polystyrene.

1. Introduction

At the Second International Liquid Crystal Conference, we have described the different liquid-crystalline structures exhibited by block copolymers in solution in a preferential solvent of one block. We have also shown the influence on the structural types and structural parameters of different factors: concentration and nature of the solvent, molecular weight and composition of the copolymer, nature of the blocks.[1] In this paper we shall study the influence of the temperature on binary systems: block-copolymer/preferential solvent of one block and describe the phase diagrams of these systems.

† Presented at the Third International Liquid Crystal Conference in Berlin, August 24–28, 1970.

The interest of such a study is both practical and theoretical. First it allows the determination of the stability of the liquid-crystalline structures and the discovery of eventual phase transitions. Then it may allow the evaluation of the role played by the configurational entropy of the macromolecular chain in liquid crystalline structures and may help the explanation of the formation of these structures in a theoretical point of view.

Three cases are possible for the binary systems block-copolymer/solvent of one block. The first one is a copolymer with two amorphous blocks in solution in a preferential solvent of one block; the second one is a copolymer with an amorphous block and a crystallizable block in solution in a preferential solvent of the amorphous block; the third one is a polymer with an amorphous block and a crystallizable block in solution in a preferential solvent of the crystallizable block. We shall take as example of the three cases the following systems:

—copolymer polystyrene-polybutadiene/toluene (PS-PB/Tol.)
—copolymer polystyrene-polyethyeneoxide/diethylphtalate (PS-POE/Diet. Phtal.)
—copolymer polystyrene-polyethyleneoxide/Nitromethane (PS-POE/Nit)

For studying these systems, we have used simultaneously X-ray diffraction and differential scanning calorimeter; DSC has allowed us to determine both phase transitions and boundaries of the domains of stability of pure phases. X-ray diffraction has allowed us to perform the detailed determination of the structure of the different phases and the study of the variation of the structural parameters with temperature and concentration.

2. Experimental

Polystyrene-polybutadiene(PS-PB) and polystyrene-polyethyleneoxide(PS-POE) block copolymers were prepared by anionic polymerization, under high vacuum, in an all glass apparatus, in THF solution with cumyl potassium as initiator.

Molecular weights of copolymers were measured by light scattering, osmometry and Gel Permeation Chromatography (Table I).

TABLE 1 Molecular Weights and Compositions of the
Copolymers Studied

Cop.	M_w PS	% PS	M_w total
SP. 3	16.500	41	40.200
SB. 1	71.000	61	117.000

G.P.C. curves and fractionation experiments have shown that our copolymers are free of homopolymers.

The D.S.C. experiments were performed with a Perkin-Elmer Differential scanning Calorimeter, type DSC 1B, equipped with tight cells.

X-ray diffraction measurements were performed with 3 different cameras: a Debye-Scherrer camera for studying large Bragg angles and 2 focusing cameras (one for middle angles and one for small angles). The two focusing cameras operating in vacuum, were equipped with both a bent quartz monochromator and a device for recording the diagrams of samples heated at high temperatures (kept constant to $\pm 0.5\,°C$).

3. Structures

All X-ray diffraction patterns from pure liquid-crystalline phases can be indexed (in the small-angles region) as a series of three (001) reflections, typical of a layered structure.

Therefore, the structure is lamellar and consists of a set of plane, parallel, equidistant sheets; each sheet results from the superposition of two layers; one formed by the insoluble block, the other by the solution in the preferential solvent of the soluble block. The inter-sheet spacing d is directly given by X-ray experiments; the thickness d_A of the soluble layer, the thickness d_B of the insoluble layer and the average area S available to a molecule are calculated by the following formulae based on simple geometry:

$$d_B = d\left[1 + \frac{\rho_B}{\rho_{AS}}\frac{1-CX_B}{CX_B}\right]^{-1}$$

$$S = \frac{2M_B}{Nd_B\,\rho_B}$$

$$\rho_{AS} = \rho_A \cdot \rho_S(1 - CX_B)\left[\rho_A + c(\rho_S - \rho_A - X_B\rho_s)\right]^{-1}$$

with c = polymer concentration in the solution

X_B = concentration of the insoluble block in the copolymer

M_B = molecular weight of the insoluble block

ρ_A = density of the soluble block

ρ_B = density of the insoluble block

ρ_S = density of the solvent.

From the examination of the wide Bragg angles region of the diffraction diagrams we have established the existence of two types of lamellar structure : the type L.C. characterized by sharp lines situated in the region of large Bragg angles and resulting from folded and crystallized macromolecular chains ; the type L.L. characterized by a diffuse halo characteristic of amorphous or melt macromolecular chains.

3.1. System Polystyrene-Polybutadiene/Toluene

(1) *Phase diagram*

By heating from -50 to $+250\,°C$ (at $20\,°C/mn$) mesomorphic gels containing less than 45% of toluene, one obtains on the thermogram : at first a signal in shape of step stairs, then an exothermic pike (Fig. 1).

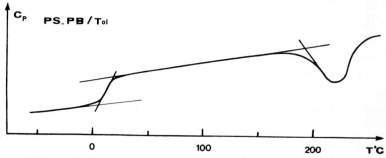

Figure 1.   Example of thermogram of the system PS–PB/Tol.

The first signal results from the glass transition of the polybutadiene block and shows that toluene is a solvent of polystyrene and does not enter the polybutadiene regions.[2]

The exothermic pike takes place at temperatures lower than $185\,°C$. As it is demonstrated by X-ray diffraction, this pike results from the disparition of a mesomorphic lamellar structure through a reversible transition.

Such thermograms obtained for different solvent concentrations have allowed us to draw the phase diagram pictured in Fig. 2.

This diagram exhibits only one mesomorphic phase with a lamellar structure of L.L. type.

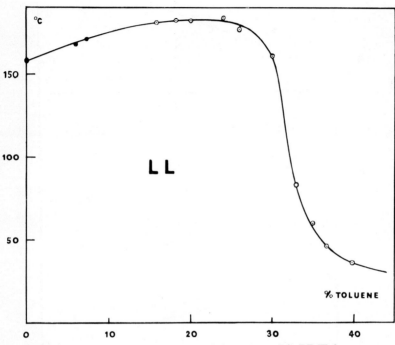

Figure 2. Phase diagram of the system PS–PB/Tol.

(2) *Influence of the temperature on structural parameters*

The variation of the structural parameters (calculated from X-ray diffraction patterns) versus temperature is pictured in Figs. 3 and 4.

The Fig. 3 where we have plotted the structural parameters versus temperature, for a constant concentration of toluene (25%) shows that, when temperature increases:

—the inter-sheet spacing d, the insoluble polybutadiene layer thickness d_B, and the soluble polystyrene layer thickness d_A decrease,
—the specific surface S increases.

In Fig. 4, we have plotted the structural parameters versus concentration for 4 constant temperatures: 25, 75, 125 and 170 °C.

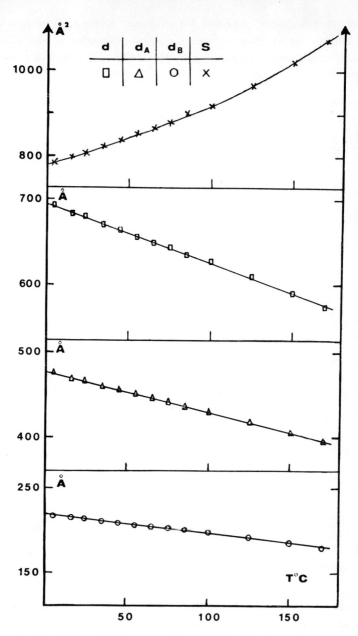

Figure 3. Variation of the parameters of the lamellar structure of the copolymer SB.I at a constant concentration of toluene (25%), versus temperature.

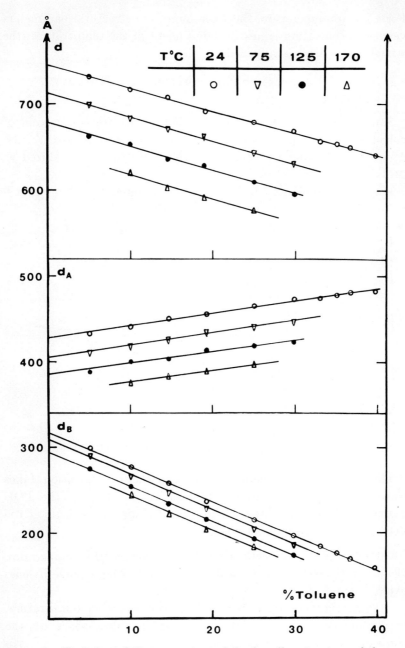

Figure 4. Variation of the parameters of the lamellar structure of the co-polymer SB.I versus toluene concentration.

For a given temperature, the variation of the structural parameters versus concentration is nearly independent of the temperature (the straight lines are nearly parallel).

3.2. SYSTEM POLYSTYRENE-POLYETHYLENEOXIDE/DIETHYL-PHTALATE

Samples of this system (in which diethylphtalate is a solvent of polystyrene) were prepared by direct weighing of the constituents. After homogenizing by heating at 80 °C, they are crystallized at 24 °C.

For such samples, with diethylphtalate content varying from 0 to 70%, the thermograms show 2 peaks (Fig. 5).

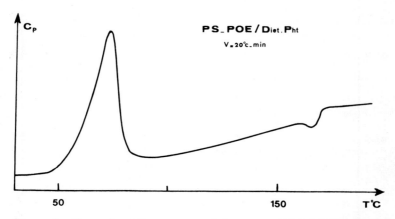

Figure 5.   Example of thermogram of the system PS–POE/Diet. Phtal.

The first peak, corresponding to an endothermic transition, takes place at about 50 °C and results from the melting of the POE chains.[3]   Why does this transition result from the melting of the POE block?   For three reasons :

—First, the endothermic peak takes place in the temperature vicinity of the melting point of the corresponding homopolyethylene-oxide,

—Then, the spherulitic texture observed at room temperature, by examination in polarization microscopy disappears at the temperature where the endothermic peak appears,

—Finally, the sharp lines characteristic of the monoclinic structure of the crystallized chains of polyethyleneoxide, in the region of large Bragg angles of the diffraction patterns, disappear at this temperature and give place to a diffuse halo characteristic of melt polyethyleneoxide chains.

Therefore, the first transition coincides with the change from a lamellar structure L.C. with folded and crystallized POE chains to a lamellar structure L.L. with melted POE chains.

The second peak, generally found at about 175 °C, results from the disappearance of the mesomorphic phase L.L. with melted POE chains, as it is proved by X-ray diffraction.

The phase diagram (concentration/temperature) pictured in Fig. 6, exhibits two mesomorphic phases, both with a lamellar structure but differing by the state of the polyethyleneoxide chains: folded and crystallized at room temperature in the structure L.C., melt at high temperature in the structure L.L.

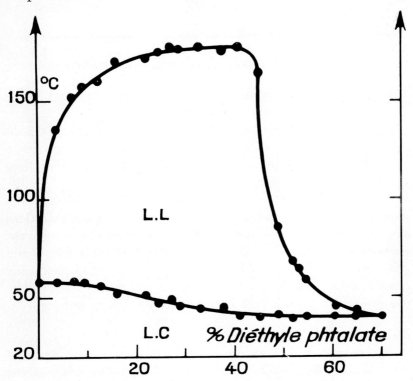

Figure 6.   Phase diagram of the system PS–POE/Diet. Phtal.

3.3. System Polystyrene-Polyethyleneoxide/Nitromethane

(1) *Phase diagram*

Samples of PS-POE/Nit. system were prepared in a manner similar to those with diethylphtalate.

Thermograms from samples with nitromethane content between 0 and 25% show two peaks: an endothermic peak at about 40 °C and an exothermic peak at high temperature (Fig. 7).

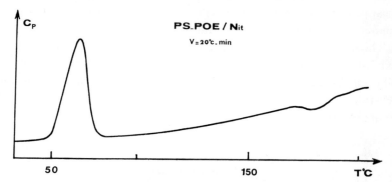

Figure 7.   Example of thermogram of the system PS–POE/Nit.

Thermograms from samples with nitromethane content between 25 and 40% show only the exothermic peak.

For the same reasons as in the case of the system PS-POE/diethylphtalate, the endothermic peak results from the disappearance of the crystallinity of the POE chains and the exothermic peak from the crash of the mesomorphic structure L.L.

The phase diagram of the system PS-POE/NM presents two mesophases (Fig. 8). In the domain of nitromethane concentrations smaller than 25% and of temperatures lower than about 40 °C, the mesophase exhibits the lamellar structure L.C. with folded and crystallized POE chains. In the domain of higher nitromethane concentrations and higher temperatures, the mesophase exhibits the structure L.L. with POE chains dissolved in nitromethane.

(2) *Structure L.C.*

The structure L.C. needs come comments in the case of PS-POE/NM systems. We must recall that their X-ray diffraction patterns are characterized by:

—in the small angles region: sharp lines (001) typical of a layered structure,

—in the large angles region: sharp lines characteristic of crystallized POE chains.

(a) *Variation of the structural parameters with concentration.*

It is interesting to examine the variation of the structural parameters versus concentration at room temperature (this variation is plotted in Fig. 9). We note a discontinuity in the variation of the intersheet spacing at the nitromethane concentration of 25% where the structure L.C. disappears and where the endothermic peak also

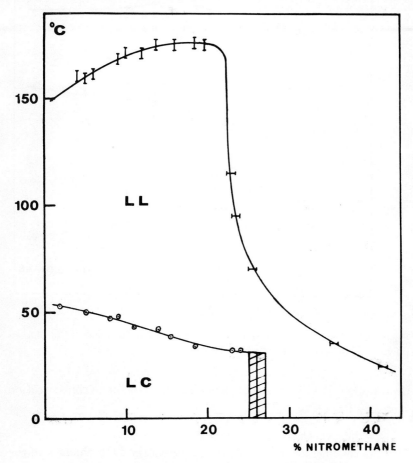

Figure 8. Phase diagram of the system PS–POE/Nit.

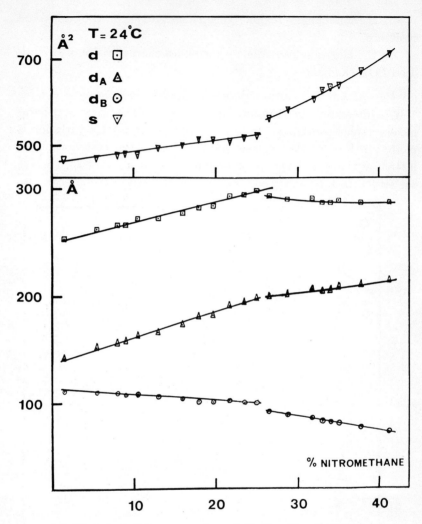

Figure 9.   Variation of the parameters of the lamellar structure of the co-polymer SP.3 versus Nitromethane concentration.

disappears. We also see that, when the nitromethane concentration increases from 0 to 25% :

—the intersheet spacing d linearly increases,
—the thickness d_A of the layer containing the POE chains and the nitromethane increases,

—the thickness d_B of the layer containing the insoluble polystyrene chains decreases,

—the average surface S available for a molecule increases.

(b) *Localization of the nitromethane*

The layer d_A contains both the POE folded and crystallized chains and the nitromethane. What are the respective positions of POE chains and nitromethane in the layer d_A? How can the coexistence of the POE crystallized chains with the nitromethane in this layer and the variation of the thickness d_A with concentration be explained?

One can think that the layer d_A results from the superposition of two layers: one formed by the crystallized POE chains, the other by the nitromethane. If this hypothesis is true, one must find a constant thickness for the POE layer and a thickness of nitromethane increasing with the solvent concentration.

With this hypothesis:

$$d_{\text{POE}} = d_A \left[1 + \frac{1 - c^1}{c^1} \frac{\rho_{\text{POE}}}{\rho_{\text{Nit}}} \right]^{-1} \quad \text{with} \quad c^1 = \frac{\text{Nit}}{\text{POE} + \text{Nit}} \text{ in weight.}$$

The results of such calculations are pictured in the Fig. 10.

One can see that, when the nitromethane concentration increases:

—the thickness of the POE layer remains constant and equal to the thickness of the POE in the dry copolymer, till $\text{Nit}/\text{POE} = 0.22$, where there is a change in the number of folding of the POE chains[4]

—the nitromethane layer thickness increases linearly.

Therefore, our hypothesis is true and we can infer the following model: the layer d_A results from the superposition of 3 layers; two layers of equal and constant thickness, formed by crystallized POE chains are separated by a nitromethane layer. When the nitromethane concentration increases, the nitromethane layer thickness increases separating the POE layers but without dissolving the POE chains. When the nitromethane layer thickness reaches a value incompatible with the stability of the structure, the POE chains melt in nitromethane and give to the structure L.L.

4. Comments

It is interesting to compare the influence of the nature of the blocks (crystallizable or amorphous) and of the nature of the solvent

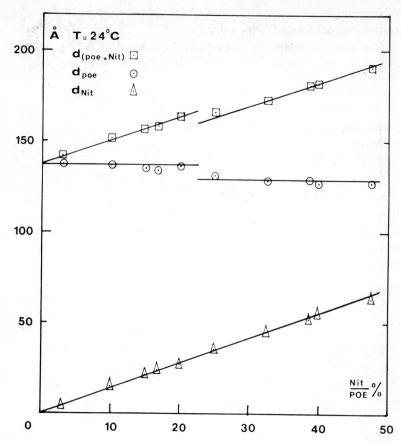

Figure 10.   Variation of the thickness of the layers of Polyetyleneoxide and Nitromethane with Nitromethane concentration.

(preferential of the crystallizable block or of the amorphous block), on the thermic behavior of binary systems: block copolymers/ preferential solvent of one block.   Block copolymers possessing two amorphous blocks exhibit only one mesophase whose structure is of the lamellar type L.L. when lengths of the two blocks are comparable. Block copolymers with an amorphous block and a crystallizable block exhibit two mesophases; both with a lamellar structure but differing by the state of the crystallizable block (melt in the structure L.L., but crystallized in the structure L.C.).   If the nature of the blocks settles the number of the mesophases, the nature of the solvent only determines the domain of stability of the mesophases: the lamellar structure L.C. disappears at lower solvent concentrations and at lower temperatures if the solvent used is a solvent of the crystallizable block than if it is a solvent of the amorphous block.

REFERENCES

1. Douy, A., Mayer, R., Rossi, J. and Gallot, B., *Mol. Cryst. and Liq. Cryst.*, **7**, 103 (1969).
2. Douy, A., Gervais, M. and Gallot, B., *C.R. Acad. Sci. Paris*, **270**, 1646 (1970).
3. Gervais, M. and Gallot, B., *C.R. Acad. Sci. Paris*, **270**, 784 (1970).
4. Gervais, M. and Gallot, B., unpublished results.